AN INTRODUCTION TO THE ANALYTIC THEORY OF NUMBERS

MATHEMATICAL SURVEYS · *Number 10*

AN INTRODUCTION TO THE ANALYTIC THEORY OF NUMBERS

BY

RAYMOND AYOUB

1963

AMERICAN MATHEMATICAL SOCIETY

190 Hope Street, Providence, Rhode Island

This research was supported in whole or in part by the United States Air Force under Contract No. AF 49(638)-291 monitored by the AF Office of Scientific Research of the Air Research and Development Command

Library of Congress Catalog Number: 63-11989

Contents

INTRODUCTION

There exist relatively few books, especially in English, devoted to the analytic theory of numbers and virtually none suitable for use in an introductory course or suitable for a first reading. This is not to imply that there are no excellent books devoted to some of the ideas and theorems of number theory. Mention must certainly be made of the pioneering and monumental work of Landau and in more recent years of the excellent books of Estermann, Ingham, Prachar, Vinogradoff and others. For the most part, however, these works are aimed at the specialist rather than at the general reader. No further apology therefore will be made for adding to the vast and growing list of mathematical treatises.

The subject of analytic number theory is not very clearly defined and while the choice of topics included here is to some extent arbitrary, the topics themselves represent some important problems of number theory to which generations of outstanding mathematicians have contributed.

The book is divided into five chapters.

Chapter I. This is devoted to an old and famous theorem—that of Dirichlet on primes in an arithmetic progression.

The chapter begins with some elementary considerations concerning the infinitude of primes and then lays the basis for the introduction of L-series. Characters are introduced and some of their properties derived and this is followed by some general theorems on ordinary Dirichlet series. A version of the classical proof of Dirichlet's theorem is then given with an analytic proof that $L(1, \chi) \neq 0$. The chapter ends with a definition of Dirichlet density and it is noted that the primes in the progression $kn + m$ have D.D. $1/\varphi(k)$.

Apart from the interest of the theorem itself, the methods and ideas introduced by Dirichlet have had an important influence on number theory as well as other branches of mathematics. The beginning reader would then do well to read this chapter in its entirety.

Chapter II. This chapter is devoted to the prime number theorem and to certain auxiliary arithmetic functions arising in a natural way. The p. n. t. is first proved with a modest error term following the general idea of Riemann's proof as completed by Landau. This requires the development of some properties of the zeta function and the proof leads rather directly to $\pi(x)$ (§ 5). It is then shown that the analysis becomes simpler if mean values and absolutely convergent integrals are introduced and then coupled with a Tauberian argument. At this stage, the error is improved to give the result of de la Vallée Poussin (§ 6B). The next step is to reduce further the analytic requirements and couple the discussion with a deeper Tauberian theorem. This is the Hardy-Littlewood proof (§ 6C). The final proof is that of Wiener, as simplified by Ikehara and Landau (§ 6D). Here the Tauberian element plays the primary role. Wiener's proof completes the equivalence of $\psi(x) \sim x$

with $\zeta(1 + it) \neq 0$.

The final section is devoted to other arithmetic functions and applications of the p.n.t. to their asymptotic properties (§ 7).

The chapter is planned so as to give the reader a flexible program. He may wish to read the direct proof of

$$(1) \qquad \pi(x) = \operatorname{li} x + O(xe^{-c(\log x)^{1/10}}) \qquad (\S\,5)$$

or of

$$(2) \qquad \psi(x) = x + O(xe^{-c(\log x)^{1/10}}) \qquad (\S\,6A)\,.$$

He may read a proof of

$$(3) \qquad \psi_2(x) = \tfrac{1}{2}x^2 + O(x^2e^{-c(\log x)^{1/2}}) \qquad (\S\,6B)$$

and then deduce that

$$(4) \qquad \pi(x) = \operatorname{li} x + O(xe^{-c(\log x)^{1/2}})\,.$$

With a slight rearrangement he may read a proof of (4) directly.

On the other hand, a direct reading of the Hardy-Littlewood or Wiener proof is possible.

The material on arithmetic functions again allows a certain measure of latitude.

Chapter III. This chapter is devoted to the theory of partitions. The chapter begins with proofs of some elementary results and the subsequent material is again arranged to provide options to the reader. It is first proved that

$$(1) \qquad p(n) \sim \frac{1}{4n\sqrt{3}}\, e^{k\sqrt{n}} \qquad (k = \pi\sqrt{(2/3)})$$

with the help of the little known but elegant proof of Uspensky (§ 2). Then Siegel's beautifully simple proof of

$$(2) \qquad \eta\left(-\frac{1}{\tau}\right) = \sqrt{\frac{\tau}{i}}\, \eta(\tau)$$

is given (§ 3).

This is followed by the introduction of the modular transformation and it is proved that the set of modular transformations forms a group with two generators. This allows us to prove that

$$(3) \qquad \eta\left(\frac{a\tau + b}{c\tau + d}\right) = \varepsilon(c\tau + d)^{1/2}\eta(\tau)\,,$$

where ε is a 24th root of unity whose nature is as yet undetermined (§ 3).

The next step is to give Rademacher's adaptation of Siegel's method to another derivation of (3) and an explicit determination of ε in terms of Dedekind sums (§ 4).

Finally, Rademacher's convergent series for $p(n)$ is derived and proved (§ 6).

The reader has 3 options. He may be content with a proof of (1) and (2) (§§ 2 and 3). He may wish to read a proof of (3) and follow this by a proof of Rademacher's formula (§§ 3 and 6), or finally, he may wish to evaluate ε in (3) and then read a proof of Rademacher's formula (§§ 4 and 6).

Chapter IV. This chapter is devoted to Waring's problem for kth powers. The general plan is to discuss first the contribution from the major arc. This is followed by Weyl's estimate for trigonometric sums. No effort is made to present the deeper and much more difficult estimates of Vinogradoff. For those the interested reader may consult the excellent book of Vinogradoff.

The asymptotic formula for the number of representations of n as a sum of s kth powers is proved to hold for

$$s \geqq k2^k + 1 \qquad (\S\,6,\ \text{Theorem } 6.6)\,. \tag{1}$$

This is then strengthened (§ 6, Theorem 6.7), with the help of a theorem of Hua to

$$s \geqq 2^k + 1 \tag{2}$$

which for small values of k is superior to Vinogradoff's result.

The next section is devoted to a discussion of Vinogradoff's upper bounds for $G(k)$ (§ 7).

With very little additional effort it is shown that (Theorem 7.3)

$$G(k) = O(k^2 \log k) \tag{3}$$

and with further estimates on the minor arc, that (Theorem 7.6)

$$G(k) = O(k \log k)\,. \tag{4}$$

The constants are more precisely determined.

The last section is devoted to a discussion of the singular series and kth power Gauss sums.

The reader has several options. He may read the account on the major arcs (§ 4), and then prove either (1), (2), (3) or (4) since they are essentially independent of one another.

Chapter V. The class number of quadratic fields and the related problem of L functions with real characters are discussed here.

The chapter begins by assuming an elementary knowledge of quadratic fields. The concept of class number h is introduced. It is shown that h is finite and that there exists a constant α such that

$$\alpha h = L(1, \chi)$$

for a certain real character χ.

The reader who is unacquainted with the theory of quadratic fields may take this as the definition of h and interpret subsequent results as theorems on $L(1, \chi)$. The next step is to sum the series $L(1, \chi)$ and derive the Gauss-Dirichlet formula for h. A mean value theorem for $h(d)$ is then derived and proved. This necessitates an estimate for sums of characters. The chapter culminates in Siegel's proof that

$$\log h(d)R \sim \tfrac{1}{2} \log |d|\,.$$

The reader may read §§1 to 3 and derive the Gauss-Dirichlet formula for $h(d)$, then read §5 for the mean value of $h(d)$ and proceed to §6 where Siegel's theorem is proved. He may on the other hand omit §§1 to 3 (except for the discussion of the Kronecker symbol) and proceed directly to §6 or be content to stop after reading §§4 and 5.

The mathematical preparation required to read this book is relatively modest. The elements of number theory and algebra, especially group theory, are required. In addition, however, a good working knowledge of the elements of complex function theory and general analytic processes is assumed. The subject matter of the book is of varying difficulty and there is a tendency to leave more to the reader as the book progresses. The first chapter can be read with relative ease, the subsequent chapters require that they be read more and more "with pen in hand."

It is a pleasure at this juncture to acknowledge my indebtedness during the writing of this book. First to the American Mathematical Society who through a contract with the Air Force Office of Scientific Research enabled me to devote a full year to its writing; to Professor R. Webber of the University of Toronto for his careful and critical reading of Chapters I and II. Many of his suggestions have been incorporated. To Professor C. L. Siegel for his generous help in the proof of Theorem 5.4 of Chapter V. Further the author wishes to thank Dr. Gordon Walker for recommending that the book be published in the American Mathematical Society's distinguished Survey Series. As to the mechanics of publication, the author is most grateful to Mrs. Ellen Burns and Mrs. Helen Striedieck for typing and other secretarial help and to Miss Ellen Swanson and her staff at the American Mathematical Society (especially S. Ramanujam) for preparing a chaotic manuscript for the printer.

There is in addition an indebtedness of more abstract character which the author wishes to acknowledge. No devotee of the analytic theory of numbers can help but be influenced by the brilliant writings of Professors H. A. Rademacher, C. L. Siegel, I. M. Vinogradoff, and the late Professor G. H. Hardy. If the reader detects little originality in the present work, it stems merely from the fact that the work of these scholars can hardly be improved upon. It has indeed been the author's hope that some specialists whose knowledge is broader and whose understanding is deeper than his might have undertaken to write a book of the present type. Perhaps the shortcomings of this work will induce them to do so.

State College, Pennsylvania
November, 1962

NOTATION

We make extensive use of the order notation (O, o, $\sim$) in this book, and for the benefit of those readers who have not encountered it before, we give a brief summary of the definition and principal properties. The notation was first introduced by Bachmann in analytic theory of numbers and has by now made its way into general analytic processes.

A. **Big O.** Let a be any real number including the possibilities $\pm\infty$. Let $f(x)$ and $g(x)$ be two functions defined in some neighborhood of a and suppose that $g(x) > 0$. We say that $f(x)$ is "big O of $g(x)$" and we write

$$f(x) = O(g(x)) ,$$

if there exists a constant $K > 0$ and a neighborhood $N(a)$ of a such that

$$|f(x)| \leqq Kg(x)$$

for all x in $N(a)$.

In particular, the notation

$$f(x) = O(1)$$

means that $f(x)$ is bounded in absolute value in a suitable neighborhood of a.

EXAMPLES. (i) Suppose that $a = 0$. Then

$$\sin x = O(x) , \qquad x^3 = O(x^2) .$$

(ii) If $a = \infty$, then

$$\sin x = O(1) , \qquad x = O(x^2) .$$

Some simple properties follow at once.

I. If $f_i(x) = O(g_i(x))$, $i = (1, 2)$, then

$$f_1(x) + f_2(x) = O(g_1(x) + g_2(x)) ,$$
$$f_1(x)f_2(x) = O(g_1(x)g_2(x)) .$$

II. If c is a constant and

$$f(x) = O(g(x)) ,$$

then

$$cf(x) = O(g(x)) .$$

The notation is frequently used with functions of more than one variable and here some care must be exercised in its use and interpretation. For example, we frequently encounter a function $f(s)$ of the complex variable $s = \sigma + it$ and write

$$f(s) = O(g(t)) \qquad (t \to \infty) .$$

The constant K whose existence is implied by the O is dependent upon σ, and the dependence may be such that $K = K(\sigma)$ is unbounded for σ in some neighborhood. Sometimes the dependence of K on the auxiliary variables or parameters is explicitly stated and sometimes it is implied by the context.

We use the notation for sequences as well—the sequences may be sequences of functions or sequences of real or complex numbers. For example,

$$f(n) = O(g(n))$$

means that there exists a constant K and an integer N_0 such that if $n > N_0$, then

$$|f(n)| \leqq Kg(n) .$$

To allow for greater flexibility and to use the O symbolism as effectively as possible, it is convenient to define $O(g(x))$ standing by itself. By $O(g(x))$, we shall mean the class of functions $C(g)$ such that $f \in C(g)$ if and only if

$$f(x) = O(g(x)) .$$

Thus in particular, $O(1)$ is the class of bounded functions. If

$$C(g) \subset C(h) ,$$

we write

$$O(g) = O(h) .$$

The reader will readily adapt himself to the mathematical anarchy in which the symbol of equality is used for a relation which is not symmetric. Surprisingly enough, this almost never leads to confusion! We define the sum and product of two O's. By

$$O(g) + O(h)$$

we mean the class of functions C consisting of sums $f_1 + f_2$ where $f_1 \in C(g)$ and $f_2 \in C(h)$. Similarly with $O(g)O(h)$. In addition to a finite sum, we often take an infinite sum of O's.

The following examples will illustrate some of the points.

(i) If

$$f(x) = x \sin (1/x) ,$$

then, as $x \to \infty$,

$$f(x) = O(x)O(1) = O(x) = O(x \log x) .$$

Note carefully that although

$$O(x) = O(x \log x) ,$$
$$O(x \log x) \neq O(x)!$$

(ii) If $f(x) = x \cos x \, e^{-\sqrt{(\log x)}} + x \sin x \log^{-9} x$, then, as $x \to \infty$,

$$f(x) = O(xe^{-\sqrt{(\log x)}}) + O(x \log^{-9} x)$$
$$= O(x \log^{-9} x) = O(x) .$$

(iii) If $s = \sigma + it$, and

$$f(s) = \sum_{n=1}^{\infty} \frac{\sin n}{n^s},$$

then, as $t \to \infty$,

$$\begin{aligned} f(s) &= \sum_{n=1}^{\infty} O(n^{-\sigma}) \\ &= O\left(\sum_{n=1}^{\infty} n^{-\sigma}\right) \\ &= O(1), \end{aligned}$$

if $\sigma > 1$. However the constant implied by the O depends on σ in a critical manner.

B. Little o. Suppose that $f(x)$ and $g(x)$ are defined in a neighborhood of a, and suppose that $g(x) > 0$. Then we say that $f(x)$ is "little o of $g(x)$" and we write

$$f(x) = o(g(x))$$

if

$$\lim_{x \to a} \frac{f(x)}{g(x)} = 0 .$$

In a similar manner, we define "little o" for sequences. We write

$$f(n) = o(g(n))$$

if

$$\lim_{n \to \infty} \frac{f(n)}{g(n)} = 0 .$$

It is easily seen that if

$$f_i = o(g_i) \qquad (i = 1, 2),$$

then

$$f_1 f_2 = o(g_1 g_2) .$$

As for "big O," we define $o(g)$ as the class of functions $D(g)$ with the property that $f \in D$ if and only if $f = o(g)$. Then we can define

$$o(g) + o(h) \quad \text{and} \quad o(g)o(h) .$$

If $D(g) \subset D(h)$, we write

$$o(g) = o(h) .$$

If $C(g)$ is the class of functions which are $O(g)$, and $C(g) \subset D(h)$, we write

$$O(g) = o(h) .$$

Thus we encounter statements of the following types:

$$\begin{aligned} f &= g_1 + g_2 \\ &= O(g_3) + O(g_4) \\ &= O(g_5) = o(g_6) \end{aligned}$$

and

$$\begin{aligned} f &= O(g_1) + O(g_2) \\ &= o(g_3) + o(g_4) \\ &= o(g_5) \,. \end{aligned}$$

C. Asymptotic equality. Finally we define $\sim$. If f and g are two functions defined in a neighborhood of a, we say that f is asymptotic to g and write

$$f \sim g$$

if

$$\lim_{x \to a} \frac{f}{g} = 1 \,.$$

The definition applies to both functions of real or complex variables and to sequences. The relation is evidently symmetric and transitive.

CHAPTER I

Dirichlet's Theorem on Primes in an Arithmetic Progression

1. Introduction and elementary results. The fundamental theorem of arithmetic places the prime numbers in a dominant position among sets of integers; their distribution was, therefore, among the first problems in arithmetic to be studied extensively and systematically. We may obtain two types of results about the distribution of primes—results of a "qualitative" and "quantitative" kind. This chapter is devoted to results of a qualitative character.

Euclid's was the first recorded proof of the theorem that there exist infinitely many primes and about 20 centuries elapsed before Euler gave a fundamentally different proof and thereby laid the foundations of analytic number theory. His proof, which we present below, contains the fundamental technique which led Dirichlet in 1837 to study the problem of the distribution of primes in various arithmetic progressions and hence provide a stimulus for a close association of analysis and number theory. Before proceeding with Euler's and Dirichlet's theorems, let us look closely at Euclid's proof.

THEOREM 1.1. *There exist infinitely many primes.*

PROOF. Suppose on the contrary that there are only finitely many, say $p_1, p_2, \cdots, p_k$. We form the number

$$N = \prod_{i=1}^{k} p_i + 1 . \tag{1}$$

Then either N is a prime distinct from $p_1, \cdots, p_k$ or is divisible by a prime p. p cannot be any of $p_1, \cdots, p_k$, for we should then have from (1),

$$p \mid N , \qquad p \,\Big|\, \prod_{i=1}^{k} p_i ,$$

and hence

$$p \mid N - \prod_{i=1}^{k} p_i ,$$

i.e., $p \mid 1$ which is impossible. Thus in any case, we have determined a prime p distinct from $p_1, p_2, \cdots, p_k$, contradicting our hypothesis.

We may formulate this result in another way: we may assert that there exist infinitely many primes in the progression $2n + 1$ or again that there exist infinitely many primes $p \equiv 1 \pmod 2$.

When the theorem is stated in these terms, it becomes natural to enquire whether the theorem is true for the arbitrary progression $kn + a$ for fixed k and a; i.e., are there infinitely many primes $p \equiv a \pmod k$?

It is immediately clear that if $n \neq 0$ and $kn + a$ is a prime, then $(k,a) = 1$. That the converse is true, i.e., that there exist infinitely many primes in the progression $kn + a$ if $(k,a) = 1$, is the great achievement of Dirichlet.

Let us return to Euclid's argument and note that his proof may be adapted to a variety of progressions. Indeed, using his argument, we may prove

THEOREM 1.2. *There exist infinitely many primes of the form* $4n + 3$.

PROOF. Suppose as above, that there exist only finitely many, say $p_1, p_2, \cdots, p_k$. We form the number

$$N = 4\prod_{i=1}^{k} p_i - 1 . \tag{2}$$

Then either N is prime and $\equiv -1 \equiv 3 \pmod 4$ or N is composite. Not all prime factors of N can be of the form $4n + 1$, for otherwise N itself would be $\equiv 1 \pmod 4$. This is easily seen from the simple remark that if $s \equiv 1 \pmod 4$ and $t \equiv 1 \pmod 4$, then $st \equiv 1 \pmod 4$. There exists, therefore, at least one prime factor $p \equiv 3 \pmod 4$. Again, as above, p cannot be any one of $p_1, p_2, \cdots, p_k$, for if it were, then from (2),

$$4\prod_{i=1}^{k} p_i \equiv 0 \pmod p \text{ and } N = 4\prod_{i=1}^{k} p_i - 1 \equiv 0 \pmod p ,$$

thus

$$-1 \equiv 0 \pmod p ,$$

a contradiction.

With the help of the quadratic law of reciprocity of Gauss-Legendre, we may prove the corresponding theorem for other progressions. For example,

THEOREM 1.3. *There exist infinitely many primes in the progression* $6n + 1$.

PROOF. Suppose on the contrary that there are only finitely many, say $p_1, p_2, \cdots, p_k$. We form the number

$$N = 12\Big(\prod_{i=1}^{k} p_i\Big)^2 + 1 . \tag{3}$$

Then evidently, $N \equiv 1 \pmod 6$. Now N is prime or composite. If N is prime, we have our contradiction; otherwise, we wish to show that N is divisible by a prime p of the form $6n + 1$ that is distinct from $p_1, p_2, \cdots, p_k$. If $p \neq 2, 3$, and $p \mid N$, then from (3), the congruence

$$3x^2 + 1 \equiv 0 \pmod p$$

is solvable; i.e.,

$$(3x)^2 \equiv -3 \pmod p .$$

Thus

$$\left(\frac{-3}{p}\right) = 1 ,$$

but by the quadratic law of reciprocity

$$\left(\frac{-3}{p}\right) = \left(\frac{-1}{p}\right)\left(\frac{3}{p}\right) = (-1)^{(p-1)/2}(-1)^{(p-1)/2}\left(\frac{p}{3}\right) = \left(\frac{p}{3}\right).$$

Therefore

$$\left(\frac{p}{3}\right) = 1 ;$$

i.e., $p \equiv 1 \pmod 3$ and since p is odd, $p \equiv 1 \pmod 6$. There exists, therefore, at least one prime divisor p of N and $p \equiv 1 \pmod 6$. p cannot be one of $p_1, \cdots, p_k$; for if it were, then p would have to be a factor of 1 which is a contradiction.

By a combination of these and other related devices, it is possible to prove Dirichlet's theorem for a variety of arithmetic progressions by elementary arithmetic means. No simple arithmetic proof for the general case is known, however.

We turn our attention now to Euler's proof of Euclid's theorem. Let s be real and consider the series

$$\sum_{n=1}^{\infty} \frac{1}{n^s}.$$

This series converges for $s > 1$ and diverges for $s \leqq 1$; we denote the series and its sum for $s > 1$ by $\zeta(s)$. The connection between this function and prime numbers is given by Euler's fundamental

THEOREM 1.4. *For* $s > 1$,

(4) $$\zeta(s) = \prod_p (1 - p^{-s})^{-1},$$

where the product is taken over all primes p.

This result may be thought of as the analytic analogue of the fundamental theorem of arithmetic, viz., that every integer is uniquely a product of primes. It asserts a little more in that the product on the right converges for $s > 1$.

PROOF. Let

(5) $$P(x) = \prod_{p \leqq x} (1 - p^{-s})^{-1},$$

then expanding the parenthesis, we have from (5),

$$P(x) = \prod_{p \leqq x} \sum_{k=0}^{\infty} \frac{1}{p^{ks}}.$$

Since the series involved are absolutely convergent, we arrange the product in the form $(p_1^{\alpha_1} \cdots p_r^{\alpha_r})^s = m^s$ (say).

By the fundamental theorem of arithmetic, every integer is uniquely the product of primes; it follows that

$$P(x) = \sum \frac{1}{m^s},$$

where the sum ranges over all m having no prime factor $>x$ and each such m occurs only once. Hence the difference

$$\zeta(s) - P(x) = \sum \frac{1}{m^s}, \tag{6}$$

where the sum on the right now ranges over those integers m having at least one prime factor $> x$. Therefore from (6),

$$\zeta(s) - P(x) \leqq \sum_{m \geqq x} \frac{1}{m^s};$$

the right-hand sum now extending over all integers $m \geqq x$. Since $\zeta(s)$ converges for $s > 1$, $\sum_{m \geqq x} 1/m^s \to 0$ as $x \to \infty$, and the theorem follows.

This is a specific instance of a more general theorem which will be useful in what follows later. We recall that a numerical function $f(n)$ is called multiplicative if $f(mn) = f(m)f(n)$ for $(m,n) = 1$, and completely multiplicative if $f(mn) = f(m)f(n)$ without restriction.

For multiplicative functions we prove the following

THEOREM 1.5. *If $f(n)$ is multiplicative, then*

$$\sum_{n=1}^{\infty} f(n) = \prod_p (1 + f(p) + f(p^2) + \cdots + f(p^k) + \cdots) = \prod_p \sum_{k=0}^{\infty} f(p^k) \tag{7}$$

provided that either side is absolutely convergent. If $f(n)$ is completely multiplicative, then the right-hand side may be written in the form $\prod_p (1 - f(p))^{-1}$. In both instances the product is taken over all primes p.

PROOF. The proof follows the procedure of Theorem 1.4. First, we note that since $f(1)f(1) = f(1)$, then $f(1) = 1$ if we exclude the trivial case $f(1) = 0$.

Suppose that the left-hand side converges absolutely. We consider as above

$$P(x) = \prod_{p \leqq x} \sum_{k=0}^{\infty} f(p^k). \tag{8}$$

Since by hypothesis the series on the right converge absolutely, we may multiply them together and rearrange the terms. By the fundamental theorem of arithmetic, we get by (8),

$$P(x) = \sum f(m), \tag{9}$$

where again the sum on the right is over all m having no prime factor exceeding x, and each such m occurs precisely once. It follows from (9), that

$$\left| \sum_{m=1}^{\infty} f(m) - P(x) \right| = \left| \sum f(m) \right|;$$

the sum on the right extends over those m having at least one prime divisor $>x$. Then

$$\left| \sum f(m) - P(x) \right| \leqq \sum_{m \geqq x} f(m)$$

and the right-hand side $\to 0$ as $x \to \infty$. If now $\prod_p \sum_{k=0}^{\infty} f(p^k)$ converges absolutely, we argue in much the same way. The details are left to the reader. Finally, the second part of the theorem follows at once if we note that for a completely multiplicative function $f(n)$, we have $f(p^k) = (f(p))^k$, and we then sum the geometric progression.

To prove that there exist infinitely many primes, Euler's objective is to prove that the series $\sum_p 1/p$ diverges. To isolate a series involving primes only, it is natural to take logarithms in (4) and then to allow s to tend to 1^{+0}. Here is Euler's argument

THEOREM 1.6.

$$\lim_{s \to 1+0} \sum_p \frac{1}{p^s} \to \infty ,$$

where the sum is over all primes p. There exist therefore infinitely many primes.

PROOF. From (4), taking logarithms on both sides and expanding the logarithm, we have

$$\begin{aligned} \log \zeta(s) &= - \sum_p \log (1 - p^{-s}) \\ &= \sum_p \sum_{k=1}^{\infty} \frac{1}{kp^{ks}} \qquad (10) \\ &= \sum_p \frac{1}{p^s} + \sum_p \sum_{k=2}^{\infty} \frac{1}{kp^{ks}} , \end{aligned}$$

where we have broken the sum into two parts: one with $k = 1$, and the other with $k \geqq 2$. When $s \to 1$, $\log \zeta(s) \to \infty$ and so if we could prove that the second sum remains bounded as $s \to 1$, then we would have proved the theorem. We denote the second sum in (10) by $R(s)$, then

$$\begin{aligned} |R(s)| &\leqq \frac{1}{2} \sum_p \sum_{k=2}^{\infty} \frac{1}{p^{ks}} \\ &\leqq \frac{1}{2} \sum_p \frac{p^{-2s}}{1-p^{-s}} \\ &\leqq \frac{1}{2} \frac{1}{1-2^{-s}} \sum_p p^{-2s} \\ &< \frac{1}{2} \frac{1}{1-2^{-s}} \zeta(2s) . \end{aligned}$$

Since $\zeta(2s)$ remains bounded as $s \to 1$ (its value actually being $\pi^2/6$), it follows that $R(s)$ remains bounded and we deduce that

$$\lim_{s \to 1+0} \sum_p \frac{1}{p^s} \to \infty .$$

COROLLARY 1. *As a simple corollary, we infer that $\sum_p 1/p$ diverges.*

For if $\sum_p 1/p$ converges to a, then for all $s > 1$,

$$\sum_p \frac{1}{p^s} < a ,$$

and this contradicts the statement of the theorem. It is possible to prove the divergence of $\sum 1/p$ independently of the above theorem. We simply modify the argument and get more precise inequalities. Indeed,

$$P(x) = \prod_{p \leqq x} \left(1 - \frac{1}{p}\right)^{-1} \Sigma' , \tag{11}$$

where the dash indicates that only those m having all prime factors $\leqq x$ are to be included. Thus

$$P(x) \geqq \sum_{m \leqq x} \frac{1}{m} > \int_1^x \frac{dt}{t} = \log x . \tag{12}$$

If we take logs in (11), and argue as above, we get

$$\sum_{p \leqq x} \frac{1}{p} + \sum_{p \leqq x} \sum_{k=2}^{\infty} \frac{1}{kp^k} = \log\left(\Sigma' \frac{1}{m} \right) > \log \log x . \tag{13}$$

If we denote the second sum on the left of (13) by $T(x)$, we get

$$T(x) < \frac{1}{2} \sum_{p \leqq x} \sum_{k=2}^{\infty} \frac{1}{p^k} < \frac{1}{2} \sum_{p \leqq x} \frac{p^{-2}}{1-p^{-1}} < \sum_{p \leqq x} \frac{1}{p^2} < \sum_{n=1}^{\infty} \frac{1}{n^2} = \zeta(2) .$$

Thus from (13)

$$\sum_{p \leqq x} \frac{1}{p} + \zeta(2) > \log \log x , \tag{14}$$

and the proof is complete.

Dirichlet patterns the proof that there exist infinitely many primes of the form $kn + a$, $(k,a) = 1$ on Euler's proof. Important modifications are necessary, however. To introduce these modifications, it is necessary to define a numerical function which will separate the primes into individual residue classes. The function was called a character by Dirichlet and the series

$$\sum_{n=1}^{\infty} \frac{\chi(n)}{n^s}$$

denoted by $L(s, \chi)$. We may induce some of the "desirable" properties of $\chi(n)$. In order to use Theorem 1.5, we require that $\chi(n)$ be completely multiplicative; i.e., $\chi(mn) = \chi(m)\chi(n)$. Moreover it suffices to require that $\chi(n)$ depend only on the residue class modulo k to which n belongs. Finally, we wish to exclude those n which have a factor in common with k. We do this by requiring that $\chi(n) = 0$ if $(n,k) > 1$. This does not destroy the multiplicative character of $\chi(n)$, for if $(n,k) > 1$, then so is $(mn,k) > 1$, thus

$$\chi(m)\chi(n) = \chi(m) \cdot 0 = 0 = \chi(mn) .$$

To illustrate, we give the Dirichlet proof for the progression $4n + 1$.

THEOREM 1.7.
$$\lim_{s \to 1+0} \sum_{p \equiv 1 \pmod 4} \frac{1}{p^s} \to \infty .$$
There exist therefore infinitely many primes in the progression $4n + 1$.

PROOF. We first define our character. Let

(15)
$$\chi(n) = \begin{cases} (-1)^{(n-1)/2} & \text{for odd } n, \\ 0 & \text{for even } n; \end{cases}$$

i.e., $\chi(n) = 1$ if $n \equiv 1 \pmod 4$ and $\chi(n) = -1$ if $n \equiv 3 \pmod 4$.

If m, n are odd, then

$$\chi(n)\chi(m) = (-1)^{(n-1)/2+(m-1)/2}$$

and

$$\chi(mn) = (-1)^{(mn-1)/2} .$$

In order that $\chi(mn) = \chi(m)\chi(n)$, we must show that the exponents have the same parity. We have in fact

$$\frac{mn-1}{2} - \frac{(n-1)+(m-1)}{2} = \frac{mn-m-n+1}{2} = \frac{(m-1)(n-1)}{2} \equiv 0 \pmod 2.$$

Thus $\chi(n)$ is multiplicative if m, n are odd. The fact is obvious if m or n is even.

Consider now for real s the series

(16)
$$L(s, \chi) = \sum_{n=1}^{\infty} \frac{\chi(n)}{n^s} = 1 - \frac{1}{3^s} + \frac{1}{5^s} - \frac{1}{7^s} + \cdots .$$

From the elementary theory of infinite series, it follows that this series converges for $s > 0$, converges absolutely for $s > 1$ and diverges for $s < 0$. Hence by Theorem 1.5, for $s > 1$, we have

$$L(s,\chi) = \prod_{\text{odd } p} \left(1 - \frac{\chi(p)}{p^s}\right)^{-1} .$$

Taking logarithms, we get

(17)
$$\begin{aligned} \log L(s,\chi) &= \sum_{\text{odd } p} \sum_{k=1}^{\infty} \frac{\chi(p)^k}{kp^{ks}} = \sum_{\text{odd } p} \frac{\chi(p)}{p^s} + \sum_{\text{odd } p} \sum_{k=2}^{\infty} \frac{\chi(p^k)}{kp^{ks}} \\ &= \sum_{p\equiv 1 (\text{mod } 4)} \frac{1}{p^s} - \sum_{p\equiv 3(\text{mod } 4)} \frac{1}{p^s} + R_1(s) , \end{aligned}$$

where we have called the second sum $R_1(s)$. As in Euler's proof we have

$$\begin{aligned} |R_1(s)| &\leqq \frac{1}{2} \sum_{\text{odd } p} \sum_{k=2}^{\infty} \frac{1}{p^{ks}} < \frac{1}{2} \sum_p \frac{p^{-2s}}{1-p^{-s}} < \frac{1}{2} \cdot \frac{1}{1-2^{-s}} \sum \frac{1}{p^{2s}} \\ &< \frac{1}{2} \frac{1}{1-2^{-s}} \zeta(2s) . \end{aligned}$$

Therefore $R_1(s)$ remains bounded as $s \to 1^{+0}$. In order to isolate the primes $p \equiv 1 \pmod 4$, we add the sum over all primes p which we write in the form obtained in Euler's proof, viz.

(18)
$$\begin{aligned} \log \zeta(s) &= \sum_p \frac{1}{p^s} + R(s) = \frac{1}{2^s} + \sum_{p \text{ odd}} \frac{1}{p^s} + R(s) \\ &= \frac{1}{2^s} + \sum_{p\equiv 1(\text{mod } 4)} \frac{1}{p^s} + \sum_{p\equiv 3(\text{mod } 4)} \frac{1}{p^s} + R(s) , \end{aligned}$$

where it will be recalled $R(s)$ was shown to remain bounded as $s \to 1^{+0}$. We get from (17) and (18),

$$\log L(s, \chi) + \log \zeta(s) = \frac{1}{2^s} + 2 \sum_{p \equiv 1 (\mathrm{mod}\ 4)} \frac{1}{p^s} + R_1(s) + R(s) .$$

We know that $\log \zeta(s) \to \infty$ as $s \to 1^{+0}$ and the terms 2^{-s}, $R_1(s)$, $R(s)$ all remain bounded as $s \to 1^{+0}$. Also, $L(s,\chi) \to L(1,\chi)$ a convergent series. Our theorem would then be proved if we knew that $L(1,\chi) \neq 0$. In this particular case

$$L(1,\chi) = 1 - \frac{1}{3} + \frac{1}{5} - \frac{1}{7} + \cdots = \frac{\pi}{4} \neq 0 ,$$

thus proving the theorem.

The proof that $L(1,\chi) \neq 0$ in this case may be seen more simply as follows

$$L(1,\chi) = \left(1 - \frac{1}{3}\right) + \left(\frac{1}{5} - \frac{1}{7}\right) + \cdots > 0 .$$

On the other hand no such simple proof is available for the general case. Indeed, the proof that $L(1,\chi) \neq 0$ becomes the main difficulty in Dirichlet's proof of his theorem.

To prepare for the general case, we now turn our attention to the general theory of characters.

2. Characters and their properties. It will be recalled that the most important property we required of a character was that it be a completely multiplicative function of the residue classes modulo k—the most important of these being the reduced ones. The reduced residue classes form an Abelian group under multiplication and indeed the theory of finite Abelian groups is the most convenient setting for our purposes. We therefore start with an Abelian group of order h.

The reduced residue classes modulo k form an Abelian group of order $\varphi(k)$, $\varphi(k)$ being Euler's function; the identity of the group is the residue class of which the representative is 1 and the inverse of the element represented by a is the element whose representative is a solution of the congruence $ax \equiv 1 \pmod{k}$. We first develop the general theory of characters for an Abelian group of order h and then apply the theory to this particular instance.

Let g be an element of G. We define a function $\chi(g)$ from G to the complex numbers which is multiplicative; i.e., if a and b are elements of G, then $\chi(ab) = \chi(a)\chi(b)$. In the language of algebra, χ is a homomorphism from G to the complex numbers, but we prove any properties of a homomorphism which we require. If $\chi(a) = 0$ for every element of the group, then $\chi(a)$ satisfies the multiplicative property but we agree to exclude this trivial instance of a character once for all.

If $\chi(a) = 1$ for every a in the group, then $\chi(a)$ is multiplicative and we call this the *principal character* and denote it by $\chi_1(a)$. It is not immediately clear that there exist any other characters but we shall show in fact that there are h and only h distinct characters.

A few properties follow directly from the definition.

THEOREM 2.1. *If e is the identity of the group, then* $\chi(e) = 1$.

PROOF. We have

$$\chi(e) = \chi(e^2) = (\chi(e))^2 .$$

Whence $\chi(e) = 0$ or $\chi(e) = 1$. If $\chi(e) = 0$, then $\chi(a) = \chi(ae) = \chi(a)\chi(e) = 0$, for every a in G and we have excluded this case.

THEOREM 2.2. $\chi(a)$ *is different from* 0 *for every* a *in* G.

PROOF. Suppose on the contrary that for some a in $G, \chi(a) = 0$. Then $\chi(e) = \chi(aa^{-1}) = \chi(a)\chi(a^{-1}) = 0$. But we showed in the preceding theorem that $\chi(e) = 0$ implies $\chi(a) = 0$ for all a in G, and this case we have ruled out.

THEOREM 2.3. $\chi(a)$ *is an hth root of unity; i.e.,* $\chi(a)$ *satisfies the equation* $\chi^h = 1$.

PROOF. $\chi(a^h) = \chi(e) = 1$; but $\chi(a^h) = (\chi(a))^h$, thus $\chi^h(a) = 1$.

Before proceeding with the discussion, we construct as examples, the characters for the reduced residues modulo 12 and modulo 7. Representatives of the classes modulo 12 may be taken as 1, 5, 7, 11. We have first the principal character

$$\chi_1(1) = \chi_1(5) = \chi_1(7) = \chi_1(11) = 1 .$$

Since $\chi^2(5) = \chi(5^2) = \chi(25) = \chi(1)$, it follows that $\chi(5) = \pm 1$. In like manner, $\chi^2(7) = \chi^2(11) = 1$; i.e., $\chi(7) = \pm 1$, $\chi(11) = \pm 1$. To decide on the proper signs we note that

$$\chi(5)\chi(7) = \chi(5 \cdot 7) = \chi(11), \qquad \chi(5)\chi(11) = \chi(5 \cdot 11) = \chi(7)$$

and

$$\chi(7)\chi(11) = \chi(7 \cdot 11) = \chi(5) .$$

Thus, there are 4 possible characters, viz.

$$\chi_1(1) = \chi_1(5) = \chi_1(7) = \chi_1(11) = 1 ,$$
$$\chi_2(1) = \chi_2(5) = 1, \quad \chi_2(7) = -1, \quad \chi_2(11) = -1 ,$$
$$\chi_3(1) = 1, \quad \chi_3(5) = -1, \quad \chi_3(7) = -1, \quad \chi_3(11) = 1 ,$$
$$\chi_4(1) = 1, \quad \chi_4(5) = -1, \quad \chi_4(7) = 1, \quad \chi_4(11) = -1 ,$$

and it is easily seen that they are indeed characters.

We consider now the characters for the group of residues modulo 7. We take the representatives of the residue classes to be 1, 2, 3, 4, 5, 6 and since 7 is prime, there exists a primitive root; i.e., the group is cyclic. A generator is 3, for we have

$$3 \equiv 3, \ 3^2 \equiv 2, \ 3^3 \equiv 6, \ 3^4 \equiv 4, \ 3^5 \equiv 5, \ 3^6 \equiv 1 \pmod 7 .$$

We construct the characters as follows: Since $\chi^6(3) = 1$, then we let $\chi(3)$ be a sixth root of unity. We show that all 6 possible choices enable us to construct an admissible character.

Let

$$\chi_1(3) = 1, \quad \chi_2(3) = \exp\left(\frac{2\pi i}{6}\right), \quad \chi_3(3) = \exp\left(\frac{2\pi i}{6}\cdot 2\right),$$

$$\chi_4(3) = \exp\left(\frac{2\pi i}{6}\cdot 3\right), \quad \chi_5(3) = \exp\left(\frac{2\pi i}{6}\cdot 4\right), \quad \chi_6(3) = \exp\left(\frac{2\pi i}{6}\cdot 5\right).$$

We show how to construct, for example, χ_2.

$$\chi_2(1) = 1\,;$$

$$\chi_2(2) = \chi_2(3^2) = \chi_2^2(3) = \exp\left(\frac{2\pi i}{6}\cdot 2\right);$$

$$\chi_2(3) = \exp\left(\frac{2\pi i}{6}\right);$$

$$\chi_2(4) = \chi_2(3^4) = \chi_2^4(3) = \exp\left(\frac{2\pi i}{6}\cdot 4\right);$$

$$\chi_2(5) = \chi_2(3^5) = \chi_2^5(3) = \exp\left(\frac{2\pi i}{6}\cdot 5\right);$$

$$\chi_2(6) = \chi_2(3^3) = \chi_2^3(3) = \exp\left(\frac{2\pi i}{6}\cdot 3\right).$$

The remaining characters are constructed in the same way; the details are left to the reader.

The procedure used in both these cases leads to a general principle which is based on the fundamental theorem on Abelian groups. We state this theorem in the following form.

THEOREM. *Let G be an Abelian group of order h; then there exist in G elements $a_1, a_2, \cdots, a_m$ of orders $r_1, r_2, \cdots, r_m$, respectively so that every element g of G may be written uniquely in the form*

$$g = a_1^{k_1} a_2^{k_2} \cdots a_m^{k_m} \text{ where } 0 \leqq k_i \leqq r_i - 1 \qquad (i = 1, 2, \cdots, m).$$

Moreover $r_1 \cdot r_2 \cdots r_m = h$.

PROOF. A proof may be found for example in *Theory of groups* by Marshall Hall. Since

$$(1) \qquad \chi(g) = \chi^{k_1}(a_1) \cdots \chi^{k_m}(a_m),$$

it follows that the value of a character for an element g of the group G is completely determined by the value of the character for the basis elements $a_1, a_2, \cdots, a_m$. Furthermore, $\chi(a_i)$ is an r_ith root of unity; i.e., if $\chi(a_i) = \rho_i$, then $\rho_i^{r_i} = 1$. Since there are r_i choices for ρ_i, the above argument with (1) suggests that there are $r_1 \cdot r_2 \cdots r_m = h$ possible characters. Indeed, we have

THEOREM 2.4. *There are precisely h different characters for a group G of order h.*

PROOF. Let $a_1, \cdots, a_m$ be a basis for G and let r_j be the order of a_j $(j = 1, 2, \cdots, m)$. We define

$$\chi(a_j) = \rho_j \qquad (j = 1, \cdots, m)\,, \tag{2}$$

and since ρ_j is an r_jth root of unity, let

$$\rho_j = \exp\left(\frac{2\pi i}{r_j} \cdot n_j\right) \qquad 0 \leqq n_j \leqq r_j - 1\,. \tag{3}$$

If

$$g = a_1^{k_1} \cdots a_r^{k_r}\,,$$

let

$$\chi(g) = \rho_1^{k_1} \cdots \rho_r^{k_r}\,. \tag{4}$$

Then the χ so defined is a character, for if a and b are two elements of the group G, we have

$$a = a_1^{s_1} a_2^{s_2} \cdots a_m^{s_m}\,,$$

and

$$b = a_1^{t_1} a_2^{t_2} \cdots a_m^{t_m}\,.$$

Hence from (4)

$$\chi(a) = \rho_1^{s_1} \cdots \rho_m^{s_m}\,,$$

and

$$\chi(b) = \rho_1^{t_1} \cdots \rho_m^{t_m}\,,$$
$$\chi(ab) = \chi(a_1^{s_1+t_1} \cdots a_m^{s_m+t_m})\,.$$

Suppose that $s_i + t_i \equiv u_i \pmod{r_i}$, $0 \leqq u_i \leqq r_i - 1$ then from (3)

$$\chi(ab) = \rho_1^{u_1} \rho_2^{u_2} \cdots \rho_m^{u_m}\,;$$

on the other hand

$$\chi(a)\chi(b) = \rho_1^{s_1+t_1} \rho_2^{s_2+t_2} \cdots \rho_m^{s_m+t_m}\,.$$

But $\rho_j^l = \rho_j^n$ if $l \equiv n \pmod{r_j}$ and hence $\chi(ab) = \chi(a)\chi(b)$. The number of possible choices for n_j is r_j and hence the total number of possible choices for

$$\chi(g) = \chi(a_1^{k_1} \cdots a_m^{k_m})$$

is $r_1 \cdot r_2 \cdots r_m = h$. Moreover, no two distinct choices lead to the same character. For, if χ_u and χ_v are two characters defined by

$$\chi_u(a_j) = \exp\left(\frac{2\pi i}{r_j} \cdot u_j\right), \qquad 0 \leqq u_j \leqq r_j - 1\,,$$

and

$$\chi_v(a_j) = \exp\left(\frac{2\pi i}{r_j} \cdot v_j\right), \qquad 0 \leqq v_j \leqq r_j - 1\,,$$

then for some $j, u_j \neq v_j$. Thus, there exists an element g in G for which

$$\chi_u(g) \neq \chi_v(g) ,$$

the element being namely $g = a_j$. There are, therefore, at least h characters. On the other hand if χ is a character, then $\chi(g) = \chi(a_1^{k_1}) \cdots \chi(a_m^{k_m})$. Each of the factors is an r_ith root of unity and so $\chi(g)$ must coincide with one of the above choices. There are, therefore, exactly h distinct characters.

Characters may be combined in the following way: Let χ and ψ be two characters on the group G. We define for g in G

$$\chi\psi(g) = \chi(g)\psi(g) .$$

Let $\varphi = \chi\psi$, and note that $\psi\chi = \chi\psi$; moreover φ is a character for

$$\begin{aligned}\varphi(ab) = \chi\psi(ab) = \chi(ab)\psi(ab) &= \chi(a)\chi(b)\psi(a)\psi(b) = \chi(a)\psi(a)\chi(b)\psi(b) \\ &= (\chi\psi(a))(\chi\psi(b)) = \varphi(a)\varphi(b) .\end{aligned}$$

Theorem 2.5. *Under this rule of composition, the characters of a group G form themselves an Abelian group.*

Proof. The set of characters is closed under the above definition and the associate law follows immediately. The principal character χ_1 acts as an identity for

$$\chi_1\chi(a) = \chi_1(a)\chi(a) = \chi(a);$$

thus

$$\chi_1\chi = \chi .$$

If χ is a character and a is an element of G, then

(5) $$\chi(a) = \rho_1^{k_1} \cdots \rho_m^{k_m} .$$

Let

(6) $$\psi(a) = \rho_1^{-k_1} \cdots \rho_m^{-k_m} .$$

Since $|\rho_i| = 1$, $\rho_i^{-k_i} = \overline{\rho_i^{k_i}}$ and hence from (5) and (6), $\psi(a) = \bar{\chi}(a)$ and ψ is evidently a character. We have

$$\chi(a)\psi(a) = 1 = \chi_1(a)$$

and it follows that $\psi = \bar{\chi}$ is the inverse of the character χ.

We prove now two theorems which will be very useful in our later work.

Theorem 2.6.

(7) $$\sum_{g \in G} \chi(g) = \begin{cases} h & \text{if } \chi = \chi_1 , \\ 0 & \text{if } \chi \neq \chi_1 , \end{cases}$$

the sum being for a fixed character summed over all the elements of the group.

Proof. If $\chi = \chi_1$, then $\chi_1(g) = 1$ for all elements g in G and so $\sum_{g \in G}\chi_1(g) = h$ and the first assertion is proved.

Suppose $\chi \neq \chi_1$, and let

(8) $$S=\sum_{g\in G}\chi(g)\,.$$

Suppose that a is an element of G for which $\chi(a)\neq 1$. Such an element must exist for otherwise χ would be the principal character. As g ranges over the elements of G, then so does ag once and only once. Then from (8),

$$S=\sum_{g\in G}\chi(g)=\sum_{g\in G}\chi(ag)=\chi(a)\sum_{g\in G}\chi(g)=\chi(a)S$$

and since $\chi(a)\neq 1$, it follows that $S=0$.

We now prove the so-called dual of this theorem.

THEOREM 2.7.

(9) $$\sum_{\chi}\chi(g)=\begin{cases} h & \text{if } g=e\,,\\ 0 & \text{otherwise}\,,\end{cases}$$

the sum taken over all characters χ for a fixed element g of G.

PROOF. If $g=e$, then $\chi(e)=1$ for all characters by Theorem 2.1. Suppose $g\neq e$; we first show that there exists a character χ such that $\chi(g)\neq 1$. To this end we let

$$g=a_1^{k_1}\cdots a_m^{k_m}\,;$$

since $g\neq e$; then for some $j, k_j\not\equiv 0 \pmod{r_j}$. We define

$$\chi(a_j)=\exp\left(\frac{2\pi i}{r_j}\right),$$

$$\chi(a_1)=\cdots=\chi(a_{j-1})=\chi(a_{j+1})=\cdots=\chi(a_m)=1\,.$$

Then, as we saw above χ defines a character and $\chi(g)=\rho_j^{k_j}\neq 1$.

Now we let

(10) $$S=\sum_{\chi}\chi(g)$$

and since by Theorem 2.5 $\psi\chi$ ranges over all characters wherever χ does, we suppose that ψ has been selected in accordance with the above principle; i.e., $\psi(g)\neq 1$, then by (10),

$$S=\sum_{\chi}\chi(g)=\sum_{\chi}\psi\chi(g)=\sum_{\chi}\psi(g)\chi(g)=\psi(g)\sum_{\chi}\chi(g)=\psi(g)S$$

and since $\psi(g)\neq 1$, it follows that $S=0$.

With these essential properties of characters established, we turn our attention now to the general theory of Dirichlet series.

3. The general theory of Dirichlet series. We study in this section the theory of Dirichlet series to the extent to which it will be useful in the further development of the subject. Though Dirichlet used only functions of real variables in his proof, we shall use the more general case in several instances.

A series of the form

$$\sum_{n=1}^{\infty} \frac{a(n)}{n^s} \tag{1}$$

with $s = \sigma + it$ and $a(n)$ a sequence of real or complex numbers, is called an ordinary Dirichlet series. We shall denote the series and its sum when it converges in the same way. Moreover we follow the standard but curious notation of denoting the real part of the complex variable s by the Greek letter σ and the imaginary part by the Latin letter t. We first establish a few results about the region of convergence of such a series and determine the connection with the coefficients. These results are analogues of the corresponding results for power series.

THEOREM 3.1. *If the series* (1) *converges for* $s_0 = \sigma_0 + it_0$, *then it converges for all* s *for which* $\sigma > \sigma_0$. *Moreover, the convergence is uniform inside any angle for which* $|\arg(s - s_0)| \leqq \pi/2 - \delta$ *for* $0 < \delta < \pi/2$.

The proof is based on a lemma for partial integration of Stieltjes integrals which we state in the following form.

LEMMA 3.1. *Let* $x \geqq 1$ *and let* $\varphi(x)$ *be a function with continuous derivative for* $x \geqq 1$. *Let* $S(x) = \sum_{n \leqq x} C(n)$ *where* $C(n)$ *are real or complex numbers. Then*

$$\sum_{n \leqq x} C(n)\varphi(n) = S(x)\varphi(x) - \int_1^x S(t)\varphi'(t)dt . \tag{2}$$

We observe that if we use Stieltjes integrals, the left-hand side may be written in the form

$$\int_1^x \varphi(t)\, dS(t) .$$

Thus integrating by parts, we get the right-hand side. However, we do not assume a knowledge of Stieltjes integration, and prove the theorem directly. The proof uses Abel's method of partial summation which is the discrete analogue of partial integration. Let k be an integer such that $k \leqq x < k + 1$; then in this interval we have

$$S(x) = \sum_{n \leqq x} C(n) = \sum_{n \leqq k} C(n) = S(k) . \tag{3}$$

We define $S(0) = 0$, and get

$$\begin{aligned}
\sum_{n \leqq x} C(n)\varphi(n) &= \sum_{n \leqq k} C(n)\varphi(n) \\
&= \sum_{n=1}^{k} (S(n) - S(n-1))\varphi(n) \\
&= \sum_{n=1}^{k} S(n)\varphi(n) - \sum_{n=1}^{k} S(n-1)\varphi(n) \\
&= \sum_{n=1}^{k} S(n)\varphi(n) - \sum_{n=1}^{k-1} S(n)\varphi(n+1)
\end{aligned}$$

on changing the index in the second sum. Proceeding, we get

$$\begin{aligned}\sum_{n\leq x} C(n)\varphi(n) &= \sum_{n=1}^{k-1}(\varphi(n)-\varphi(n+1))S(n)+S(k)\varphi(k)\\ &= \sum_{n=1}^{k-1}(\varphi(n)-\varphi(n+1))S(n)+S(k)(\varphi(k)-\varphi(x))+S(k)\varphi(x)\\ &= -\sum_{n=1}^{k-1}S(n)\int_n^{n+1}\varphi'(t)dt - S(k)\int_k^x \varphi'(t)dt + S(x)\varphi(x)\\ &= S(x)\varphi(x)-\sum_{n=1}^{k-1}\int_n^{n+1}S(t)\varphi'(t)dt - \int_k^x S(t)\varphi'(t)dt\\ &= S(x)\varphi(x)-\int_1^x S(t)\varphi'(t)dt\,.\end{aligned}$$

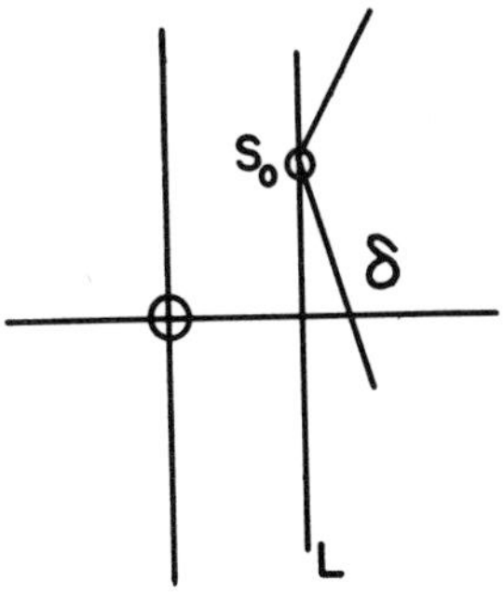

We have made use of (3).

We return now to a proof of Theorem 3.1. The theorem asserts that if the series converges for $s = s_0$, then it converges for all s in the half plane to the right of the line L. Furthermore that the convergence is uniform for all s in the angle indicated.

We put

$$\sum_{n=1}^{\infty}\frac{a(n)}{n^s} = \sum_{n=1}^{\infty}\frac{a(n)}{n^{s_0}}\cdot\frac{1}{n^{s-s_0}} \tag{4}$$

and $C(n) = a(n)/n^{s_0}$, $\varphi(x) = x^{-(s-s_0)}$, then

$$S(x) = \sum_{n\leq x}\frac{a(n)}{n^{s_0}}\,, \tag{5}$$

and $\varphi'(x) = -(s-s_0)x^{-1-(s-s_0)}$. We now apply the above lemma, using (4) and (5)

$$\begin{aligned}\sum_{n=N+1}^{M}\frac{a(n)}{n^s} &= \sum_{n=1}^{M}\frac{a(n)}{n^s}-\sum_{n=1}^{N}\frac{a(n)}{n^s} = S(M)M^{-(s-s_0)}+(s-s_0)\int_1^M S(t)t^{-1-(s-s_0)}dt\\ &\quad - S(N)N^{-(s-s_0)}-(s-s_0)\int_1^N S(t)t^{-1-(s-s_0)}dt\\ &= (S(M)-S(N))M^{-(s-s_0)}+S(N)(M^{-(s-s_0)}-N^{-(s-s_0)})\\ &\quad + (s-s_0)\int_N^M S(t)t^{-1-(s-s_0)}dt\,.\end{aligned} \tag{6}$$

The second term of (6) may be written in the form

$$-(s-s_0)\int_N^M t^{-1-(s-s_0)}S(N)dt$$

and we then get from (6)

$$\sum_{n=N+1}^{M}\frac{a(n)}{n^s} = (S(M)-S(N))M^{-(s-s_0)}+(s-s_0)\int_N^M (S(t)-S(N))t^{-1-(s-s_0)}dt\,. \tag{7}$$

Since we have assumed that $\sum_{n=1}^{\infty} a(n)/n^{s_0}$ converges, then for $\varepsilon > 0$ there exists N_0 such that for all $x \geqq N > N_0$, we have $|S(x) - S(N)| < \varepsilon$; thus by (7),

$$(8)\qquad \left| \sum_{n=N+1}^{M} \frac{a(n)}{n^s} \right| \leqq |S(M) - S(N)|\,|M^{-(s-s_0)}| + \varepsilon\,|s - s_0| \left| \int_N^M \right| t^{-1-(s-s_0)}|\,dt\,.$$

For $\sigma > \sigma_0$, we have

$$(9)\qquad \int_N^M |t^{-1-(s-s_0)}|\,dt = \int_N^M t^{-1-(\sigma-\sigma_0)}\,dt = \frac{N^{-(\sigma-\sigma_0)} - M^{-(\sigma-\sigma_0)}}{\sigma - \sigma_0}\,.$$

Now since $|s - s_0| \geqq \sigma - \sigma_0$, we get using (9) in (8),

$$(10)\qquad \left| \sum_{n=N+1}^{M} \frac{a(n)}{n^s} \right| \leqq \varepsilon \frac{|s - s_0|}{\sigma - \sigma_0} \{M^{-(\sigma-\sigma_0)} + N^{-(\sigma-\sigma_0)} - M^{-(\sigma-\sigma_0)}\}$$

$$\leqq \varepsilon \frac{|s - s_0|}{\sigma - \sigma_0} N^{-(\sigma-\sigma_0)}\,.$$

Since ε is arbitrary, (10) implies that $\sum_{N+1}^{M} a(n)/n^s$ may be made arbitrarily small for a fixed $\sigma > \sigma_0$. Hence the series converges. To complete the proof of the second part of the theorem, let s be a point in the angle. Then we have (see the figure)

$$\frac{|s - s_0|}{|\sigma - \sigma_0|} = \frac{1}{\sigma - \sigma_0} \cdot \frac{\sigma - \sigma_0}{\cos \arg |s - s_0|} \leqq \frac{1}{\cos(\pi/2 - \delta)} = \frac{1}{\sin \delta}\,.$$

Hence, from (10),

$$\left| \sum_{N+1}^{M} \frac{a(n)}{n^s} \right| < \frac{\varepsilon}{\sin \delta}$$

and the convergence is thus uniform inside the angle.

COROLLARY. *If*

$$\sum_{n=1}^{\infty} \frac{a(n)}{n^{s_0}}$$

converges, and

$$f(s) = \sum_{n=1}^{\infty} \frac{a(n)}{n^s}\,,$$

then

$$\lim_{s \to s_0} f(s) = \sum \frac{a(n)}{n^{s_0}}$$

where $s \to s_0$ through values in the region of uniform convergence described above.

The proof is a consequence of the simple remark that if a series converges uniformly, then the processes of summation and passage to a limit may under the given hypothesis be interchanged.

We now define an analogue of the radius of convergence. We divide the real numbers γ into two classes R and L. γ belongs to R if the series converges for all values of $\sigma > \gamma$. Otherwise, γ is placed in L. By what we have just proved, every member of R is to the right of every member of L. These two classes, therefore, define a Dedekind cut. Let α be the real number defined by this cut. α is then called the abscissa of convergence. The series converges if $\sigma > \alpha$ and diverges if $\sigma < \alpha$. For those values of s for which $\sigma = \alpha$, the behaviour of the series is in general undetermined. This is analogous to the situation for power series where behaviour on the circle of convergence may be simple or chaotic.

We note that a Dirichlet series may converge for no values of s as is the case for the series

$$\sum_{n=1}^{\infty} \frac{n!}{n^s}$$

or for every value of s as is the case for the series

$$\sum_{n=1}^{\infty} \frac{1}{n!n^s} .$$

We have just shown that a Dirichlet series has a half plane as its region of convergence. Inside the circle of convergence, a power series represents an analytic function. We prove the analogue for Dirichlet series.

THEOREM 3.2. *A Dirichlet series*

$$\sum_{n=1}^{\infty} \frac{a(n)}{n^s}$$

whose abscissa of convergence is α, represents an analytic function in the half plane $\sigma > \alpha$.

PROOF. Let $s_0 = \sigma_0 + it_0$ and suppose that $\sigma_0 > \alpha$. Then there exists a neighborhood of s_0 lying in a region of uniform convergence. Since each term of the series is analytic, it follows that the sum of the series is a analytic function, for the series converges uniformly in the prescribed neighborhood of s_0.

A power series has a singularity on its circle of convergence. For our purposes, we prove

THEOREM 3.3. *If $a(n) \geqq 0$, and $f(s)$ is the function determined by $\sum_{n=1}^{\infty} a(n)/n^s$, then $f(s)$ has a singularity at $s = \alpha$, the abscissa of convergence.*

PROOF. The proof is similar to its power series analogue. Let $\sigma_1 > \alpha$ and expand $f(s)$ in a Taylor series about σ_1. We get

$$f(s) = \sum_{k=0}^{\infty} \frac{f^{(k)}(\sigma_1)}{k!} (s - \sigma_1)^k . \tag{11}$$

If α is not a singular point, then the interior of the circle with centre σ_1 and radius $\sigma_1 - \alpha$ lies in the half plane $\sigma > \alpha$ and has only regular points on its boundary. Hence the radius of convergence r is greater than $\sigma_1 - \alpha$ since the circle of convergence has a singularity on its boundary. The idea of

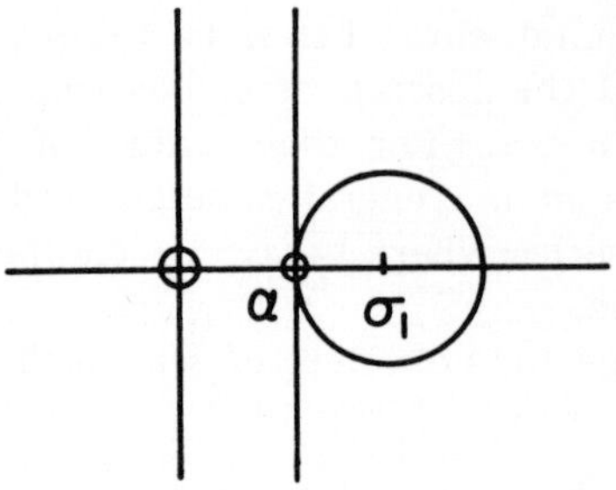

the proof is that the circle of convergence goes to the left of α and so there must be a point to the left of $\sigma = \alpha$ at which the Dirichlet series converges. This contradicts the choice of α. Here are the details:

Choose $\varepsilon > 0$ so that $r > \sigma_1 - \alpha + \varepsilon > \sigma_1 - \alpha$. Then from (11),

$$f(\alpha - \varepsilon) = \sum_{k=0}^{\infty} f^{(k)}(\sigma_1) \frac{(\alpha - \varepsilon - \sigma_1)^k}{k!} \tag{12}$$

converges. Since $f(\sigma_1) = \sum_{n=1}^{\infty} a(n)/n^{\sigma_1}$, we get

$$f^{(k)}(\sigma_1) = \sum_{n=1}^{\infty} \frac{(-\log n)^k a(n)}{n^{\sigma_1}}$$

which we substitute in the series for $f(\alpha - \varepsilon)$ in (12).

$$\begin{aligned} f(\alpha - \varepsilon) &= \sum_{k=0}^{\infty} \frac{(\alpha - \varepsilon - \sigma_1)^k}{k!} \sum_{n=1}^{\infty} \frac{(-\log n)^k a(n)}{n^{\sigma_1}} \\ &= \sum_{k=0}^{\infty} \sum_{n=1}^{\infty} \frac{(\sigma_1 - \alpha + \varepsilon)^k (\log n)^k a(n)}{k!\ n^{\sigma_1}} . \end{aligned} \tag{13}$$

Since by hypothesis $a(n) \geqq 0$ and $\sigma_1 - \alpha + \varepsilon > 0$, all terms involved in the double sum are non-negative; we may, therefore, interchange the order of summation in (13), and get

$$\begin{aligned} f(\alpha - \varepsilon) &= \sum_{n=1}^{\infty} \frac{a(n)}{n^{\sigma_1}} \sum_{k=0}^{\infty} \frac{(\sigma_1 - \alpha + \varepsilon)^k (\log n)^k}{k!} \\ &= \sum_{n=1}^{\infty} \frac{a(n)}{n^{\sigma_1}} \exp((\log n)(\sigma_1 - \alpha + \varepsilon)) \\ &= \sum_{n=1}^{\infty} \frac{a(n)}{n^{\sigma_1}} \cdot \frac{1}{n^{\alpha - \varepsilon - \sigma_1}} = \sum_{n=1}^{\infty} \frac{a(n)}{n^{\alpha - \varepsilon}} . \end{aligned}$$

Thus the series with $s = \alpha - \varepsilon$ converges contradicting the fact that α was the abscissa of convergence.

In the case of power series we obtain information about the radius of convergence from the order of magnitude of the coefficients. In the case of Dirichlet series, some information is deduced from the sum function for the coefficients. For our purposes we prove the following:

THEOREM 3.4. *Let* $S(n) = \sum_{k=1}^{n} a(k)$. *If* $\beta > 0$ *and* $S(n) = O(n^\beta)$, *then the abscissa of convergence* α *is* $\leqq \beta$. *Thus if* γ *is the lower bound of numbers* β *for which* $S(n) = O(n^\beta)$, *then* $\alpha \leqq \gamma$.

PROOF. The proof uses Abel summation. We have for $M > N$

$$\begin{aligned}
\sum_{n=N}^{M} \frac{a(n)}{n^s} &= \sum_{n=N}^{M} \frac{S(n)-S(n-1)}{n^s} \\
&= \sum_{n=N}^{M} \frac{S(n)}{n^s} - \sum_{n=N}^{M} \frac{S(n-1)}{n^s} \\
&= \sum_{n=N}^{M} S(n)\left\{\frac{1}{n^s} - \frac{1}{(n+1)^s}\right\} - \frac{S(N-1)}{N^s} + \frac{S(M)}{(M+1)^s} \\
&= \sum_{n=N}^{M} S(n)\cdot s\int_n^{n+1} \frac{dx}{x^{s+1}} - \frac{S(N-1)}{N^s} + \frac{S(M)}{(M+1)^s} \\
&= s\sum_{n=N}^{M} \int_n^{n+1} \frac{S(x)}{x^{s+1}}\,dx - \frac{S(N-1)}{N^s} + \frac{S(M)}{(M+1)^s} \\
&= s\int_N^{M+1} \frac{S(x)}{x^{s+1}}\,dx - \frac{S(N-1)}{N^s} + \frac{S(M)}{(M+1)^s} \\
&= O\left\{|s|\int_N^{M+1} \frac{|S(x)|\,dx}{x^{\sigma+1}}\right\} + O\left(\frac{1}{N^{\sigma-\beta}}\right) + O\left(\frac{1}{M^{\sigma-\beta}}\right) \\
&= O\left(|s|\int_N^{M+1} x^{-\sigma-1+\beta}dx\right) + O(N^{\beta-\sigma}) + O(M^{\beta-\sigma}) \\
&= O\left(|s|\frac{1}{\sigma-\beta}((M+1)^{\beta-\sigma} - N^{\beta-\sigma})\right) + O(N^{\beta-\sigma}) + O(M^{\beta-\sigma}) \,.
\end{aligned}$$

If $\sigma > \beta$, then the right-hand side $\to 0$ as $N \to \infty$, thus proving that the series converges.

One of the most important examples of a Dirichlet series is the Riemann zeta function. This function plays a fundamental role in the theory of the distribution of primes. We shall study its properties extensively in the next chapter but will require one property in the present discussion. The function is defined as

$$\zeta(s) = \sum_{n=1}^{\infty} \frac{1}{n^s} \,, \tag{14}$$

where $s = \sigma + it$.

We prove the following

THEOREM 3.5. *The function $\zeta(s)$ is analytic in the half plane $\sigma > 0$ except for a simple pole at $s = 1$ with residue* 1.

The series converges for $\sigma > 1$; since $S(n) = n$, the abscissa of convergence by Theorem 3.3 is $\geqq 1$. On the other hand since the series diverges for $s = 1$, the abscissa of convergence is $= 1$. The continuation of the function to the line $\sigma = 0$ is effected by the important Euler-MacLaurin formula which we state as

LEMMA 3.2. *Let $\varphi(x)$ be defined and continuous for $n \leqq x \leqq m$, where m, n are positive integers; then*

$$\sum_{k=n}^{m} \varphi(k) = \frac{\varphi(n)}{2} + \frac{\varphi(m)}{2} + \int_n^m \varphi(x)dx + \int_n^m \varphi'(x)\left(x - [x] - \frac{1}{2}\right)dx \,. \tag{15}$$

Here $[x]$ *denotes the greatest integer in* x.

This formula enables us to replace a sum by an integral and at the same time gives us a precise value for the difference. For the proof, we start with the last term on the right. We have

$$\begin{aligned}\int_n^m \varphi'(x)\left(x-[x]-\frac{1}{2}\right)dx &= \sum_{k=n}^{m-1}\int_k^{k+1}\varphi'(x)\left(x-k-\frac{1}{2}\right)dx \\ &= \sum_{k=n}^{m-1}\int_k^{k+1}\varphi'(x)x\,dx - \sum_{k=n}^{m-1}k\int_k^{k+1}\varphi'(x)\,dx \\ &\quad -\frac{1}{2}\sum_{k=n}^{m-1}\int_k^{k+1}\varphi'(x)dx\,. \end{aligned}\tag{16}$$

If we integrate the first integral on the right of (16) by parts, we get

$$\sum_{k=n}^{m-1}\int_k^{k+1}\varphi'(x)x\,dx = \sum_{k=n}^{m-1}((k+1)\,\varphi(k+1) - k\,\varphi(k)) - \sum_{k=n}^{m-1}\int_k^{k+1}\varphi(x)\,dx\,.\tag{17}$$

Therefore, combining (16) and (17), we have

$$\begin{aligned}\int_n^m \varphi'(x)\left(x-[x]-\frac{1}{2}\right)dx &= \sum_{k=n}^{m-1}((k+1)-\varphi(k+1))k\varphi(k) - \sum_{k=n}^{m-1}\int_k^{k+1}\varphi(x)\,dx \\ &\quad - \sum_{k=n}^{m-1}k(\varphi(k+1)-\varphi(k)) - \frac{1}{2}(\varphi(m)-\varphi(n)) \\ &= \sum_{k=n}^{m-1}\varphi(k+1) - \int_n^m\varphi(x)\,dx - \frac{1}{2}(\varphi(m)-\varphi(n)) \\ &= \sum_{k=n}^{m}\varphi(k) - \int_n^m\varphi(x)\,dx - \varphi(n) - \frac{1}{2}(\varphi(m)-\varphi(n))\,.\end{aligned}$$

The lemma is thus established.

We return to the proof of the continuation of $\zeta(s)$. In the above lemma we put $\varphi(x)=x^{-s}$ for $s\neq 1$ and investigate the remainder of the series for the zeta function. Using the above formula (15), we then get

$$\begin{aligned}\sum_{k=n}^{m}\frac{1}{k^s} &= \frac{1}{2n^s}+\frac{1}{2m^s}+\int_n^m x^{-s}dx \\ &\quad - s\int_n^m x^{-s-1}\left(x-[x]-\frac{1}{2}\right)dx\,.\end{aligned}\tag{18}$$

We investigate the last term on the right. Since $|x-[x]-\frac{1}{2}|\leqq 1$, it follows that

$$\begin{aligned}s\int_n^m x^{-s-1}\left(x-[x]-\frac{1}{2}\right)dx &= O\left(s\int_n^m x^{-\sigma-1}dx\right) \\ &= O\left(\frac{|s|}{\sigma}\left(\frac{1}{n^\sigma}-\frac{1}{m^\sigma}\right)\right) \\ &= O\left(\frac{|s|}{\sigma}\frac{1}{n^\sigma}\right)\,.\end{aligned}\tag{19}$$

Hence if $\sigma>0$, the second integral of (18) converges absolutely and uniformly as $m \to \infty$. We, therefore, let $m \to \infty$ in (18), and deduce after integrating the first integral,

$$\sum_{k=n}^{\infty} \frac{1}{k^s} = \frac{1}{2n^s} - \frac{n^{1-s}}{1-s} - s\int_n^{\infty} x^{1-s}\left(x - [x] - \frac{1}{2}\right) dx . \tag{20}$$

It now follows from (14) and (20) that

$$\begin{aligned} \zeta(s) &= \sum_{k=1}^{\infty} \frac{1}{k^s} = \sum_{k=1}^{n-1} \frac{1}{k^s} + \sum_{k=n}^{\infty} \frac{1}{k^s} \\ &= \sum_{k=1}^{n-1} \frac{1}{k^s} + \frac{1}{2n^s} - \frac{n^{1-s}}{1-s} - s\int_n^{\infty} x^{1-s}\left(x - [x] - \frac{1}{2}\right) dx . \end{aligned} \tag{21}$$

This is true for all n. In particular, (21) is true for $n = 1$, in which case the first sum is empty and we get

$$\zeta(s) = \frac{1}{2} - \frac{1}{1-s} - s\int_1^{\infty} x^{1-s}\left(x - [x] - \frac{1}{2}\right) dx . \tag{22}$$

The integral in (22) represents an analytic function for $\sigma > 0$ and hence $\zeta(s)$ is analytic for $\sigma > 0$ except for the simple pole at $s = 1$ where its residue is 1. The proof of Theorem 3.5 is therefore complete.

We shall complete this section with two additional results. The first asserts that the function arising from a Dirichlet series is uniquely determined by the coefficients and the second asserts that the product of two Dirichlet series is itself a Dirichlet series.

THEOREM 3.6. *If*

$$f(s) = \sum_{n=1}^{\infty} \frac{a(n)}{n^s}$$

and

$$g(s) = \sum_{n=1}^{\infty} \frac{b(n)}{n^s}$$

and the series converge for $\sigma > \sigma_0$ *and if*

$$f(s) = g(s) \ \textit{for} \ \sigma > \sigma_0 ,$$

then

$$a(n) = b(n) , \qquad n = 1, 2, \cdots .$$

PROOF. It evidently suffices to prove that if

$$\sum_{n=1}^{\infty} \frac{c(n)}{n^s} = 0 \quad \text{for } \sigma > \sigma_0 , \tag{23}$$

then

$$c(n) = 0 \qquad (n = 1, 2, \cdots) .$$

The proof is by induction on n. Indeed, by Theorem 3.1, there exists a region enclosing the real axis for $s > \sigma_0$ in which the series (23) converges uniformly. Letting $s \to \infty$ through real values of s, we infer that $c(1) = 0$.

Suppose that $c(k) = 0$ for $k < n$,
then

$$\sum_{m=1}^{\infty} \frac{c(m)}{m^s} = \sum_{m=n}^{\infty} \frac{c(m)}{m^s} = 0 .$$

That is,

$$\sum_{m=n}^{\infty} \frac{c(m)}{\left(\frac{m}{n}\right)^s} = 0 . \tag{24}$$

Again, letting $s \to \infty$, in (24), it follows that $c(n) = 0$. We shall occasionally refer to this theorem as the identity theorem.

THEOREM 3.7. *If*

$$f(s) = \sum_{n=1}^{\infty} \frac{a(n)}{n^s}$$

and

$$g(s) = \sum_{n=1}^{\infty} \frac{b(n)}{n^s}$$

converge absolutely for $\sigma > \sigma_0$, *then for* $\sigma > \sigma_0$,

$$\begin{aligned} f(s)g(s) &= \sum_{n=1}^{\infty} \frac{a(n)}{n^s} \cdot \sum_{n=1}^{\infty} \frac{b(n)}{n^s} \\ &= \sum_{n=1}^{\infty} \frac{c(n)}{n^s}, \end{aligned} \tag{25}$$

where

$$\begin{aligned} c(n) &= \sum_{jk=n} a(j)b(k) = \sum_{k|n} a(k)b\left(\frac{n}{k}\right) \\ &= \sum_{k|n} a\left(\frac{n}{k}\right)b(k) , \end{aligned} \tag{26}$$

the summation in the first expression being over all terms $a(j)b(k)$ *for which* $jk = n$ *and in the second and third expressions over all factors* k *of* n.

PROOF. Since for $\sigma > \sigma_0$, the series for $f(s)$ and $g(s)$ are absolutely convergent, we may multiply them together and rearrange the terms. We have for $\sigma > \sigma_0$,

$$f(s)\cdot g(s) = \sum_{j=1}^{\infty} \frac{a(j)}{j^s} \cdot \sum_{k=1}^{\infty} \frac{b(k)}{k^s} = \sum_{j,k}^{1,\infty} \frac{a(j)b(k)}{(jk)^s} . \tag{27}$$

Putting $jk = n$ in (27), we get,

$$f(s)g(s) = \sum_{n=1}^{\infty} \frac{1}{n^s} \cdot \sum_{jk=n} a(j)b(k) = \sum_{n=1}^{\infty} \frac{c(n)}{n^s}$$

as required.

We shall refer to this as the multiplication theorem.

4. Proof of Dirichlet's theorem. We now have all the necessary tools to prove Dirichlet's theorem. We wish to prove that there exist infinitely many primes in any arithmetic progression $kn + a$ where $(k,a) = 1$.

We first construct the necessary Dirichlet series and then argue as we did in §1.

Let χ be a character on the group of reduced residues modulo k. We complete the definition of χ by requiring that $\chi(m) = 0$ if $(m,k) > 1$. χ remains completely multiplicative, for, when $(m,n) = 1$, $\chi(mn) = \chi(m)\chi(n)$ by the definition of χ, and when $(m,k) > 1$, then $(mn,k) > 1$, and we get $\chi(m) = 0$, $\chi(mn) = 0$, thus $\chi(mn) = \chi(m)\chi(n)$.

We define the Dirichlet L-series

$$L(s,\chi) = \sum_{n=1}^{\infty} \frac{\chi(n)}{n^s} \qquad (s = \sigma + it) \tag{1}$$

and derive some important properties.

THEOREM 4.1. *If $\chi \neq \chi_1$, the principal character, then $L(s,\chi)$ converges for $\sigma > 0$.*

PROOF. We wish to apply Theorem 3.4 and try to determine the magnitude of $S(n) = \sum_{m=1}^{n} \chi(m)$. By Theorem 2.6, the sum of the value of the character summed over a reduced residue system is 0 but since the value of χ on residue classes not prime to k is defined to be 0, the theorem remains true when the sum is extended over a complete residue system modulo k. Thus, we may expect that the sum of every k terms in $S(n)$ is 0. In detail we break the sum as follows: Let $n = qk + r$ where $0 \leqq r < k$, then

$$S(n) = \left(\sum_{m=1}^{k} + \sum_{m=k+1}^{2k} + \cdots + \sum_{m=(q-1)k+1}^{qk} + \sum_{m=qk}^{n} \right) \chi(m) . \tag{2}$$

Each of the first q sums is 0 since in each case m ranges over a complete residue system modulo k. The last sum has $r < k$ terms. Thus from (2)

$$|S(n)| \leqq \sum_{m=qk}^{n} |\chi(m)| = \sum_{m=qk}^{n} 1 = r .$$

Hence $S(n) = O(1) = O(n^{\beta})$ for every $\beta > 0$ and by Theorem 3.4 $L(s,\chi)$ converges for $\sigma > 0$.

COROLLARY. *The abscissa of convergence is actually 0 since for $\sigma < 0$, the nth term does not even tend to 0.*

The relation between $L(s,\chi)$ and prime numbers is given by

THEOREM 4.2. *For $\sigma > 1$*

$$L(s,\chi) = \prod_{p} \left(1 - \frac{\chi(p)}{p^s}\right)^{-1} . \tag{3}$$

PROOF. We have by definition

$$L(s,\chi) = \sum_{n=1}^{\infty} \frac{\chi(n)}{n^s}\,, \tag{4}$$

and since $|\chi(n)| \leqq 1$, the series in (4) converges absolutely. Theorem 1.5 is then applicable and the result (3) follows.

We now wish to examine the L-series for the principal character. We have

$$\begin{aligned}\chi_1(p) &= 1 \quad \text{if } (p,k) = 1\,,\\ &= 0 \quad \text{if } (p,k) > 1, \text{ i.e., if } p\,|\,k\,.\end{aligned}$$

Using the above theorem, we get

$$\begin{aligned}L(s,\chi_1) &= \prod_p \left(1 - \frac{\chi_1(p)}{p^s}\right)^{-1}\\ &= \prod_{(p,k)=1} \left(1 - \frac{\chi_1(p)}{p^s}\right)^{-1} \prod_{p|k}\left(1 - \frac{\chi_1(p)}{p^s}\right)^{-1}\\ &= \prod_{(p,k)=1} \left(1 - \frac{1}{p^s}\right)^{-1}\\ &= \prod_p \left(1 - \frac{1}{p^s}\right)^{-1} \prod_{p|k}\left(1 - \frac{1}{p^s}\right).\end{aligned}$$

Calling the second factor $g(s)$, we therefore deduce that

$$L(s,\chi_1) = \zeta(s)\cdot g(s)\,. \tag{5}$$

The second factor $g(s)$ contains only finitely many terms; each term is analytic and so, therefore, is the product. Applying Theorem 3.4, we get

THEOREM 4.3. *$L(s,\chi_1)$ for the principal character χ_1 is analytic for $\sigma > 0$ except for a simple pole at $s = 1$. The residue at $s = 1$ is*

$$\prod_{p|k}\left(1 - \frac{1}{p}\right) = \frac{\varphi(k)}{k} = \frac{h}{k}\,.$$

To prove Dirichlet's theorem, we proceed as in Euler's proof of Euclid's theorem. The function $L(s,\chi)$ is complex valued and its logarithm is multiple valued. But we choose that branch of $\log L(s,\chi)$ which is real when s is real and $\sigma > 1$. We then get for $\sigma > 1$,

$$\log L(s,\chi) = \log \prod_p \left(1 - \frac{\chi(p)}{p^s}\right)^{-1} = -\sum_p \log\left(1 - \frac{\chi(p)}{p^s}\right). \tag{6}$$

Since $|\chi(p)/p^s| = 1/p^\sigma < 1$, we may expand the logarithm and get from (6),

$$\log L(s,\chi) = \sum_p \sum_{n=1}^{\infty} \frac{\chi(p^n)}{np^{ns}}\,. \tag{7}$$

We break the sum (7) into two parts—one sum with $n = 1$ and one sum with $n \geqq 2$.

$$(8)\qquad \log L(s,\chi) = \sum_p \frac{\chi(p)}{p^s} + \sum_p \sum_{n=2}^{\infty} \frac{\chi(p^n)}{np^{ns}} = \sum_p \frac{\chi(p)}{p^s} + R(s)\,.$$

Arguing as we did in Euler's proof, we get

$$|R(s)| \leqq \sum_p \sum_{n=2}^{\infty} \frac{1}{np^{n\sigma}} \leqq \frac{1}{2} \sum_p \sum_{n=2}^{\infty} \frac{1}{p^{n\sigma}} \leqq \frac{1}{2} \sum_p \frac{p^{-2\sigma}}{1-p^{-\sigma}}$$
$$\leqq \frac{1}{2} \cdot \frac{1}{1-2^{-\sigma}} \sum_p p^{-2\sigma} \leqq \frac{1}{2} \frac{1}{1-2^{-\sigma}} \zeta(2\sigma)\,.$$

Since $\zeta(2\sigma)$ is bounded, it follows that as $s \to 1^{+0}$, $R(s)$ remains bounded.

We wish to isolate these terms in the first sum with $p \equiv a \pmod{k}$. If we consider first the simpler case with $a = 1$, we need only sum (8) over all characters mod k and get

$$(9)\qquad \sum_\chi \log L(s,\chi) = \sum_\chi \sum_p \frac{\chi(p)}{p^s} + \sum_\chi R(s) = \sum_p \frac{1}{p^s} \sum_\chi \chi(p) + \sum_\chi R(s)\,.$$

But by Theorem 2.7, the inner sum in the first term is 0 or $h = \varphi(k)$ according as $p \not\equiv 1$, or $p \equiv 1 \pmod{k}$. It follows from (9) that

$$(10)\qquad \sum_\chi \log L(s,\chi) = h \sum_{p\equiv 1 (\mathrm{mod}\ k)} \frac{1}{p^s} + \sum_\chi R(s)\,.$$

For the more general case we first find a^* such that

$$(11)\qquad a\,a^* \equiv 1 \pmod{k}\,.$$

We multiply both sides of (8) by $\chi(a^*)$ and sum over all characters χ.

$$\sum_\chi \chi(a^*) \log L(s,\chi) = \sum_\chi \chi(a^*) \sum_p \frac{\chi(p)}{p^s} + \sum_\chi \chi(a^*)R(s)\,,$$
$$(12)\qquad = \sum_p \frac{1}{p^s} \sum_\chi \chi(a^*)\chi(p) + R^*(s)$$
$$= \sum_p \frac{1}{p^s} \sum_\chi \chi(a^*p) + R^*(s)\,.$$

By Theorem 2.7, the inner sum of the first term, however, is 0 or h according as $a^*p \not\equiv 1 \pmod{k}$ or $a^*p \equiv 1 \pmod{k}$. That is

$$\sum_\chi \chi(a^*p) = \begin{cases} h \text{ if } a^*p \equiv 1 \pmod{k}\,, \\ 0 \text{ otherwise}\,. \end{cases}$$

But by (11) $a^*p \equiv 1 \pmod{k}$ if and only if $aa^*p \equiv a \pmod{k}$ or $p \equiv a \pmod{k}$. Therefore,

$$(13)\qquad \sum_\chi \chi(a^*) \log L(s,\chi) = h \sum_{p\equiv a (\mathrm{mod}\ k)} \frac{1}{p^s} + R^*(s)\,.$$

However, $R(s)$ remains bounded as $s \to 1^{+0}$ and so then does $R^*(s)$. $L(s,\chi)$ for $\chi \neq \chi_1$ by Theorem 4.1, is analytic at $s = 1$ and so remains bounded as $s \to 1^{+0}$. By Theorem 4.3, $L(s,\chi_1) \to \infty$ as $s \to 1^{+0}$. It follows that the sum

$$\sum_{p\equiv a(\text{mod } k)} \frac{1}{p^s} \tag{14}$$

must $\to \infty$ as $s \to 1^{+0}$ *provided* $L(1,\chi) \neq 0$ for $\chi \neq \chi_1$ since the terms on the left of (13) involve the logarithm of these functions.

We must, therefore, prove that $L(1,\chi) \neq 0$ for $\chi \neq \chi_1$, and it will then follow that the series (14) must contain infinitely many terms.

Though requiring considerable preparation, the argument to this stage is from an arithmetic point of view comparatively simple and could very readily be carried out entirely in the real domain, as indeed it was by Dirichlet. The proof, therefore, of the fact that $L(1,\chi) \neq 0$, has attracted considerable attention and several proofs have been given.

Dirichlet considered two cases—the one for which the character χ assumes only real values and that for which χ assumes some complex values. The former case turns out to be the more difficult one. The argument for the complex character is as follows:

If $L(1,\chi) = 0$, then $\overline{L(1,\chi)} = L(1,\bar{\chi}) = 0, \bar{\chi}$ denoting the conjugate character. Since $L(s,\chi)$ $(\chi \neq \chi_1)$ is analytic at $s = 1$, it follows that

$$L'(1,\chi) = \lim_{s\to 1} \frac{L(s,\chi)}{s-1},$$

$$L'(1,\bar{\chi}) = \lim_{s\to 1} \frac{L(s,\bar{\chi})}{s-1}$$

both exist. Therefore, there exists a constant C such that

$$\lim_{s\to 1} \frac{\prod_{\chi\neq\chi_1} L(s,\chi)}{(s-1)^2} = C. \tag{15}$$

But by Theorem 4.3, we deduce that

$$\lim_{s\to 1} (s-1)L(s,\chi_1) = \frac{h}{k}; \tag{16}$$

whence, by (15), (16),

$$\lim_{s\to 1} \prod_{\chi} L(s,\chi) = \lim_{s\to 1} \{(s-1)L(s,\chi_1)\}(s-1)\frac{\prod_{\chi\neq\chi_1} L(s,\chi)}{(s-1)^2} = \frac{h}{k}\cdot 0\cdot C = 0. \tag{17}$$

On the other hand, we calculate the limit of this product in another way. Taking logs, we have

$$\sum_{\chi} \log L(s,\chi) = \sum_{\chi}\sum_{p}\sum_{n=1}^{\infty} \frac{\chi(p^n)}{np^{ns}} = \sum_{p}\sum_{n=1}^{\infty} \frac{1}{np^{ns}} \sum_{\chi} \chi(p^n) = h \sum_{p^n\equiv 1(\text{mod } k)} \sum_{p,n} \frac{1}{np^{ns}} \tag{18}$$

by Theorem 2.7. Each term of this series in (18) is positive, hence

$$\liminf_{s\to 1} \sum_{\chi} \log L(s,\chi) \geqq 0;$$

i.e.,

$$\liminf_{s\to 1}\prod_{\chi} L(s,\chi) \geqq e^0 = 1 .$$

This contradicts (17).

Dirichlet then showed that for real characters, $L(1,\chi)$ is a factor of the class number of binary quadratic forms belonging to a certain discriminant. The class number being necessarily $\geqq 1$, it followed that $L(1,\chi) \neq 0$.

With the development of the theory of algebraic numbers and the zeta function associated with these fields, it was discovered that $\prod_{\chi\neq\chi_1} L(1,\chi)$ is a multiple of the class number of ideals of a cyclotomic field. The advantage of this argument is that it eliminated the necessity for distinguishing between the two types of characters. We present here a function theoretic modification of this argument.

THEOREM 4.4. *If* $\chi \neq \chi_1$, $L(1,\chi_1) \neq 0$.

PROOF. From (18)

$$\begin{aligned}\log\prod_{\chi} L(s,\chi) &= \frac{1}{h}\sum_{n=1}^{\infty}\sum_{p^n\equiv 1(\text{mod } k)}\frac{1}{np^{ns}} \\ &= \sum_{m=1}^{\infty}\frac{a(m)}{m^s} = f(s) \text{ (say)} ,\end{aligned} \tag{19}$$

where $a(m)$ denote the coefficients of the Dirichlet series. We may investigate the nature of $a(m)$ more closely but we need only the fact that $1 \geqq a(m) \geqq 0$. Let the abscissa of convergence be α. Accordingly,

$$\prod_{\chi} L(s,\chi) = e^{f(s)} = 1 + f(s) + \frac{f^2(s)}{2!} + \cdots = \sum_{n=0}^{\infty}\frac{f^n(s)}{n!} . \tag{20}$$

Since the product of two Dirichlet series is, by Theorem 3.6, a Dirichlet series, it follows that

$$\frac{f^n(s)}{n!} = \sum_{k=1}^{\infty}\frac{a^{(n)}(k)}{k^s} \qquad (a^{(1)}(k) = a(k)) , \tag{21}$$

and moreover $a^{(n)}(k) \geqq 0$ as is evident by induction. Thus, by (19) and (20), if $\sigma > \alpha$,

$$\begin{aligned}\prod_{\chi} L(s,\chi) &= 1 + \sum_{m=1}^{\infty}\sum_{k=1}^{\infty}\frac{a^{(m)}(k)}{k^s} \\ &= 1 + \sum_{k=1}^{\infty}\frac{1}{k^s}\sum_{m=1}^{\infty} a^{(m)}(k) = \sum_{k=1}^{\infty}\frac{b(k)}{k^s} ,\end{aligned} \tag{22}$$

the interchange of summations being justified by absolute convergence (the terms are all non-negative). The inner sum converges as is easily seen by induction.

The idea of the proof, that $L(1,\chi) \neq 0$, is as follows. The left-hand side of (22) has a simple pole at $s = 1$ arising from $L(s,\chi_1)$, the other L series being regular at $s = 1$. If $L(1,\chi) = 0$, then this zero would cancel the pole making the left-hand side regular. But we shall show that the right-hand side has a singularity in the interval $0 < s \leqq 1$. This is a contradiction.

In the first place (by (19)), if $\sigma > 1$,

$$\left| \sum_{n=1}^{\infty} \frac{a(n)}{n^s} \right| \leqq \sum_{n=1}^{\infty} \frac{a(n)}{n^\sigma} \leqq \sum_{n=1}^{\infty} \frac{1}{n^\sigma} .$$

The series for $f(s)$ thus converges if $\sigma > 1$. This means that $\alpha \leqq 1$. Indeed, $\alpha > 1/h$ since the following argument shows that the series for $f(s)$ diverges for $s = 1/h$ $(h = \varphi(k))$: We consider only these terms of $f(s)$ for which $m = jh$. If $p \nmid k$, $p^m \equiv p^{jh} \equiv 1 \pmod k$ by the Euler-Fermat theorem. Hence, by (19)

$$f\left(\frac{1}{h}\right) = h \sum_{p^m \equiv 1 \pmod k} \frac{1}{mp^{(m/h)}} > h \sum_{p^{jh} \equiv 1 \pmod k} \frac{1}{jhp^j}$$

$$> \sum_{p \nmid k} \sum_{j=1}^{\infty} \frac{1}{jp^j} > \sum_{p \nmid k} \frac{1}{p} = \sum_{p} \frac{1}{p} - \sum_{p \mid k} \frac{1}{p} .$$

By Theorem 1.6, however, $\sum_p 1/p$ diverges and the second sum has only finitely many terms. Thus the series for $f(1/h)$ diverges and therefore $\alpha > 1/h$.

The coefficients of the series for $f(s)$ are all positive; $f(s)$, therefore, has a singularity at $s = \alpha$ by Theorem 3.3. Suppose that the Dirichlet series for $\exp(f(s))$ has abscissa of convergence β. If $f(s)$ converges, then so must $\exp(f(s))$; hence, $\beta \leqq \alpha$. On the other hand, if $\exp(f(s))$ converges, then so must $f(s)$. Therefore, $\beta \geqq \alpha$; that is, $\alpha = \beta$. Since the coefficients of $\exp(f(s))$ are positive, $\exp(f(s))$ has a singularity at $\beta = \alpha$. This means that $\prod_\chi L(s,\chi)$ has a singularity at β and $1/h < \beta \leqq 1$. On the other hand, since $L(s,\chi)$ for $\chi \neq \chi_1$ is regular for $\sigma > 0$, it follows that $\prod_\chi L(s,\chi)$ is regular for $0 < \sigma \leqq 1$ except possibly for a simple pole at $s = 1$, since $L(s,\chi_1)$ is regular except for a simple pole at $s = 1$.

If now $L(1,\chi) = 0$ for some χ (say $\chi = \chi_2$), then

$$\lim_{s \to 1} \frac{L(s,\chi_2)}{s-1} = A$$

some finite constant. Therefore, using Theorem 4.3,

$$\lim_{s \to 1} \prod_\chi L(s,\chi) = \lim_{s \to 1} (s-1)L(s,\chi_1) \frac{L(s,\chi_2)}{s-1} \prod_{\chi \neq \chi_1, \chi_2} L(s,\chi)$$

$$= \frac{h}{k} \cdot A \prod_{\chi \neq \chi_1, \chi_2} L(1,\chi) = \text{finite limit} .$$

That is, $\prod_\chi L(s,\chi)$ is regular for $0 < \sigma \leqq 1$. This contradicts the fact that it has a singularity at β.

The proof of the nonvanishing of $L(1,\chi)$ and hence of Dirichlet's theorem is therefore complete.

5. Some consequences of Dirichlet's theorem. The proof as given above, required an excursion into the theory of complex functions. This is not actually necessary as suggested above. Indeed, infinite series may be avoided altogether as two distinct proofs have recently shown. However, part of the significance of the above discussion stems from the fact that it has been extended to the general theory of the "qualitative" distribution of prime ideals. The argument actually reveals a result of a quantitative character in the following way.

Let A be any set of prime numbers. We wish to construct a measure of that proportion of all primes which are contained in the set A. One such measure is defined by the following limit when it exists:

$$\lim_{s\to 1+0} \frac{\sum_{p\in A} \frac{1}{p^s}}{\sum_p \frac{1}{p^s}} = d\,. \tag{1}$$

The lower sum is over all primes and the upper sum only over those primes in the set A. This limit is called the Dirichlet density which we abbreviate as D. D.

The above analysis will show that for arithmetic progressions the D. D. exists and is in fact independent of the residue class to which p belongs. Indeed we have

THEOREM 5.1.

$$\lim_{s\to 1+0} \frac{\sum_{p\equiv a(\mathrm{mod}\ k)} \frac{1}{p^s}}{\sum_p \frac{1}{p^s}} = \frac{1}{\varphi(k)}\ .$$

The primes are thus "equidistributed" in all residue classes modulo k.

We note incidentally that the existence of a positive Dirichlet density for a set A implies the infinitude of primes in that set. For if the D. D. is $d > 0$, and if there were only finitely many primes in A, then the numerator would have a finite limit, whereas the denominator $\to \infty$; the ratio would therefore $\to 0$.

PROOF. We have from equation (13) of §4,

$$\log L(s,\chi_1) + \sum_{\chi\neq\chi_1} \chi(a^*) \log L(s,\chi) = h \sum_{p\equiv a(\mathrm{mod}\ k)} \frac{1}{p^s} + R^*(s)\,, \tag{2}$$

where it will be remembered $R^*(s)$ remains bounded as $s \to 1^{+0}$, and $\log L(s,\chi)$ for $\chi \neq \chi_1$, remains bounded as $s \to 1^{+0}$.

Also, by equation (5) of §4,

$$L(s,\chi_1) = \zeta(s) \prod_{p|k} \left(1 - \frac{1}{p^s}\right), \tag{3}$$

and since from equation (10) of §1 we have

$$\log \zeta(s) = \sum_p \frac{1}{p^s} + R(s)\,, \tag{4}$$

where $R(s)$ remains bounded as $s \to 1^{+0}$, we get by (3)

$$\log L(s,\chi_1) = \log \zeta(s) + \log \prod_{p|k} \left(1 - \frac{1}{p^s}\right). \tag{5}$$

Therefore from (3), (4) and (5),

$$\sum_p \frac{1}{p^s} + R(s) + \log \prod_{p|k} \left(1 - \frac{1}{p^s}\right) + \sum_{\chi \neq \chi_1} \chi(a^*) \log L(s,\chi) = h \sum_{p \equiv a (\mathrm{mod}\ k)} \frac{1}{p^s} + R^*(s).$$

If we now divide by $\sum_p 1/p^s$ which we showed $\to \infty$ as $s \to 1^{+0}$, we conclude that

$$\lim_{s \to 1+0} h \frac{\sum_{p \equiv a (\mathrm{mod}\ k)} \frac{1}{p^s}}{\sum_p \frac{1}{p^s}} \to 1,$$

or

$$\frac{\sum_{p \equiv a (\mathrm{mod}\ k)} \frac{1}{p^s}}{\sum_p \frac{1}{p^s}} \to \frac{1}{h} = \frac{1}{\varphi(k)}.$$

Another, and in some ways more natural, measure of the ratio of primes in a set A is obtained as follows. Let $\pi(x)$ denote the number of all primes $\leqq x$ and $\pi_A(x)$ the number of primes $\leqq x$ but lying in the set A. Then

$$\lim_{x \to \infty} \frac{\pi_A(x)}{\pi(x)}$$

when it exists is called the natural density of the set of primes A. It is not difficult to show that when the natural density exists, then so does the D. D. The converse problem is one of the central problems in the theory of the distribution of prime ideals in algebraic number fields. The D. D. for sets of prime ideals plays an important role in the analytic theory of prime ideals—in particular, in analytic class field theory. The techniques developed here are applicable with suitable changes to ideals of algebraic number fields. It is only necessary to develop the theory of the zeta function over algebraic fields and a generalization of the notion of "arithmetic progressions" for ideals.

Problems

1. Use the fact that $\pi^2/6$ is irrational to prove that there exist infinitely many primes.
2. Prove, using Euclid's argument, that there exist infinitely many primes of the form $6n + 5$.
3. Prove by using the quadratic law of reciprocity that there exist infinitely many primes of the form $4n + 1$.

4. Prove that there are infinitely many primes of the form $8n+5$.

5. Construct the characters modulo 8, modulo 9.

6. Show directly that for each character $(\chi \neq \chi_1)$ modulo 8, $L(1,\chi) \neq 0$.

7. Prove Euclid's theorem as follows: Let $\pi(x)$ denote the number of primes $\leqq x$; then Euclid's theorem asserts that $\pi(x) \to \infty$. Prove first by induction using $N = p_1 \cdots p_k + 1$, that if p_n is the nth prime

$$p_n < 2^{2^n}.$$

Then, if $n \geqq 4$, and x is chosen so that $e^{e^{n-1}} < x < e^{e^n}$

$$\pi(x) \geqq n.$$

Deduce that

$$\pi(x) \geqq \log\log x.$$

8. Let $F_n = 2^{2^n} + 1$. These are called Fermat numbers and represent an attempt by Fermat to find an expression which represents primes only. Show that $F_n | F_{n+k} - 2$. Deduce that no two Fermat numbers have a factor in common. Hence conclude that there are infinitely many primes and that

$$p_n \leqq F_n = 2^{2^n} + 1.$$

9. Let g be an element of a group G. Let G have order h and g have order m. Prove that

(i) $\chi(g)$ is an mth root of unity.

(ii) If $\chi_1(g), \chi_2(g), \cdots, \chi_h(g)$ are the values of the h characters for the argument g, then each mth root of unity occurs equally often in this set, viz. h/m times.

Let ρ be an mth root of unity and sum the expression

$$S = \sum_{n=1}^{h} (\rho^{-1}\chi_n(g) + \rho^{-2}\chi_n(g^2) + \cdots + \rho^{-m}\chi_n(g^m))$$

in two ways.

10. Prove that if χ and ψ are two characters, then

$$\sum_{g \in G} \chi(g)\bar{\psi}(g) = \begin{cases} h & \text{if } \chi = \psi, \\ 0 & \text{otherwise}. \end{cases}$$

11. Let A be the matrix $((\chi_i(g_j)))$ where g_j are the elements of the group G and χ_i ranges over all the characters. Prove

$$A\bar{A}^T = hI,$$

and deduce that $A/\sqrt{h}$ is a unitary matrix. Also deduce that

$$\sum_{\chi} \chi(g_1)\bar{\chi}(g_2) = \begin{cases} h & \text{for } g_1 = g_2, \\ 0 & \text{otherwise}. \end{cases}$$

12. Using 11, prove that the solution of the system of equations

$$\sum_{g} \chi(g)\, x_g = y_\chi$$

is

$$x_g = \frac{1}{h} \sum_{\chi} \bar{\chi}(g) y_\chi ,$$

and conversely.

13. Prove that there are precisely h characters for a group of order h as follows. If H is a subgroup of index k with cyclic factor group G/H, then a character on H may be extended to a character for G in precisely k ways.

[If $a \in G$, then $a = c^m b$ ($m = 0, 1, 2, \cdots, k-1$) where $b \in H$ and c is a representative of the coset generating G/H. Construct a chain $e \subset H_1 \subset H_2 \subset \cdots \subset H_r = G$, whose factor groups H_i/H_{i-1} are cyclic and apply the above result.]

Characters for residue classes may be developed entirely independently of group theory.

A number theoretic function χ is called a character mod k if

(i) $\chi(a) = 0$ if $(a,k) > 1$,

(ii) $\chi(a)$ is not identically 0 ,

(iii) $\chi(a_1 a_2) = \chi(a_1)\,\chi(a_2)$,

(iv) $\chi(a_1) = \chi(a_2)$ if $a_1 \equiv a_2 \pmod{k}$.

Prove the following

14. $\chi(1) = 1$.

15. $\chi(a)$ is a $\varphi(k)$th root of unity if $(a,k) = 1$.

16. If $\chi(a)$ is a character, then so is $\bar{\chi}(a)$.

17.

$$\sum_{a \bmod k} \chi(a) = \begin{cases} 0 & \text{if } \chi \neq \chi_1 , \\ \varphi(k) & \text{if } \chi = \chi_1 , \end{cases}$$

the summation being over a complete residue system mod k.

18. If χ_1 and χ_2 are characters, then so is $\chi_1\chi_2$.

19. There exist only finitely many characters.

20. If χ ranges over all characters, and ψ is a character, then $\chi\psi$ ranges over all characters.

21. If $d > 0$, $(d,k) = 1$, $d \not\equiv 1 \pmod{k}$, then there exists a character χ for which $\chi(d) \neq 1$.

[If $d \not\equiv 1 \pmod{k}$, then there exists $p^l \mid k$, $p > 2$, $l > 0$ or $2^l \mid k$ so that $d \not\equiv 1 \pmod{p^l}$ or mod 2. Let g be a primitive root mod p^l and $\zeta = \exp[2\pi i/\varphi(p^l)]$. If $a \equiv g^b \pmod{k}$, define $\chi(d) = \zeta^b$ and consider in a similar way the case $2^l \mid k$, recalling that ± 5 generate the residues mod 2^l.]

22. Show that if c is the number of characters,

$$\sum_{\chi} \chi(a) = \begin{cases} c & \text{if } a \equiv 1 \pmod{k} , \\ 0 & \text{otherwise} . \end{cases}$$

23. Show that $c = \varphi(k)$.

24. Using Theorem 3.6, determine the arithmetic nature of the coefficients of

$$\zeta^2(s) = \sum_{n=1}^{\infty} \frac{d(n)}{n^s} .$$

$$\frac{1}{\zeta(s)} = \prod_p \left(1 - \frac{1}{p^s}\right) = \sum_{n=1}^{\infty} \frac{\mu(n)}{n^s} .$$

In the following series of problems, we derive a proof that for real χ, $L(1,\chi) \neq 0$.

25. Show by partial summation that

$$\sum_{n \geqq x} \frac{\chi(n)}{\sqrt{n}} = O\left(\frac{1}{\sqrt{x}}\right) .$$

26. For some constant B, show that

$$\sum_{n \leqq x} \frac{1}{\sqrt{n}} = 2\sqrt{x} + B + O\left(\frac{1}{\sqrt{x}}\right) ,$$

by using the Euler-Maclaurin formula.

27. If

$$f(n) = \sum_{d \mid n} \chi(d) ,$$

then $f(m)f(n) = f(mn)$ if $(m,n) = 1$. Deduce that since for real χ, $\chi(p) = \pm 1$, then $f(n) \geqq 0$ for all n and $f(m^2) \geqq 1$.

28. Let

$$G(x) = \sum_{n \leqq x} \frac{f(n)}{\sqrt{n}} .$$

Show, using 27, that $G(x) \to \infty$ as $x \to \infty$.

29. Evaluate $G(x)$ in another way, viz. show that

$$G(x) = \sum_{m \leqq \sqrt{x}} \frac{\chi(m)}{\sqrt{m}} \cdot \sum_{n \leqq x/m} \frac{1}{\sqrt{n}} + \sum_{n \leqq \sqrt{x}} \frac{1}{\sqrt{n}} \sum_{m \leqq x/n} \frac{\chi(m)}{\sqrt{m}} - \sum_{n \leqq \sqrt{x}} \frac{1}{\sqrt{n}} \sum_{m \leqq \sqrt{x}} \frac{\chi(m)}{\sqrt{m}} .$$

Use (25) and (26) to deduce that

$$G(x) = 2L(1,\chi)\sqrt{x} + O(1) .$$

Infer from (28) that $L(1,\chi) \neq 0$.

30. Let $f(s) = \sum_{n=1}^{\infty} a(n)/n^s$ with $s = \sigma + it$. Define the abscissa of absolute convergence β as the g.l.b. of numbers σ for which

$$\sum_{n=1}^{\infty} \frac{|a(n)|}{n^{\sigma}}$$

converges.

(a) Show that for the L functions $\beta = 1$.

(b) Show that $(1 - 1/2^{s-1})\zeta(s) = \sum_{n=1}^{\infty} (-1)^{n+1}/n^s$ and show that for this series $\alpha = 0$, and $\beta = 1$, where α is the abscissa of convergence.

(c) Prove for any Dirichlet series that $\beta - \alpha \leqq 1$. [If $\sum_{n=1}^{\infty} a(n)/n^s$ converges, then $a(n)/n^{\sigma}$ is bounded as $n \to \infty$.]

31. The analogue of Cauchy's nth root test for power series is as follows. Let

$$f(s) = \sum_{n=1}^{\infty} \frac{a(n)}{n^s},$$

and

$$S(n) = \sum_{k=1}^{n} a(k),$$

and when $\sum_{n=1}^{\infty} a(n)$ converges, let

$$r(n) = \sum_{k=n+1}^{\infty} a(k).$$

Put

$$\gamma = \limsup_{n\to\infty} \frac{\log |S(n)|}{\log n}, \qquad \delta = \limsup \frac{\log |r(n)|}{\log n}.$$

Then $\alpha = \gamma$ if $\sum_{k=1}^{\infty} a(k)$ diverges and $\alpha = \delta$ otherwise. [Consider real values of s for which the series converges and apply partial summation to $S(n) = \sum b(n)n^s$ where $b(n) = a(n)n^{-s}$.] Apply the above to determine the abscissa of convergence of the series with $a(n) = 1$, $a(n) = (-1)^n$, $a(n) = n^{-1/2}$, $a(n) = \log n$, $a(n) = \chi(n)$ a character mod k.

32. The theory of the cyclotomic equations may be used to prove that there exist infinitely many primes in the progressions $kn \pm 1$. As an example let p be a fixed prime and let

$$f_p(x) = x^{p-1} + x^{p-2} + \cdots + x + 1$$

be the cyclotomic polynomial belonging to p. Prove that if a prime $q \mid f_p(x)$, then $q \equiv 1 \pmod p$ by noticing that if $q \mid f_p(x)$, then $x^p \equiv 1 \pmod q$. Deduce that there exist infinitely many primes $\equiv 1 \pmod p$. [Suppose that there are only finitely many primes $\equiv 1 \pmod p$ say $p_1, p_2, \cdots, p_r$. Let $x_r = pp_1p_2\cdots p_r$ and show that

$$f(x_r) \equiv 1 \pmod p, \text{ that a prime } q \equiv 1 \pmod p$$

divides $f(x_r)$ and that $q \neq p_1, p_2, \cdots, p_r$.]

Notes to Chapter I

1. Euclid's theorem is found in the *Elements*, Book 9, Proposition 20. This book is devoted primarily to propositions of an arithmetic character.

Since the time of Euclid, many proofs of a substantially different nature have been given. Those in the text are supplemented by three proofs in the problem set. One such proof uses the difficult result that π^2 is irrational.

Euler's proof of Euclid's theorem is given in his "Introductio..." but was first published in the Proceedings of the Imperial Academy of Sciences of St. Petersburg, 1737 in a communication entitled "Variae observationes circa series infinitas."

There exist theorems of a general character concerning the arithmetic properties of primes dividing prescribed polynomials such as is used in

Theorem 1.3. One such property is given in the problems and the proof may be extended to prove Dirichlet's theorem for the progressions $kn \pm 1$ for all k. Other results may be found in *Introduction to number theory* by T. Nagell. Proofs of theorems dealing with quadratic polynomials rely for the most part on the reciprocity law.

2. For a purely arithmetic discussion of characters, the reader may consult the section on characters in *Vorlesungen über Zahlentheorie*, Vol. 1, by E. Landau. See Problems 14-23.

The reader who is better acquainted with the theory of groups and the notion of factor group, may find a simpler derivation of the properties of characters in the problem set. The derivation avoids the comparatively difficult fundamental theorem on abelian groups but requires a knowledge of the elementary properties of factor groups.

Characters were discussed in detail for the first time by Dirichlet although Euler used quadratic characters and Gauss used 4th roots of unity in discussing the theory of biquadratic residues. Since the time of Dirichlet, characters and their properties have been developed extensively, and the idea pervades much of the modern theory of representations.

3. An extensive account of the general theory of Dirichlet series may be found in the Cambridge tract of Hardy and Riesz, or in the *Theory of functions* by E. C. Titchmarsh.

4. Dirichlet first published a proof of the theorem which now bears his name in 1837 in Proceedings of the Royal Prussian Academy of Sciences and only minor modifications were made in his proof until recently. These earlier modifications centered about a proof of the fact that $L(1,\chi) \neq 0$ $(\chi \neq \chi_1)$. Dirichlet based his proof on the fact that for real characters $L(1,\chi)$ is a factor of the class number of binary quadratic forms belonging to a suitable discriminant, while for complex characters, his proof is substantially that given in the text. Many proofs have since been published but these are mainly of three types—the first uses elementary estimates to obtain a lower bound for $L(1,\chi)$; see problems 25-29. The second uses the idea that $L(1,\chi)$ is a factor of the class number of ideals of a suitable cyclotomic field and the third uses function-theoretic proofs which are generally based on Theorem 2.8.

Recent proofs were given by H. Zassenhaus [Comment. Math. Helv. **22** (1949), 232-259] and A. Selberg [Ann. of Math. (2) **50** (1949), 297-304]. The former removes the transcendental elements from Dirichlet's proof by using only finite series but otherwise makes no fundamental change. The latter uses an ingenious method for finding a lower bound for $\pi_k(x,a)$ the number of primes less than x and belonging to the residue class a modulo k.

5. If we use a notation introduced by H. Hasse, the analysis of this section may be somewhat simplified. $f(s) \approx g(s)$ means that $f(s) - g(s) = O(1)$ (as $s \to 1^{+0}$), then it is easy to see that

$$\zeta(a) \approx \frac{1}{s-1}\,, \text{ and } \sum_p \frac{1}{p^s} \approx \log \zeta(s) \approx \log \frac{1}{s-1}\,.$$

Dirichlet density may therefore be defined as

$$\lim_{s\to 1+0} \frac{\sum_{p\in A} \frac{1}{p^s}}{\log \frac{1}{s-1}} .$$

We have actually proved that

$$\lim_{s\to 1+0} \frac{\sum_{p\equiv a_1} \frac{1}{p^s}}{\sum_{p\equiv a_2} \frac{1}{p^s}} = 1 .$$

Dirichlet himself conjectured that

$$\lim_{x\to\infty} \frac{\pi_k(x,a_1)}{\pi_k(x,a_2)} = 1$$

though this was not proved until some time later.

Chapter II

Distribution of Primes

1. Introduction. In this chapter, we give a detailed discussion of the prime number theorem and some consequences thereof. We shall give a variety of proofs—some similar in nature others using basically different ideas. The common thread, if there be any, is the basic dependence on the Riemann zeta function. It is true that the proof of the prime number theorem given by A. Selberg in collaboration with P. Erdös, avoids any mention of the zeta function; we shall, however, restrict our attention only to "analytic" proofs and refer the reader to several books on elementary number theory for accounts of the Selberg-Erdös proof.

The theory of the distribution of primes has been a focal point of mathematical interest for many years. Indeed, in 1751, Euler wrote "Mathematicians have tried in vain to this day to discover some order in the sequence of prime numbers, and we have reason to believe that it is a mystery into which the human mind will never penetrate. To convince ourselves, we have only to cast a glance at tables of primes (which some have constructed to values beyond 100,000) and we should perceive at once that there reigns neither order nor rule."

His assertion that there is neither rule nor order is indeed the first impression we get on examining a table of primes. Closer observation, however, reveals the following facts:

(i) Gaps between successive primes tend on the whole to increase in size.

(ii) Instances of "twin primes," which is to say primes whose difference is 2, occur as far as the tables go.

(iii) There are instances of very wide gaps between successive primes.

We shall formulate these descriptive properties mathematically.

Let

$$p_1, p_2, \cdots, p_n, \cdots$$

denote the sequence of prime numbers and let

$$\chi(n) = \begin{cases} 1 & \text{if } n \text{ is a prime,} \\ 0 & \text{otherwise} \end{cases}$$

be the characteristic function of the primes.

We may infer that Euler's main concern was with the behavior of p_n. The determination of $\chi(n)$ is equivalent to giving a rule which will enable us to decide whether or not a given integer is a prime. Several such rules are known; the simplest example being the rule inferred from Wilson's theorem and its converse: n is a prime if and only if $n! + 1$ is divisible by n. No one of these rules, however, gives a practical decision procedure.

Euler, moreover, would have been content with a formula for p_n in terms of $p_1, p_2, \cdots, p_{n-1}$, and he thought it likely that such a formula would be discovered in virtue of the fact he had discovered such a formula for $\sigma(n)$ the sum of the divisors of n.

It seemed to him that the irregularities of $\sigma(n)$ must be "at least as great" as those of p_n since $\sigma(n) = n + 1$ if and only if n is prime. We shall derive Euler's celebrated result in Chapter III. Unfortunately no satisfactory formula for p_n has been discovered to date.

If we put

$$\delta(n) = p_n - p_{n-1},$$

then the celebrated conjecture involved in (ii) is that $\delta(n) = 2$ infinitely often, i. e., $\liminf \delta(n) = 2$. In other words there exist infinitely many twin primes. This conjecture has not yet been decided.

On the other hand, the following argument allows us to interpret (iii) as meaning

$$\limsup_{n\to\infty} \delta(n) = \infty .$$

The proof is simple and perhaps well-known. For the set of integers

$$n! + 2, n! + 3, \cdots, n! + n$$

are all composite having respectively the factors $2, 3, \cdots, n$, and the conclusion follows directly.

Thus the questions about the functions $\chi(n)$, and p_n in the form proposed by Euler are indeed difficult ones, and it is not very surprising that not much progress in this direction has been made.

On the other hand, if we are content with asymptotic relations of these and other functions and their averages, we are in a more favorable position. The prime numbers, in spite of their seemingly irregular character, do exhibit some features of regularity. These features may be stated in precise mathematical form and have been the object of intense mathematical research for many years. We devote this chapter to some of the consequences of this research.

2. Some preliminary results. The function with which we shall be primarily concerned is

$$\pi(x) = \sum_{n \leqq x} 1 = \text{no. of primes} \leqq x .$$

We notice that $\pi(x)$ is defined for all real x; it is a step function with jumps occurring at the primes. It should be observed that $\pi(n)$, for n an integer, may be regarded as an average since

$$\frac{\pi(n)}{n} = \frac{1}{n} \sum_{k=1}^{n} \chi(k)$$

is an average of $\chi(n)$. As we noted above, the function $\pi(x)$ and the question concerning the diminishing frequency of primes attracted the attention of mathematicians from the earliest times. Indeeed, in 1780, Legendre arrived at an empirical formula which is remarkable for the precision with which it represents $\pi(x)$ for relatively small values of x. The formula is

$$\pi(x) = \frac{x}{\log x - c},$$

where Legendre gave 1.08 for the approximate value of the constant c. So surprising was the simplicity of this formula that Abel in 1823 called it "the most remarkable in all mathematics."

Independently, Gauss (at age about 15), around 1792 suggested the following answer to the question about the diminishing frequency of the primes: the number of primes per unit interval is $1/\log x$. He therefore proposed the formula

$$\int_2^x \frac{dt}{\log t}$$

for the function $\pi(x)$.

It is not clear from their statements in what precise sense either author intended his formula to represent $\pi(x)$. We may presume that they intended an asymptotic relation with a relatively small error term. We may even infer that Legendre implied a bounded error for his formula. That is,

$$\pi(x) = \frac{x}{\log x - 1.08} + O(1) .$$

What either intended precisely is not perhaps important. It is sufficiently remarkable that either had arrived at so simple a formula for so erratic a function.

The first result that we prove is that the primes are relatively sparse.

THEOREM 2.1.

(1) $$\pi(x) = o(x);$$

that is,

$$\lim_{x\to\infty} \frac{\pi(x)}{x} = 0 .$$

This is often expressed by saying "the probability that an integer, chosen at random, should be prime is zero."

PROOF. The proof makes use of the idea of the "sieve" of Eratosthenes. This ancient principle has been developed by Viggo Brun and others into a fruitful general method which, skilfully applied, leads to deep and interesting results of number theory. In one of the adaptations, Brun proved that the sum of the reciprocals of the twin primes converges. Eratosthenes' sieve is simple; if we wish to determine all primes $\leqq n$, we consider all primes $p \leqq \sqrt{n}$ and simply strike out from the sequence $1, 2, \cdots, n$, all multiples of these primes. We modify this idea slightly. Let

$$\alpha(x, r) \tag{2}$$

denote the number of integers $\leqq x$ which are not divisible by $p_1, p_2, \cdots, p_r$. For example, $\alpha(10, 1) = 5$, since $p_1 = 2$; $\alpha(15, 2) = 5$; and in particular $\pi(x) = \alpha(x, r) + r$, where r is chosen so that $p_r \leqq \sqrt{x}$.

To calculate $\alpha(x, r)$, we subtract from $[x]$ all multiples of $p_1, p_2, \cdots, p_r$; there are

$$\sum_{i=1}^{r} \left[\frac{x}{p_i}\right]$$

of these. In doing so, however, we have subtracted multiples of $p_i p_j$ twice, of $p_i p_j p_k$ thrice and in general multiples of $p_{i_1} \cdots p_{i_k}$ k times. We first replace multiples of $p_i p_j$. There are

$$\sum_{1 \leq i < j \leq r} \left[\frac{x}{p_i p_j}\right]$$

of these, but in doing so we have replaced multiples of $p_i p_j p_k$ thrice since any multiple of $p_i p_j p_k$ is a multiple of $p_i p_j$, $p_i p_k$, $p_j p_k$. We therefore subtract multiples of $p_i p_j p_k$, and so on. This leads to

$$\alpha(x, r) = [x] - \sum_{1 \leq i \leq r} \left[\frac{x}{p_i}\right] + \sum_{1 \leq i < j \leq r} \left[\frac{x}{p_i p_j}\right] - \sum_{1 \leq i < j < k \leq r} \left[\frac{x}{p_i p_j p_k}\right] + \cdots. \tag{3}$$

To see this formula clearly, let n be an integer $\leqq x$ which is divisible by $p_1, p_2, \cdots, p_k$ but no other primes. Then n contributes 1 to $[x]$, 1 to exactly k of $[x/p_i]$, 1 to exactly $C_{k,2}$ of $[x/p_i p_j]$, and in general, 1 to exactly $C_{k,m}$ of $[x/p_{i_1} \cdots p_{i_m}]$, where $C_{k,m}$ is the binomial coefficient. Hence, if $k \geqq 1$, the amount contributed by n to the right-hand side of (3) is

$$1 - \binom{k}{1} + \binom{k}{2} - \cdots = (1-1)^k = 0.$$

On the other hand, if n is not divisible by $p_1, \cdots, p_r$, then it contributes exactly 1 to the right-hand side. This completes the proof of (3).

Now evidently

$$\pi(x) \leqq \alpha(x, r) + r, \tag{4}$$

for the primes between p_r and x are certainly included among the primes not divisible by $p_1, \cdots, p_r$.

$$\begin{aligned} \pi(x) \leqq x - \sum_{1 \leq i \leq r} \frac{x}{p_i} + \sum_{1 \leq i < j \leq r} \frac{x}{p_i p_j} - \cdots + r \\ + [x] - x + \sum_{1 \leq i \leq r} \left(\left(\frac{x}{p_i}\right) - \left[\frac{x}{p_i}\right]\right) + \cdots. \end{aligned} \tag{5}$$

Since $\xi - [\xi] \leqq 1$, and

$$\sum_{1 \leq i_1 < i_2 < \cdots < i_m \leq r} \left\{\left(\frac{x}{p_{i_1} \cdots p_{i_m}}\right) - \left[\frac{x}{p_{i_1} \cdots p_{i_m}}\right]\right\} \leqq \sum_{1 \leq i_1, \cdots, i_m \leq r} 1 = C_{m,r} \tag{6}$$

we conclude from (5) and (6) that

$$\pi(x) \leqq x\left(1 - \sum_{1\leqq i\leqq r} \frac{1}{p_i} + \sum_{1\leqq i<j\leqq r} \frac{1}{p_i p_j} - \sum_{1\leqq i<j<k\leqq r} \frac{1}{p_i p_j p_k} + \cdots\right)$$

$$(7) \qquad + r + 1 + \binom{r}{1} + \cdots + \binom{r}{m} + \cdots + 1$$

$$\leqq x \prod_{i=1}^{r}\left(1 - \frac{1}{p_i}\right) + r + 2^r .$$

We showed, in Chapter I, § 1, (12), that $\prod_p (1 - 1/p)^{-1}$ diverges; indeed, that

$$\prod_{p\leqq y}\left(1 - \frac{1}{p}\right)^{-1} > \log y .$$

It is therefore possible to choose r so large that

$$(8) \qquad \prod_{i=1}^{r}\left(1 - \frac{1}{p_i}\right) < \frac{\varepsilon}{2} .$$

Then from (7) and (8),

$$\pi(x) < \frac{x}{2}\varepsilon + r + 2^r$$

$$< \frac{x}{2}\varepsilon + 2^{r+1}$$

$$< x\left(\frac{\varepsilon}{2} + \frac{2^{r+1}}{x}\right).$$

If x is sufficiently large, $2^{r+1}/x < \varepsilon/2$, and hence

$$\pi(x) < \varepsilon x ,$$

as was to be proved.

We shall now show that the conjecture

$$(9) \qquad \pi(x) \sim \frac{x}{\log x}$$

is reasonable. In order to do so, we shall require several preliminary results. The first relates the behavior of $\pi(n)$ to that of p_n.

THEOREM 2.2. *If p_n represents the nth prime, then*

$$(10) \qquad \pi(n) \sim \frac{n}{\log n}$$

if and only if

$$(11) \qquad p_n \sim n \log n .$$

PROOF. If

$$\pi(n) \sim \frac{n}{\log n} ,$$

then

(12)
$$n = \pi(p_n) \sim \frac{p_n}{\log p_n} .$$

Hence

(13)
$$\log n \sim \log p_n - \log\log p_n \sim \log p_n$$

since $p_n \to \infty$ and $\log\log p_n/\log p_n \to 0$.

From (12) and (13), it follows that

$$p_n \sim n \log p_n \sim n \log n .$$

Conversely, suppose that

(14)
$$p_n \sim n \log n .$$

Choose k so that

(15)
$$p_n \leqq k < p_{n+1} ,$$

then

$$n = \pi(p_n) = \pi(k) .$$

Since from (14),

$$\frac{p_n}{p_{n+1}} \sim \frac{n \log n}{(n+1)\log(n+1)} \sim 1 ,$$

it follows from (15) that

(16)
$$p_n \sim k .$$

In other words, from (14) and (16),

(17)
$$n \log n \sim k ,$$

or

$$\log n + \log\log n \sim \log k ,$$

and this implies that

(18)
$$\log n \sim \log k .$$

Consequently, from (17), (18),

$$n \sim \frac{k}{\log n} \sim \frac{k}{\log k} ,$$

and therefore

$$\pi(k) \sim \frac{k}{\log k} ,$$

as required.

Before proceeding, we derive some consequences of the Euler-MacLaurin theorem. These results are estimates for certain frequently used sums.

THEOREM 2.3. *If* $x \geqq 2$, *then*

(19)
$$\sum_{1\leqq n\leqq x} \log n = x\log x - x + O(\log x)\ .$$

PROOF. This is a first approximation to Stirling's formula. From the Euler-MacLaurin formula, Chapter I, Lemma 3.2, we have, with $\varphi(x) = \log x$,

$$\begin{aligned}\sum_{1\leqq n\leqq x} \log n &= \frac{\log x}{2} + \int_1^x \log t\,dt + \int_1^x \Big(t - [t] - \frac{1}{2}\Big)\frac{dt}{t}\\ &= \frac{\log x}{2} + x(\log x - 1) + O\Big(\int_1^x \frac{dt}{t}\Big)\\ &= x\log x - x + O(\log x)\ ,\end{aligned}$$

since $|t - [t] - \frac{1}{2}| \leqq 1$.

THEOREM 2.4. *If* $x \geqq 1$, *then*

(20)
$$\sum_{1\leqq n\leqq x} \frac{1}{n} = \log x + \gamma + O\Big(\frac{1}{x}\Big)\,,$$

where

$$\gamma = \lim_{N\to\infty}\Big(\sum_{n=1}^{N}\frac{1}{n} - \log N\Big) = .577\cdots$$

is Euler's constant.

PROOF. In the Euler-MacLaurin formula, we put $\varphi(x) = 1/x$, then

(21)
$$\begin{aligned}\sum_{1\leqq n\leqq x} \frac{1}{n} &= \frac{1}{2} + \frac{1}{2x} + \int_1^x \frac{dt}{t} - \int_1^x \Big(t - [t] - \frac{1}{2}\Big)\frac{dt}{t^2}\\ &= \frac{1}{2} + O\Big(\frac{1}{x}\Big) + \log x - \int_1^x \frac{t - [t] - \frac{1}{2}}{t^2}\,dt\ .\end{aligned}$$

On the other hand,

(22)
$$\int_x^\infty \frac{t - [t] - \frac{1}{2}}{t^2}\,dt = O\Big(\int_x^\infty \frac{dt}{t^2}\Big) = O\Big(\frac{1}{x}\Big)\,;$$

hence, from (21) and (22),

(23)
$$\sum_{1\leqq n\leqq x} \frac{1}{n} = \log x + O\Big(\frac{1}{x}\Big) + \frac{1}{2} - \int_1^\infty \frac{t - [t] - \frac{1}{2}}{t^2}\,dt\ .$$

Since the integral in (23) converges (as (22) shows), we could define

$$\gamma = \frac{1}{2} - \int_1^\infty \frac{t - [t] - \frac{1}{2}}{t^2}\,dt\ .$$

It may be of interest, however, to express this value in the form given in the theorem. Indeed,

$$\begin{aligned}\int_1^\infty \frac{t - [t] - \frac{1}{2}}{t^2}\,dt &= \lim_{N\to\infty}\int_1^N \frac{t - [t] - \frac{1}{2}}{t^2}\,dt\\ &= \lim_{N\to\infty}\sum_{n=1}^{N-1}\int_n^{n+1} \frac{t - [t] - \frac{1}{2}}{t^2}\,dt\ .\end{aligned}$$

In the interval $n \leqq t < n+1$, $[t] = n$, and therefore

$$\int_n^{n+1} \frac{t-[t]-\frac{1}{2}}{t^2}\,dt = \log(n+1) - \log n + n\left(\frac{1}{n+1} - \frac{1}{n}\right) + \frac{1}{2}\left(\frac{1}{n+1} - \frac{1}{n}\right),$$

$$\frac{1}{2} - \lim_{N\to\infty} \sum_{n=1}^{N-1} \int_n^{n+1} \frac{t-[t]-\frac{1}{2}}{t^2}\,dt = \frac{1}{2} - \lim_{N\to\infty}\left\{\log N - \sum_{n=1}^{N-1} \frac{1}{n+1} + \frac{1}{2N} - \frac{1}{2}\right\}$$
$$= \lim_{N\to\infty}\left\{\sum_{n=1}^{N} \frac{1}{n} - \log N\right\}.$$

Theorem 2.5. *If $x \geqq 2$, there exists a constant B such that*

$$\sum_{2\leqq n\leqq x} \frac{1}{n\log n} = \log\log x + B + O\left(\frac{1}{x\log x}\right). \tag{24}$$

Proof. In the Euler-MacLaurin formula, we put $\varphi(x) = 1/x\log x$, then

$$\sum_{2\leqq n\leqq x} \frac{1}{n\log n} = \frac{1}{4\log 2} + \frac{1}{2x\log x} + \int_2^x \frac{dt}{t\log t} - \int_2^x \frac{t-[t]-\frac{1}{2}}{(t\log t)^2}(1+\log t)dt\,.$$

Since

$$\frac{t-[t]-\frac{1}{2}}{(t\log t)^2}(1+\log t) = O\left(\frac{1}{t^2\log t}\right),$$

then

$$\int_2^\infty \frac{t-[t]-\frac{1}{2}}{(t\log t)^2}(1+\log t)dt$$

converges to C_1 (say). Hence

$$\sum_{2\leqq n\leqq x} \frac{1}{n\log n} = B_1 + \log\log x + O\left(\frac{1}{x\log x}\right) + C_1 + O\left(\int_x^\infty \frac{1+\log t}{(t\log t)^2}\,dt\right)$$
$$= \log\log x + B + O\left(\frac{1}{x\log x}\right).$$

With the help of these estimates, we shall now give two arguments which show that the conjecture

$$p_n \sim n\log n$$

or, by Theorem 2.2, the equivalent statement

$$\pi(n) \sim \frac{n}{\log n},$$

is indeed reasonable.

We showed in Chapter I, § 1, (10), that

$$\log\zeta(s) \sim \sum_p \frac{1}{p^s}$$

as $s \to 1^{+0}$, the second sum ranging over all primes p. In that event, we may reasonably expect that

$$\log \sum_{1 \leqq n \leqq x} \frac{1}{n} \sim \sum_{p \leqq x} \frac{1}{p},$$

as $x \to \infty$. Using Theorem 2.4, this leads us to expect that

$$\sum_{p \leqq x} \frac{1}{p} \sim \log \log x . \tag{25}$$

Now (25) is in fact correct and may be proved by an elementary argument. On the other hand, by Theorem 2.6,

$$\sum_{2 \leqq n \leqq x} \frac{1}{n \log n} \sim \log \log x$$

and we conclude that $p_n \sim n \log n$ is consistent with (25).

An important decisive step toward a proof of the prime number theorem was taken in 1848 by Tchebycheff. He proved that if the limit

$$\lim_{x \to \infty} \frac{\pi(x) \log x}{x}$$

exists, then its value must be 1; and in addition determined constants A and B for which the relations

$$A \frac{x}{\log x} \leqq \pi(x) \leqq B \frac{x}{\log x} \tag{26}$$

hold. He thus showed that $x/\log x$ is the correct order of magnitude of $\pi(x)$.

We shall give another argument due in essence to Tchebycheff which, once again, supports the truth of the prime number theorem.

THEOREM 2.6.

$$\sum_{p \leqq n} \frac{\log p}{p} \sim \log n . \tag{27}$$

PROOF. From elementary arithmetic, we know that the power of the prime p dividing $n!$ is

$$\sum_{i=1}^{\infty} \left[\frac{n}{p^i} \right].$$

The series is in reality finite and terminates when $p^i > n$. Thus

$$n! = \prod_{p \leqq n} p^{\sum_{i=1}^{\infty}[n/p^i]}$$

or, on taking logarithms,

$$\log n! = \sum_{p \leqq n} \log p \left[\frac{n}{p} \right] + \sum_{p \leqq n} \log p \left(\left[\frac{n}{p^2} \right] + \left[\frac{n}{p^3} \right] + \cdots \right). \tag{28}$$

The second sum in (28) is

$$O\Big(n \sum_{p \leq n} \log p\Big(\frac{1}{p^2} + \frac{1}{p^3} + \cdots\Big)\Big),$$

since $[n/p] \leq n/p$. Moreover,

$$\begin{aligned}\sum_{p \leq n} \log p\Big(\frac{1}{p^2} + \frac{1}{p^3} + \cdots\Big) &= O\Big(\sum_{p \leq n} \log p \frac{1}{p(p-1)}\Big) \\ &= O\Big(\sum_{p \leq n} \frac{\log p}{p^2}\Big) = O\Big(\sum_{p \leq n} \frac{1}{p^{2-\varepsilon}}\Big) \\ &= O\Big(\sum_{k \leq n} \frac{1}{k^{2-\varepsilon}}\Big) = O\Big(\sum_{k=2}^{\infty} \frac{1}{k^{2-\varepsilon}}\Big) = O(1).\end{aligned}$$

Consequently, the second sum in (28) is $O(n)$.

In the first sum, we replace $[\xi]$ by ξ and calculate the error:

$$\sum_{p \leq n} \Big(\frac{n}{p}\Big) \log p = \sum_{p \leq n} \Big[\frac{n}{p}\Big] \log p + \sum_{p \leq n} \Big\{\Big(\frac{n}{p}\Big) - \Big[\frac{n}{p}\Big]\Big\} \log p.$$

Since $(n/p) - [n/p] \leq 1$, the second sum is

$$O\Big(\sum_{p \leq n} \log p\Big) = O\Big(\log n \sum_{p \leq n} 1\Big) = O(\log n\, \pi(n)).$$

By Theorem 2.1, $\pi(n) = o(n)$, hence

$$\sum_{p \leq n} \Big(\frac{n}{p}\Big) \log p = \sum_{p \leq n} \Big[\frac{n}{p}\Big] \log p + o(n \log n). \tag{29}$$

Therefore, from (28) and (29),

$$\log n! = \sum_{p \leq n} \frac{n}{p} \log p + o(n \log n). \tag{30}$$

But by Theorem 2.3,

$$\log n! = n \log n + O(n).$$

Putting this value in (30) we get the required result.

COROLLARY. *Note that if we assume the truth of* (26), *then* $\pi(n) = O(n/\log n)$, *the error in* (29) *is replaced by* $O(n)$, *and we deduce the sharper result*

$$\sum_{p \leq n} \frac{\log p}{p} = \log n + O(1).$$

(27) however is again consistent with the supposition that $p_n \sim n \log n$.

The next decisive step toward a proof of the prime number theorem was taken in 1859 by Riemann. In a research paper celebrated for its great wealth of ideas, he formulated an analytic approach to the problem. His proof of the prime number theorem contained certain gaps, however, which were not filled in until some years later. It was essentially his method, however, which was carried to fruition in 1895 independently by Hadamard and de la Vallée Poussin.

We shall give in this chapter several different proofs of the prime number theorem. The first, which is due to Landau, 1903 and 1912, proceeds directly to the function $\pi(x)$ but involves a nonabsolutely convergent integral. As a consequence, some of the steps require detailed analysis. In later sections we shall give alternative proofs. In some instances these avoid the analytic difficulties caused by the nonabsolute convergence but on the other hand require a so-called Tauberian theorem to derive the relation for $\pi(x)$.

In addition to the asymptotic relation

$$\pi(x) \sim \frac{x}{\log x},$$

we shall be concerned with the question of the closeness of approximation. For this purpose, we replace $x/\log x$ by a slight modification of the integral suggested by Gauss. Let

$$\operatorname{li} x = \int_0^x \frac{dt}{\log t} = \lim_{\varepsilon\to 0}\left(\int_{1+\varepsilon}^x \frac{dt}{\log t} + \int_0^{1-\varepsilon} \frac{dt}{\log t}\right). \tag{31}$$

We notice first that

$$\operatorname{li} x = \int_2^x \frac{dt}{\log t} + \int_0^2 \frac{dt}{\log t},$$

so that

$$\operatorname{li} x = \int_2^x \frac{dt}{\log t} + O(1).$$

Now we remark on the relationship between $\operatorname{li} x$ and the function $x/\log x$.

If we integrate the integral in (31) successively m times by parts, we find

$$\operatorname{li} x = \frac{x}{\log x} + \frac{x}{\log^2 x} + \cdots + \frac{(m-1)!\,x}{\log^m x} + m!\int_0^x \frac{dt}{\log^{m+1} t}.$$

On the other hand,

$$\int_0^x \frac{dt}{\log^{m+1} t} = \int_0^{\sqrt{x}} + \int_{\sqrt{x}}^x \frac{dt}{\log^{m+1} t} = O(\sqrt{x}) + O\left(\frac{x-\sqrt{x}}{\log^{m+1}\sqrt{x}}\right) = O\left(\frac{x}{\log^{m+1} x}\right).$$

Hence

$$\operatorname{li} x = \frac{x}{\log x} + \cdots + \frac{(m-1)!\,x}{\log^m x} + O\left(\frac{x}{\log^{m+1} x}\right).$$

In particular $\operatorname{li} x \sim x/(\log x)$. We shall use the observations shortly. The result we shall prove is the following:

THEOREM A. *There exists a constant $c > 0$ such that*

$$\pi(x) = \operatorname{li} x + O(x \exp[-c(\log x)^{1/10}]).$$

We shall have more to say about the error later on, but note in anticipation that we shall show that the error term in Theorem A has smaller order of magnitude than $x/\log^m x$ for any m. It will then follow from the above remarks, that $\operatorname{li} x$ is ultimately a better approximation to $\pi(x)$ than $x/\log x$ or any sum of the type

$$\frac{x}{\log x} + \frac{x}{\log^2 x} + \cdots + \frac{(m-1)!\,x}{\log^m x} .$$

To gain insight into a proof of Theorem A, we look first at Riemann's argument. The analytic approach stems once again from Euler's formula

$$\zeta(s) = \sum_{n=1}^{\infty} \frac{1}{n^s} = \prod_p \left(1 - \frac{1}{p^s}\right)^{-1} , \tag{32}$$

where $s = \sigma + it$ and $\sigma > 1$ to ensure convergence. Choosing that branch of the logarithm which is real when s is real, we get from (32),

$$\log \zeta(s) = -\sum_p \log\left(1 - \frac{1}{p^s}\right) = \sum_p \sum_{k=1}^{\infty} \frac{1}{kp^{ks}} .$$

In order to write this as a Dirichlet series, we introduce the following arithmetic function. Let

$$\Lambda_1(m) = \begin{cases} 1/k & \text{if } m = p^k , \\ 0 & \text{otherwise ,} \end{cases} \tag{33}$$

then

$$\log \zeta(s) = \sum_{m=1}^{\infty} \frac{\Lambda_1(m)}{m^s} . \tag{34}$$

In the case of power series, we can easily derive a formula for the sum of the coefficients up to a given value. Suppose that this can be done for the Dirichlet series (34). What is the relation between the sum

$$\sum_{m \leq x} \Lambda_1(m)$$

and $\pi(x)$? This is given by

THEOREM 2.7. *If*

$$\psi_1(x) = \sum_{m \leq x} \Lambda_1(m) ,$$

then

$$\psi_1(x) = \pi(x) + O(x^{1/2} \log x) . \tag{35}$$

PROOF. The proof proceeds directly from the definition of $\psi_1(x)$. In fact

$$\begin{aligned} \psi_1(x) &= \sum_{m \leq x} \Lambda_1(m) = \sum_{p \leq x} 1 + \sum_{p^2 \leq x} \frac{1}{2} + \cdots + \sum_{p^r \leq x} \frac{1}{r} + \cdots \\ &= \pi(x) + \frac{1}{2}\pi(x^{1/2}) + \cdots + \frac{1}{r}\pi(x^{1/r}) + \cdots , \end{aligned} \tag{36}$$

the series terminating when $x^{1/(r+1)} < 2$. The last nonzero term occurs, as is readily seen, when $r = r_0$ where

$$r_0 = \left[\frac{\log x}{\log 2}\right]. \tag{37}$$

It remains to estimate the terms in (36) beginning with $r = 2$. Since $\pi(x) < x$, we get

$$\frac{1}{2}\pi(x^{1/2}) + \cdots + \frac{1}{r_0}\pi(x^{1/r_0}) < \frac{1}{2}x^{1/2} + \cdots + \frac{1}{r_0}x^{1/r_0} < \frac{x^{1/2}}{2}r_0$$
$$\leqq \frac{x^{1/2}}{2}\left[\frac{\log x}{\log 2}\right] = O(x^{1/2}\log x) .$$

This completes the proof.

To prove Theorem A, it therefore suffices to prove

THEOREM B. *There exists a constant $c > 0$ such that*

(38) $$\psi_1(x) = \mathrm{li}\, x + O(x \exp[-c(\log x)^{1/10}]) .$$

Returning to (34), we express the right-hand side as an integral with the help of Lemma 3.1, Chapter I. In that result, we put $\varphi(x) = x^{-s}$, $c(n) = \Lambda_1(n)$, $S(x) = \psi_1(x)$ and we are led to

$$\sum_{n=1}^{k} \frac{\Lambda_1(n)}{n^s} = \frac{\psi_1(k)}{k^s} + s\int_1^k \psi_1(x)x^{-s-1}dx ,$$

with s real and $s > 1$. If we let $k \to \infty$, we deduce

(39) $$\frac{\log \zeta(s)}{s} = \int_1^\infty \psi_1(x)x^{-s-1}dx ,$$

this formula holding by analytic continuation for complex s with $\mathscr{R}(s) > 1$.

Riemann's next step is to invert the relation (39), for on putting $s = \sigma + it$, we see that the integral in (39) is essentially a Fourier transform. The result of his argument is this: for $a > 1$,

(40) $$\psi_1(x) = \frac{1}{2\pi i}\int_{a-i\infty}^{a+i\infty} \log \zeta(s) \frac{x^s}{s} ds .$$

It is interesting to note that he reaches this conclusion without the use of Cauchy's theorem.

We do not repeat his argument here since we derive the conclusion as a particular case of a more general theorem. (40) is in fact the fundamental starting point for our first proof of Theorem B.

The integrand in (40) is in absolute value

$$\frac{|\log \zeta(s)|}{|s|}x^\sigma$$

and the integral does not therefore converge absolutely. Since $\sigma = a > 1$, and we wish to prove that

$$\psi_1(x) \sim \frac{x}{\log x} ,$$

it is reasonable to expect that one effective method for evaluating (40) is to move the path of integration to the left of the line $\sigma = 1$. In order to do so, however, we shall require a more detailed knowledge of $\zeta(s)$. In particular, we need

(a) Analytic continuation of $\zeta(s)$ to the left of $\sigma = 1$.

(b) An estimate for $\zeta(s)$ to the left of $\sigma = 1$.

(c) Some knowledge of the zeros of $\zeta(s)$ in a region to the left of $\sigma = 1$ since the zeros of $\zeta(s)$ are singularities of the integrand.

The next two sections are devoted to a proof of (40) and the derivation of information relevant to (a), (b), (c).

3. The sum of the coefficients of a Dirichlet series. Let

$$f(s) = \sum_{n=1}^{\infty} \frac{a(n)}{n^s} \tag{1}$$

be a Dirichlet series whose abscissa of convergence is α. Our primary object is to prove

THEOREM 3.1. *If* $a > \alpha, a > 0$,

$$S(x) = \sum_{n \leq x} a(n), \tag{2}$$

then

$$S(x) = \frac{1}{2\pi i} \lim_{T\to\infty} \int_{a-iT}^{a+iT} f(s) \frac{x^s}{s} ds, \tag{3}$$

provided x is not an integer.

A proof of this basic result may be made to depend upon a simple instance of this theorem.

THEOREM 3.2. *If* $a > 0$, *then*

$$\frac{1}{2\pi i} \lim_{T\to\infty} \int_{a-iT}^{a+iT} \frac{x^s}{s} ds = \begin{cases} 0 & \text{if } 0 \leq x < 1, \\ 1 & \text{if } x > 1. \end{cases} \tag{4}$$

PROOF. Since

$$\left| \frac{x^s}{s} \right| = \frac{x^a}{|s|},$$

the integral does not converge absolutely; it is therefore advantageous to integrate by parts:

$$\int_{a-iT}^{a+iT} \frac{x^s}{s} ds = \frac{x^s}{s \log x}\Big]_{a-iT}^{a+iT} + \frac{1}{\log x} \int_{a-iT}^{a+iT} \frac{x^s}{s^2} ds. \tag{5}$$

However,

$$\frac{x^{a \pm iT}}{(a \pm iT) \log x} = O\left(\frac{x^a}{(a^2 + T^2)^{1/2}} \frac{1}{\log x} \right) = o(1), \tag{6}$$

as $T \to \infty$. It suffices then to evaluate the integral on the right-hand side of (5). This integral contains the term

$$x^s = e^{a \log x}(\cos(t \log x) + i \sin(t \log x)),$$

which, along the straight line path of (5), oscillates irregularly as $t \to \infty$. To avoid this difficulty, we alter the path of integration in such a manner as to make σ play the dominant role. Several possibilities suggest themselves but in integrals of this type, one of the most convenient is the following: We first draw a circle which has its center at the origin and which passes through the points $a+iT$, $a-iT$. We consider two cases.

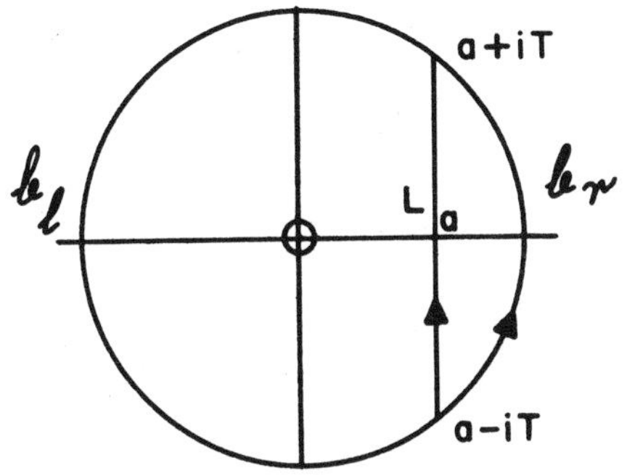

Case (i). $x > 1$. In this case we replace the line L by the curve $\mathscr{C}_l$ (see the figure) so as to make σ relatively small. Inside the contour bounded by L and $\mathscr{C}_l$, the integrand of the integral in (5) has a double pole at $s = 0$. Since

$$x^s = e^{s \log x} = 1 + s \log x + \frac{s^2 \log^2 x}{2!} + \cdots,$$

the residue of x^s/s^2 is $\log x$. Consequently, from (5) and (6) and Cauchy's theorem,

(7) $$\frac{1}{2\pi i} \int_{a-iT}^{a+iT} \frac{x^s}{s}\, ds = o(1) + \log x - \frac{1}{2\pi i} \int_{\mathscr{C}_l} \frac{x^s}{s^2}\, dx\,.$$

It remains to show that the integral on the right of (7) is $o(1)$. On $\mathscr{C}_l$, let $s = \sigma + it$, and let the radius of the circle be ρ so that $\rho^2 = a^2 + T^2$. Then, since $\sigma \leqq a$, and $x > 1$,

$$\int_{\mathscr{C}_l} \frac{x^s}{s^2} ds = O\left(\int_{\mathscr{C}_l} \frac{x^a}{|s|^2} |ds|\right) = O\left(\frac{x^a}{\rho^2} \int_{\mathscr{C}_l} |ds|\right) = O\left(\frac{x^a}{\rho^2} \cdot 2\pi\rho\right) = o(1)\,,$$

as $T \to \infty$. This proves the first part of the theorem.

Case (ii). $0 \leqq x < 1$. In this case, by Cauchy's theorem,

$$\int_L + \int_{\mathscr{C}_r} = 0\,.$$

Consequently, since here $\sigma \leqq a$ and $x < 1$,

$$\int_{\mathscr{C}_r} \frac{x^s}{s^2} ds = O\left(\frac{x^a 2\pi\rho}{\rho^2}\right) = o(1)\,.$$

This completes the proof of the theorem. $(1/2\pi i)\int_{a-i\infty}^{a+i\infty}(x^s/s)\,ds$ does not converge for $x=1$, but its Cauchy principal value is $\frac{1}{2}$. This is seen as follows:

$$\lim_{T\to\infty}\frac{1}{2\pi i}\int_{a-iT}^{a+iT}\frac{ds}{s}=\lim_{T\to\infty}\log\frac{a+iT}{a-iT}=\frac{1}{2\pi i}\log(-1)=\frac{1}{2\pi i}\pi i=\frac{1}{2}\,. \tag{8}$$

We return now to a proof of Theorem 3. 1.

We could infer the result of Theorem 3. 1, with the help of Theorem 3.2, by arguing formally as follows:

$$\begin{aligned}\frac{1}{2\pi i}\int_{a-i\infty}^{a+i\infty}f(s)\frac{x^s}{s}\,ds&=\frac{2\pi i}{1}\int_{a-i\infty}^{a+i\infty}\sum_{n=1}^{\infty}\frac{a(n)}{n^s}\frac{x^s}{s}\,ds\\&=\frac{1}{2\pi i}\sum_{n=1}^{\infty}a(n)\int_{a-i\infty}^{a+i\infty}\left(\frac{x}{n}\right)^s\frac{1}{s}\,ds=\sum_{n\leqq x}a(n)\,,\end{aligned} \tag{9}$$

provided $x/n\neq 1$, that is, x is not an integer. To justify this formal argument, we must prove in effect that the interchange of the order of summation and integration is valid. To do this, we digress and prove a general theorem on the order of magnitude of a function represented by a Dirichlet series.

LEMMA 3.1. *If*

$$f(s)=\sum_{n=1}^{\infty}\frac{a(n)}{n^s}$$

has abscissa of convergence α, *then*

$$f(s)=O(|t|^{1-(\sigma-\alpha)+\varepsilon}) \tag{10}$$

for every value of σ *satisfying*

$$\alpha<\sigma<\alpha+1. \tag{11}$$

Moreover, (10) *holds uniformly in any half plane to the right of any line with* $\mathscr{R}(s)=\sigma$ *for* σ *satisfying* (11).

PROOF. The proof uses partial summation.

Case (i). Suppose $\alpha=0$ but that $\sum_{n=1}^{\infty}a(n)$ converges. Then $a(n)$ and $S(n)=\sum_{k=1}^{n}a(k)$ are both bounded. Thus, using partial summation as given in Chapter I, Lemma 3.1, we get, with $\varphi(x)=x^{-s}$,

$$\begin{aligned}\sum_{n=1}^{N}\frac{a(n)}{n^s}&=\sum_{n=1}^{M}\frac{a(n)}{n^s}+\sum_{n=M+1}^{N}\frac{a(n)}{n^s}\\&=\sum_{n=1}^{M}\frac{a(n)}{n^s}+\frac{S(N)}{N^s}-\frac{S(M)}{M^s}+s\int_{M}^{N}\frac{S(x)}{x^{s+1}}\,dx\,.\end{aligned} \tag{12}$$

Letting $N\to\infty$, we deduce from (12), with $\sigma>0$

$$\begin{aligned}f(s)&=O\Big(\sum_{n=1}^{M}\frac{1}{n^\sigma}+|s|\int_{M}^{\infty}\frac{dx}{x^{\sigma+1}}+\frac{1}{M^\sigma}\Big)\\&=O\Big(M^{1-\sigma}+\frac{|s|}{\sigma}M^{-\sigma}+M^{-\sigma}\Big)\,.\end{aligned} \tag{13}$$

Putting $M=[t]$ in (13), we infer that for $0<\sigma<1$,

$$f(s) = O(|t|^{1-\sigma}).$$

If $0 < \sigma_0 < 1$, then we get for all $\sigma \geqq \sigma_0$,

$$f(s) = O(|t|^{1-\sigma_0}).$$

Case (ii). If $\sum_{n=1}^{\infty} a(n)$ does not converge, we write the series for $f(s)$ in the form

$$f(s) = \sum \frac{a(n)}{n^{\alpha+\varepsilon}} \cdot \frac{1}{n^{s-\alpha-\varepsilon}} = \sum \frac{b(n)}{n^{s-\alpha-\varepsilon}}, \tag{14}$$

where $b(n) = a(n)/n^{\alpha+\varepsilon}$.

From the definition of α, the series $\sum_{n=1}^{\infty} b(n)$ converges and we are then in Case (i). Thus,

$$f(s) = O(|t|^{1-(\sigma-\alpha)+\varepsilon})$$

as required. The uniformity follows as above.

Proof of Theorem 3.1. Let $\bar{a}$ be the abscissa of absolute convergence for $f(s)$.

Case (i). Let $a > \bar{a}$ and consider the integral

$$I(U,T) = \frac{1}{2\pi i}\int_{a-iU}^{a+iT} f(s)\frac{x^s}{s}\,ds. \tag{15}$$

By Theorem 3.1, Chapter I, the series for $f(s)$ converges absolutely and uniformly in a region enclosing the path of integration. Therefore, from (15),

$$\begin{aligned} I(U,T) &= \frac{1}{2\pi i}\sum_{n=1}^{\infty} a(n)\int_{a-iU}^{a+iT}\left(\frac{x}{n}\right)^s\frac{ds}{s} \\ &= \frac{1}{2\pi i}\sum_{n=1}^{\infty} a(n)\int_{a-i\infty}^{a+i\infty}\left(\frac{x}{n}\right)^s\frac{ds}{s} - \frac{1}{2\pi i}\sum_{n=1}^{\infty} a(n)\int_{a+iT}^{a+i\infty}\left(\frac{x}{n}\right)^s\frac{ds}{s} \\ &\quad - \frac{1}{2\pi i}\sum_{n=1}^{\infty} a(n)\int_{a-i\infty}^{a-iU}\left(\frac{x}{n}\right)^s\frac{ds}{s}. \end{aligned} \tag{16}$$

By Theorem 3.2, it therefore suffices to show that

$$\sum_{n=1}^{\infty} a(n)\int_{a+iT}^{a+i\infty}\left(\frac{x}{n}\right)^s\frac{ds}{s} = o(1) \qquad \text{as } T \to \infty \tag{17}$$

and similarly for U.

For fixed x (since x is not an integer), we have

$$\begin{aligned} \int_{a+iT}^{a+i\infty}\left(\frac{x}{n}\right)^s\frac{ds}{s} &= \left(\frac{x}{n}\right)^s \frac{1}{s\log\dfrac{x}{n}}\Bigg]_{a+iT}^{a+i\infty} + \frac{1}{\log\dfrac{x}{n}}\int_{a+iT}^{a+i\infty}\left(\frac{x}{n}\right)^s\frac{ds}{s^2} \\ &= O\left(\frac{1}{n^a T}\,\frac{1}{\left|\log\dfrac{x}{n}\right|}\right) \end{aligned}$$

and therefore

$$\sum_{n=1}^{\infty} a(n) \int_{a+iT}^{a+i\infty} \left(\frac{x}{n}\right)^s \frac{ds}{s} = O\left(\frac{1}{T}\right) \sum_{n=1}^{\infty} \frac{|a(n)|}{n^a \left|\log \frac{x}{n}\right|} = o(1) \qquad \text{as } T \to \infty$$

by the assumption on a. This proves (17).

Case (ii). $\alpha < a \leqq \bar{\alpha}$. Let $b > \bar{\alpha}$ and consider the rectangle $\mathscr{C}$ with vertices at $b + iT, b - iU, a + iT, a - iU$. Because $a > 0$, the integrand in (15) is regular in $\mathscr{C}$ and by Cauchy's theorem, we infer that

$$\int_{b-iU}^{b+iT} f(s) \frac{x^s}{s} ds = \int_{a-iU}^{a+iT} f(s) \frac{x^s}{s} ds + \int_{b-iU}^{a-iU} f(s) \frac{x^s}{s} ds + \int_{b+iT}^{a+iT} f(s) \frac{x^s}{s} ds . \tag{18}$$

But by the above Lemma 3.1,

$$f(s) \frac{x^s}{s} = O(|t|^{\alpha-\sigma+\varepsilon}) = O(|t|^{\alpha-a+\varepsilon}) .$$

Accordingly, the second and third integrals on the right of (18) are $o(1)$ as $T, U \to \infty$. Therefore

$$\int_{b-i\infty}^{b+i\infty} f(x) \frac{x^s}{s} ds = \int_{a-i\infty}^{a+i\infty} f(s) \frac{x^s}{s} ds$$

and since $b > \bar{\alpha}$, we revert to Case (i).

The difficulties which are inherent in Theorem 3.1 are largely avoided by

THEOREM 3.3. *If k is any positive integer, $a > 0$, $x \geqq 0$, then*

$$\frac{1}{2\pi i} \int_{a-i\infty}^{a+i\infty} \frac{x^s ds}{s(s+1)\cdots(s+k)} = \begin{cases} 0 & \textit{if } x \leqq 1 , \\ \dfrac{1}{k!}\left(1 - \dfrac{1}{x}\right)^k & \textit{if } x \geqq 1 . \end{cases} \tag{19}$$

PROOF. Since the integrand is $O(x^a |t|^{-k-1})$ on the line of integration, and $k \geqq 1$, the integral is absolutely convergent. The argument proceeds very much as in the proof of Theorem 3.2. We construct the same circle and consider two cases.

Case (i). $x \geqq 1$. We have

$$\frac{1}{2\pi i} \int_{a-iT}^{a+iT} \frac{x^s ds}{s(s+1)\cdots(s+k)} = -\frac{1}{2\pi i} \int_{\mathscr{C}_l} \frac{x^s ds}{s(s+1)\cdots(s+k)} + \sum \text{residues}. \tag{20}$$

The integrand has simple poles at $s = 0, -1, \cdots, -k$. Let R_m denote the residue at $-m$. Then

$$R_m = \frac{x^{-m}}{-m(-m+1)\cdots(-1)1\cdot 2\cdots(k-m)} = \frac{(-1)^m x^{-m}}{m!(k-m)!} .$$

Consequently,

$$\begin{aligned} \sum_{m=0}^{k} R_m &= \frac{1}{k!} \sum_{m=0}^{k} \frac{k! x^{-m}(-1)^m}{m!(k-m)!} = \frac{1}{k!} \sum_{m=0}^{k} \binom{k}{m} \left(-\frac{1}{x}\right)^m \\ &= \frac{1}{k!}\left(1 - \frac{1}{x}\right)^k . \end{aligned} \tag{21}$$

Let ρ be the radius of the circle chosen so that $\rho \geqq 2k$. Then on $\mathscr{C}_l$, since $x \geqq 1$,

$$\sigma \leqq a, |x^s| = x^\sigma \leqq x^a, \qquad |s+m| \geqq \rho - k \geqq \frac{\rho}{2};$$

hence

$$\frac{1}{2\pi i} \cdot \int_{\mathscr{C}_l} \frac{x^s ds}{s(s+1)\cdots(s+k)} = O\left(\frac{1}{2\pi} \frac{x^a}{\left(\frac{\rho}{2}\right)^{k+1}} 2\pi\rho\right) = O\left(\frac{x^a}{T^k}\right) = o(1),$$

as $T \to \infty$. This, together with (20) and (21), proves the second part of the theorem.

Case (ii). $x \leqq 1$. If $x \leqq 1$, then we replace the line L by the arc to the right of L. The integrand is analytic within this contour and Cauchy's theorem yields

$$\frac{1}{2\pi i} \int_{a-iT}^{a+iT} \frac{x^s}{s(s+1)\cdots(s+k)} ds = -\frac{1}{2\pi i} \int_{\mathscr{C}_r} \frac{x^s}{s(s+1)\cdots(s+k)} ds.$$

The integral on the right, however, is

$$O\left(\frac{x^a}{\rho^k}\right) = O\left(\frac{x^a}{T^k}\right) = o(1),$$

as $T \to \infty$. This completes the proof.

As a corollary, we prove an analogue of Theorem 3.1.

Theorem 3.4. *If α is the abscissa of convergence of*

$$f(s) = \sum_{n=1}^{\infty} \frac{a(n)}{n^s},$$

and

$$S(x) = \sum_{n \leqq x} a(n),$$

then for $a > \alpha$

$$\frac{1}{x} \sum_{n \leqq x} a(n)(x-n) = \frac{1}{x} \int_1^x S(y)dy = \int_{a-i\infty}^{a+i\infty} f(s) \frac{x^s}{s(s+1)} dx. \tag{22}$$

Proof. Since $a > \alpha$ the abscissa of convergence, it follows that

$$\int_{a-iU}^{a+iT} f(s) \frac{x^s}{s(s+1)} dx = \sum_{n=1}^{\infty} a(n) \int_{a-iU}^{a+iT} \left(\frac{x}{n}\right)^s \frac{ds}{s(s+1)}.$$

Thus, it suffices by Theorem 3.3 to prove that

$$\int_{a+iT}^{a+i\infty} f(s) \frac{x^s}{s(s+1)} ds = o(1) \qquad \text{as } T \to \infty$$

and likewise for U.

By Lemma 3.1,

$$\int_{a+iT}^{a+i\infty} f(s)\frac{x^s}{s(s+1)}ds = O\left(\int_T^\infty \frac{t^{1-(a-\alpha)+\varepsilon}dt}{|s(s+1)|}\right) = O\left(\int_T^\infty t^{-1-(a-\alpha)+\varepsilon}dt\right)$$
$$= O(T^{-(a-\alpha)+\varepsilon}) = o(1),$$

and similarly for U. On the other hand, by Lemma 3.1, Chapter I, with $\varphi(y) = x - y$,

$$\sum_{n \leqq x} a(n)(x-n) = \int_1^x S(y)dy,$$

as required.

4. The behavior of $\zeta(s)$ for $\sigma > 0$. From § 2, (34), we had

$$\log \zeta(s) = \sum_{n=1}^\infty \frac{\Lambda_1(n)}{n^s} = \sum_{p,k} \frac{1}{kp^{ks}}$$

and if to this Dirichlet series we apply Theorem 3.1, we get

THEOREM 4.1. *If $a > 1$ and x is not an integer,*

(1) $$\psi_1(x) = \sum_{n \leqq x} \Lambda_1(n) = \frac{1}{2\pi i}\int_{a-i\infty}^{a+i\infty} \log \zeta(s)\frac{x^s}{s}ds.$$

As we noted above, this is Riemann's starting point. He now evaluates the integral by assuming that

$$\zeta(s) = \frac{e^{bs}}{2(s-1)\Gamma\left(\frac{s}{2}+1\right)}\prod_\rho \left(1-\frac{s}{\rho}\right)e^{s/\rho},$$

where the product ranges over all the zeros of $\zeta(s)$ and b is some constant (which can be given explicitly). This formula was not proved rigorously until about 1892 when Hadamard constructed his general theory of entire functions. Landau showed that it is possible to avoid this theory and it is this proof which we give.

Instead of moving the line of integration to the left across the singularities of $\log \zeta(s)$, we shall find a region to the left of $\sigma = a$ in which the integrand is analytic except for the singularity at $s = 1$. This is to say, we find a region in which $\zeta(s) \neq 0$. The integral, moreover, does not converge absolutely and this forces us to exercise considerable care in discussing it. Furthermore, it is evidently advantageous to move the line of integration in such a way as to make the real part of s as small as possible, but as we shall see, a compromise is necessary since the behavior of $\zeta(\sigma + it)$ is irregular as $t \to \infty$.

The principal barrier which stands in the way of moving the line of integration stems from the zeros of $\zeta(s)$ for the zeros of $\zeta(s)$ are singularities of the integrand in (1). Indeed, the location of these zeros constitutes the main unsolved problem in the theory of the zeta function and hence of the error term in the prime number theorem. For it can be shown that the magnitude of the error is directly dependent on the greatest lower bound θ

of values σ ($0 \leqq \sigma \leqq 1$) for which

$$\zeta(\sigma + it) \neq 0 .$$

The celebrated Riemann hypothesis asserts that all the complex zeros of $\zeta(s)$ have real part $\sigma = \frac{1}{2}$.

Our objectives in this section will then be twofold:

(i) To find a positive lower bound for $|\zeta(s)|$ in a region as far to the left as possible from the line $\sigma = 1$.

(ii) To find an upper bound for $|\zeta(s)|$ in this region.

We consider the second problem first. The natural starting point is to use some suitable continuation for $\zeta(s)$; we employ the continuation § 3, (21), developed in Chapter I. The formula in question is

$$\zeta(s) = \sum_{k=1}^{n-1} \frac{1}{k^s} + \frac{n^{-s}}{2} + \frac{n^{1-s}}{s-1} - s\int_n^\infty x^{-1-s}\left(x - [x] - \frac{1}{2}\right)dx , \tag{2}$$

which is valid for $\sigma > 0$.

If we argue in a straightforward manner from (2), we find a satisfactory bound in a suitable region. Though the character of the region may seem at first sight somewhat odd, it is a natural consequence of our calculations.

Theorem 4.2. *Let $T \geqq e^2$, $\sigma_0 = 1 - (1/\log T)$, then for any s in the rectangle with vertices $\sigma_0 + iT, \sigma_0 - iT, 2 + iT, 2 - iT$, we have*

$$\zeta(s) - \frac{1}{s-1} = O(\log T) . \tag{3}$$

Proof. Let

$$\Delta(s) = \zeta(s) - \frac{1}{s-1} ,$$

then from (2)

$$\Delta(s) = \sum_{k=1}^{n-1} \frac{1}{k^s} + \frac{1}{2} n^{-s} + \frac{n^{1-s}}{s-1} - \frac{1}{s-1} - s\int_n^\infty x^{-s-1}\left(x - [x] - \frac{1}{2}\right)dx . \tag{4}$$

Since

$$\frac{n^{1-s} - 1}{s-1} = -\int_1^n x^{-s} dx ,$$

and $|x - [x] - \frac{1}{2}| \leqq \frac{1}{2}$,

$$\begin{aligned} |\Delta(s)| &< \sum_{k=1}^{n-1} k^{-\sigma} + \frac{1}{2} n^{-\sigma} + \int_1^n x^{-\sigma} dx + \frac{|s|}{2}\int_n^\infty x^{-1-\sigma} dx \\ &< \sum_{k=1}^{n} k^{-\sigma} + \int_1^n x^{-\sigma}\, dx + \frac{|s|}{2}\int_n^\infty x^{-1-\sigma} dx . \end{aligned} \tag{5}$$

Moreover,

$$\sum_{k=1}^{n} k^{-\sigma} < 1 + \int_1^n x^{-\sigma} dx ,$$

which, coupled with (5), gives

$$
\begin{aligned}
|\Delta(s)| &< 1 + 2\int_1^n x^{-\sigma}dx + \frac{|s|}{2}\int_n^\infty x^{-1-\sigma}dx \\
&< 1 + \frac{2(n^{1-\sigma}-1)}{1-\sigma} + \frac{|s|}{2}\frac{n^{-\sigma}}{\sigma} \qquad (6)\\
&< \frac{2n^{1-\sigma}}{1-\sigma} + \frac{|s|}{2}\frac{n^{-\sigma}}{\sigma}\,.
\end{aligned}
$$

The left-hand side does not depend on n; we therefore choose n and σ so as to minimize the right-hand side. Let $n = [T]$, then for s in the rectangle $|s| < 2 + T$ and for $\sigma > \frac{1}{2}$,

$$\frac{|s|}{2\sigma} < \frac{2+T}{2\sigma} < 2 + T\,.$$

Equation (6) then leads to

$$\Delta(s) < \frac{2T^{1-\sigma}}{1-\sigma} + \frac{2+T}{T^\sigma} = T^{1-\sigma}\left(\frac{2}{1-\sigma} + \frac{2+T}{T}\right). \tag{7}$$

We choose σ in such a way as to make $T^{1-\sigma}$ in (7) as small as possible. Let σ_0 be chosen so that

$$T^{1-\sigma_0} = c_1\,,$$

where c_1 is a constant. This means that

$$1 - \sigma_0 = \frac{c_2}{\log T}\,,$$

or

$$\sigma_0 = 1 - \frac{c_2}{\log T}\,;$$

then for any $s = \sigma + it$ for which $\sigma > \sigma_0$ and $|t| > T$, the inequality

$$\Delta(s) < T^{1-\sigma_0}\left[\frac{2}{1-\sigma_0} + \frac{2+T}{T}\right] \tag{8}$$

holds since replacing σ by σ_0 in (7) preserves the inequality. Thus

$$\Delta(s) < c_3\left[\frac{2\log T}{c_2} + 1 + \frac{2}{T}\right] = 2c_4\log T + c_5\left(1 + \frac{2}{T}\right) < c_6 \log T\,,$$

provided $1 + 2/T \leqq \log T$. This inequality is assured if $T \geqq e^2$. We could avoid some of the calculations if we were content with the less precise statement that the inequalities hold for $T \geqq T_0$, where T_0 is some suitably large value.

COROLLARY 1. *In particular,*

$$\zeta(s) = O(\log T)$$

in the same region.

COROLLARY 2.

$$\zeta(s) = O(T^{1/2}) \qquad \text{for } \sigma \geqq \tfrac{1}{2}\,.$$

PROOF. The proof of this inequality follows directly from (7). For

$$\Delta(s) = O(T^{1/2}) \qquad \text{if } \sigma \geqq \tfrac{1}{2}$$

and hence $\zeta(s) = O(T^{1/2})$ in the same region.

It may be well to remark parenthetically that the question which has arisen in this theorem concerning the minimization of the right-hand side of (7) is one of very frequent occurrence in analytic theory of numbers. Stated somewhat generally, a typical class of such problems is characterized as follows. There is given a sum $f_1(x, y) + f_2(x, y)$ of two functions of two variables and to fix the ideas, one of the variables, say x, may be selected arbitrarily as a function of the other and we are required to minimize $f_1(x, y) + f_2(x, y)$. For any selection of x as a function of y, each of the terms $f_1(x, y)$ and $f_2(x, y)$ has a certain order of magnitude. The order of magnitude of the sum is then that of the maximum of the two terms. We then wish to select x so as to balance the effect of the terms. In other words we require $\min_x \max_y (f_1(x, y), f_2(x, y))$. While some general rules may be formulated for a solution of this and other problems of this type, it is frequently best to treat separately each problem which is encountered. This is in part because the "ideal" solution is frequently very tedious and is not significantly better than that arrived at by general considerations.

The general argument used for $\zeta(s)$ enables us to prove an inequality for $\zeta'(s)$. We have

THEOREM 4.3. *Let* $T \geqq e^2$, $\sigma_0 = 1 - (1/\log T)$, *then in the rectangle with vertices* $\sigma_0 - iT, \sigma_0 + iT, 2 + iT, 2 - iT$, *we have*

$$\zeta'(s) + \frac{1}{(s-1)^2} = O(\log^2 T)\,. \tag{9}$$

PROOF. We differentiate the relation (4) with respect to s. This gives

$$\begin{aligned} E(s) &= \zeta'(s) + \frac{1}{(s-1)^2} \\ &= -\sum_{k=1}^{n-1} k^{-s} \log k - \frac{n^{-s}}{2} \log n + \int_1^n x^{-s} \log x\, dx \\ &\quad - \int_n^\infty x^{1-s}\left(x - [x] - \frac{1}{2}\right) dx + s\int_n^\infty x^{-1-s}\left(x - [x] - \frac{1}{2}\right) \log x\, dx\,. \end{aligned}$$

Hence

$$|E(s)| < \log n \left\{\sum_{k=1}^{n} k^{-\sigma} + \int_1^n x^{-\sigma} dx\right\} + \frac{1}{2}\int_n^\infty x^{-1-\sigma} dx + \frac{|s|}{2}\int_n^\infty x^{-1-\sigma} \log x\, dx. \tag{10}$$

On the other hand, for $\sigma > \frac{1}{2}$,

$$\int_n^\infty x^{-1-\sigma} dx = \frac{n^{-\sigma}}{\sigma} < \frac{1}{\sigma} < 2\,, \tag{11}$$

and if we integrate the last integral in (10) by parts, we get

$$\int_n^\infty x^{-1-\sigma}\log x\,dx = \frac{n^{-\sigma}}{\sigma}\log n + \frac{n^{-\sigma}}{\sigma^2} < c_2 n^{-\sigma}\log n\,. \tag{12}$$

Furthermore, the braces in (10) are

$$< 1 + 2\int_1^n x^{-\sigma}\,dx = 1 + 2\,\frac{n^{1-\sigma}-1}{1-\sigma} < 2\,\frac{n^{1-\sigma}}{1-\sigma}\,. \tag{13}$$

From (10), (11), (12), (13), we get, on putting $n = [T]$,

$$\begin{aligned} |E(s)| &< 2\,\frac{T^{1-\sigma_0}}{1-\sigma_0}\log T + 2 + c_3\,\frac{T+2}{2}\,T^{-\sigma_0}\log T \\ &< \log T\left[e\log T + 2 + c_3\left(1+\frac{2}{T}\right)\right] < c_4\log^2 T\,, \end{aligned}$$

if $T \geqq e^2$ exactly as in Theorem 4.2.

Corollary. *$\zeta'(s) = O(\log^2 T)$ in the same region.*

We turn now to the first problem we posed—that of finding an inequality for $1/|\zeta(s)|$ or what is the same thing, a lower bound for $|\zeta(s)|$. In particular, we should like to prove that the zeta function does not vanish for $\sigma = 1$. The Euler product

$$\zeta(s) = \prod_p (1-p^{-s})^{-1}$$

implies that $\zeta(s)$ does not vanish for $\sigma > 1$. For if $\sigma > 1$,

$$\begin{aligned} |\zeta(s)| &\geqq \prod_p (1+p^{-\sigma})^{-1} = \exp\left(-\sum_p \log\left(1+\frac{1}{p^\sigma}\right)\right) \\ &= \exp\left(\sum_p\left(-\frac{1}{p^\sigma}+\frac{1}{2p^{2\sigma}}-\cdots\right)\right) > \exp\left(-\sum_p \frac{1}{p^\sigma}\right) > 0\,, \end{aligned}$$

since $\sum 1/p^\sigma$ converges for $\sigma > 1$.

Theorem 4.4.

$$\zeta(1+it) \neq 0\,. \tag{14}$$

This fact is fundamental in all known so-called "analytic" proofs of the prime number theorem. Indeed Wiener has shown that this is the only essential information needed about the zeta function in order to prove that

$$\pi(x) \sim \frac{x}{\log x}\,. \tag{15}$$

We shall later prove that $\zeta(1+it) \neq 0$ is both necessary and sufficient for the truth of (15).

There are several proofs known for the basic property (14). Its truth may be seen roughly as follows: We showed in Chapter I, § 1, (10), that

$$\log\zeta(s) = \sum_p \frac{1}{p^s} + g(s)\,, \tag{16}$$

where $g(s)$ is regular for $\sigma > \frac{1}{2}$. In particular, as $\sigma \to 1^{+0}$,

$$\log \zeta(\sigma) \sim \sum_p \frac{1}{p^\sigma}. \tag{17}$$

On the other hand, $\zeta(s)$ has a simple pole at $s = 1$,

$$\log \zeta(\sigma) \sim \log \frac{1}{\sigma - 1}, \tag{18}$$

which, taken together with (17), means that

$$\sum_p \frac{1}{p^\sigma} \sim \log \frac{1}{\sigma - 1}. \tag{19}$$

If we take real parts in (16), $s = \sigma + it_0, t_0 \neq 0$, we get

$$\sum_p \frac{\cos(t_0 \log p)}{p^\sigma} = \log |\zeta(s)| - \mathscr{R}(g(s)),$$

and if $\zeta(1 + it_0) = 0$, we get as $\sigma \to 1^{+0}$

$$\sum_p \frac{\cos(t_0 \log p)}{p^\sigma} \sim \log(\sigma - 1), \tag{20}$$

since the only singularity of $\zeta(s)$ is at $s = 1$.

Equation (20), together with (19), means that $\cos t_0 \log p$ must in some sense be close to -1 most of the time. This implies that $t_0 \log p$ is "usually" π or that $\cos 2t_0 \log p$ is "usually" 1. In that event, however,

$$\begin{aligned}\log |\zeta(\sigma + 2it_0)| &\sim \sum_p \frac{\cos(2t_0 \log p)}{p^\sigma} \\ &\sim \sum_p \frac{1}{p^\sigma} \sim \log \frac{1}{\sigma - 1};\end{aligned}$$

and this implies that $1 + 2it_0$ is a pole of $\zeta(s)$ which is a contradiction.

Although this argument can be "rigorized," we give a somewhat simpler one due to de la Vallée Poussin in which, once again, a relation between $\zeta(\sigma + it)$ and $\zeta(\sigma + 2it)$ is basic. The relation, however, is used more effectively. We first require a simple lemma.

Lemma 4.1. *If* $|\omega| = 1$, *then*

$$\mathscr{R}(\omega^2 + 4\omega + 3) \geqq 0.$$

Proof. Since $\bar{\omega} = 1/\omega$,

$$\begin{aligned}\mathscr{R}(\omega^2 + 4\omega + 3) &= \frac{\omega^2 + \omega^{-2}}{2} + \frac{4(\omega + \omega^{-1})}{2} + 3 \\ &= \frac{1}{2}(\omega^2 + 4\omega + 6 + 4\omega^{-1} + \omega^{-2}) \\ &= \frac{1}{2}(\omega^{1/2} + \omega^{-1/2})^4 \geqq 0.\end{aligned}$$

Proof of Theorem 4.4. The relation we get is among $\zeta(\sigma+it)$, $\zeta(\sigma+2it)$ and $\zeta(\sigma)$. In fact, we have

$$\mathscr{R}\{\log\zeta(\sigma+2it)+4\log\zeta(\sigma+it)+3\log\zeta(\sigma)\} \tag{21}$$
$$=\mathscr{R}\left\{\sum_{n=1}^{\infty}\frac{\Lambda_1(n)}{n^{\sigma}}(n^{-2it}+4n^{-it}+3)\right\}.$$

Applying the above lemma to $n^{-2it}+4n^{-it}+3$ with $\omega=n^{-it}$, we see that

$$\mathscr{R}(n^{-2it}+4n^{-it}+3)\geqq 0.$$

This, together with (21) implies that

$$\mathscr{R}\{\log\zeta(\sigma+2it)+4\log\zeta(\sigma+it)+3\log\zeta(\sigma)\}\geqq 0. \tag{22}$$

This means that

$$\log|\zeta(\sigma+2it)\zeta^4(\sigma+it)\zeta^3(\sigma)|\geqq 0,$$

or

$$|\zeta(\sigma+2it)\zeta^4(\sigma+it)\zeta^3(\sigma)|\geqq 1. \tag{23}$$

If $\zeta(1+it)=0\,(t\neq 0)$, then

$$\lim_{\sigma\to 1}\frac{\zeta(\sigma+it)}{\sigma-1}=\lim_{\sigma\to 1}\frac{\zeta(\sigma+it)-\zeta(1+it)}{(\sigma+it)-(1+it)}=\zeta'(1+it),$$

and $\zeta'(1+it)$ is regular. Consequently from (23),

$$\left|\zeta(\sigma+2it)\,\frac{\zeta^4(\sigma+it)}{(\sigma-1)^4}\,(\sigma-1)^3\zeta^3(\sigma)(\sigma-1)\right|\geqq 1. \tag{24}$$

Now as $\sigma\to 1$, $\zeta(\sigma+2it)$, $\zeta^4(\sigma+it)/(\sigma-1)^4$, $(\sigma-1)^3\zeta^3(\sigma)$, are all bounded, whereas $\sigma-1$ tends to 0. The left-hand side of (24) may therefore be made as small as we please and this is a contradiction.

As a corollary we deduce

Theorem 4.5. *If* $1<\sigma\leqq 2$,

$$|\zeta(s)|\geqq|\zeta(\sigma+2it)|^{-1/4}(\zeta(\sigma))^{-3/4}. \tag{25}$$

Proof. The proof is obvious from (23).

For $2t<T$, the corollary of Theorem 4.2 tells us that $\zeta(\sigma+2it)=O(\log T)$. Furthermore, $(\sigma-1)\zeta(\sigma)$ remains bounded as $\sigma\to 1$ and being continuous has an upper bound for $1<\sigma\leqq 2$. Consequently from (25) we get for $1<\sigma\leqq 2$,

$$|\zeta(s)|\geqq|\zeta(\sigma+2it)|^{-1/4}(\zeta(\sigma))^{-3/4}(\sigma-1)^{-3/4}(\sigma-1)^{3/4} \tag{26}$$
$$>K(\log T)^{-1/4}(\sigma-1)^{3/4},$$

for some constant K, by Corollary 1, Theorem 4.2.

We showed that $\zeta(1+it)\neq 0$ and that $\zeta(s)$ is regular except for $s=1$; hence there is a region to the left of $\sigma=1$ in which $\zeta(s)$ does not vanish. The next theorem establishes a left-hand boundary for this region.

Theorem 4.6. *Let* $s=\sigma+it$, $\log T\geqq|t|>1$, *then there exist positive constants* c_1 *and* c_2 *such that for*

(27) $$1-\frac{c_1}{(\log T)^9}\leqq\sigma\leqq 2\,,$$

we have

(28) $$|\zeta(s)|>\frac{c_2}{(\log\ T)^7}\,.$$

Proof. The inequality (26), which we proved above, is valid for $\sigma>1$; our object now is to establish an inequality in a region extending to the left of $\sigma=1$. This is accomplished by relating $\zeta(s)$ for $\sigma>1$ to $\zeta(s)$ for $\sigma<1$.

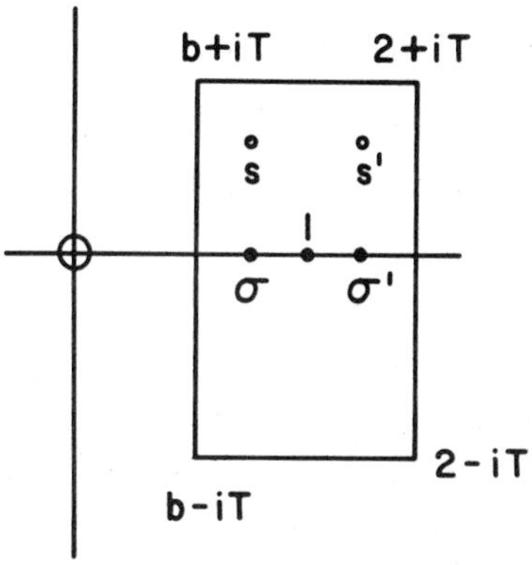

Let $s=\sigma+it,\ s'=\sigma'+it$, where $\sigma'-1=1-\sigma,\ \sigma'>1,\ \sigma<1$ (see the figure); s and s' are symmetrically placed in relation to the line $\sigma=1$. Then

(29) $$\zeta(s')-\zeta(s)=\int_s^{s'}\zeta'(\alpha)d\alpha;$$

from which it follows that

(30) $$\begin{aligned}|\zeta(s)|&\geqq|\zeta(s')|-\left|\int_s^{s'}\zeta'(\alpha)d\alpha\right|\\&\geqq|\zeta(s')|-\int_\sigma^{\sigma'}|\zeta'(\alpha)||d\alpha|\,.\end{aligned}$$

We now use the inequality of the corollary to Theorem 4.3 and (26). These, together with (30), give

(31) $$|\zeta(s)|\geqq c_3(\sigma'-1)^{3/4})\log T)^{-1/4}-c_4(\sigma'-\sigma)\log^2 T.$$

Moreover, $\sigma'-\sigma=2(\sigma'-1)=2(1-\sigma)$, and therefore

(32) $$|\zeta(s)|\geqq(1-\sigma)^{3/4}\{c_3(\log T)^{-1/4}-2c_4(1-\sigma)^{1/4}\log^2 T\}\,.$$

Once again, in order to maximize the parenthesis (see the remark after Theorem 4.2), we put

$$c_3(\log T)^{-1/4}=3c_4(1-\sigma)^{1/4}\log^2 T\,,$$

from which it follows that

$$c_5 \log^{-9} T = (1 - \sigma),$$

or

$$\sigma = 1 - c_5(\log T)^{-9};$$

and hence from (32),

$$|\zeta(s)| \geqq c_4 (\log T)^{-27/4} (\log T)^{-1/4} = c_4 (\log T)^{-7}.$$

The same inequality holds for $2 \geqq \sigma \geqq 1 + c_5/\log^9 T$ and the theorem is proved with $c_1 = c_5$.

Combining this result with the corollary of Theorem 4.3, we get

THEOREM 4.7. *There exists a constant c such that if* $s = \sigma + it$, $\log T \geqq |t| > 1$,

$$2 \geqq \sigma \geqq 1 - c(\log T)^{-9},$$

then

$$\frac{\zeta'(s)}{\zeta(s)} = O(\log^9 T). \tag{33}$$

As an illustration of the magnitude of the constants implied in these calculations, we note that a careful accounting yields the result:

If $1 - 10^{-6}/\log^9 T \leqq \sigma \leqq 2$, $T > 10$, then $|\zeta'(s)/\zeta(s)| < 10^7 \log^9 T$.

We establish the validity of an inequality of the type given by Theorem 4.7 for the function $\log \zeta(s)$ since this is the function which enters into the integral in (1)

THEOREM 4.8. *There exists a constant c such that if* $s = \sigma + it$, $\log T \geqq |t| > 1$,

$$1 - c(\log T)^{-9} \leqq \sigma \leqq 2,$$

then

$$\log \zeta(s) = O(\log^9 T). \tag{34}$$

Moreover, the same inequality holds if $\sigma = 1 - c/\log^9 T$ *and* $|t| \leqq 1$.

PROOF. Using Theorem 4.7, we have

$$\begin{aligned} \log \zeta(s) - \log \zeta(2 + it) &= \int_2^\sigma \frac{\zeta'(u + it)}{\zeta(u + it)} du \\ &= O((\sigma - 2) \log^9 T). \end{aligned} \tag{35}$$

Hence from (35),

$$\begin{aligned} \log \zeta(s) &= \log \zeta(2 + it) + O((\sigma - 2) \log^9 T) \\ &= O(1) + O(\log^9 T) = O(\log^9 T), \end{aligned} \tag{36}$$

provided $T \geqq T_0$, where T_0 is some sufficiently large constant. On the other hand, if $\sigma = 1 - c/\log^9 T$, $|t| < 1$, with c sufficiently small, we have in the rectangle bounded on the right by $\sigma_1 < 1$,

$$\begin{aligned}\log \zeta(s) &= \log (s-1)\zeta(s) - \log (s-1) \\ &= O(1) + O(\log \log^{-9} T) \\ &= O(\log T) = O(\log^9 T).\end{aligned} \tag{37}$$

Equations (36) and (37) complete the proof.

We now have all the necessary inequalities for a proof of our main theorem. As we stated earlier, these inequalities may be sharpened considerably but only at the expense of more elaborate analysis. Moreover, the improvement in the error term which these sharper estimates imply is still far short of that which the Riemann hypothesis implies.

5. First proof of the prime number theorem. We had from § 4, (1) for $a > 1$

$$\psi_1(x) = \frac{1}{2\pi i}\int_{a-i\infty}^{a+i\infty} \log \zeta(s)\, \frac{x^s}{s}\, ds,$$

and we recall that our objective was to move the path of integration suitably far to the left but avoiding the singularities of the integrand. In § 4 we established the necessary inequalities for $\log \zeta(s)$; in addition, however, $\log \zeta(s)$ has a logarithmic singularity at $s = 1$ and we must take careful account of this fact.

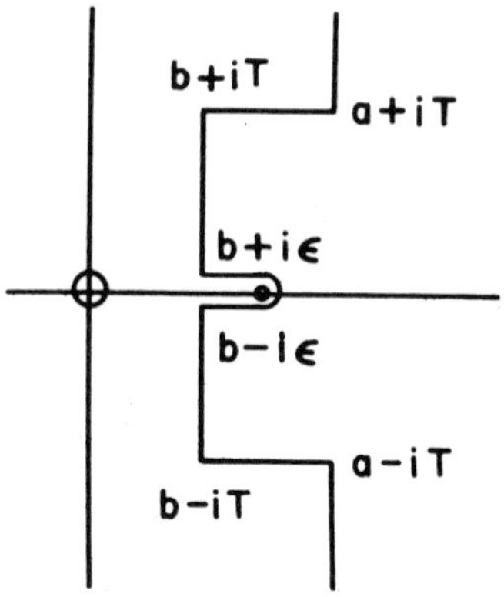

We therefore change the path as follows. Let T be fixed and

$$b = 1 - c\log^{-9} T, \qquad a = 1 + c\log^{-9} T, \tag{1}$$

where c is the constant of Theorem 4.8. Then the segment from $a - iT$ to $a + iT$ is deformed so as to go horizontally from $a - iT$ to $b - iT$, vertically from $b - iT$ to $b - i\varepsilon$, around an indentation or cut avoiding the point $s = 1$, with a semicircle of radius ε and center 1, vertically from $b + i\varepsilon$ to $b + iT$ and horizontally from $b + iT$ to $a + iT$. Since, by Theorem 4.8, the integrand is analytic in the region so defined, we get by Cauchy's theorem

$$\frac{1}{2\pi i}\int_{a-i\infty}^{a+i\infty}\log\zeta(s)\frac{x^s}{s}\,ds=\frac{1}{2\pi i}\left(\int_{a-i\infty}^{a-iT}+\int_{a-iT}^{b-iT}+\int_{b-iT}^{b-i\varepsilon}+\int_{\text{cut}}+\int_{b+i\varepsilon}^{b+iT}+\int_{b+iT}^{a+iT}+\int_{a+iT}^{a+i\infty}\right)\log\zeta(s)\frac{x^s}{s}\,ds. \tag{2}$$

Call these integrals $I_1, I_2, I_3, I_4, I_5, I_6, I_7$, respectively. We estimate these integrals.

I. *The integrals* I_1 *and* I_7. Since I_1 and I_7 are similar in character, an estimate for one can be carried out in a similar way for the other. We consider I_7.

We have already noted that the integral

$$\frac{1}{2\pi i}\int_{a-i\infty}^{a+i\infty}\log\zeta(s)\frac{x^s}{s}\,ds$$

does not converge absolutely; we must therefore exercise some care in estimating I_7. The argument is a repetition of that used in the proof of Theorem 3.1. We have in fact, for $U > T$,

$$\begin{aligned} I_7&=\lim_{U\to\infty}\frac{1}{2\pi i}\int_{a+iT}^{a+iU}\log\zeta(s)\frac{x^s}{s}\,ds\\ &=\lim_{U\to\infty}\frac{1}{2\pi i}\int_{a+iT}^{a+iU}\sum_{n=1}^{\infty}\frac{\Lambda_1(n)}{n^s}\frac{x^s}{s}\,ds \\ &=\lim_{U\to\infty}\frac{1}{2\pi i}\sum_{n=1}^{\infty}\Lambda_1(n)\int_{a+iT}^{a+iU}\left(\frac{x}{n}\right)^s\cdot\frac{1}{s}\,ds,\end{aligned} \tag{3}$$

the interchange of summation and integration being justified by Theorem 3.1, or alternatively by the fact that the path of integration is in a region of uniform convergence. To estimate the integral, we integrate by parts

$$\begin{aligned}\int_{a+iT}^{a+iU}\left(\frac{x}{n}\right)^s\frac{ds}{s}&=\left.\frac{\left(\frac{x}{n}\right)^s}{s\log\frac{x}{n}}\right]_{a+iT}^{a+iU}+\frac{1}{\log\frac{x}{n}}\int_{a+iT}^{a+iU}\left(\frac{x}{n}\right)^s\frac{ds}{s^2}\\ &=O\left(\frac{\left(\frac{x}{n}\right)^a}{|a+iU|\left|\log\frac{x}{n}\right|}+\frac{\left(\frac{x}{n}\right)^a}{|a+iT|\left|\log\frac{x}{n}\right|}\right.\\ &\qquad\left.+\frac{1}{\left|\log\frac{x}{n}\right|}\left(\frac{x}{n}\right)^a\int_T^U\frac{dt}{a^2+t^2}\right)\\ &=O\left(\frac{\left(\frac{x}{n}\right)^a}{T\left|\log\frac{x}{n}\right|}\right),\end{aligned}$$

since $U > T$. Moreover, because $\Lambda_1(n) < 1$, this leads by (3) to

(4) $$I_7 = O\left(\frac{x^a}{T}\sum_{n=1}^{\infty}\frac{n^{-a}}{\left|\log\frac{x}{n}\right|}\right).$$

Whenever x is close to n, the denominator is small. In order to deal with the series, we therefore divide the sum into three parts in accordance with the conditions

$$\text{(i)}\quad n < \frac{x}{2}, \quad \text{(ii)}\quad \frac{x}{2} \leqq n \leqq \frac{3x}{2}, \quad \text{(iii)}\quad n > \frac{3x}{2}.$$

For the range (i),

$$\left|\log\frac{x}{n}\right| > \log 2;$$

while for the values of n in (iii),

$$\left|\log\frac{x}{n}\right| = \left|\log\frac{n}{x}\right| > \log\frac{3}{2}.$$

In either case,

$$\left|\log\frac{x}{n}\right| > \log\frac{3}{2} > \frac{1}{3};$$

and then,

(5) $$\sum_{n<x/2}\frac{n^{-a}}{\left|\log\frac{x}{n}\right|} = O\left(\sum_{n<x/2} n^{-a}\right) = O\left(\frac{1}{a-1}\right),$$

and

(6) $$\sum_{n>3x/2}\frac{n^{-a}}{\left|\log\frac{x}{n}\right|} = O\left(\sum_{n>3x/2} n^{-a}\right) = O\left(\frac{1}{a-1}\right).$$

For values of n in class (ii),

$$-\frac{1}{2} \leqq 1 - \frac{n}{x} \leqq \frac{1}{2},$$

and if we put $z = 1 - n/x$, then $|z| \leqq \frac{1}{2}$,

$$\log\frac{x}{n} = \log(1-z)^{-1}$$
$$= z\left(1 + \frac{z}{2} + \frac{z^2}{3} + \cdots\right).$$

If, however, $z \geqq 0$, then

$$1 + \frac{z}{2} + \frac{z^2}{3} + \cdots \geqq 1,$$

while if $-\frac{1}{2} \leqq z \leqq 0$, then

$$1 + \frac{z}{2} + \frac{z^2}{3} + \cdots \geqq \frac{3}{4}.$$

In either case, for some constant $c_1 > 0$,

$$\left| \log\left(\frac{x}{n}\right) \right| \geqq c_1 z ,$$

from which it follows that

$$\frac{1}{\left| \log \frac{x}{n} \right|} \leqq \frac{c_2}{|z|} \leqq \frac{c_2 x}{|x-n|}. \tag{7}$$

Therefore from (7)

$$\sum_{x/2 \leqq n \leqq 3x/2} \frac{n^{-a}}{\left| \log \frac{x}{n} \right|} = O\Big(x \sum_{x/2 \leqq n \leqq 3x/2} \frac{n^{-a}}{|x-n|}\Big) = O\Big(x^{1-a} \sum_{x/2 \leqq n \leqq 3x/2} \frac{1}{|x-n|}\Big). \tag{8}$$

Let $x = [x] + \xi$ ($\xi \neq 0$, since x is not an integer); then as n ranges over the set $x/2 \leqq n \leqq 3x/2$, $|x-n|$ will range over the set

$$\xi, |\xi \pm 1|, |\xi \pm 2|, \cdots \left| \xi \pm \frac{[x]}{2} \right|.$$

Inserting these values in (8), we get

$$\sum_{x/2 \leqq n \leqq 3x/2} \frac{1}{|x-n|} < \Big(\frac{1}{\xi} + \sum_{k=1}^{[x]} \frac{1}{k}\Big) = O(\log x). \tag{9}$$

From (4), (5), (6), (9), it follows that

$$I_7 = O\Big\{\frac{x^a}{T}\Big(\frac{1}{a-1} + x^{1-a} \log x\Big)\Big\}. \tag{10}$$

I_1 is estimated in exactly the same way.

II. *The integrals I_2 and I_6.* We consider now the pair I_2 and I_6 and focus our attention on I_6. We have

$$I_6 = \frac{1}{2\pi i} \int_{b+iT}^{a+iT} \log \zeta(s) \frac{x^s}{s} \, ds$$

$$= O\Big(\int_b^a |\log \zeta(\sigma + iT)| \frac{|x^{\sigma+iT}|}{|\sigma + iT|} d\sigma\Big),$$

and this, by Theorem 4.8, is

$$O\Big(x^a \frac{1}{T} \log^9 T\Big). \tag{11}$$

I_2 yields the same estimate.

III. *The integrals I_3 and I_5.* Next, we consider I_3 and I_5:

$$I_5 = \frac{1}{2\pi i} \int_{b+i\varepsilon}^{b+iT} \log \zeta(s) \frac{x^s}{s} \, ds$$

$$= O\Big(\int_\varepsilon^T |\log \zeta(b + it)| \frac{|x^{b+it}|}{|b+it|} dt\Big).$$

Once again, by Theorem 4.8, this is

$$O\left(x^b \int_0^T \frac{dt}{(b^2+t^2)^{1/2}} \log^9 T\right) = O(x^b \log^9 T \log T) \tag{12}$$
$$= O(x^b \log^{10} T).$$

IV. *The integral I_4*. There remains I_4. Here we have

$$I_4 = \frac{1}{2\pi i}\int_c \log \zeta(s) \frac{x^s}{s}\, ds$$
$$= \frac{1}{2\pi i}\int_c \log [(s-1)\zeta(s)] \frac{x^s}{s}\, ds - \frac{1}{2\pi i}\int_c \log (s-1) \frac{x^s}{s}\, ds .$$

The first integral is zero because $\log (s-1)\zeta(s)$ is regular and single-valued along the cut c; the integrand is regular therefore, and the integral along the upper side cancels the integral along the lower side. To evaluate the second integral, let $s-1 = \varepsilon e^{i\theta}$ with $-\pi < \theta < \pi$; then $\log(s-1) = (\log \varepsilon) + i\theta$ so that the value of $\log(s-1)$ along the lower part differs from that along the upper part by $2\pi i$. We let ε tend to 0. Then

$$\frac{1}{2\pi i}\int_c \log (s-1) \frac{x^s}{s}\, ds = \frac{1}{2\pi i}\int_b^1 ((\log \varepsilon) - i\pi) \frac{x^s}{s}\, ds$$
$$+ \frac{1}{2\pi i}\int_1^b ((\log \varepsilon) + i\pi) \frac{x^s}{s}\, ds \tag{13}$$
$$+ \frac{1}{2\pi i}\int_\gamma ((\log \varepsilon) + i\theta) \frac{x^s}{s}\, ds ,$$

where in the last integral γ is a semi-circle of radius ε drawn around the point 1.

$$\int_\gamma ((\log \varepsilon) + i\theta) \frac{x^s}{s}\, ds = O((\log(\varepsilon+\pi)x^{1+\varepsilon}2\pi\varepsilon) = o(1) \qquad \text{as } \varepsilon \to 0. \tag{14}$$

For the other integrals in (13) we have

$$\frac{1}{2\pi i}\int_b^1 ((\log \varepsilon) - i\pi) \frac{x^s}{s}\, ds - \frac{1}{2\pi i}\int_b^1 ((\log \varepsilon) + i\pi) \frac{x^s}{s}\, ds = -\int_b^1 \frac{x^s}{s}\, ds .$$

From (13), (14),

$$I_4 = \int_b^1 \frac{x^s}{s}\, ds . \tag{15}$$

If we put $x^s = u$, then

$$I_4 = \int_{x^b}^x \frac{du}{\log u} = \int_2^x \frac{du}{\log u} + \int_{x^b}^2 \frac{du}{\log u} ,$$

and since $\log u > \log 2$ for $2 \leqq u \leqq x^b$, we get the estimate

$$\int_2^{x^b} \frac{du}{\log u} = O(x^b) ,$$

which, together with (15), gives

(16)
$$I_4 = \int_2^x \frac{du}{\log u} + O(x^b)\,.$$

V. *Completion of the proof.* We gather our results. From Theorems 2.7 and 4.1 and equations (2), (10), (11), (12), (16) we get:

$$\pi(x) = \psi_1(x) + O(x^{1/2}) = \int_2^x \frac{du}{\log u} + R(x)$$

where

(17)
$$R(x) = O\left\{\left(\frac{x^a}{T}\right)\cdot\frac{1}{a-1} + \frac{x\log x}{T} + \frac{x^a}{T}\log^9 T + x^b\log^{10}T + x^b + x^{1/2}\right\}.$$

We encounter once again the problem of selecting T as a function of x so as to make the order of magnitude of $R(x)$ as small as possible. The dominant terms are $(x^a\log^9 T)/T$ and $x^b\log^{10} T$. We balance their effect by putting

$$\frac{x^a}{T}\log^9 T = x^b\log^{10} T;$$

that is,

$$T\log T = x^{a-b}\,.$$

It will serve our purposes equally well to choose

$$T = x^{a-b}\,.$$

Then

$$\log x = \frac{\log T}{a-b}\,,$$

and since, from (1),

(18)
$$a - b = 1 + \frac{c}{\log^9 T} - \left(1 - \frac{c}{\log^9 T}\right) = \frac{2c}{\log^9 T}\,,$$

we get

(19)
$$\log x = \frac{\log^{10} T}{2c}\,,$$

and

$$a - 1 = c\log^{-9} T\,.$$

Therefore by (18) and (19)

$$R(x) = O(x^b\log^{10} T + x^{1+b-a}\log^{10} T + x^b\log^{10} T + x^b\log^{10} T) = O\,(x^b\log^{10} T)\,,$$

since $a > 1$, and $x^{1+b-a} = O(x^b)$. On the other hand,

$$\begin{aligned} O(x^b\log^{10} T) &= O(x^{1-c(\log T)^{-9}}\;\log^{10} T) \\ &= O(x\exp[-c(\log T)^{-9}\log x + 10\log\log T]) \\ &= O(x\exp[-c_1\log T]) \\ &= O(x\exp[-c_2(\log x)^{1/10}]), \end{aligned}$$

on account of (19).

This completes the proof; that is,

$$\pi(x) = \int_2^x \frac{du}{\log u} + O(xe^{-\lambda(x)}), \tag{20}$$

where $\lambda(x) = c(\log x)^{1/10}$.

Notice that

$$\lim_{x\to\infty} e^{-\lambda(x)} \log^k x = \lim_{x\to\infty} \frac{\log^k x}{1 + \lambda(x) + \dfrac{\lambda^2(x)}{2!} + \cdots} \to 0 \qquad \text{for every } k > 0.$$

That is, $e^{-\lambda(x)}$ tends to zero "infinitely more rapidly" than any negative power of $\log x$. On the other hand,

$$\lim_{x\to\infty} e^{-\lambda(x)} x^m = \lim_{x\to\infty} x^m\left(1 - \lambda(x) + \frac{\lambda^2(x)}{2!} - \cdots\right) \to \infty \qquad \text{for every } m > 0.$$

In other words, $e^{-\lambda(x)}$ tends to 0 "infinitely less rapidly" than any negative power of x. Thus $e^{-\lambda(x)}$ is intermediate in order of magnitude between $1/\log^k x$ $(k > 0)$ and x^{-m} $(m > 0)$. Returning to the remark we made after the statement of Theorem A, we see, therefore, that

$$\int_2^x \frac{dt}{\log t}$$

is indeed a better approximation to $\pi(x)$ than the sum

$$\frac{x}{\log x} + \frac{x}{\log^2 x} + \cdots + \frac{(k-1)!\,x}{\log^k x}$$

for any k.

The function $\lambda(x)$ in the error term has gone through a succession of ameliorations but the accompanying analysis becomes elaborate. About the best value known to date is

$$\lambda(x) = c(\log x)^{3/5}.$$

On the other hand, if

$$R(x) = \pi(x) - \int_2^x \frac{du}{\log u},$$

then on the assumption of the unproved Riemann hypothesis, it can be shown that

$$R(x) = O(x^{1/2} \log x);$$

indeed, if θ is the lower bound of numbers σ for which

$$\zeta(\sigma + it) \neq 0,$$

then

$$R(x) = O(x^\theta \log x). \tag{21}$$

If it should turn out that $\theta < 1$, then the error in (21) is "infinitely" better than that given in (20) for

$$\lambda(x) = c(\log x)^r$$

for any r. On the other hand, it is just possible that the Riemann hypothesis is false and that $\theta = 1$!

It can furthermore be shown that if (21) holds, then

$$\zeta(\sigma + it) \neq 0$$

for $\sigma > \theta$.

Thus the zeros of $\zeta(s)$ impose a decided limitation on the accuracy with which $\operatorname{li} x$ can represent $\pi(x)$.

6. Other proofs of the prime number theorem. The proof given in § 5 had some disadvantages, namely

(i) The function "naturally" associated with $\log \zeta(s)$ is not $\pi(x)$ but the function we called $\psi_1(x)$.

(ii) $\log \zeta(s)$ is multiple-valued and we had to avoid the singularity at $s = 1$.

(iii) Some of the integrals were not absolutely convergent and necessitated careful treatment.

Of these, the most troublesome was (iii). On the other hand, it was a very simple step to go from $\psi_1(x)$ to $\pi(x)$ and therefore the arithmetic discussion was reduced to a minimum.

We can avoid the difficulties implied by (ii) working with the derivative of $\log \zeta(s)$, namely $\zeta'(s)/\zeta(s)$. We show first that $\zeta'(s)/\zeta(s)$ may be written as a Dirichlet series and then determine some properties of the coefficients.

THEOREM 6.1. *If*

(1) $$\Lambda(n) = \begin{cases} \log p & \text{when } n = p^k , \\ 0 & \text{otherwise} , \end{cases}$$

then for $\sigma > 1$,

(2) $$-\frac{\zeta'(s)}{\zeta(s)} = \sum_{n=1}^{\infty} \frac{\Lambda(n)}{n^s} .$$

PROOF. We had

$$\log \zeta(s) = \sum_{n=1}^{\infty} \frac{\Lambda_1(n)}{n^s} .$$

Differentiating, we get

$$-\frac{\zeta'(s)}{\zeta(s)} = \sum_{n=1}^{\infty} \frac{\Lambda_1(n) \log n}{n^s} .$$

If we put

(3) $$\Lambda(n) = \Lambda_1(n) \log n ,$$

we get

$$\Lambda(n) = \begin{cases} \frac{1}{k}\log p^k & \text{if} \quad n = p^k\,, \\ 0 & \text{otherwise}\,, \end{cases}$$

$$= \begin{cases} \log p & \text{if} \quad n = p^k\,, \\ 0 & \text{otherwise}\,, \end{cases}$$

and this completes the proof.

Let

(4)
$$\psi(x) = \sum_{n \leq x} \Lambda(n)\,;$$

then we can discuss the first variant of the proof given in § 5.

A. *Proof using* $\psi(x)$. In this case we have by Theorem 3.1 for $a > 1$,

(5)
$$\psi(x) = \int_{a-i\infty}^{a+i\infty} \left(-\frac{\zeta'(s)}{\zeta(s)}\right)\frac{x^s}{s}\,ds\,.$$

We are required to evaluate this integral. In the first place $\zeta(s)$ has a Laurent expansion about $s = 1$ given by

(6)
$$\zeta(s) = \frac{1}{s-1} + a_0 + a_1(s-1) + \cdots\,.$$

Consequently,

(7)
$$-\frac{\zeta'(s)}{\zeta(s)} = \frac{1}{s-1} + b_0 + b_1(s-1) + \cdots\,,$$

from which it follows that $-\zeta'(s)/\zeta(s)$ has a simple pole at $s = 1$ with residue 1. This fact, together with the inequalities developed in § 4, allows us to prove

THEOREM 6.2. *There exists a constant* c *such that*

(8)
$$\psi(x) = x + O(xe^{-c(\log x)^{1/10}})\,.$$

Before proceeding with the proof, let us infer the relationship between $\pi(x)$ and $\psi(x)$. We prove

THEOREM 6.3. *If* $\lambda(x) = (\log x)^r$ *for* $0 < r < 1$, *then for constants* c_1, c_2 *and* c_3

(9)
$$\psi(x) = x + O(x\exp[-c_1\lambda(x)])$$

if and only if

(10)
$$\pi(x) = \operatorname{li} x + O(x\exp[-c_2\lambda(x)])$$

if and only if

(11)
$$\psi_1(x) = \operatorname{li} x + O(x\exp[-c_3\lambda(x)])\,.$$

PROOF. We bear in mind that li x and $\int_2^x dt/\log t$ differ by a constant. The equivalence is established as follows: the equivalence of (10) with (11) has already been proved; we prove that (9) implies (11). Suppose there exists a constant c_1 such that

$$\psi(x) = x + O(x\exp[-c_1\lambda(x)])\,.$$

We have

$$\psi_1(x) = \sum_{n\leq x} \Lambda_1(n) = \sum_{2\leq n\leq x} \frac{\Lambda(n)}{\log n}\,.$$

Using Lemma 3.1 of Chapter I with $\phi(x) = 1/\log x$ and $c_n = \Lambda(n)$, we get

$$\psi_1(x) = \frac{\psi(x)}{\log x} + \frac{\psi(2)}{2} + \int_2^x \frac{\psi(t)}{\log^2 t}\cdot\frac{dt}{t}\,. \tag{12}$$

On the other hand, if we integrate by parts, we find

$$\int_2^x \frac{dt}{\log t} = \frac{x}{\log x} - \frac{2}{\log 2} + \int_2^x \frac{dt}{\log^2 t}\,,$$

which, taken with (12), implies that

$$\begin{aligned}\psi_1(x) - \int_2^x \frac{dt}{\log t} &= \frac{\psi(x)-x}{\log x} + \int_2^x \frac{\psi(t)-t}{t\log^2 t}\,dt + \frac{\psi(2)}{2} - \frac{2}{\log 2}\\ &= O\Big(\frac{x}{\log x}\exp[-c_1\lambda(x)]\Big) + O\Big(\int_2^x \frac{\exp[-c_1\lambda(t)]}{\log^2 t}\,dt\Big)\\ &= O(x\exp[-c_1\lambda(x)]) + O\Big(\int_2^x \exp[-c_1\lambda(t)]\,dt\Big)\\ &= O(x\exp[-c_1\lambda(x)]) + O\Big(\Big(\int_2^{\sqrt{x}} + \int_{\sqrt{x}}^x\Big) \exp[-c_1\lambda(t)]\,dt\Big)\\ &= O(x\exp[-c_1\lambda(x)]) + O(\sqrt{x}) + O((x-\sqrt{x})\exp[-c_1\lambda(\sqrt{x})])\\ &= O(x\exp[-c_3\lambda(x)])\,.\end{aligned}$$

We leave the converse that (11) implies (9) as an exercise—the proof is very much the same.

PROOF OF THEOREM 6.2. For the proof of Theorem 6.2, we fix T and choose $a = 1 + c/\log^9 T$, $b = 1 - c/\log^9 T$, where c is the constant of Theorem 4.7 and deform the path between $a - iT$ and $a + iT$ so as to go horizontally from $a - iT$ to $b - iT$, vertically from $b - iT$ to $b + iT$ and horizontally from $b + iT$ to $a + iT$. Since $-\zeta'(s)/\zeta(s)$ has a simple pole at $s = 1$ with residue 1, we get by Cauchy's theorem

$$\begin{aligned}\frac{1}{2\pi i}\int_{a-iT}^{a+iT}\Big(-\frac{\zeta'(s)}{\zeta(s)}\Big)\frac{x^s}{s}\,ds &= x + \frac{1}{2\pi i}\Big(\int_{a-iT}^{b-iT} + \int_{b-iT}^{b+iT} + \int_{b+iT}^{a+iT}\Big(-\frac{\zeta'(s)}{\zeta(s)}\Big)\frac{x^s}{s}\,ds\Big)\\ &= x + I_1 + I_2 + I_3\,.\end{aligned} \tag{13}$$

Consequently, by (5) and (13) we have

$$\begin{aligned}\psi(x) &= x + \frac{1}{2\pi i}\int_{a-i\infty}^{a-iT}\Big(-\frac{\zeta'(s)}{\zeta(s)}\Big)\frac{x^s}{s}\,ds + \frac{1}{2\pi i}\int_{a+iT}^{a+i\infty}\Big(-\frac{\zeta'(s)}{\zeta(s)}\Big)\frac{x^s}{s}\,ds + I_1 + I_2 + I_3\\ &= x + I_4 + I_5 + I_1 + I_2 + I_3\,.\end{aligned} \tag{14}$$

Estimates for I_1, I_2, I_3, I_4 and I_5 follow exactly as in § 5. In fact, by Theorem 4.7,

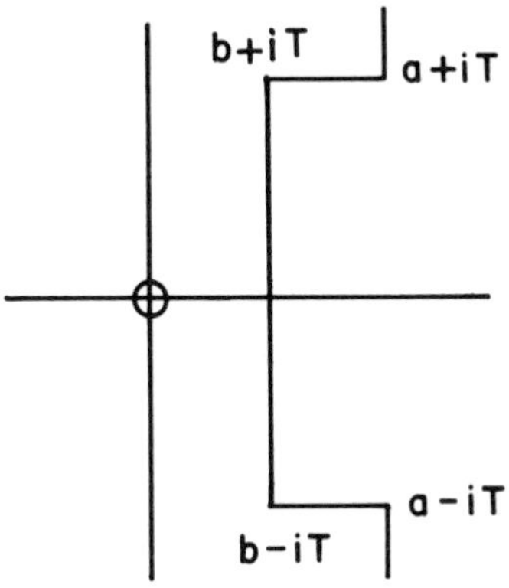

$$(15)\qquad I_1 + I_3 = O\left(\int_b^a \left|\frac{\zeta'(\sigma+iT)}{\zeta(\sigma+iT)}\right| \frac{x^\sigma}{|\sigma+iT|}\, d\sigma\right) = O\left(x^a \frac{1}{T}\log^9 T\right),$$

$$(16)\qquad I_2 = O\left(\int_{-T}^{T} \left|\frac{\zeta'(b+it)}{\zeta(b+it)}\right| \frac{x^b}{|\sigma+it|}\, dt\right) = O(x^b \log^{10} T),$$

$$I_4 + I_5 = O\left(\frac{x^a}{T}\left(\frac{1}{a-1} + x^{1-a}\log x\right)\log T\right).$$

Combining these, we get exactly as in § 5,

$$\psi(x) = x + R(x),$$

with

$$R(x) = O(x^b \log^{10} T) = O(x \exp[-c(\log x)^{1/10}]).$$

In this proof we still had to contend with nonabsolutely convergent integrals. The next variant uses an absolutely convergent integral.

B. *Proof with improved error using absolutely convergent integrals.* Our natural resource here is Theorem 3.3 with $k = 1$. This is

$$(17)\qquad \frac{1}{2\pi i}\int_{a-i\infty}^{a+i\infty} \frac{x^s}{s(s+1)}\, ds = \begin{cases} 0 & \text{if } x \leqq 1, \\ \left(1 - \dfrac{1}{x}\right) & \text{if } x \geqq 1, \end{cases}$$

which is absolutely convergent. Then by Theorem 3.4 with $f(s) = -\zeta'(s)/\zeta(s)$, we get for $a > 1$,

$$(18)\qquad \frac{1}{2\pi i}\int_{a-i\infty}^{a+i\infty}\left(-\frac{\zeta'(s)}{\zeta(s)}\right)\frac{x^s}{s(s+1)}\, ds = \frac{1}{x}\int_1^x \psi(t)dt.$$

Actually, we may deduce (18) directly from (17) without the help of Theorem 3.4. The right-hand side of (18) represents the arithmetic mean of the function $\psi(x)$. Let

$$(19)\qquad \psi_2(x) = \int_1^x \psi(t)dt = \sum_{n \leqq x} \Lambda(n)(x-n);$$

then we may expect that the mean value $\psi_2(x)/x$ will admit of simpler treatment than $\psi(x)$ itself. Moreover a direct argument shows that if

$$\psi(x) \sim x ,$$

then

$$\psi_2(x) \sim \frac{x^2}{2} .$$

Suppose that we prove

$$\psi_2(x) = \tfrac{1}{2}x^2 + O(x^2 \exp[-c_1\lambda(x)]) ,$$

with $\lambda(x) = (\log x)^r$ for some r between 0 and 1. What can we infer about $\psi(x)$? We prove

THEOREM 6.4. *For some constants c_1 and c_2,*

$$\psi_2(x) = \tfrac{1}{2}x^2 + O(x^2 \exp[-c_1\lambda(x)]) \tag{20}$$

if and only if

$$\psi(x) = x + O(x \exp[- c_2\lambda(x)]) , \tag{21}$$

where $\lambda(x) = (\log x)^r$ for $0 < r < 1$.

PROOF. That (20) implies (21) is a simple deduction from the definition (19) of $\psi_2(x)$. For the converse, suppose that $x \geqq 4$ and suppose that $h(x)$ is a function satisfying the inequality

$$0 < h(x) < \frac{x}{2} . \tag{22}$$

Since $\psi(x)$ is a nondecreasing function of x,

$$\frac{1}{h}\int_{x-h}^{x} \psi(t)dt \leqq \psi(x) \leqq \frac{1}{h}\int_{x}^{x+h} \psi(t)dt . \tag{23}$$

On the other hand

$$\begin{aligned} \frac{1}{h}\int_{x-h}^{x} \psi(t)dt &= \frac{1}{h}(\psi_2(x) - \psi_2(x-h)) \\ &= \frac{1}{h}\left\{\frac{x^2}{2} + O(x^2 \exp[- c_1\lambda(x)]) - \frac{(x-h)^2}{2}\right. \\ &\qquad \left. + O(x^2 \exp[-c_1\lambda(x-h)])\right\} . \end{aligned} \tag{24}$$

But $\lambda(x)$ is an increasing function of x and by (22),

$$\tfrac{1}{2}x < x - h < x ,$$

and therefore, from (24),

$$\frac{1}{h}\int_{x-h}^{x} \psi(t)dt = x - \frac{h}{2} + O\left(\frac{x^2 \exp\left[-c_1\lambda\left(\frac{x}{2}\right)\right]}{h}\right) . \tag{25}$$

By exactly the same argument,

$$\frac{1}{h}\int_x^{x+h}\psi(t)dt = x + \frac{h}{2} + O\left(\frac{x^2 \exp\left[-c_1\lambda\left(\frac{x}{2}\right)\right]}{h}\right). \tag{26}$$

However, since

$$\frac{\lambda\left(\frac{x}{2}\right)}{\lambda(x)} = \left(1 - \frac{\log 2}{\log x}\right)^r > \frac{1}{2^r} \qquad \text{if } x \geqq 4\,,$$

it follows that

$$\exp\left[-c_1\lambda\left(\frac{x}{2}\right)\right] = O(\exp[-c_3\lambda(x)])\,.$$

Hence from (23), (25), (26),

$$O\left(\frac{x^2}{h}e^{-c_3\lambda(x)}\right) - \frac{h}{2} \leqq \psi(x) - x \leqq \frac{h}{2} + O\left(\frac{x^2}{h}e^{-c_3\lambda(x)}\right). \tag{27}$$

If we choose

$$h(x) = \frac{x}{2}e^{-c_4\lambda(x)}\,,$$

then $0 < h(x) < \frac{1}{2}$, and the conclusion follows from (27), with some constant c_2.

The main theorem we prove in this subsection is the following:

THEOREM 6.5. *There exists a constant c such that*

$$\psi_2(x) = \frac{x^2}{2} + O(x^2 e^{-c\lambda(x)})\,, \tag{28}$$

where

$$\lambda(x) = (\log x)^{1/2}\,. \tag{29}$$

From this will follow directly, using Theorems 6.3 and 6.2, the

COROLLARY. *There exists a constant c such that*

$$\pi(x) = \operatorname{li} x + O(xe^{-c\lambda(x)})\,,$$

where $\lambda(x) = (\log x)^{1/2}$.

It will be observed that we have here replaced the value $\frac{1}{10}$ by $\frac{1}{2}$ in the exponent of the logarithm. The additional labor required to effect this is comparatively small. We require an enlarged region which is free of the zeros of $\zeta(s)$ and an improved estimate for $-\zeta'(s)/\zeta(s)$. The original proof by de la Vallée Poussin made use of the formula

$$\zeta(s) = \frac{e^{bs}}{2(s-1)\Gamma\left(\frac{s}{2}+1\right)}\prod_\rho\left(1 - \frac{s}{\rho}\right)e^{s/\rho}$$

or

$$\frac{\zeta'(s)}{\zeta(s)} = b - \frac{1}{s-1} - \frac{1}{2}\frac{\Gamma'\left(\frac{s}{2}+1\right)}{\Gamma\left(\frac{s}{2}+1\right)} + \sum_{\rho}\left(\frac{1}{s-\rho}+\frac{1}{\rho}\right)$$

which is a consequence of Hadamard's general theory of entire functions. Landau showed, however, that it is possible to establish the required inequalities using only a knowledge of $\zeta(s)$ for $\sigma > 0$.

The relevant theorems are based on some preliminary results whose principal application is to a proof of Theorem 6.5. Theorem 6.7 is the crucial lemma.

THEOREM 6.6. *Let $f(z)$ be analytic for $|z| \leqq R$,*

$$M(a) = \max_{|z|=a} |f(z)|, \qquad A(a) = \max_{|z|=a} \mathscr{R} f(z)\,;$$

then for $0 < r < R$, we have the inequality

$$M(r) \leqq \frac{R+r}{R-r}\left\{A(R) + |f(0)|\right\}. \tag{30}$$

PROOF. The object of this theorem is to give an upper bound to the modulus of $f(z)$ inside a smaller circle in terms of the magnitude of the real part on the larger circle. If $f(z)$ is constant, there is nothing to prove. Suppose that $f(z)$ is not constant and consider first the case $f(0) = 0$. We construct the function

$$\varphi(z) = \frac{f(z)}{2A(R) - f(z)}. \tag{31}$$

Since $\mathscr{R}(2A(R) - f(z)) = 2A(R) - \mathscr{R} f(z) \neq 0$, it follows that $\varphi(z)$ is regular for $|z| \leqq R$. Moreover, if $f(z) = u + iv$, then $u \leqq 2A(R) - u$, and hence

$$|\varphi(z)| \leqq \frac{|f(z)|}{|2A(R) - f(z)|} \leqq \left[\frac{u^2+v^2}{(2A(R)-u)^2+v^2}\right]^{1/2} \leqq 1\,.$$

$\varphi(0) = 0$, and therefore $\varphi(z)/z$ is regular for $|z| \leqq R$, and

$$\left|\frac{\varphi(z)}{z}\right| \leqq \frac{1}{R} \qquad \text{for } |z| = R\,.$$

Therefore by the maximum modulus principle, for $|z| = r < R$, we have

$$|\varphi(z)| \leqq \frac{r}{R}\,.$$

Solving (31) for $f(z)$, we get

$$|f(z)| = \left|\frac{2A(R)\varphi(z)}{1+\varphi(z)}\right| \leqq \frac{2A(R)\frac{r}{R}}{1-\frac{r}{R}} = \frac{2rA(R)}{R-r} \leqq A(R)\frac{R+r}{R-r}\,. \tag{32}$$

If $f(0) \neq 0$, we put $g(z) = f(z) - f(0)$. Then from (32), with $A(R)$ replaced by $\max_{|z|=R} \mathscr{R}(g(z))$, we get

$$|g(z)| \leqq \frac{2r}{R-r} \max_{|z|=R} \mathscr{R}(g(z)) \leqq \frac{2r}{R-r}\{A(R) + |f(0)|\} .$$

In other words,

$$|f(z)| \leqq \frac{2r}{R-r}\{A(R) + |f(0)|\} + |f(0)| \leqq \frac{R+r}{R-r}\{A(R) + |f(0)|\} .$$

This completes the proof.

THEOREM 6.7. *If $M > 1$, $f(s)$ is regular and*

$$\left|\frac{f(s)}{f(s_0)}\right| < e^M \tag{33}$$

in the circle $|s - s_0| \leqq r$, then

$$\left|\frac{f'(s)}{f(s)} - \sum_\rho \frac{1}{s-\rho}\right| < \frac{c_1 M}{r} , \tag{34}$$

for $|s - s_0| \leqq \frac{1}{4}r$, where ρ runs through the zeros of $f(s)$ for which $|\rho - s_0| \leqq \frac{1}{2}r$.

PROOF. We shall shortly take $f(s)$ to be $\zeta(s)$.
Let

$$g(s) = f(s) \prod_\rho (s-\rho)^{-1} ,$$

then $g(s)$ is regular for $|s - s_0| \leqq r$ and $g(s) \neq 0$ for $|s - s_0| \leqq r/2$ since the zeros of $f(s)$ have been cancelled. On $|s - s_0| = r$, we have

$$|s-\rho| \geqq \tfrac{1}{2}r \geqq |s_0 - \rho| ,$$

and therefore on $|s - s_0| = r$,

$$\left|\frac{g(s)}{g(s_0)}\right| = \left|\frac{f(s)}{f(s_0)} \prod_\rho \left(\frac{s_0-\rho}{s-\rho}\right)\right| \leqq \left|\frac{f(s)}{f(s_0)}\right| < e^M . \tag{35}$$

By the maximum modulus principle, this inequality holds for $|s - s_0| \leqq r$. Since we are interested in the left-hand side of (35), we put

$$h(s) = \log\left(\frac{g(s)}{g(s_0)}\right) .$$

This function is regular for $|s - s_0| \leqq \frac{1}{2}r$, and $h(s_0) = 0$, $\mathscr{R}(h(s)) < M$, on $|s - s_0| = r$ by (35). Theorem 6.6 is applicable (with a translation to s_0) and we have for $|s - s_0| \leqq (3/8)r$,

$$|h(s)| < c_2 M .$$

Consequently for $|s - s_0| \leqq r/4$,

$$|h'(s)| = \left|\frac{1}{2\pi i}\int_{|z-s|=r/8} \frac{h(z)}{(z-s)^2} dz\right| < \frac{c_3 M}{r} .$$

The proof is complete and the theorem leads to two important corollaries.

Theorem 6.8. *If $f(s)$ satisfies the hypotheses of Theorem 6.7, and has no zeros in the right-hand half of the circle $|s - s_0| = r$, then*

$$-\mathscr{R}\left\{\frac{f'(s_0)}{f(s_0)}\right\} < \frac{c_4 M}{r}. \tag{36}$$

If $f(s)$ has a zero ρ_0 in the domain $|s - s_0| \leqq \frac{1}{2}r\ \mathscr{R}(s - s_0) \leqq 0$, then

$$-\mathscr{R}\left\{\frac{f'(s_0)}{f(s_0)}\right\} < \frac{c_4 M}{r} - \mathscr{R}\frac{1}{s_0 - \rho_0}. \tag{37}$$

Proof. From Theorem 6.7,

$$-\mathscr{R}\left(\frac{f'(s_0)}{f(s_0)}\right) < \frac{c_3 M}{r} - \sum \mathscr{R}\frac{1}{s_0 - \rho_0}.$$

Since by the hypothesis for the first case $\mathscr{R}(1/(s_0 - \rho)) \geqq 0$ for every ρ, the conclusion follows. The second case follows in exactly the same way.

Theorem 6.9. *Suppose that $f(s)$ satisfies the hypotheses of Theorem 6.7 and in addition let*

$$\left|\frac{f'(s_0)}{f(s_0)}\right| < \frac{M}{r}. \tag{38}$$

Suppose, furthermore, that $f(s) \neq 0$ in the part $\sigma \geqq \sigma_0 - 2r'$ of the circle $|s - s_0| \leqq r$, where $0 < r' < \frac{1}{4}r$, then

$$\left|\frac{f'(s)}{f(s)}\right| < \frac{c_5 M}{r}, \tag{39}$$

for $|s - s_0| \leqq r'$.

Proof. By Theorem 6.7,

$$-\mathscr{R}\left(\frac{f'(s)}{f(s)}\right) < \frac{c_4 M}{r} - \sum \mathscr{R}\left(\frac{1}{s - \rho}\right) < \frac{c_4 M}{r}$$

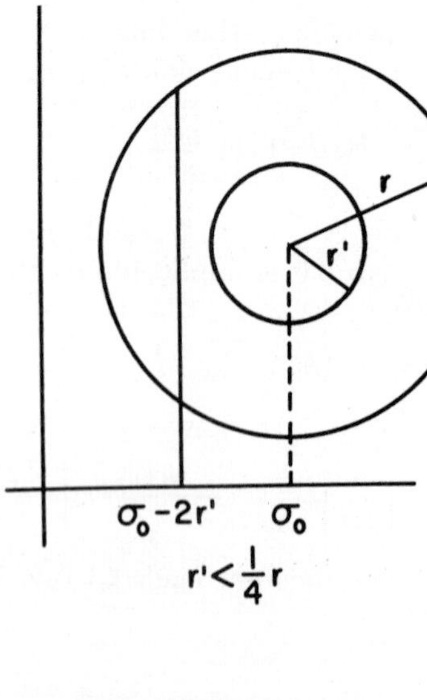

for all s in the region $|s - s_0| \leqq \frac{1}{4}r$, $\sigma \geqq \sigma_0 - 2r'$ since each term of the sum is positive in this region as can be readily verified. We now apply Theorem 6.6 to the function $-f'(s)/f(s)$ and the circles $|s - s_0| = 2r'$, $|s - s_0| = r'$. This gives for $|s - s_0| < r'$,

$$\left|\frac{f'(s)}{f(s)}\right| < 3\left\{\frac{c_4 M}{r} + \frac{c_5 M}{r}\right\} = \frac{c_6 M}{r} .$$

These results allow us to establish improved inequalities for $\zeta(s)$ and $\zeta'(s)/\zeta(s)$.

THEOREM 6.10. *There exists a constant* $c > 0$ *such that*

$$\zeta(s) \neq 0$$

in the region defined by

$$\sigma > 1 - \frac{c}{\log t}$$

for $|t| \geqq 2$.

PROOF. The proof is based on an inequality similar to that used in the proof of Theorem 4.4 coupled with the preceding theorems. The relation in question is the following

$$\begin{aligned}(40)\qquad \mathscr{R}\left\{-\frac{\zeta'(\sigma+2i\gamma)}{\zeta(\sigma+2i\gamma)} - 4\frac{\zeta'(\sigma+i\gamma)}{\zeta(\sigma+i\gamma)} - 3\frac{\zeta'(\sigma)}{\zeta(\sigma)}\right\} \\ = \sum_{n=1}^{\infty} \frac{\Lambda(n)}{n^{\sigma}} \mathscr{R}\left(\frac{1}{n^{2i\gamma}} + \frac{4}{n^{i\gamma}} + 3\right) .\end{aligned}$$

By Lemma 4.1, $\mathscr{R}(n^{-2i\gamma} + 4n^{-i\gamma} + 3) \geqq 0$, and, therefore, from (40),

$$(41)\qquad -\mathscr{R}\left(\frac{\zeta'(\sigma+2i\gamma)}{\zeta(\sigma+2i\gamma)}\right) - 4\mathscr{R}\left(\frac{\zeta'(\sigma+i\gamma)}{\zeta(\sigma+i\gamma)}\right) - 3\frac{\zeta'(\sigma)}{\zeta(\sigma)} \geqq 0 .$$

Our object is to use Theorems 6.7 and 6.8 to establish inequalities for the first two terms on the left of (41). We first recall that in the corollary of Theorem 4.2, we showed that if $s = \sigma + it$,

$$(42)\qquad \zeta(s) = O(t^{1/2})$$

uniformly for $\sigma \geqq \frac{1}{2}$. Let us suppose that $\beta + i\gamma$ is a zero of $\zeta(s)$ with $\gamma \geqq 0$. In order to apply Theorem 6.8, we require an upper bound for $|\zeta'(s)/\zeta(s)|$ as well as a zero free right half circle. Indeed, let

$$(43)\qquad 2 \geqq \sigma_0 \geqq 1 + \frac{1}{(2\gamma+1)^{1/2}} ,$$

where σ_0 will be fixed more precisely shortly, and to apply Theorem 6.8,

$$(44)\qquad s_0 = \sigma_0 + i\gamma, \qquad r = \tfrac{1}{2} .$$

We are considering the circle $|s - s_0| \leqq \frac{1}{2}$. Now on the one hand by Theorem 1.4, Chapter I, for $\sigma > 1$,

$$(45)\qquad \left|\frac{1}{\zeta(s)}\right| = \left|\prod_p\left(1 - \frac{1}{p^s}\right)\right| \leqq \sum_n \frac{1}{n^{\sigma}} < 1 + \frac{1}{\sigma - 1}$$

and, therefore, by (42), and (45),

$$\left|\frac{\zeta(s)}{\zeta(s_0)}\right| = O(\gamma^{1/2}(2\gamma+1)^{1/2}) = O(\exp c_2 \log \gamma)$$

in the circle

$$|s - s_0| \leqq \tfrac{1}{2}\,. \tag{46}$$

$\zeta(s)$ has no zeros in the right half of the circle in (46) and, therefore, from the first part of Theorem 6.8 with $M = \log \gamma$, we get

$$-\mathscr{R}\left(\frac{\zeta'(\sigma_0+i\gamma)}{\zeta(\sigma_0+i\gamma)}\right) < c_3 \log \gamma\,.$$

Exactly the same argument gives us

$$-\mathscr{R}\left(\frac{\zeta'(\sigma_0+2i\gamma)}{\zeta(\sigma_0+2i\gamma)}\right) < c_4 \log \gamma\,. \tag{47}$$

On the one hand, if

$$\beta > \sigma_0 - \tfrac{1}{4}\,, \tag{48}$$

then by (37) of Theorem 6.8, with $r = \frac{1}{2}$,

$$-\mathscr{R}\left(\frac{\zeta'(\sigma_0+i\gamma)}{\zeta(\sigma_0+i\gamma)}\right) < c_4 \log \gamma - \frac{1}{\sigma_0 - \beta}\,. \tag{49}$$

We have inequalities for the first two terms of (41). For the third term we notice that as $\sigma_0 \to 1$,

$$-\frac{\zeta'(\sigma_0)}{\zeta(\sigma_0)} \sim \frac{1}{\sigma_0 - 1}$$

and, therefore, we can choose α as close to 1 as we please (for proper choice of σ_0) such that

$$-\frac{\zeta'(\sigma_0)}{\zeta(\sigma_0)} < \frac{\alpha}{\sigma_0 - 1}\,. \tag{50}$$

The inequalities (47), (49) and (50) inserted in (41) impose a limitation on β. Indeed, from these relations we get

$$\frac{3\alpha}{\sigma_0 - 1} + 5c_4 \log \gamma - \frac{4}{\sigma_0 - \beta} \geqq 0\,.$$

Solving for $1-\beta$, we get

$$1 - \beta \geqq \frac{1 - \dfrac{3\alpha}{4} + (1-\sigma_0)\dfrac{5c_4}{4}\log\gamma}{\dfrac{3\alpha}{4(\sigma_0 - 1)} + \dfrac{5c_4}{4}\log\gamma}\,. \tag{51}$$

Now we choose $\sigma_0 = 1 + c_5/\log \gamma$, where c_5 will be chosen shortly. Then

$$1 - \beta \geqq \frac{4 - 3\alpha - 5c_4c_5}{\left(\dfrac{3\alpha}{c_5} + 5c_4\right)\log \gamma} > \frac{c}{\log \gamma}$$

if α, γ and c_5 are suitably chosen in the order given. If, on the other hand, (47) does not hold, then

$$\beta \leqq \sigma_0 - \frac{1}{4} = 1 + \frac{c_5}{\log \gamma} - \frac{1}{4}$$

and

$$1 - \beta \geqq \frac{1}{4} - \frac{c_5}{\log \gamma} \geqq \frac{c_6}{\log \gamma},$$

if c_6 is sufficiently small. Thus, in either case, the proof is complete.

There follows as a consequence the important

Theorem 6.11. *There exists a constant $c > 0$ such that if $|t| \geqq 2$,*

$$\frac{\zeta'(s)}{\zeta(s)} = O(\log t) \tag{52}$$

uniformly in the region defined by

$$\sigma \geqq 1 - \frac{c}{\log t}. \tag{53}$$

Proof. We use Theorems 6.9 and 6.10. In Theorem 6.9, let t_0 be given, and $\sigma_0 = 1 + c_1/\log t_0$

$$s_0 = \sigma_0 + it_0, \qquad r = \tfrac{1}{2}.$$

In the circle $|s - s_0| \leqq \frac{1}{2}$, we have by (42) and (45),

$$\frac{\zeta(s)}{\zeta(s_0)} = O\left(\frac{t^{1/2}}{\sigma_0 - 1}\right) = O(t_0^{1/2}\log t_0) = O\left(\exp\left[c_2 \log t_0\right]\right) \tag{54}$$

and

$$\frac{\zeta'(s_0)}{\zeta(s_0)} = O\left(\frac{1}{\sigma_0 - 1}\right) = O(\log t_0). \tag{55}$$

Thus, we have yet to choose r'. Because by Theorem 6.10, $\zeta(s) \neq 0$ for

$$\sigma \geqq 1 - \frac{c}{\log t}, \tag{56}$$

let

$$r' = \frac{c_4}{\log t_0}. \tag{57}$$

Then, by (54), (55), (56), and (57) the hypotheses of Theorem 6.9 are fulfilled with $M = c_3 \log t$ and, therefore,

(58) $$\frac{\zeta'(s)}{\zeta(s)} = O(\log t_0)$$

for

(59) $$|s - s_0| \leqq \frac{c_4}{\log t_0}$$

and in particular when $t = t_0$ and $c_1 < c_4$,

(60) $$\sigma \geqq 1 - \frac{c_5}{\log t_0} .$$

This is the required conclusion with t_0 in place of t.

We return now to a proof of Theorem 6.5.

PROOF. We had for $a > 1$,

(61) $$\frac{\psi_2(x)}{x} = \frac{1}{2\pi i}\int_{a-i\infty}^{a+i\infty}\left(-\frac{\zeta'(s)}{\zeta(s)}\right)\frac{x^s}{s(s+1)}ds .$$

We fix T and choose

(62) $$a = 1 + \frac{c}{\log T} ,$$

(63) $$b = 1 - \frac{c}{\log T} ,$$

where c is the constant of Theorem 6.11. Now we deform the path from

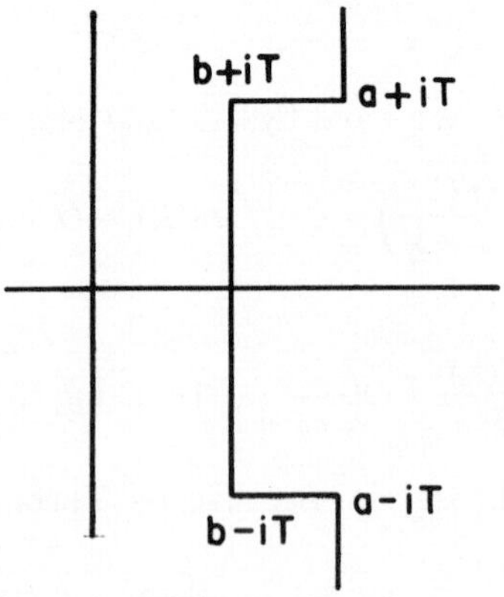

$a - iT$ to $a + iT$ as shown. Then, because $(-\zeta'(s)/\zeta(s))$ has a simple pole with residue 1 at $s = 1$, we get, by Cauchy's theorem

(64) $$\frac{1}{2\pi i}\int_{a-iT}^{a+iT}\left(-\frac{\zeta'(s)}{\zeta(s)}\right)\frac{x^s}{s(s+1)}ds = \frac{x}{2} + I_1 + I_2 + I_3 ,$$

where I_1, I_2, I_3 denote the integrals along the paths $a - iT$ to $b - iT$, $b - iT$ to $b + iT$, $b + iT$ to $a + iT$, respectively. From (64)

(65) $$\frac{\psi_2(x)}{x} = \frac{x}{2} + I_1 + I_2 + I_3 + I_4 + I_5 \,,$$

where I_4 and I_5 denote the integrals from $a - i\infty$ to $a - iT$ and $a + iT$ to $a + i\infty$, respectively.

We estimate these:

(66) $$\begin{aligned} I_4 + I_5 &= O\left|\int_T^{\infty}\left(-\frac{\zeta'(a \pm it)}{\zeta(a \pm it)}\right)\frac{x^{a\pm it}}{(a \pm it)(a \pm it + 1)}dt\right| \\ &= O\left(x^a\int_T^{\infty}\log t\frac{dt}{t^2}\right) = O\left(\frac{x^a}{T}\log T\right), \end{aligned}$$

since for $a > 1$, $\zeta'(s)/\zeta(s) = O(\log t)$ uniformly in a by Theorem 6.11. Moreover, by Theorem 6.11,

(67) $$\begin{aligned} I_1 + I_3 &= O\left(\int_a^b\left|\frac{\zeta'(\sigma \pm iT)}{\zeta(\sigma \pm iT)}\right|\left|\frac{x^{\sigma+iT}}{(\sigma \pm iT)(\sigma \pm iT + 1)}\right|d\sigma\right) \\ &= O\left(x^a\log T\int_a^b\frac{d\sigma}{\sigma^2 + T^2}\right) \\ &= O\left(x^a\,\frac{1}{T^2}\,\log T\right). \end{aligned}$$

Again, by Theorem 6.11, the inequality holding for $|t| \leqq 2$,

(68) $$\begin{aligned} I_2 &= O\left(\int_0^T\left|\frac{\zeta'(b \pm it)}{\zeta(b \pm it)}\right|\frac{x^b}{|(b \pm it)(b \pm it + 1)|}dt\right) \\ &= O\left(x^b\log T\int_0^T\frac{dt}{b^2 + t^2}\right) = O(x^b\log T)\,. \end{aligned}$$

Collecting our results, we get from (65), (66), (67) and (68),

(69) $$\frac{\psi_2(x)}{x} = \frac{x}{2} + R(x)\,,$$

where

$$\begin{aligned} R(x) &= O\left(\frac{x^a\log T}{T} + \frac{x^a\log T}{T^2} + x^b\log T\right) \\ &= O\left(\frac{x^a\log T}{T} + x^b\log T\right). \end{aligned}$$

For large T, the first term is small but the second is large. Since, by (62) and (63), $b = 1 - c/\log T$, to balance the terms, we put

$$\frac{x^a\log T}{T} = x^b\log T, \qquad a - b = \frac{\log T}{\log x}\,,$$

and, therefore, solving for T,

$$T = \exp\left(c_4(\log x)^{1/2}\right).$$

For this value of T,

$$R(x) = O(x^b \log T) = O(x \exp[-c_5(\log x)^{1/2} + c_6 \log\log x]) = O(x \exp[-c_7(\log x)^{1/2}])$$

since $\log\log x$ is infinitely smaller than $(\log x)^{1/2}$. The proof is, therefore, complete.

We now turn to another proof.

C. *The Hardy-Littlewood proof.* It is instructive to recapitulate the main ideas in the proofs we have so far presented. As we simplified the function theory, we made more difficult the transition from the relevant function back to the function $\pi(x)$. The proof may therefore be considered as entailing three steps.

(i) We first went from $\psi(x)$ to its mean value $\psi_2(x)/x$. In general, a theorem which deduces information about the average of a function from the behavior of the function itself is called an Abelian theorem. The name stems from Abel's theorem on the continuity of power series, viz.: If $\sum_{n=0}^{\infty} a(n)z^n$ converges to $f(z)$ for $|z| < 1$ and if $\sum_{n=0}^{\infty} a(n)$ converges, then $\lim_{z\to 1} f(z) = \sum_{n=0}^{\infty} a(n)$.

(ii) In the second step, we invoked Cauchy's theorem as well as function theoretic arguments about $\zeta(s)$. From these we deduced as in the preceding proof

$$\psi_2(x) \sim \tfrac{1}{2}x^2 .$$

(iii) The third step necessitated a return to

$$\psi(x) \sim x ,$$

and thence to $\pi(x) \sim x/\log x$.

Such a theorem which proceeds from a knowledge of an average of a function to a knowledge of the function itself is referred to as a Tauberian theorem. The name stems from Tauber's provisional converse of Abel's theorem, viz.: If $\sum a(n)z^n$ converges to $f(z)$ for $|z| < 1$, and $\lim_{z\to 1} f(z)$ exists, then $\sum_{n=0}^{\infty} a(n)$ converges *provided* $a(n) = o(1/n)$.

The converse of an Abelian theorem is not in general true without some additional hypothesis. For example, the direct converse of Abel's theorem is false, as the example

$$\sum_{n=0}^{\infty} (-1)^n z^n = \frac{1}{1+z}$$

clearly shows.

A comparison of the preceding proofs given of the prime number theorem suggests that the function theoretic part may be simplified at the expense of making the Tauberian part more difficult. In other words, the simpler the Abelian deduction, the stronger must be the Tauberian element. Let us prove an Abelian theorem.

THEOREM 6.12. *If*

$$f(s) = \sum_{n=1}^{\infty} \frac{a(n)}{n^s}$$

and

(70) $$S(n) = \sum_{k=1}^{n} a(k) \sim \beta n, \qquad \text{as } n \to \infty ,$$

then

(71) $$f(s) \sim \frac{\beta}{s-1} \qquad \text{as } s \to 1 .$$

PROOF. In the first place the abscissa of convergence of the series is $\leqq 1$ by Theorem 3.4 of Chapter I. In fact, it is exactly 1 as can be shown by modifying the argument of Theorem 3.4 slightly. For a proof of (71), we observe that by Lemma 3.1 of Chapter I,

$$\begin{aligned}\sum_{n=1}^{N} \frac{a(n)}{n^s} &= s\int_1^N \frac{S(x)}{x^{s+1}}dx + \frac{S(N)}{N^s} \\ &= s\int_1^N \frac{S(x)-\beta x}{x^{s+1}}dx + \beta s\int_1^N \frac{dx}{x^s} + \frac{S(N)}{N^s} \\ &= s\int_1^N \frac{S(x)-\beta x}{x^{s+1}}dx + \frac{\beta s}{s-1} + O(N^{1-\sigma}) .\end{aligned}$$

Letting $N \to \infty$, we get

$$f(s) = s\int_1^\infty \frac{S(x)-\beta x}{x^{s+1}}dx + \frac{\beta s}{s-1} .$$

Thus

(72) $$(s-1)f(s) - \beta s = (s-1)s\int_1^\infty \frac{S(x)-\beta(x)}{x^{s+1}}dx .$$

Since $S(x) - \beta x = o(x)$, as $x \to \infty$, for $\varepsilon > 0$, we choose x_0 so large that $|S(x) - \beta x| < \varepsilon_1 x$ for $x > x_0$, where ε_1 will be chosen shortly, and therefore by (72), if $C(x_0)$ denotes a constant depending only on x_0,

$$\begin{aligned}|(s-1)f(x) - s\beta| &\leqq |(s-1)s| \int_1^{x_0}\left|\frac{S(x)-\beta x}{x^{s+1}}\right|dx \\ &\quad + |(s-1)s| \int_{x_0}^{\infty}\left|\frac{S(x)-\beta x}{x^{s+1}}\right|dx \\ &\leqq |(s-1)s|\,C(x_0) + |(s-1)|\,|s| \int_{x_0}^\infty \frac{\varepsilon_1}{x^\sigma}dx \\ &\leqq |s|\,|s-1|\,C(x_0) + |s-1|\,|s| \frac{x_0^{-\sigma+1}}{|\sigma-1|}\varepsilon_1 \\ &\leqq |s|\,|s-1|\,C(x_0) + \frac{|s|\,|s-1|}{|\sigma-1|}\varepsilon_1 .\end{aligned}$$

Letting $\varepsilon_1 = (\varepsilon/2)\cdot|\sigma-1|/(|s|\,|s-1|)$ and choosing s so close to 1 that $|s|\,|s-1|\,C(x_0) < \varepsilon/2$ we conclude that for s sufficiently close to 1,

$$|(s-1)f(x) - s\beta| < \varepsilon .$$

This is the required conclusion.

Now suppose that the corresponding Tauberian theorem were true. Suppose in other words that the assumption

$$f(s) \sim \frac{\beta}{s-1}$$

implied that $S(n) \sim \beta n$. Then the prime number theorem would follow very simply, for

$$\sum_{n=1}^{\infty} \frac{\Lambda(n)}{n^s} = -\frac{\zeta'(s)}{\zeta(s)} \sim \frac{1}{s-1},$$

as we know by Theorem 6.7, and therefore

$$\psi(n) = \sum_{k \leqq n} \Lambda(k) \sim n,$$

which is equivalent to the prime number theorem.

This Tauberian theorem, however, is false, as the following example shows. If $a(n) = n$ when $n = 2^m$ and $a(n) = 0$ otherwise, then

$$f(s) = \sum_{n=1}^{\infty} \frac{a(n)}{n^s} = \sum_{m=0}^{\infty} \frac{2^m}{2^{ms}} = \sum_{m=0}^{\infty} \frac{1}{(2^{s-1})^m}$$

$$= \frac{1}{1-2^{1-s}} \sim \frac{1}{\log 2}\left(\frac{1}{s-1}\right).$$

On the other hand, suppose that $2^k = N$, then

$$S(N) = \sum_{m=1}^{N} a(m) = \sum_{j=0}^{k} 2^j = 2^{k+1} - 1 = 2N - 1,$$

while if $N = 2^{k+1} - 1$,

$$S(N) = 2^{k+1} - 1 = N,$$

and so the limit $S(N)/N$ does not exist.

Various efforts have been made to reduce the function theoretic part of the proof of the prime number theorem to a minimum at the expense of the Tauberian part. There is some justification for this procedure since there exist many Tauberian theorems which hold out some hope of success. In particular Hardy and Littlewood proved the following Tauberian theorem.

THEOREM 6.13. *If $a(n) \geqq 0$, and*

$$\sum_{n=0}^{\infty} a(n)z^n \sim \frac{\alpha}{1-z} \quad (\text{as } z \to 1^{-0}),$$

then

$$\sum_{k \leqq u} a(k) \sim \alpha u.$$

PROOF. We may without loss of generality assume that $\alpha = 1$. For, if $\alpha \neq 1$, we consider the series with $b(n) = a(n)/\alpha$. Thus, we are given that

$$\lim_{z\to 1}(1-z)\sum_{n=0}^{\infty} a(n)z^n = 1 \tag{73}$$

and we are required to prove that

$$\sum_{k\leqq u} a(k) \sim u\,.$$

The proof we give is one due to Karamata and assumes known the classical theorem of Weierstrass: Every continuous function is the uniform limit of a sequence of polynomials.

For any given series $\sum_{n=0}^{\infty} a(n)z^n$ satisfying (73), we consider the class $\mathscr{C}$ of functions in the closed interval $[0, 1]$, defined as follows: $g(z)$ is in $\mathscr{C}$ if

$$\lim_{z\to 1}(1-z)\sum_{n=0}^{\infty} a(n)z^n g(z^n) = \int_0^1 g(t)dt\,. \tag{74}$$

The class $\mathscr{C}$ clearly contains the function 1 by (73).

Since

$$\sum_{n=0}^{\infty} a(n)z^n z^{mn} = \sum_{n=0}^{\infty} a(n)(z^{(m+1)})^n = \frac{1-z^{m+1}}{1-z^{m+1}}\sum_{n=0}^{\infty} a(n)(z^{m+1})^n$$

and, therefore, by assumption,

$$\lim_{z\to 1}(1-z)\sum_{n=0}^{\infty} a(n)z^n z^{mn} = \lim_{z\to 1}\frac{1-z}{1-z^{m+1}}\lim_{z\to 1}(1-z^{m+1})\sum_{n=0}^{\infty} a(n)(z^{m+1})^n$$

$$= \frac{1}{m+1} = \int_0^1 t^m dt\,;$$

it follows that $\mathscr{C}$ contains the function t^m. If $\mathscr{C}$ contains the functions g_1 and g_2, it clearly contains the function

$$c_1g_1 + c_2g_2$$

for any constants c_1 and c_2. Thus, by induction, $\mathscr{C}$ contains all polynomials. If g_k converges uniformly to g, and g_k are in $\mathscr{C}$, then so is g. For,

$$\lim_{z\to 1}(1-z)\sum_{n=0}^{\infty} a(n)z^n g(z^n) = \lim_{k\to\infty}\lim_{z\to 1}(1-z)\sum_{n=0}^{\infty} a(n)z^n g_k(z^n)$$

$$= \lim_{k\to\infty}\int_0^1 g_k(t)dt = \int_0^1 g(t)dt\,.$$

Thus, it follows by Weierstrass' theorem, that $\mathscr{C}$ contains all continuous functions. We shall show that $\mathscr{C}$ contains in particular the function $g_0(t)$ defined as follows:

$$g_0(t) = \begin{cases} 0 & \text{if } 0 \leqq t < \dfrac{1}{e}\,, \\[2mm] \dfrac{1}{t} & \text{if } \dfrac{1}{e} \leqq t \leqq 1\,. \end{cases} \tag{75}$$

Suppose that we have done this, then the enunciation of the theorem is easily proved. For,

$$\lim_{z\to 1}(1-z)\sum_{n=0}^{\infty} a(n)z^n g_0(z^n) = \int_0^1 g_0(t)dt = 1\,.$$

But $g_0(z^n) = 0$ if $z^n < 1/e$ and $g_0(z^n) = 1/z^n$ if $z^n \geqq 1/e$, and therefore,

$$\lim_{z\to 1}(1-z)\sum_{n\leqq 1/\log(1/z)} a(n) = 1\,.$$

If we put $\log(1/z) = 1/u$, $z = e^{-1/u}$, we deduce that

$$\sum_{n\leqq u} a(n) \sim \frac{1}{1-e^{-1/u}} \sim u\,.$$

It remains to show that the class $\mathscr{C}$ contains the function $g_0(t)$ defined by (75). Indeed, we define a sequence for $k \geqq 3$

$$g_k(t) = \begin{cases} g_0(t) & \text{if } \dfrac{1}{e} \leqq t \leqq 1\,, \\ 0 & \text{if } 0 \leqq t < \left(\dfrac{1}{e} - \dfrac{2}{ek}\right), \\ \text{linearly joining the points} \left(\dfrac{2}{ek}, 0\right) \text{ and } \left(\dfrac{1}{e}, e\right). \end{cases}$$

Then $g_k(t)$ converges decreasingly toward $g_0(t)$. Moreover,

$$\lim_{k\to\infty}\int_0^1 (g_k(t) - g_0(t))dt = \lim_{k\to\infty}\frac{1}{k} = 0\,.$$

Therefore since $g_k(t)$ is continuous, it is easy to see from (74) that the function $g_0(t)$ in (75) belongs to $\mathscr{C}$ and the proof is complete.

If, in particular, we choose $a(n) = \Lambda(n)$, then the prime number theorem would follow from the statement

$$f(z) = \sum_{n=1}^{\infty} \Lambda(n)z^n \sim \frac{1}{1-z}\,.$$

A proof of this is the object of the next theorem.

THEOREM 6.14. *If*

$$f(z) = \sum_{n=1}^{\infty} \Lambda(n)z^n$$

then as $z\to 1$,

$$f(z) \sim \frac{1}{1-z}\,.$$

PROOF. For the proof, we use Mellin's transform. This states that

$$e^{-ny} = \frac{1}{2\pi i}\int_{c-i\infty}^{c+i\infty} y^{-s}n^{-s}\Gamma(s)ds\,, \qquad (c>1)$$

where $\Gamma(s)$ is Euler's gamma function. The integral is absolutely convergent. For a proof as well as properties of $\Gamma(s)$, we refer the reader to Appendix A.

It is natural to transform $f(z)$ by putting $z = e^{-\xi}$, and we are then required to prove that

$$f(e^{-\xi}) \sim \frac{1}{\xi},$$

as $\xi \to 0$ since

$$\frac{1}{1-e^{-\xi}} \sim \frac{1}{\xi} \qquad \text{as } \xi \to 0 .$$

We have from the above integral, for $c > 1$,

$$(76) \qquad \begin{aligned} f(e^{-\xi}) &= \sum_{n=1}^{\infty} \Lambda(n) e^{-n\xi} = \frac{1}{2\pi i} \sum_{n=1}^{\infty} \Lambda(n) \int_{c-i\infty}^{c+i\infty} \xi^{-s} n^{-s} \Gamma(s) ds \\ &= \frac{1}{2\pi i} \int_{c-i\infty}^{c+i\infty} \xi^{-s} \sum_{n=1}^{\infty} \frac{\Lambda(n)}{n^s} \Gamma(s) ds = \frac{1}{2\pi i} \int_{c-i\infty}^{c+i\infty} \xi^{-s} \left(-\frac{\zeta'(s)}{\zeta(s)} \right) \Gamma(s) ds , \end{aligned}$$

the interchange of order of summation being justified by the absolute convergence of sum and integral.

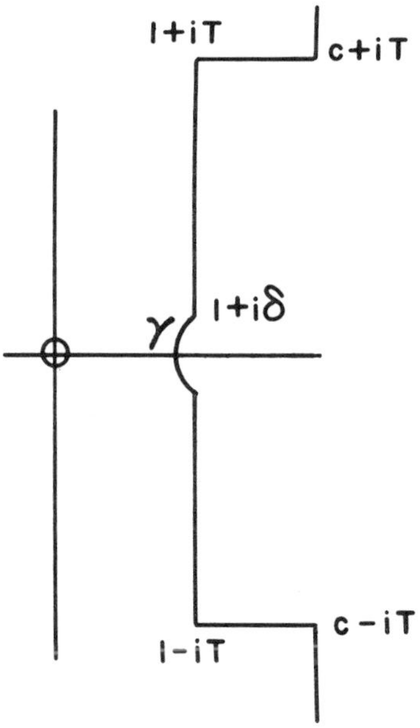

We now move the path of integration to $\sigma = 1$. For this purpose, we need only to assume that $-\zeta'(s)/\zeta(s)$ is regular for $\sigma \geqq 1$, except for a simple pole at $s = 1$ with residue 1, and the very weak condition

$$-\frac{\zeta'(s)}{\zeta(s)} = O(e^{k|t|})$$

uniformly for $\sigma \geqq 1$ and $k < \pi/2$. In other words, we need no essential knowledge of the zeta function for $\sigma < 1$ except for a neighborhood of $s=1$. The requisite properties (and more) have already been established in Corollary 2 of Theorem 4.2. From (76), we get

$$f(e^{-\xi}) = \lim_{T\to\infty} \frac{1}{2\pi i}\int_{c-iT}^{c+iT} \Gamma(s)\left(-\frac{\zeta'(s)}{\zeta(s)}\right)\xi^{-s}ds\,. \tag{77}$$

If we deform the path from $c - iT$ to $c + iT$ as shown in the figure with a semicircle γ of radius δ circling the point 1, we get by Cauchy's theorem

$$f(e^{-\xi}) = \lim_{T\to\infty} \frac{1}{2\pi i}\left\{\left(\int_{c-iT}^{1-iT} + \int_{1-iT}^{1-i\delta} + \int_{\gamma} + \int_{1+i\delta}^{1+iT} + \int_{1+iT}^{c+iT}\right)\Gamma(s)\left(-\frac{\zeta'(s)}{\zeta(s)}\right)\xi^{-s}ds\right\} \tag{78}$$
$$+ \text{ residue at } s=1\,.$$

The residue at $s=1$ is $\lim_{s\to1}(s-1)\Gamma(s)(-\zeta'(s)/\zeta(s))\xi^{-s} = \Gamma(1)/\xi = 1/\xi$, since $\Gamma(1)=1$.

We call the integrals on the right of (78) I_1, I_2, I_3, I_4, and I_5, respectively. Let us, furthermore, assume (as we prove in Appendix A) that

$$\Gamma(\sigma + it) = O(e^{-\pi|t|/2}\,|t|^{\sigma-1/2})\,. \tag{79}$$

We show that the integrals along the horizontal sides $\to 0$ as $T\to\infty$. Indeed, using (77) and (79),

$$\begin{aligned} I_5 &= O\left(\int_c^1 |\Gamma(\sigma+iT)|\left|\frac{\zeta'(\sigma+iT)}{\zeta(\sigma+iT)}\right|\xi^{-\sigma}d\sigma\right) \\ &= O(e^{(-\pi/2+k)T}T^{c-1/2})\int_c^1 \xi^{-\sigma}d\sigma \\ &= o(1) \quad \text{as } T\to\infty \end{aligned} \tag{80}$$

because of the assumption on k. Similarly for the integral I_1 using the estimates for $\zeta'(s)/\zeta(s)$ and $\Gamma(s)$. Moreover since,

$$\begin{aligned} I_4 &= O\left(\int_\delta^T |\Gamma(1+it)|\left|\frac{\zeta'(1+it)}{\zeta(1+it)}\right|\xi^{-1}dt\right) \\ &= O\left(\xi^{-1}\int_\delta^T e^{(-\pi/2+k)t}t^{1/2}\,dt\right) \\ &= O(1) \quad \text{as } T\to\infty\,, \end{aligned} \tag{81}$$

it follows from (78), (80) and (81) that

$$\begin{aligned} f(\xi) &= \frac{1}{\xi} + \frac{1}{2\pi i}\int_\gamma \Gamma(s)\left(-\frac{\zeta'(s)}{\zeta(s)}\right)\xi^{-s}ds \\ &\quad + \frac{1}{2\pi i}\int_{1+i\delta}^{1+i\infty} \Gamma(s)\left(-\frac{\zeta'(s)}{\zeta(s)}\right)\xi^{-s}ds \\ &\quad + \frac{1}{2\pi i}\int_{1-i\infty}^{1-i\delta} \Gamma(s)\left(-\frac{\zeta'(s)}{\zeta(s)}\right)\xi^{-s}ds\,. \end{aligned} \tag{82}$$

As $\xi\to0$, by the Riemann-Lebesgue theorem, the second and third integrals in (82) are $o(1/\xi)$ since, for example,

$$\int_{1+i\delta}^{1+i\infty} \Gamma(s)\left(-\frac{\zeta'(s)}{\zeta(s)}\right)\xi^{-s}ds = \xi^{-1}\int_{\delta}^{\infty} \Gamma(1+it)\left(-\frac{\zeta'(1+it)}{\zeta(1+it)}\right)\xi^{-it}dt$$

and the integral is by (81) absolutely convergent.

It therefore remains to appraise the behavior of the first integral of (82). We have on γ, $s = 1 + \delta e^{i\theta}$ and therefore as $\xi \to 0$,

$$\begin{aligned}\frac{1}{2\pi i}\int_{\gamma} \Gamma(s)\left(-\frac{\zeta'(s)}{\zeta(s)}\right)\xi^{-s}ds &= O\left(\xi^{-1}\int_{\pi/2}^{3\pi/2} \xi^{-\delta\cos\theta}d\theta\right) = O\left(\xi^{-1}\int_{0}^{\pi} \xi^{\delta\sin\theta}d\theta\right) \\ &= O\left(\xi^{-1}\int_{0}^{\pi/2} \xi^{\delta\sin\theta}d\theta\right) = O\left(\xi^{-1}\int_{0}^{\pi/2} \xi^{2\delta\theta/\pi}d\theta\right) \\ &= O\left(\xi^{-1}\frac{1}{|\log\xi|}\right) = o\left(\frac{1}{\xi}\right).\end{aligned}$$

The proof is thus complete using the fact that $\sin\theta \geqq 2\theta/\pi$ for $0 \leqq \theta \leqq \pi/2$.

Theorems 6.13 and 6.14 together, then, imply

THEOREM 6.15. *If $-\zeta'(s)/\zeta(s)$ is regular for $\sigma \geqq 1$ except for a simple pole at $s=1$, and $|\zeta'(s)/\zeta(s)| = O(e^{k|t|})$ uniformly for $\sigma \geqq 1$, $k < \pi/2$, then*

$$\psi(n) \sim n\,.$$

Let us summarize the salient features of this proof:

(i) We took a strong average of $\Lambda(n)$, viz.:

$$f(z) = \sum_{n=1}^{\infty} \Lambda(n)z^n\,.$$

(ii) We proved that $f(z) \sim 1/(1-z)$ with the assumption of the relatively weak order relation

$$-\frac{\zeta'(s)}{\zeta(s)} = O(e^{k|t|})\,, \qquad k < \frac{\pi}{2}\,,$$

and the fact that $-\zeta'(s)/\zeta(s)$ was analytic for $\sigma \geqq 1$ except for a pole at $s=1$.

(iii) We applied the deep Tauberian theorem of Hardy and Littlewood. It had been felt for some time after the publication of this proof that the order condition in (ii) was superfluous. Wiener showed that this was indeed the case.

D. *The Wiener proof.* The relevant theorem here is the Tauberian analogue of Theorem 6.13.

The general theorem is the following:

Suppose that

(i) $$a(n) \geqq 0\,,$$

(ii) $$F(s) = \sum_{n=1}^{\infty} \frac{a(n)}{n^s}$$

is absolutely convergent for $\sigma > 1$,

(iii) $$F(s) - \frac{1}{s-1}$$

is regular for $\sigma \geqq 1$, *and* $|t| \leqq T$, *then*

$$S(x) = \sum_{n \leqq x} a(n) \sim x .$$

If in particular $F(s) = \zeta'(s)/\zeta(s)$, *then it will follow from this result that* $\psi(x) \sim x$.

We shall not prove this result, which in the above form is due to Ikehara, but will present Landau's "distillation" as it is directly applicable to $a(n) = \Lambda(n)$,

$$F(s) = -\frac{\zeta'(s)}{\zeta(s)} .$$

Notice that in this case, condition (iii) is equivalent to the fact that

$$\zeta(1 + it) \neq 0 .$$

The essential underlying idea of Wiener's proof is derived from the theory of Fourier transforms and while we shall not use the theory as such, it will make Landau's version of the proof more transparent if we first place it in its general setting.

We recall that two functions $f(x)$ and $F(x)$ are said to be Fourier transforms of each other if

$$f(x) = \frac{1}{\sqrt{(2\pi)}} \int_{-\infty}^{\infty} F(t) e^{-ixt} dt \tag{83}$$

implies

$$F(x) = \frac{1}{\sqrt{(2\pi)}} \int_{-\infty}^{\infty} f(t) e^{ixt} dt ,$$

and conversely. If in (83) we replace x by $x - y$, then

$$f(x - y) = \frac{1}{\sqrt{(2\pi)}} \int_{-\infty}^{\infty} F(t) e^{iyt} e^{-ixt} dt ,$$

and it follows that $f(x - y)$ and $F(x)e^{iyt}$ are transforms of each other. We shall not concern ourselves with questions of convergence, etc., since we never use the transform theory. The important relation here is the so-called Parseval equality: If $\varphi(x)$ and $\Phi(x)$ are transforms of each other and $\theta(x)$, $\Theta(x)$ are transforms of each other, then

$$\int_{-\infty}^{\infty} \varphi(x)\theta(x) dx = \int_{-\infty}^{\infty} \Phi(x)\Theta(x) dx . \tag{84}$$

Our object now is to obtain analytic relations which allow us to deduce an equality such as (84).

As in the preceding proofs of the prime number theorem, we start by taking a suitable average of $\psi(x)$. The average we use is a mean, weighted by the so-called Fejér kernel,

$$K_\lambda(x) = \frac{\sin^2 \lambda x}{\lambda x^2} .$$

We first transform $\psi(x)$. Exactly as in § 2, (39), we have for $\sigma > 1$,

(85) $$-\frac{\zeta'(s)}{\zeta(s)} = s\int_1^\infty \psi(x)x^{-s-1}dx ,$$

or, on putting $x = e^u$,

$$-\frac{\zeta'(s)}{\zeta(s)} = s\int_0^\infty \psi(e^u)e^{-us}du .$$

What we wish to prove is that

$$\psi(e^u) \sim e^u ,$$

or, equivalently, that

(86) $$g(u) = e^{-u}\psi(e^u) - 1 \to 0 .$$

However,

$$\psi(e^u) = e^u(g(u) + 1) ;$$

hence

$$-\frac{\zeta'(s)}{\zeta(s)} = s\int_0^\infty e^u(g(u) + 1)e^{-su}du$$
$$= s\int_0^\infty g(u)e^{-u(s-1)}du + s\int_0^\infty e^{-u(s-1)}du .$$

If we integrate the second integral on the right, and transpose, we deduce for $\sigma > 1$

(87) $$\int_0^\infty g(u)e^{-u(s-1)}du = \frac{1}{s}\left(-\frac{\zeta'(s)}{\zeta(s)} - \frac{s}{s-1}\right).$$

Let

(88) $$h(s) = \frac{1}{s}\left(-\frac{\zeta'(s)}{\zeta(s)} - \frac{s}{s-1}\right),$$

then since by Theorem 4.4 $\zeta(1 + it) \neq 0$, and $-\zeta'(s)/\zeta(s)$ has a simple pole with residue 1 at $s = 1$, it follows that $h(s)$ is regular for $\sigma \geqq 1$. We are required to show that under these conditions,

$$g(u) \to 0 .$$

Consider the weighted mean

$$g_\lambda(u) = \int_0^\infty g(t)K_\lambda(t - u)dt .$$

We first show that for fixed λ, $g_\lambda(u) \to c$ (a constant) as $u \to \infty$. The conclusion $g(u) \to 0$ will then follow simply. The first step is to express $g_\lambda(u)$ in terms of the known function $h(s)$ and this is where the the Parseval relation comes in.

In (87), we put $s = 1 + \delta + it$ $(\delta > 0)$; then

(89) $$\int_0^\infty g(u)e^{-\delta u}e^{-iut}du = h(1+\delta+it) .$$

Thus $h(1+\delta+it)$ and the function defined as

$$\varphi(u) = \begin{cases} g(u)e^{-\delta u} & \text{for } u \geqq 0 , \\ 0 & \text{for } u < 0 \end{cases}$$

are transforms of each other. Moreover, we shall shortly show that

$$K_\lambda(u) = 2\int_{-2\lambda}^{2\lambda}\left(1-\frac{|t|}{2\lambda}\right)e^{itu}du$$

and therefore $K_\lambda(u)$ and (for suitable constant c) the function

$$\theta(u) = \begin{cases} c(1-|u|/2\lambda) & \text{for } -2\lambda \leqq u \leqq 2\lambda , \\ 0 & \text{otherwise} \end{cases}$$

are transforms of each other. It then will follow from (84) that

(90) $$\int_0^\infty K_\lambda(t-u)\varphi(u)du = \int_{-2\lambda}^{2\lambda} h(1+\delta+iu)\left(1-\frac{|u|}{2\lambda}\right)e^{itu}du .$$

The integral on the right involves the familiar $-\zeta'(s)/\zeta(s)$ and other known functions. The left-hand side involves $g(u)$, the function we are concerned with.

Here then is Landau's modification, which derives an analogue of (90) directly. First a simple lemma.

THEOREM 6.16.

(91) $$\frac{1}{2}\int_{-2}^{2}\left(1-\frac{|t|}{2}\right)e^{iut}dt = \frac{\sin^2 u}{u^2} .$$

PROOF. The left-hand side is

$$I = \frac{1}{2}\int_0^2\left(1-\frac{t}{2}\right)e^{iut}dt + \frac{1}{2}\int_{-2}^0\left(1+\frac{t}{2}\right)e^{iut}dt .$$

Replacing t by $-t$ in the second integral and combining, we get

(92) $$I = \int_0^2\left(1-\frac{t}{2}\right)\cos ut\,dt = \frac{1-\cos 2u}{2u^2} = \frac{\sin^2 u}{u^2} .$$

This follows directly by integration by parts.

We now derive the analogue of (90).

THEOREM 6.17. *If $\delta > 0$, then*

(93) $$\int_{-\infty}^{\lambda u} g\left(u-\frac{v}{\lambda}\right)\frac{\sin^2 v}{v^2}e^{-\delta(u-v/\lambda)}dv = \frac{\lambda}{2}\int_{-2}^{2}\left(1-\frac{|t|}{2}\right)e^{i\lambda ut}h(1+\delta+i\lambda t)dt .$$

PROOF. In (87), we put $s = 1+\delta+i\lambda t$, multiply by

$$\frac{\lambda}{2}\left(1-\frac{|t|}{2}\right)e^{i\lambda ut} ,$$

and integrate with respect to t between -2 and 2; then

$$\frac{\lambda}{2}\int_{-2}^{2}\left(1-\frac{|t|}{2}\right)e^{i\lambda ut}dt\int_{0}^{\infty}g(v)e^{-(\delta+i\lambda t)v}dv \tag{94}$$
$$=\frac{\lambda}{2}\int_{-2}^{2}\left(1-\frac{|t|}{2}\right)e^{i\lambda ut}h(1+\delta+i\lambda t)\,dt\,.$$

For fixed δ, we may interchange the order of integration on the left-hand side, for the inner integral converges uniformly with respect to u in the finite interval $(-2, 2)$. This is because the integrand is

$$O(g(v)e^{-\delta v})=O(ve^{-\delta v})\,.$$

The left-hand side is therefore

$$\frac{\lambda}{2}\int_{0}^{\infty}g(v)e^{-\delta v}dv\int_{-2}^{2}\left(1-\frac{|t|}{2}\right)e^{it(\lambda u-\lambda v)}dt\,. \tag{95}$$

In order to apply Theorem 6.16, we change variables in the inner integral of (95). We put

$$\lambda u-\lambda v=w, \quad \text{then} \quad v=u-\frac{w}{\lambda}$$

and (95) becomes

$$\frac{\lambda}{2}\int_{-\infty}^{\lambda u}g\left(u-\frac{w}{\lambda}\right)e^{-\delta(u-w/\lambda)}dw\int_{-2}^{2}\left(1-\frac{|t|}{2}\right)e^{itw}dt$$
$$=\int_{-\infty}^{\lambda u}g\left(u-\frac{w}{\lambda}\right)e^{-\delta(u-w/\lambda)}\frac{\sin^2 w}{w^2}dw\,.$$

This, together with (94), gives (93).

If now we let $\delta\to 0$, in (93), we may expect

THEOREM 6.18.

$$\int_{-\infty}^{\lambda u}g\left(u-\frac{t}{\lambda}\right)\frac{\sin^2 t}{t^2}dt=\frac{\lambda}{2}\int_{-2}^{2}\left(1-\frac{|t|}{2}\right)e^{i\lambda ut}h(1+i\lambda t)dt\,. \tag{96}$$

PROOF. For fixed u as $\delta\to 0$, the right-hand side of (93) exists since $h(s)$ is regular for $\sigma\geqq 1$. On the other hand,

$$\lim_{\delta\to 0}\lim_{N\to\infty}\int_{-N}^{\lambda u}\frac{\sin^2 t}{t^2}g\left(u-\frac{t}{\lambda}\right)e^{-\delta(u-t/\lambda)}dt$$
$$=\lim_{\delta\to 0}\lim_{N\to\infty}\left\{\int_{-N}^{\lambda u}\frac{\sin^2 t}{t^2}e^{-(u-t/\lambda)}\phi\left(u-\frac{t}{\lambda}\right)e^{-\delta(u-t/\lambda)}dt\right. \tag{97}$$
$$\left.-\int_{-N}^{\lambda u}\frac{\sin^2 t}{t^2}e^{-\delta(u-t/\lambda)}dt\right\}$$
$$=\lim_{\delta\to 0}\lim_{N\to\infty}(A_u(N,\delta)-B_u(N,\delta))\,.$$

The integrand in $A_u(N,\delta)$ is positive and therefore $A_u(N,\delta)$ increases as N increases and increases as δ decreases since in the range $-\infty<t<\lambda u$,

$u - t/\lambda \geqq 0$.

Consequently, the iterated limit exists, that is

$$\lim_{\delta \to 0} \lim_{N \to \infty} A_u(N, \delta) = L .$$

In other words, for each $\varepsilon > 0$, there exist $\delta(\varepsilon)$, $N(\varepsilon)$ so that

$$L - \varepsilon < A_u(N, \delta) < L$$

for $\delta < \delta(\varepsilon)$ and $N > N(\varepsilon)$. This means, however, that for fixed $N > N(\varepsilon)$,

$$L - \varepsilon < \lim_{\delta \to 0} A_u(N, \delta) < L ;$$

consequently,

$$\lim_{\delta \to 0} \lim_{N \to \infty} A_u(N, \delta) = \lim_{N \to \infty} \lim_{\delta \to 0} A_u(N, \delta) .$$

A similar argument applies to $B_u(N, \delta)$. The conclusion of the theorem follows from (97). We now let $u \to \infty$.

Theorem 6.19. *If*

(98) $$\Phi(u) = \int_{-\infty}^{\lambda u} g\left(u - \frac{t}{\lambda}\right) \frac{\sin^2 t}{t^2} dt ,$$

then

$$\lim_{u \to \infty} \Phi(u) = 0 .$$

Proof. The proof is a consequence of the Riemann-Lebesgue theorem applied to the right-hand side of (96). For the right-hand side of (96) is the Fourier coefficient of a continuous function. For a direct argument, we note that if

(99) $$f(t) = \left(1 - \frac{|t|}{2}\right) h(1 + i\lambda t) ,$$

then, since $\zeta'(s)/\zeta(s) + s/(s-1)$ is regular for $\sigma \geqq 1$, it follows that $h(1 + i\lambda t)$ as a function of t is absolutely continuous because the segment $1 - 2\lambda i$ to $1 + 2\lambda i$ is entirely contained in the domain of regularity of the function $h(1 + i\lambda t)$. Thus we may integrate the right-hand side of (96) by parts and get

(100) $$\Phi(u) = \frac{\lambda}{2} \frac{f(1 + i\lambda t) e^{i\lambda u t}}{i\lambda u} \Bigg]_{-2}^{2} - \frac{1}{2iu} \int_{-2}^{2} f'(1 + i\lambda t) e^{i\lambda u t} dt$$

the integral on the right-hand side is $O(1)$ and the conclusion follows.

Theorem 6.20.

$$\lim_{u \to \infty} \int_{-\infty}^{\lambda u} e^{-(u - t/\lambda)} \psi\left(u - \frac{t}{\lambda}\right) \frac{\sin^2 t}{t^2} dt = \int_{-\infty}^{\infty} \frac{\sin^2 t}{t^2} dt .$$

Proof. The proof follows directly from Theorem 6.19 and the definition (86) of $g(u)$.

For simplicity, let

$$\int_{-\infty}^{\infty} \frac{\sin^2 t}{t^2} dt = P. \tag{101}$$

The value of P is π but we do not need this fact. Let us put in addition

$$k(u) = e^{-u}\psi(e^u). \tag{102}$$

THEOREM 6.21. *We have the inequalities*

$$(e^{-2/\sqrt{\lambda}})k\left(u - \frac{1}{\sqrt{\lambda}}\right) \leqq k\left(u - \frac{t}{\lambda}\right) \leqq (e^{2/\sqrt{\lambda}})k\left(u + \frac{1}{\sqrt{\lambda}}\right) \tag{103}$$

for $-\sqrt{\lambda} \leqq t \leqq \sqrt{\lambda}$.

PROOF. Since $\psi(u)$ is a monotone increasing function, we have

$$k(u_2) \geqq k(u_1)e^{u_1 - u_2}. \tag{104}$$

By hypothesis,

$$u - \frac{1}{\sqrt{\lambda}} \leqq u - \frac{t}{\lambda} \leqq u + \frac{1}{\sqrt{\lambda}} \tag{105}$$

and therefore, from (104)

$$\begin{aligned} k\left(u - \frac{t}{\lambda}\right) &\geqq k\left(u - \frac{1}{\sqrt{\lambda}}\right)e^{t/\lambda - 1/\sqrt{\lambda}} \\ &\geqq k\left(u - \frac{1}{\sqrt{\lambda}}\right)e^{-2/\sqrt{\lambda}}. \end{aligned} \tag{106}$$

On the other hand

$$\begin{aligned} k\left(u + \frac{1}{\sqrt{\lambda}}\right) &\geqq k\left(u - \frac{t}{\lambda}\right)e^{-t/\lambda - 1/\sqrt{\lambda}} \\ &\geqq k\left(u - \frac{t}{\lambda}\right)e^{-2/\sqrt{\lambda}}. \end{aligned} \tag{107}$$

The conclusion of the theorem follows from (106) and (107). We can now prove the fundamental

THEOREM 6.22

$$\psi(x) \sim x.$$

PROOF. By Theorems 6.20 and 6.21

$$\begin{aligned} P &\geqq \limsup_{u\to\infty} \int_{-\sqrt{\lambda}}^{\sqrt{\lambda}} k\left(u - \frac{t}{\lambda}\right)\frac{\sin^2 t}{t^2} dt \\ &\geqq \limsup_{u\to\infty} e^{-2/\sqrt{\lambda}} k\left(u - \frac{1}{\sqrt{\lambda}}\right)\int_{-\sqrt{\lambda}}^{\sqrt{\lambda}} \frac{\sin^2 t}{t^2} dt \end{aligned} \tag{108}$$

and, therefore, from (108) we have

$$\text{(109)}\qquad \begin{aligned}\limsup_{u\to\infty} k(u) = \limsup_{u\to\infty} k\left(u - \frac{1}{\sqrt{\lambda}}\right) &\leqq \frac{Pe^{2/\sqrt{\lambda}}}{\displaystyle\int_{-\sqrt{\lambda}}^{\sqrt{\lambda}} \frac{\sin^2 t}{t^2}\,dt} \\ &\leqq \lim_{\lambda\to\infty} \frac{Pe^{2/\sqrt{\lambda}}}{\displaystyle\int_{-\sqrt{\lambda}}^{\sqrt{\lambda}} \frac{\sin^2 t}{t^2}\,dt} = 1\,.\end{aligned}$$

Thus, in any event, $k(u) \leqq c$.

On the other hand, using Theorems 6.20 and 6.21 again, we have

$$\text{(110)}\qquad \begin{aligned} P &= \lim_{u\to\infty} \int_{-\infty}^{\lambda u} k\left(u - \frac{t}{\lambda}\right)\frac{\sin^2 t}{t^2}\,dt \\ &\leqq \liminf_{u\to\infty} \left(\int_{-\infty}^{-\sqrt{\lambda}} + \int_{-\sqrt{\lambda}}^{\sqrt{\lambda}} + \int_{\sqrt{\lambda}}^{\infty} k\left(u - \frac{t}{\lambda}\right)\frac{\sin^2 t}{t^2}\,dt \right).\end{aligned}$$

In the first and third integrals, we use the fact that $k(u) \leqq c$ whereas in the second we use (107). Thus from (110)

$$\text{(111)}\qquad \begin{aligned} P &\leqq \frac{2c}{\sqrt{\lambda}} + \liminf_{u\to\infty} k\left(u + \frac{1}{\sqrt{\lambda}}\right) e^{2/\sqrt{\lambda}} \int_{-\sqrt{\lambda}}^{\sqrt{\lambda}} \frac{\sin^2 t}{t^2}\,dt \\ &\leqq \frac{2c}{\sqrt{\lambda}} + \liminf_{u\to\infty} k\left(u + \frac{1}{\sqrt{\lambda}}\right) e^{2/\sqrt{\lambda}} P\,.\end{aligned}$$

If we let $\lambda \to \infty$ in (111), we deduce

$$\text{(112)}\qquad 1 \leqq \liminf_{u\to\infty} k(u)\,.$$

Equations (109) and (112) imply that

$$\lim_{u\to\infty} k(u) = 1\,.$$

This, however, by (102), means that

$$\lim_{u\to\infty} e^{-u}\psi(e^u) = 1$$

and the enunciation of the theorem follows.

There are two interesting features of this proof:

(i) Cauchy's theorem is avoided altogether.

(ii) The only analytic fact used about $\zeta(s)$ is that $\zeta(1 + it) \neq 0$.

We shall prove now a theorem in the converse direction to (ii).

Theorem 6.23. *If $\psi(x) \sim x$, then $\zeta(1 + it) \neq 0$.*

Proof. We start with (87), with e^u replaced by x. This is

$$\text{(113)}\qquad \int_1^{\infty} (\psi(x) - x)x^{-s-1}\,dx = h(s) = \frac{1}{s}\left(-\frac{\zeta'(s)}{\zeta(s)} - \frac{s}{s-1}\right), \quad \text{for } \sigma > 1\,.$$

Since by hypothesis

$$\psi(x) - x = o(x)\,,$$

for $\varepsilon > 0$ we choose $x > x_0$ so that

(114) $$\psi(x) - x < \varepsilon x .$$

Then for this fixed x_0, we have from (113)

$$h(s) = \int_1^{x_0} (\psi(x) - x)x^{-s-1}dx + \int_{x_0}^{\infty} (\psi(x) - x)x^{-s-1}dx .$$

Hence for $\sigma > 1$, from (114),

$$|h(s)| < \int_1^{x_0} \frac{|\psi(x) - x|}{x^2} dx + \int_{x_0}^{\infty} \frac{\varepsilon}{x^{\sigma}} dx .$$

The first integral is some constant $c(x_0)$ depending on x_0, while for the second, we have

(115) $$\int_{x_0}^{\infty} \frac{\varepsilon}{x^{\sigma}} dx = \frac{\varepsilon}{\sigma - 1} x_0^{1-\sigma} < \frac{\varepsilon}{\sigma - 1} ,$$

since $\sigma > 1$.

Consequently from (115) we get

$$|(\sigma - 1)h(\sigma + it)| < c(x_0)(\sigma - 1) + \varepsilon .$$

Now we choose σ sufficiently close to 1 so as to make

$$c(x_0)(\sigma - 1) < \varepsilon :$$

then

$$|(\sigma - 1)h(\sigma + it)| < 2\varepsilon ,$$

and this implies that for fixed t, as $\sigma \to 1^{+0}$

(116) $$(\sigma - 1)h(\sigma + it) \to 0 .$$

Suppose now that $s_0 = 1 + it$ is a zero of $\zeta(s)$, that is, $\zeta(s_0) = 0$. Then

(117) $$\zeta(s) = (s - s_0)^k g(s) \qquad (k \geqq 1) ,$$

where $g(s_0) \neq 0$. From (117), then,

(118) $$\frac{\zeta'(s)}{\zeta(s)} = \frac{k}{s - s_0} + \frac{g'(s)}{g(s)} ,$$

and this means that s_0 is a simple pole of $\zeta'(s)/\zeta(s)$ and therefore a simple pole of $h(s)$ with residue k. But if $1 + it$ is a simple pole of $h(s)$, then

$$\lim_{\sigma \to 1} (\sigma - 1)h(\sigma + it) = k .$$

This contradicts (116) and therefore $\zeta(1 + it) \neq 0$.

Until recently, it was generally supposed that this equivalence of the prime number theorem with the nonvanishing of $\zeta(s)$ for $\sigma = 1$, strongly suggested that the discovery of a proof of the prime number theorem not involving the zeta function in some essential way, was highly unlikely. In 1948, however, A. Selberg, in collaboration with P. Erdös, showed that it is indeed possible to give a proof requiring no use of the zeta function and only the most elementary analysis. The proof is "elementary" but by no means simple.

An excellent account may be found in Hardy and Wright's *Theory of Numbers*, third edition.

We turn to some consequences of the prime number theorem to other arithmetic functions.

7. Further arithmetic functions and some applications of the prime number theorem. We have seen that the two arithmetic functions $\Lambda_1(n)$ and $\Lambda(n)$ arose in a natural way as the coefficients of Dirichlet series allied to the zeta function. We may construct a variety of numerical functions from known Dirichlet series and conversely, we may find the Dirichlet series associated with certain known arithmetic functions, and as a result, determine their asymptotic behavior.

We consider several examples, and for this purpose, recall from Theorem 3.7, Chapter I, that if

$$\sum_{n=1}^{\infty} \frac{a(n)}{n^s} \sum_{n=1}^{\infty} \frac{b(n)}{n^s} = \sum_{n=1}^{\infty} \frac{c(n)}{n^s},$$

then

$$c(n) = \sum_{jk=n} a(j)b(k) = \sum_{j|n} a(j)b\left(\frac{n}{j}\right) = \sum_{k|n} a\left(\frac{n}{k}\right)b(k). \tag{1}$$

We shall, in this section, use these relations frequently.

We begin by getting the Dirichlet series for $1/\zeta(s)$.

THEOREM 7.1. *For* $\sigma > 1$,

$$\frac{1}{\zeta(s)} = \sum_{n=1}^{\infty} \frac{\mu(n)}{n^s}, \tag{2}$$

where

$$\mu(n) = \begin{cases} 1 & \text{if } n = 1, \\ (-1)^r & \text{if } n = p_1 p_2 \cdots p_r \qquad (p_i \neq p_j \text{ for } i \neq j), \\ 0 & \text{otherwise}. \end{cases}$$

PROOF. $\mu(n)$ is of course the familiar Möbius function.

From Euler's identity we get at once

$$\frac{1}{\zeta(s)} = \prod_p (1 - p^{-s}).$$

Since the product on the right converges absolutely, we multiply it out and find

$$\frac{1}{\zeta(s)} = 1 - \sum_p p^{-s} + \sum_{p,q} (pq)^{-s} - \cdots$$
$$= \sum_{n=1}^{\infty} \frac{\mu(n)}{n^s},$$

where $\mu(n)$ has the stated properties.

An arithmetic property of $\mu(n)$ follows at once. To facilitate the notation, we define

$$E(n) = \begin{cases} 0 & \text{if } n \neq 1, \\ 1 & \text{if } n = 1. \end{cases} \tag{3}$$

THEOREM 7.2.

$$\sum_{k|n} \mu(k) = E(n).$$

PROOF. The proof makes use of (1). In fact,

$$1 = \frac{1}{\zeta(s)} \cdot \zeta(s) = \sum_{n=1}^{\infty} \frac{\mu(n)}{n^s} \cdot \sum_{n=1}^{\infty} \frac{1}{n^s}.$$

The result then follows by (1) and the identity Theorem 3.6 for Dirichlet series.

In a similar way, we prove the Möbius inversion formula.

THEOREM 7.3. *If $f(x)$ and $g(x)$ are defined for integer values of x, and if*

$$f(n) = \sum_{k|n} g(k), \tag{4}$$

then

$$g(n) = \sum_{k|n} f(k)\mu\left(\frac{n}{k}\right), \tag{5}$$

and conversely.

PROOF. Suppose (4) holds, then by (1),

$$\sum_{n=1}^{\infty} \frac{f(n)}{n^s} = \sum_{n=1}^{\infty} \frac{g(n)}{n^s}\zeta(s). \tag{6}$$

Consequently,

$$\sum_{n=1}^{\infty} \frac{g(n)}{n^s} = \frac{1}{\zeta(s)} \sum_{n=1}^{\infty} \frac{f(n)}{n^s} = \sum_{n=1}^{\infty} \frac{\mu(n)}{n^s} \sum_{n=1}^{\infty} \frac{f(n)}{n^s}, \tag{7}$$

and again by (1) and the identity theorem the conclusion (5) follows.

Conversely, suppose that (5) holds, then (7) is valid, and this implies the validity of (6) and therefore of (4).

We should be careful to remark that there is implied in these arguments a restriction on the order of magnitude of the functions in order that the Dirichlet series may converge. Actually, however, these theorems involving only arithmetic relations which we consider may be proved directly without recourse to Dirichlet series. Moreover, it is possible to construct a formal theory of series in which convergence plays no role. For these reasons, we continue to use Dirichlet series ignoring questions of convergence since series are very convenient for suggesting new relations and new arithmetic functions.

The arithmetic properties of some functions can be determined. Let $\varphi(n)$ denote as usual, Euler's φ-function, and we recall from elementary number theory that

(8)
$$\sum_{k|n} \varphi(k) = n \,.$$

THEOREM 7.3. *For $\sigma > 2$,*

(9)
$$\sum_{n=1}^{\infty} \frac{\varphi(n)}{n^s} = \frac{\zeta(s-1)}{\zeta(s)} \,.$$

PROOF. From (8) and (1),

$$\sum_{n=1}^{\infty} \frac{\varphi(n)}{n^s} \sum_{n=1}^{\infty} \frac{1}{n^s} = \sum_{n=1}^{\infty} \frac{n}{n^s} = \zeta(s-1) \,,$$

and because $\varphi(n) < n$, the conclusion follows.

The derivative of $\zeta(s)$ has a Dirichlet series—in fact,

(10)
$$\zeta'(s) = -\sum_{n=1}^{\infty} \frac{\log n}{n^s} \,.$$

This implies a relation involving $\Lambda(n)$.

THEOREM 7.4.

(11)
$$\sum_{k|n} \Lambda(n) = \log n \,.$$

PROOF. Since

$$-\frac{\zeta'(s)}{\zeta(s)} = \sum_{n=1}^{\infty} \frac{\Lambda(n)}{n^s}$$

and

$$\zeta(s)\left(-\frac{\zeta'(s)}{\zeta(s)}\right) = -\zeta'(s) \,,$$

then

(12)
$$\sum_{n=1}^{\infty} \frac{1}{n^s} \sum_{n=1}^{\infty} \frac{\Lambda(n)}{n^s} = \sum_{n=1}^{\infty} \frac{\log n}{n^s} \,.$$

From (12), (1) and the identity theorem, we get (11).

From (11) and the Möbius inversion formula, we get at once

$$\sum_{k|n} \mu(k) \log\left(\frac{n}{k}\right) = \Lambda(n) \,.$$

We break the logarithm up into two parts

(13)
$$\sum_{k|n} \mu(k) \log n - \sum_{k|n} \mu(k) \log k = \Lambda(n) \,.$$

The first sum of (13) is 0 by Theorem 7.2 and therefore

(14)
$$-\sum_{k|n} \mu(k) \log k = \Lambda(n) \,.$$

There are several further arithmetic functions of considerable interest. These are

(15) $d(n) = \sum_{k|n} 1 = $ number of divisors of n,

(16) $\sigma(n) = \sum_{k|n} k = $ sum of the divisors of n,

(17) $\lambda(n) = \begin{cases} 1 & \text{if } n = 1\,, \\ (-1)^{\rho} & \text{where } \rho = a_1 + \cdots + a_r \text{ when } n = p_1^{a_1} \cdots p_r^{a_r}\,, \end{cases}$

(18) $\nu(n) = \begin{cases} 1 & \text{if } n = 1\,, \\ a_1 + \cdots + a_r & \text{if } n = p_1^{a_1} \cdots p_r^{a_r}\,. \end{cases}$

It is easy to get the Dirichlet series belonging to these functions.

THEOREM 7.5.

(19) $$\sum_{n=1}^{\infty} \frac{d(n)}{n^s} = \zeta^2(s), \qquad \sigma > 1\,,$$

(20) $$\sum_{n=1}^{\infty} \frac{\lambda(n)}{n^s} = \frac{\zeta(2s)}{\zeta(s)} = \prod_p \left(\sum_{n=0}^{\infty} (-1)^n p^{-ns} \right), \qquad \sigma > 1\,,$$

(21) $$\sum_{n=1}^{\infty} \frac{2^{\nu(n)}}{n^s} = \frac{\zeta^2(s)}{\zeta(2s)} = \prod_p \left(1 + 2 \sum_{n=0}^{\infty} p^{-ns} \right), \qquad \sigma > 1\,,$$

(22) $$\sum_{n=1}^{\infty} \frac{\sigma(n)}{n^s} = \zeta(s)\zeta(s-1)\,, \qquad \sigma > 2\,.$$

PROOF. The proof of (19) is immediate for

$$\zeta^2(s) = \sum_{n=1}^{\infty} \frac{1}{n^s} \sum_{n=1}^{\infty} \frac{1}{n^s}\,,$$

and (19) follows from (1).

Because

$$\frac{\zeta(2s)}{\zeta(s)} = \frac{\prod_p (1 - p^{-2s})^{-1}}{\prod_p (1 - p^{-s})^{-1}} = \prod_p (1 + p^{-s})^{-1} = \prod_p (1 - p^{-s} + p^{-2s} - \cdots)$$
$$= 1 - \sum_p p^{-s} + \sum_p p^{-2s} - \cdots + \sum_{p,q} p^{-s} q^{-s} + \sum_{p,q} p^{-2s} q^{-2s} + \cdots\,,$$

the relation (20) follows by the definition of $\lambda(n)$.

To prove (21), we observe that

$$\frac{\zeta^2(s)}{\zeta(2s)} = \frac{\prod_p (1 - p^{-s})^{-2}}{\prod_p (1 - p^{-2s})^{-1}} = \frac{\prod_p (1 - p^{-s})^{-1}}{\prod_p (1 + p^{-s})^{-1}}$$
$$= \prod_p (1 + p^{-s})(1 - p^{-s})^{-1}$$
$$= \prod_p (1 + p^{-s})(1 + p^{-s} + p^{-2s} + \cdots)$$
$$= \prod_p (1 + 2p^{-s} + 2p^{-2s} + \cdots) = \sum_{n=1}^{\infty} \frac{2^{\nu(n)}}{n^s}\,.$$

Finally, (22) will follow from (1), for

$$\zeta(s)\zeta(s-1) = \sum_{n=1}^{\infty} \frac{1}{n^s} \sum_{n=1}^{\infty} \frac{n}{n^s},$$

and this relation, together with (1) and (16), implies (22).

We are primarily concerned here with the order of magnitude of the averages of these and other arithmetic functions. To investigate the relationships among these functions, we prove

THEOREM 7.6. *If $f(x)$ and $g(x)$ are real functions defined for real values of x and if*

$$f(x) = \sum_{n \leqq x} g\left(\frac{x}{n}\right), \tag{23}$$

then

$$g(x) = \sum_{n \leqq x} \mu(n) f\left(\frac{x}{n}\right), \tag{24}$$

and conversely.

PROOF. Starting with the right-hand side of (24), we have, because

$$f\left(\frac{x}{n}\right) = \sum_{m \leqq (x/n)} g\left(\frac{x}{n}\Big/m\right),$$

$$\sum_{n \leqq x} \mu(n) f\left(\frac{x}{n}\right) = \sum_{n \leqq x} \mu(n) \sum_{mn \leqq x} g\left(\frac{x}{mn}\right). \tag{25}$$

In this relation, we put $mn = k$ and interchange the order of summation. As k ranges over the interval 1 to x, for fixed k, n ranges over the divisors of k. Therefore, from (25),

$$\sum_{n \leqq x} \mu(n) f\left(\frac{x}{n}\right) = \sum_{k \leqq x} g\left(\frac{x}{k}\right) \sum_{n \mid k} \mu(n). \tag{26}$$

By Theorem 7.2, however, the inner sum is $E(k)$ and therefore from (26),

$$\sum_{n \leqq x} \mu(n) f\left(\frac{x}{n}\right) = \sum_{k \leqq x} g\left(\frac{x}{k}\right) E(k) = g(x),$$

as required. If, conversely, (24) holds, then a similar argument shows that

$$\begin{aligned} \sum_{n \leqq x} g\left(\frac{x}{n}\right) &= \sum_{n \leqq x} \sum_{m \leqq (x/n)} \mu(m) f\left(\frac{x}{mn}\right) \\ &= \sum_{k \leqq x} f\left(\frac{x}{k}\right) \sum_{m \mid k} \mu(m) \\ &= \sum_{k \leqq x} f\left(\frac{x}{k}\right) E(k) = f(x). \end{aligned}$$

If we put $g(x) = 1$, then $f(x) = [x]$, by (23) and from (24) we get

$$\sum_{n \leqq x} \mu(n) \left[\frac{x}{n}\right] = 1. \tag{27}$$

What may we expect about the averages of some of these arithmetic functions? Let us look first at $\mu(n)$. We put

$$M(x) = \sum_{n \leqq x} \mu(n) . \tag{28}$$

Then by Theorem 3.1,

$$M(x) = \frac{1}{2\pi i} \int_{a-i\infty}^{a+i\infty} \frac{1}{\zeta(s)} \frac{x^s}{s} dx , \qquad a > 1 .$$

Since $\zeta(1+it) \neq 0$, we know that $1/\zeta(s)$ is regular for $\sigma \geqq 1$. In fact, we found a wider domain in which $1/\zeta(s)$ is regular. The integrand has no singularity in this extended domain and we may therefore expect that

$$M(x) = o(x) . \tag{29}$$

This is indeed the case, but what is particularly interesting is that this statement implies, and is implied by, the prime number theorem. There are other equally striking equivalences. If in the relation

$$\frac{1}{\zeta(s)} = \sum_{n=1}^{\infty} \frac{\mu(n)}{n^s} ,$$

we allow formally $s \to 1$ disregarding the validity of this step, we are led to expect that

$$\sum_{n=1}^{\infty} \frac{\mu(n)}{n} = 0 . \tag{30}$$

It is a highly interesting fact that this is the case and that this relation implies, and is implied by, the prime number theorem. Relation (20), coupled with an argument similar to the one we applied to $M(x)$ suggests that

$$\sum_{n \leqq x} \lambda(n) = o(x) .$$

Once again this statement is equivalent to the prime number theorem.

We shall now derive some of these equivalences. As usual, it is more convenient to use $\psi(x)$. What is the relation between $\psi(x)$ and $M(x)$? To see this, we need a relation between $\mu(n)$ and $\Lambda(n)$. The natural starting point is:

$$-\frac{\zeta'(s)}{\zeta(s)} = \sum_{n=1}^{\infty} \frac{\Lambda(n)}{n^s} \tag{31}$$

and

$$\frac{1}{\zeta(s)} = \sum_{n=1}^{\infty} \frac{\mu(n)}{n^s} . \tag{32}$$

If we multiply (31) by $-1/\zeta'(s)$, then we get (32). Unfortuately, $1/\zeta'(s)$ has no Dirichlet series and we must modify our argument. We differentiate (32) and get

(33) $$\frac{\zeta'(s)}{\zeta^2(s)} = \sum_{n=1}^{\infty} \frac{\mu(n)\log n}{n^s} .$$

On the other hand, this is

(34) $$\left(-\frac{\zeta'(s)}{\zeta(s)}\right)\left(\frac{-1}{\zeta(s)}\right) = -\sum_{n=1}^{\infty} \frac{\Lambda(n)}{n^s} \sum_{n=1}^{\infty} \frac{\mu(n)}{n^s} .$$

To derive a relation between $M(x)$ and $\psi(x)$, we require therefore a relation between the sum function of the product of two Dirichlet series and the sum function of the individual series. This is given by

THEOREM 7.7. *Let $a(n)$ and $b(n)$ be two arithmetic functions and let*

(35) $$c(n) = \sum_{jk=n} a(j)b(k) .$$

Suppose that

$$A(x) = \sum_{n \leq x} a(n) ,$$

$$B(x) = \sum_{n \leq x} b(n) ,$$

$$C(x) = \sum_{n \leq x} c(n) ,$$

and $x = yz$; then

(36) $$C(x) = \sum_{jk \leq x} a(j)b(k) = \sum_{j \leq y} a(j)B\left(\frac{x}{j}\right) + \sum_{k \leq z} b(k)A\left(\frac{x}{k}\right) - A(y)B(z) .$$

PROOF. The proof is based on a device used by Dirichlet for the particular case when $a(n) = b(n) = 1$. We draw the hyperbola $x = yz$ for fixed x, and choose a point (y, z) on it.

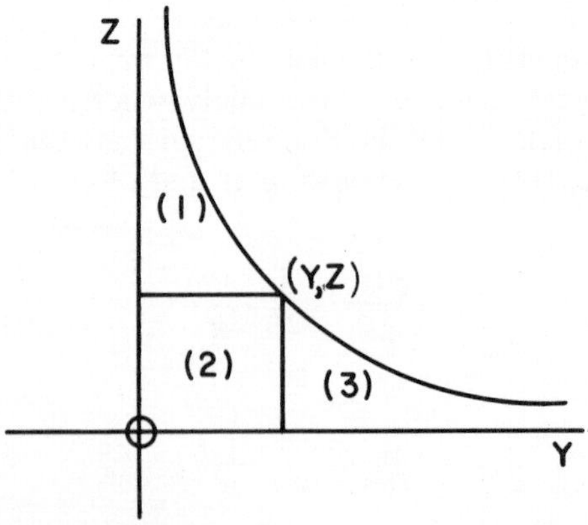

The sum on the left of (36) has a contribution from all points (j, k) with integer coordinates contained within that part of the positive quadrant which is bounded by the hyperbola and the coordinates axes. Points with integer coordinates are usually called lattice points. We break the sum into two parts —one over the lattice points contained in (1) and (2), and the second part over the lattice points of (2) and (3). In so doing, however, we have counted the lattice points of (2) twice. In this way we get

$$\begin{aligned}\sum_{jk\le x} a(j)b(k) &= \sum_{jk\le x;\, j\le y} a(j)b(k) + \sum_{jk\le x;\, k\le z} a(j)b(k) - \sum_{jk\le x;\, j\le y;\, k\le z} a(j)b(k)\\ &= \sum_{j\le y} a(j) \sum_{k\le (x/j)} b(k) + \sum_{k\le z} b(k) \sum_{j\le (x/k)} a(j) - \sum_{j\le y} a(j) \sum_{k\le z} b(k)\\ &= \sum_{j\le y} a(j)B\Big(\frac{x}{j}\Big) + \sum_{k\le z} b(k)A\Big(\frac{x}{k}\Big) - A(y)B(z)\,.\end{aligned}$$

We get an important corollary if we put $y = z = \sqrt{x}$, $a(n) = b(n) = 1$.

THEOREM 7.8.

(37) $$\sum_{n\le x} d(n) = x\log x + (2\gamma - 1)x + O(\sqrt{x})\,.$$

PROOF. With $a(n) = b(n) = 1$, $y = z = \sqrt{x}$, (19) and (36) give, since $A(x) = B(x) = [x]$,

$$\begin{aligned}\sum_{n\le x} d(n) &= \sum_{j\le\sqrt{x}} \Big[\frac{x}{j}\Big] + \sum_{k\le\sqrt{x}} \Big[\frac{x}{k}\Big] - [\sqrt{x}][\sqrt{x}]\\ &= 2\sum_{j\le\sqrt{x}} \Big[\frac{x}{j}\Big] - [\sqrt{x}][\sqrt{x}]\,.\end{aligned}$$

If we replace $[\xi]$ by ξ and calculate the error, we find

$$\begin{aligned}\sum_{n\le x} d(n) &= 2\sum_{j\le\sqrt{x}} \frac{x}{j} - 2\sum_{j\le\sqrt{x}} \Big\{\Big(\frac{x}{j}\Big) - \Big[\frac{x}{j}\Big]\Big\} - (\sqrt{x} - (\sqrt{x} - [\sqrt{x}]))^2\\ &= 2\sum_{j\le\sqrt{x}} \frac{x}{j} + O(\sqrt{x}) - x + O(\sqrt{x})\,.\end{aligned}$$

We apply Theorem 2.4 to the sum on the right. Then

$$\begin{aligned}\sum_{n\le x} d(n) &= 2x\Big(\log\sqrt{x} + \gamma + O\Big(\frac{1}{\sqrt{x}}\Big)\Big) + O(\sqrt{x}) - x\\ &= x\log x + (2\gamma - 1)x + O(\sqrt{x})\,,\end{aligned}$$

as was to be proved.

We return to relation (33). If we add 1 to both sides, we get

(38) $$\Big(\frac{\zeta'(s)}{\zeta(s)} + \zeta(s)\Big)\frac{1}{\zeta(s)} = \sum_{n=1}^{\infty} \frac{\mu(n)\log n}{n^s} + 1\,.$$

The effect of this is to make the parenthesis on the left of (38) analytic at $s = 1$ since the principal parts at the poles of $\zeta'(s)/\zeta(s)$ and $\zeta(s)$ cancel each other. We then get from (38) the relation

$$\sum_{n=1}^{\infty} \frac{1 - \Lambda(n)}{n^s} \sum_{n=1}^{\infty} \frac{\mu(n)}{n^s} = 1 + \sum_{n=1}^{\infty} \frac{\mu(n)\log n}{n^s}\,,$$

or the equivalent arithmetic relation

$$\sum_{jk=n} (1 - \Lambda(j))\mu(k) = \mu(n) \log n , \tag{39}$$

for $n \neq 1$.

Let

$$\begin{aligned} A(x) &= \sum_{n \leqq x} (1 - \Lambda(n)) = [x] - \psi(x) \\ &= x - \psi(x) + O(1) , \end{aligned} \tag{40}$$

and

$$N(x) = \sum_{n \leqq x} \mu(n) \log n . \tag{41}$$

We now prove

THEOREM 7.9. *If*

$$\psi(x) - x = o(x) , \tag{42}$$

then

$$N(x) = o(x \log x) . \tag{43}$$

That is to say, the prime number theorem implies (43).

PROOF. We apply Theorem 7.7 to $A(x)$ and $M(x)$ and get from (39)

$$\sum_{jk \leqq x} (1 - \Lambda(j))\mu(k) = 1 + \sum_{n \leqq x} \mu(n) \log n , \tag{44}$$

and then the left-hand side is

$$\sum_{jk \leqq x} (1 - \Lambda(j))\mu(k) = \sum_{j \leqq y} (1 - \Lambda(j)) M\left(\frac{x}{j}\right) + \sum_{k \leqq z} \mu(k) A\left(\frac{x}{k}\right) - A(y)M(z) , \tag{45}$$

where $x = yz$. By (40) and the hypothesis (42), $A(x) = o(x)$; hence for $\varepsilon > 0$, let y_0 be chosen so that

$$|A(y)| < \varepsilon y \qquad \text{for } y \geqq y_0 .$$

It is clear, however, that $|M(x)| \leqq x$ and therefore for fixed $y \geqq y_0$, we get from (44) and (45)

$$|1 + \sum_{n \leqq x} \mu(n) \log n| \leqq x \sum_{j \leqq y} \frac{|1 - \Lambda(j)|}{j} + \varepsilon \sum_{k \leqq z} \frac{x}{k} + \varepsilon yz . \tag{46}$$

The first sum on the right is

$$x \sum_{j \leqq y} \frac{|1 - \Lambda(j)|}{j} = xK(y) ,$$

where $K(y)$ is a constant depending only on y. The second sum is

$$\varepsilon \sum_{k \leqq z} \frac{x}{k} \leqq \varepsilon x (\log z + O(1)) .$$

Because $yz = x$, and $K(y) < \varepsilon \log x$ for x sufficiently large, it follows from (46) that

$$\left|1 + \sum_{n \leqq x} \mu(n) \log n\right| < 4\varepsilon x \log x ,$$

and this proves the theorem.

As a corollary, we prove

THEOREM 7.10. *If*

$$\psi(x) - x = o(x)$$

then

$$M(x) = o(x) . \tag{47}$$

The prime number theorem thus implies (47).

PROOF. The proof uses partial summation in the form given by Lemma 3.1, Chapter I. We have

$$M(x) = \sum_{n \leqq x} \frac{\mu(n) \log n}{\log n} ,$$

and in this relation, we put $c(n) = \mu(n) \log n$, $\varphi(x) = 1/\log x$ and apply Lemma 3.1. Then

$$\begin{aligned} M(x) &= \frac{N(x)}{\log x} + \int_2^x \frac{N(t)}{\log^2 t} \frac{dt}{t} \\ &= o(x) + O\left(\int_2^x \frac{t \log t dt}{(\log^2 t)t}\right) \\ &= o(x) + O\left(\frac{x}{\log x}\right) = o(x) . \end{aligned}$$

For the converse, which is in some ways the more interesting theorem, we use the identity

$$\frac{\zeta'(s)}{\zeta(s)} + \zeta(s) = \frac{1}{\zeta(s)}(\zeta'(s) + \zeta^2(s)) . \tag{48}$$

THEOREM 7.11. *If*

$$M(x) = o(x) ,$$

then

$$\psi(x) - x = o(x) .$$

Therefore $M(x) = o(x)$ implies the prime number theorem.

PROOF. The coefficient of the Dirichlet series of $\zeta'(s) + \zeta^2(s)$ is

$$b_1(n) = d(n) - \log n .$$

In that case

$$B_1(x) = \sum_{n \leqq x} b_1(n) = \sum_{n \leqq x} d(n) - \sum_{n \leqq x} \log n .$$

But these sums are evaluated by Theorems 7.8 and 2.3, respectively, and give

$$B_1(x) = x\log x + (2\gamma - 1)x + O(\sqrt{x}) - \left(x\log x - x + O\left(\frac{1}{x}\right)\right)$$
$$= 2\gamma x + O(\sqrt{x})\,.$$

We should like to eliminate the term $2\gamma x$ and consider instead of (48), the relation

$$(49)\qquad \begin{aligned}\zeta(s) + \frac{\zeta'(s)}{\zeta(s)} - 2\gamma &= \frac{1}{\zeta(s)}(\zeta^2(s) + \zeta'(s) - 2\gamma\zeta(s))\\ &= \sum_{n=1}^{\infty}\frac{\mu(n)}{n^s}\sum_{n=1}^{\infty}\frac{d(n) - \log n - 2\gamma}{n^s}\,.\end{aligned}$$

We get, therefore, on putting

$$(50)\qquad \begin{aligned}b(n) &= d(n) - \log n - 2\gamma = b_1(n) - 2\gamma\,,\\ B(x) &= \sum_{n\leq x} b(n) = O(\sqrt{x})\,.\end{aligned}$$

We now apply Theorem 7.7 again, with

$$a(n) = 1 - \Lambda(n)\,,$$

and deduce from (49) and (40)

$$(51)\qquad A(x) - 2\gamma = \sum_{jk\leq x}\mu(j)b(k) = \sum_{j\leq y}\mu(j)B\left(\frac{x}{j}\right) + \sum_{k\leq z}b(k)M\left(\frac{x}{k}\right) - B(y)M(z)\,.$$

By (50) the first sum on the right yields

$$(52)\qquad \left|\sum_{j\leq y}\mu(j)B\left(\frac{x}{j}\right)\right| \leqq c_1x^{1/2}\sum_{j\leq y}\frac{1}{\sqrt{j}} \leqq c_1x^{1/2}y^{1/2} \leqq c_1\frac{x}{z^{1/2}}\,.$$

We choose z so large that $c_1/z^{1/2} < \varepsilon$ and keep this z fixed.

Since by assumption $M(x) = o(x)$, we choose x_0 so large that for $x > x_0/z$, $|M(x)| < \varepsilon x/\alpha$ where α will be specified in a moment. Then the second sum is

$$(53)\qquad \left|\sum_{k\leq z}b(k)M\left(\frac{x}{k}\right)\right| \leqq \frac{\varepsilon x}{\alpha}\sum_{k\leq z}\frac{|b(k)|}{k}\,.$$

Because z is fixed, choose $\alpha = \sum_{k\leq z}|b(k)|/k$. Finally,

$$(54)\qquad B(y)M(z) = O(\sqrt{y}) = O(x^{1/2})\,,$$

and (51), (52), (53), and (54) imply that

$$|A(x) - 2\gamma| \leqq 2\varepsilon x + O(x^{1/2})\,.$$

This means, however, that $A(x) = o(x)$.

In order to prove the equivalence of the statement

$$\sum_{n=1}^{\infty}\frac{\mu(n)}{n} = 0$$

with the prime number theorem, we now prove a variation of Theorem 7.7. This result is due to Axer and is more readily and effectively applicable than Theorem 7.7.

THEOREM 7.12. *Suppose $B(x)$ is defined for all real x, $a(x)$ is defined for integral x, and*

(i) *$B(x)$ is a function of bounded variation in every finite interval,*

(ii)
$$\sum_{n\leqq x} a(n) = o(x)\,,$$

(iii) *either* (a) $B(x) = O(1)$ *and* (b) $\sum_{n\leqq x} |a(n)| = O(x)$ *or* (c) $B(x) = O(x^{\alpha})$ $(0 \leqq \alpha < 1)$ *and* (d) $a(n) = O(1)$.

Then

$$\sum_{n\leqq x} a(n)B\left(\frac{x}{n}\right) = o(x)\,. \tag{55}$$

PROOF. The proof uses the same general principles used in Theorem 7.7. Suppose that $0 < \delta < 1$,

$$A(n) = a(1) + \cdots + a(n) \qquad (A(0) = 0)\,,$$

then we apply partial summation to the left-hand side of (55), but first break the sum into two parts:

$$\sum_{n\leqq x} a(n)B\left(\frac{x}{n}\right) = \sum_{n\leqq \delta x} a(n)B\left(\frac{x}{n}\right) + \sum_{\delta x<n\leqq x} a(n)B\left(\frac{x}{n}\right) = S_1 + S_2\,.$$

Consider first the sum S_1 and suppose that (c) and (d) hold, then

$$\begin{aligned} |S_1| &\leqq \sum_{n\leqq \delta x} |a(n)| \left|B\left(\frac{x}{n}\right)\right| \leqq c_1 \sum_{n\leqq \delta x} \left(\frac{x}{n}\right)^{\alpha} \\ &\leqq c_1 x^{\alpha} \sum_{n\leqq \delta x} \frac{1}{n^{\alpha}} = O(x^{\alpha}(\delta x)^{1-\alpha}) = O(x\delta^{1-\alpha})\,. \end{aligned} \tag{56}$$

If (a) and (b) hold, then

$$|S_1| = O\left(\sum_{n\leqq \delta x} |a(n)| \left|B\left(\frac{x}{n}\right)\right|\right) = O\left(\sum_{n\leqq \delta x} |a(n)|\right) = O(\delta x)\,. \tag{57}$$

In either case, for $\varepsilon > 0$ we can choose δ so small that

$$|S_1| < \frac{\varepsilon}{2} x\,, \tag{58}$$

which is possible by (56) and (57).

Consider now S_2:

$$\begin{aligned} S_2 &= \sum_{\delta x<n\leqq x} (A(n) - A(n-1))B\left(\frac{x}{n}\right) \\ &= -A([\delta x])B\left(\frac{x}{[\delta x]+1}\right) + A([x])B\left(\frac{x}{[x]}\right) \\ &\quad + \sum_{n=[\delta x]+1}^{[x]-1} A(n)\left\{B\left(\frac{x}{n}\right) - B\left(\frac{x}{n+1}\right)\right\}, \end{aligned} \tag{59}$$

and therefore

$$|S_2| \leqq |A([\delta x])| \left|B\left(\frac{x}{[\delta x]+1}\right)\right| + |A([x])| \left|B\left(\frac{x}{[x]}\right)\right|$$
$$+ \sum_{n=[\delta x]+1}^{[x]-1} |A(n)| \left|B\left(\frac{x}{n}\right) - B\left(\frac{x}{n+1}\right)\right| .$$

Now by (i), since $B(x)$ is of bounded variation,

$$\sum_{n=[\delta x]+1}^{[x]-1} \left|B\left(\frac{x}{n}\right) - B\left(\frac{x}{n+1}\right)\right|$$

is bounded by a function which depends on δ but not on x. Moreover, if (a) and (b) hold, then

$$\left|B\left(\frac{x}{[\delta x]+1}\right)\right| \quad \text{and} \quad \left|B\left(\frac{x}{[x]}\right)\right|$$

are bounded by absolute constants. If, moreover, (c) and (d) hold, then they are bounded by functions depending at most on δ. In any case, therefore, since $A(x) = o(x)$, we get from (59)

(60) $$S_2 = o(x) f_1(\delta) + o(x) f_2(\delta) = o(x) f(\delta) ,$$

where $f(\delta)$ is a function depending only on δ.

Having chosen δ, we now choose x so large that

(61) $$|S_2| < \frac{\varepsilon}{2} x ,$$

which is possible by (60). (58) and (61) then lead to (55).

As an application, we prove

THEOREM 7.13. *Let*

(62) $$L(x) = \sum_{n \leqq x} \frac{\mu(n)}{n} .$$

Then

$$M(x) = o(x) ,$$

if and only if

$$L(x) = o(1) .$$

That is, $L(x) = o(1)$ *is equivalent to the prime number theorem.*

PROOF. Suppose that $M(x) = o(x)$, then in Theorem 7.12, we put $a(n) = \mu(n)$, $B(x) = x - [x]$. $B(x)$ is bounded and is clearly of bounded variation in every finite interval. Moreover,

$$\sum_{n \leqq x} |\mu(n)| = O(x) .$$

Thus (i), (ii) and (a), (b) of Theorem 7.12 are satisfied and we get

(63) $$\sum_{n \leqq x} \mu(n) \left(\frac{x}{n} - \left[\frac{x}{n} \right] \right) = o(x) .$$

But by (27),

$$\sum_{n\leq x}\mu(n)\left[\frac{x}{n}\right]=1\,,$$

and therefore from (63)

$$\sum_{n\leq x}\mu(n)\frac{x}{n}=o(x)\,.$$

Dividing by x, we conclude

$$L(x)=o(1)\,.$$

Suppose conversely that $L(x)=o(1)$, then by partial summation, applying Lemma 3.1, Chapter I, with $c(n)=\mu(n)/n$, $\varphi(x)=x$, we get

$$\begin{aligned} M(x)&=\sum_{n\leq x}\mu(n)=\sum_{n\leq x}\frac{\mu(n)}{n}n \\ &=xL(x)-\int_1^x L(t)dt=o(x)+o(x)=o(x)\,. \end{aligned}$$

As another application of Theorem 7.12, we prove

THEOREM 7.14. *If*

$$\psi(x)-x=o(x)$$

then

$$\sum_{n\leq x}\frac{1-\Lambda(n)}{n}=2\gamma+o(1)\,, \tag{64}$$

and conversely. Thus (64) *is equivalent to the prime number theorem.*

PROOF. Let

$$P(x)=\sum_{n\leq x}\frac{1-\Lambda(n)}{n}\,. \tag{65}$$

Since

$$-\zeta'(s)-\zeta^2(s)+2\gamma\zeta(s)=\left(-\frac{\zeta'(s)}{\zeta(s)}-\zeta(s)+2\gamma\right)\zeta(s)\,, \tag{66}$$

it follows that

$$\begin{aligned} \sum_{n\leq x}(\log n-d(n)+2\gamma)&=\sum_{jk\leq x}(\Lambda(j)-1+2\gamma E(j)) \\ &=\sum_{j\leq x}(\Lambda(j)-1+2\gamma E(j))\left[\frac{x}{j}\right]. \end{aligned} \tag{67}$$

Moreover, by (37),

$$\sum_{n\leq x}(\log n-d(n)+2\gamma)=O(\sqrt{x})\,. \tag{68}$$

In Theorem 7.12, let

$$a(n) = \Lambda(n) - 1 + 2\gamma E(n)$$

and

$$B(x) = x - [x] .$$

Then by hypothesis $\psi(x) - x = o(x)$ and therefore

$$\sum_{n \leqq x} (\Lambda(n) - 1 + 2\gamma E(n)) = o(x) , \tag{69}$$

while

$$\sum_{n \leqq x} | \Lambda(n) - 1 + 2\gamma E(n) | = O(x) .$$

Conditions (i), (ii) and (a) and (b) of Theorem 7.12 are satisfied; hence

$$\sum_{n \leqq x} (\Lambda(n) - 1 + 2\gamma E(n))\left\{\frac{x}{n} - \left[\frac{x}{n}\right]\right\} = o(x) . \tag{70}$$

But by (67) and (68),

$$\sum_{n \leqq x} (\Lambda(n) - 1 + 2\gamma E(n))\left[\frac{x}{n}\right] = O(\sqrt{x}) ,$$

and therefore from (70),

$$\sum_{n \leqq x} (\Lambda(n) - 1 + 2\gamma E(n))\frac{x}{n} = o(x) .$$

This is the same as (64).

To prove the converse, we apply partial summation:

$$\begin{aligned} -[\psi(x) - x] &= -\sum_{n \leqq x} (\Lambda(n) - 1) + O(1) \\ &= -\sum_{n \leqq x} \frac{\Lambda(n) - 1}{n} n + O(1) \\ &= P(x)\cdot x - \int_1^x P(t)dt + O(1) \\ &= 2\gamma x + o(x) - \int_1^x (2\gamma + o(1))dt + O(1) = o(x) . \end{aligned}$$

Problems

1. Using the inequality

$$\prod_{p \leqq x} \left(1 - \frac{1}{p}\right)^{-1} \leqq \prod_{k=2}^{\pi(x)+1} \left(1 - \frac{1}{k}\right)^{-1} ,$$

show that

$$\pi(x) > \log x - 1 .$$

2. Prove starting with § 2, (3), that

$$\pi(x) - \pi(\sqrt{x}) + 1 = \sum_{n | p_1 \cdots p_r} \mu(n)\left[\frac{x}{n}\right] ,$$

where $r = \pi(\sqrt{x})$.

3. Tchebycheff defined the function

$$\theta(x) = \sum_{p \leqq x} \log p .$$

Prove the following

(i) $\psi(x) = \theta(x) + \theta(x^{1/2}) + \theta(x^{1/3}) + \cdots = \theta(x) + O(x^{1/2} \log^2 x)$.

(ii) There exists a constant c so that

$$\theta(x) < cx .$$

Show that $\sum_{p \leqq n} [n/p] \log p = n \log n + O(n)$ and deduce that

$$\theta(2n) - \theta(n) = \sum_{n \leqq p \leqq 2n} \log p < c_1 n ,$$

and therefore that if $k = [\log x/\log 2] + 1$,

$$\theta(x) = \sum_{i=1}^{k} \left(\theta\left(\frac{x}{2^{i-1}}\right) - \theta\left(\frac{x}{2^i}\right)\right) < cx .$$

4. (i) Show that

$$\psi(x) = \log U(x) ,$$

where $U(x) =$ l.c.m. of all numbers $\leqq x$.

(ii) By showing that

$$\binom{2n}{n} \Big| U(2n) ,$$

prove that

$$e^{\psi(2n)} > 2^n ,$$

and deduce that there exists a constant c such that

$$\psi(x) > cx .$$

5. Deduce from Problems 3 and 4 that there exist constants $a_1, a_2, \cdots, a_6$ such that

(i) $a_1 x < \theta(x) < a_2 x$,

(ii) $a_3 x < \psi(x) < a_4 x$,

(iii) $a_5 x < \pi(x) \log x < a_6 x$.

6. Show that

$$\theta(x) \sim \pi(x) \log x \sim \psi(x) .$$

$$[\theta(x) \geqq \sum_{x^{1-\delta} < p \leqq x} \log p > (1-\delta) \log x \{\pi(x) - \pi(x^{1-\delta})\} .]$$

7. Relation (iii) of Problem 5 implies that

$$\sum_{p \leqq x} \frac{\log p}{p} = \log x + O(1) .$$

Deduce that

$$\sum_{p \leq x} \frac{1}{p} = \log \log x + O(1) .$$

8. Show that

(i) $\sum_{n \leq x} \psi(x/n) = \log [x]!$,

(ii) $\psi(n) < 2n$,

(iii) Using Stirling's formula, show that

$$\sum_{n \leq x} \psi\left(\frac{x}{n}\right)(-1)^{n+1} = x \log 2 + O(\sqrt{x}) .$$

9. Using the equation

$$\varphi(n) = n \prod_{p|n} \left(1 - \frac{1}{p}\right) ,$$

show that there exists a constant c for which

$$\varphi(n) > \frac{cn}{\log \log n} .$$

10. Prove that

$$\sum_{n \leq x} \frac{d(n)}{n} = \frac{1}{2} \log^2 x + O(\log x) ,$$

by using the relation for

$$\sum_{n \leq x} d(n) .$$

11. If $Q(x)$ denotes the number of square free integers $\leq x$, i.e.,

$$Q(x) = \sum_{n \leq x} \mu^2(n) ,$$

show that

$$Q(x) = \frac{x}{\zeta(2)} + O(\sqrt{x}) .$$

Observe that $\mu^2(n) = \sum_{d^2|n} \mu(d)$ and

$$\sum_{m \leq x} \mu^2(m) = \sum_{d \leq \sqrt{x}} \mu(d) \left[\frac{x}{d^2}\right] .$$

12. Establish the relation

$$\sum_{n \leq x} \varphi(n) = \frac{x^2}{2\zeta(2)} + O(x \log x) ,$$

using the fact that

$$\varphi(n) = \sum_{d|n} \mu(d) \frac{n}{d} .$$

13. Deduce from Problem 12 that

$$\sum_{n\leq x}\frac{\varphi(n)}{n}=\frac{x}{\zeta(2)}+O(\log x)\,.$$

14. Show that

$$\sum_{n\leq x}\frac{n}{\varphi(n)}=O(x)\,.$$

[Notice that $n/\varphi(n)=\prod_{p|n}(1-1/p)^{-1}\leqq\sum_{d|n}1/d$.] Conclude that

$$\sum_{n\leq x}\frac{1}{\varphi(n)}=O(\log x)\,.$$

15. Show that

$$f(s)=\sum_{n=1}^{\infty}\frac{(-1)^{n+1}}{n^s}$$

converges for $\sigma>0$, and that

$$\zeta(s)\left(1-\frac{1}{2^{s-1}}\right)=f(s)\,.$$

This provides a continuation of $\zeta(s)$ to $\sigma>0$.

16. Let

$$L(s,\chi)=\sum_{n=1}^{\infty}\frac{\chi(n)}{n^s}\,,$$

where χ is a character modulo k. Prove the following:

(i) $$L(s,\chi)=\prod_p\left(1-\frac{\chi(p)}{p^s}\right)^{-1}\,,$$

(ii) $$-\frac{L'(s,\chi)}{L(s,\chi)}=\sum\frac{\chi(n)\Lambda(n)}{n^s}\,,$$

(iii) $$L(s,\chi_1)=\frac{\varphi(k)k^{-1}}{\sigma-1}+O(1)\qquad\text{as }\sigma\to1\,,$$

where χ_1 is the principal character.

(iv) By considering the expression

$$3\log L(\sigma,\chi)+4\log L(\sigma+it,\chi)+\log L(\sigma+2it,\chi^2)\,,$$

show that

$$L(1+it,\chi)\neq0\,.$$

[Consider the two cases $\chi^2=\chi_1$ and $\chi^2\neq\chi_1$ separately.]

(v) Show that if $a>1$

$$\sum_{n\leq x}\chi(n)\Lambda(n)=\frac{1}{2\pi i}\int_{a-i\infty}^{a+i\infty}\left(-\frac{L'(s,\chi)}{L(s,\chi)}\right)\frac{x^s}{s}ds\,.$$

(vi) For $1\leqq l\leqq k$, $(l,k)=1$ let b be determined so that $bl\equiv1\,(\mathrm{mod}\,k)$. Then

$$\sum_{\chi} \chi(b) \sum_{n \leq x} \Lambda(n)\chi(n) = \sum_{\chi} \chi(b) \frac{1}{2\pi i} \int_{a-i\infty}^{a+i\infty} \left(- \frac{L'(s, \chi)}{L(s, \chi)} \right) \frac{x^s}{s} ds .$$

The left-hand side is

$$\varphi(k) \sum_{n \leq x;\, n \equiv l \pmod{k}} \Lambda(n) .$$

It is now possible to deduce by the same methods used for $\pi(x)$ that

$$\pi(x, k, l) = \sum_{p \leq x;\, p \equiv l \pmod{k}} 1 \sim \frac{x}{\varphi(k) \log x} .$$

17. We had for $a > 1$

$$\psi_2(x) = \frac{1}{2\pi i} \int_{a-i\infty}^{a+i\infty} \left(- \frac{\zeta'(s)}{\zeta(s)} \right) \frac{x^s}{s(s+1)} ds .$$

Show that

(1) $$\frac{\psi_2(x)}{x^2} - \frac{1}{2}\left(1 - \frac{1}{x}\right)^2 = \frac{1}{2\pi i} \int_{a-i\infty}^{a+i\infty} h(s) x^s ds ,$$

where

$$h(s) = \frac{-1}{s(s+1)} \left(\frac{\zeta'(s)}{\zeta(s)} + \frac{1}{s-1} \right) .$$

$h(s)$ is regular for $\sigma \geqq 1$. Prove the validity of (1) for $a = 1$ and deduce that

$$\frac{\psi_2(x)}{x^2} - \frac{1}{2}\left(1 - \frac{1}{x}\right)^2 = \frac{1}{2\pi} \int_{-\infty}^{\infty} h(1 + it) x^{it} dt .$$

Hence, by the Riemann-Lebesgue theorem,

$$\frac{\psi_2(x)}{x^2} - \frac{1}{2}\left(1 - \frac{1}{x}\right)^2 \to 0 \quad \text{as } x \to \infty .$$

This shows that $\psi_2(x) \sim \frac{1}{2} x^2$.

18. Show that

(i) $$\log \zeta(s) = s \int_2^\infty \frac{\pi(x)}{x(x^s - 1)} dx$$

by observing that

$$\log \zeta(s) = \sum_{n=2}^{\infty} (\pi(n) - \pi(n-1)) \log \left(1 - \frac{1}{n^s}\right) .$$

(ii) Let

$$\omega(s) = \int_2^\infty \frac{\pi(x)}{x^{s+1}(x^s - 1)} dx ;$$

then the integral converges for $\sigma \geqq \frac{1}{2} + \delta$, $\delta > 0$.

(iii) Show that

$$\frac{\log \zeta(s)}{s} - \omega(s) = \int_2^\infty \frac{\pi(x)}{x^{s+1}} dx$$

and deduce that

$$-\frac{\zeta'(s)}{s\zeta(s)}+\frac{\log\zeta(s)}{s^2}+\omega'(s)=\int_2^\infty\frac{\pi(x)\log x}{x^{s+1}}dx\,.$$

This formula can be inverted by Mellin's transform and can then be used to prove the prime number theorem.

19. Use the methods of § 3 to prove the following general theorem:
Let

$$f(s)=\sum\frac{a(n)}{n^s}$$

be absolutely convergent for $\sigma>1$ and

$$a(n)=O(g(n))\,,$$

where $g(n)$ is a nondecreasing function of n. Suppose that

$$\sum_{n=1}^\infty\frac{|a(n)|}{n^s}=O\Big(\frac{1}{(\sigma-1)^\alpha}\Big)\qquad\text{as } \sigma\to1\,.$$

Then if $c>0$, $\sigma+c>1$, x is not an integer, and N is the integer nearest to x, we have

$$\sum_{n<x}\frac{a(n)}{n^s}=\frac{1}{2\pi i}\int_{c-i\infty}^{c+i\infty}f(s+w)\frac{x^w}{w}+O\Big(\frac{x^c}{T(\sigma+c-1)^\alpha}\Big)$$
$$+O\Big(\frac{g(2x)x^{1-\sigma}\log x}{T}\Big)+O\Big(\frac{g(N)x^{1-\sigma}}{T|x-N|}\Big)\,.$$

20. Prove by the methods of Theorem 6.12, that there exists a constant c for which

$$\frac{1}{\zeta(s)}=O(\log t)\qquad\text{for } \sigma\geqq1-\frac{c}{\log t}\,.$$

21. Prove the following Tauberian theorem:
If $f(u)$ is nondecreasing and as $x\to\infty$,

$$\int_1^x\frac{f(u)}{u}du\sim x\,,$$

then

$$f(x)\sim x\,.$$

22. Prove the following Tauberian theorem:
If $a(n)\geqq0$, $A(x)=\sum_{n\leqq x}a(n)$,

$$A_1(x)=\int_0^x A(u)du=\sum_{n\leqq x}(x-n)a(n)\,,$$

and

$$A_1(x)\sim\alpha x^a\qquad\text{as } x\to\infty\,,$$

then

$$A(x) \sim \alpha a x^{\alpha-1} .$$

Observe that for $\varepsilon > 0$,

$$\frac{1}{\varepsilon x}\int_{(1-\varepsilon)x}^{x} A(u)du \leqq A(u) \leqq \frac{1}{\varepsilon x}\int_{x}^{(1+\varepsilon)x} A(u)du .$$

This allows us to deduce directly that $\psi_2(x) \sim \frac{1}{2}x^2$ implies $\psi(x) \sim x$.

23. Let $\lambda_1 < \lambda_2 < \cdots < \lambda_n < \cdots$ be an increasing sequence of real numbers and

$$f(s) = \sum a(n)e^{-\lambda_n s}$$

be a general Dirichlet series. If $\lambda_n = \log n$, we get an ordinary Dirichlet series. Show that for suitable c

$$\frac{1}{2\pi i}\int_{c-i\infty}^{c+i\infty} \frac{f(s)e^{xs}}{s^2} ds = \sum_{\lambda_n \leqq x} a(n)(x - \lambda_n) ,$$

and more generally that for suitable c

$$\frac{1}{2\pi i}\int_{c-i\infty}^{c+i\infty} \frac{f(s)e^{xs}ds}{s^\alpha} = \frac{1}{\Gamma(\alpha)} \sum_{\lambda_n \leqq x} a(n)(x - \lambda_n)^{\alpha-1} , \qquad \alpha > 1 .$$

Prove first that

$$\frac{1}{2\pi i}\int_{c-i\infty}^{c+i\infty} \frac{e^{xs}}{s^2} ds = \begin{cases} 0 & \text{if } x \leqq 0 , \\ x & \text{if } x \geqq 0 . \end{cases}$$

24. In particular, show that

$$\sum_{n \leqq x} \Lambda(n) \log \frac{x}{n} = \frac{1}{2\pi i}\int_{c-i\infty}^{c+i\infty} \left(-\frac{\zeta'(s)}{\zeta(s)}\right)\frac{x^s}{s^2} ds ,$$

and conclude that

$$\sum_{n \leqq x} \Lambda(n) \log \frac{x}{n} \sim x .$$

Show that

$$\sum_{n \leqq x} \Lambda(n) \log \frac{x}{n} = \sum_{n \leqq x} \psi(n) \log \left(1 + \frac{1}{n}\right) + \psi(x) \log \left(\frac{x}{[x]+1}\right) ,$$

and therefore successively that

(a) $$\sum_{n \leqq x} \frac{\psi(n)}{n} \sim x ,$$

(b) $$\int_1^x \frac{\psi(u)}{u} du \sim x ,$$

(c) $$\psi(x) \sim x$$

by Problem 21.

25. Let

$$f(s) = \sum_{n=1}^{\infty} \frac{a(n)}{n^s}$$

be absolutely convergent for $\sigma > 1$ and regular on $\sigma = 1$ except for a simple pole at $s = 1$ with residue 1, and for $\sigma \geqq 1$ suppose $f(\sigma + it) = O(|t|^{\alpha})$, $\alpha < 1$. Put $A(x) = \sum_{n \leqq x} a(n)$, $A_1(x) = \int_0^x A(y)dy$, and show successively that

(i) $$A_1(x) = \frac{1}{2\pi i}\int_{c-i\infty}^{c+i\infty} f(s)\frac{x^s}{s(s+1)}ds\,, \qquad c > 1\,,$$

(ii) $$\frac{x^2}{2} + O(x) = \frac{1}{2\pi i}\int_{c-i\infty}^{c+i\infty} \zeta(s)\frac{x^s}{s(s+1)}ds\,,$$

(iii) $$A_1(x) - \frac{1}{2}x^2 + O(x) = \frac{1}{2\pi i}\int_{c-i\infty}^{c+i\infty} (f(s) - \zeta(s))\frac{x^s}{s(s+1)}\,,$$

(iv) The relation (iii) is valid for $c = 1$.

(v) By the Riemann-Lebesgue theorem,

$$A_1(x) - \tfrac{1}{2}x^2 + O(x) = o(x^2)\,,$$

i.e.,

$$A_1(x) \sim \tfrac{1}{2}x^2\,.$$

26. Prove that

$$\frac{1}{\zeta(s)} = \sum_{n=1}^{\infty} \frac{\mu(n)}{n^s}$$

converges for $\sigma = 1$ and deduce that

$$\sum_{n=1}^{\infty} \frac{\mu(n)}{n} = 0\,.$$

27. Show that if $\lambda(n) = (-1)^{a_1 + \cdots + a_r}$, where $n = p_1^{a_1} \cdots p_r^{a_r}$, then

$$\sum_{n=1}^{\infty} \frac{\lambda(n)}{n^s} = \frac{\zeta(2s)}{\zeta(s)}\,;$$

and prove by complex methods that

$$\sum_{n \leqq x} \lambda(n) = O(x \exp[-c(\log x)^{\alpha}])\,,$$

for some constants c and α.

28. Show that

$$\sum_{n \leqq x} \mu(n) = O(x \exp[-c(\log x)^{\alpha}])$$

for some c and α.

29. Suppose that

(a) $F(s) = \sum_{n=1}^{\infty} a(n)/n^s$ is absolutely convergent for $\sigma > \sigma_0 > 0$.

(b) $F(s)$ is regular for $\sigma > c$ where $0 < c \leqq \sigma_0$ and continuous for $\sigma \geqq c$, then prove by the methods of §6 that

$$f(y) = \sum_{n=0}^{\infty} a(n)e^{-ny}$$

is convergent for all $y > 0$ and

$$f(y) = o(y^{-c}) \qquad \text{as } y \to 0 .$$

30. If (a), (b) of Problem 29 are satisfied and

$$a(n) = O(n^{c-1}) ,$$

then

$$A(n) = \sum_{k \leq n} a(k) = O(n^c) .$$

In particular, if $a(n) = \mu(n)$, $c = 1$, we get $F(s) = 1/\zeta(s)$, and therefore

$$M(n) = o(n) .$$

31. If under the same conditions $c = 0$, $F(s)$ is regular for $s = 0$, then $\sum_{n=1}^{\infty} a(n)$ is convergent and has sum $F(0)$. In particular, if $a(n) = \mu(n)/n$, $c = 0$, $F(s) = 1/\zeta(s+1)$, and therefore

$$\sum_{n=1}^{\infty} \frac{\mu(n)}{n} = 0 .$$

32. Suppose that p ranges over any set A of integers for which

$$\sum_{p \in A} \frac{1}{p^s}$$

converges in $\sigma > 1$.

Let

$$\prod_{p \in A} \left(1 - \frac{1}{p^s}\right)^{-1} = \sum_{n=1}^{\infty} \frac{c(n)}{n^s} = z(s) ,$$

and suppose that $z(s)$ is regular for $\sigma > 1$, has a simple pole at $s = 1$ with residue 1, and for $t \geqq t_0$, $\sigma > 1 - c/\log t$, $z(s)$ is regular, $z(s) \neq 0$ and

$$z(s) = O(\log |t|) ,$$

then

$$\pi_A(x) = \sum_{p \leq x;\, p \in A} 1 = \int_2^x \frac{du}{\log u} + O(x \exp[-\alpha\sqrt{\log x}]) .$$

33. If

$$\sigma(n) = \sum_{d|n} d = \text{sum of the divisors of } n,$$

then

$$\sum_{n=1}^{\infty} \frac{\sigma(n)}{n^s} = \zeta(s)\zeta(s-1) .$$

34. Show that

$$\sum_{n=1}^{\infty} \frac{|\mu(n)|}{n^s} = \frac{\zeta(s)}{\zeta(2s)} .$$

35. Prove that

$$\frac{\zeta^4(s)}{\zeta(2s)} = \sum_{n=1}^{\infty} \frac{d^2(n)}{n^s} .$$

36. If

$$\sigma_k(n) = \sum_{d|n} d^k ,$$

then

$$\sum \frac{\sigma_k(n)}{n^s} = \zeta(s)\zeta(s-k) .$$

37. Establish the identity

$$\frac{\zeta(s)\zeta(s-c)\zeta(s-b)\zeta(s-c-b)}{\zeta(2s-c-b)} = \sum_{n=1}^{\infty} \frac{\sigma_c(n)\sigma_b(n)}{n^s} .$$

38. The relation in 37 can be used to prove that $\zeta(1+it) \neq 0$ as follows: Put $c = ai$, $b = -ai$, and then

$$f(s) = \frac{\zeta^2(s)\zeta(s+ai)\zeta(s-ai)}{\zeta(2s)} = \sum_{n=1}^{\infty} \frac{|\sigma_{ai}(n)|^2}{n^s} ,$$

where $\sigma_{ai}(n) = \sum_{d|n} d^{ai}$. Let σ_0 be the abscissa of convergence, then $\sigma_0 \leqq 1$ and σ_0 is a singularity. If $\zeta(1+ai) = 0$, then $\zeta(1-ai) = 0$ from which it follows that $\sigma_0 \leqq 0$. This is impossible since then from the left-hand side $f(\frac{1}{2}) = 0$, and from the right, $f(\frac{1}{2}) \geqq 1$. Fill in the details.

39. From the formula

$$\zeta(s) = \frac{1}{s-1} - s\int_1^{\infty} (t-[t])t^{-s+1}dt ,$$

show that $\zeta(s) < 0$ for $0 < s < 1$.

40. If $a \neq 0$, $k = \prod p^l$, show using the fact that $\sigma_a(n)$ is multiplicative, that

$$\sum_{n=1}^{\infty} \frac{\sigma_a(kn)}{n^s} = \zeta(s)\zeta(s-a)\prod_{p|k} \frac{1 - p^{a-s} - p^{(l+1)a} + p^{(l+1)a-s}}{1-p^a} .$$

41. In Problem 40, let $a \to 0$ and deduce

$$\sum_{n=1}^{\infty} \frac{d(kn)}{n^s} = \zeta^2(s)\prod_{p|k} (l+1-lp^{-s}) .$$

Prove this directly.

42. Show that

$$\sum_p \frac{1}{p^s} = \sum_{n=1}^{\infty} \frac{\mu(n)}{n^s} \log \zeta(ns) .$$

43. If $\nu(n)$ = number of different prime factors of n, then

(i)
$$\frac{\zeta^2(s)}{\zeta(2s)} = \sum_{n=1}^{\infty} \frac{2^{\nu(n)}}{n^s},$$

(ii)
$$\sum_{n=1}^{\infty} \frac{\nu(n)}{n^s} = \zeta(s) \sum_{n=1}^{\infty} \frac{\mu(n)}{n^s} \log \zeta(ns).$$

44. If $b(n)$ = number of divisors of n which are primes or powers of primes, then

$$\sum_{n=1}^{\infty} \frac{b(n)}{n^s} = \zeta(s) \sum_{n=1}^{\infty} \frac{\varphi(n)}{n} \log \zeta(ns).$$

45. Let

$$n = p_1^{a_1} \cdots p_r^{a_r}$$

and

$$\alpha(n) = a_1 a_2 \cdots a_r$$

$$\beta(n) = \frac{3 + (-1)^{a_1}}{2} \cdots \frac{3 + (-1)^{a_r}}{2};$$

then

$$\sum_{n=1}^{\infty} \frac{\alpha(n)}{n^s} = \frac{\zeta(s)\zeta(2s)\zeta(3s)}{\zeta(6s)}$$

$$\sum_{n=1}^{\infty} \frac{\beta(n)}{n^s} = \frac{\zeta(s)\zeta(2s)}{\zeta(3s)}.$$

46. If $d_k(n)$ = number of ways of decomposing n into a product of k factors, then

$$\sum_{n=1}^{\infty} \frac{d_k(n)}{n^s} = \zeta^k(s).$$

47. Prove that if $M(x) = \sum_{n \leq x} \mu(n)$, then

(i)
$$\sum_{n \leq x} M\left(\frac{x}{n}\right) = 1,$$

(ii)
$$M(x) = 1 - \sum_{2 \leq n \leq x} (1 - d_2(n) + d_3(n) - d_4(n) - \cdots).$$

48. If

$$f(x) = \sum_{n=1}^{\infty} \frac{\pi(x^{1/n})}{n},$$

then

$$f(x) = \sum_{2 \leq n \leq x} \left(1 - \frac{d_2(n)}{2} + \frac{d_3(n)}{3} - \cdots\right).$$

49. If $g(n)$ is an arithmetic function, then

$$\sum_{i=1}^{\infty} \frac{1}{i} \sum_{p^i \leq x} g(p^i) = \sum_{n \leq x} g(n)(f(n) - f(n-1))$$

$$= \sum_{n \leq x} g(n) - \frac{1}{2} \sum_{n_1 n_2 \leq x} g(n_1 n_2)$$

$$+ \frac{1}{3} \sum_{n_1 n_2 n_3 \leq x} g(n_1 n_2 n_3) - \cdots .$$

50. Prove that

$$\sum_{n=1}^{\infty} \frac{\mu(n)}{n} \log n = -1 + o(1) .$$

51. Prove that

$$\sum_{n \leq x} \frac{\Lambda(n)}{n \log n} = \log \log x + \gamma + o(1) .$$

52. Prove the following variant of Axer's theorem:
Let $B(x)$ be a function of bounded variation in every finite interval and

$$B(x) = O(\omega(x)) ,$$

where $\omega(x)$ is nondecreasing and for $\xi > 0$,

$$\int_{\xi}^{\infty} \frac{\omega(t)}{t^2} dt < \infty .$$

If

$$\sum_{n \leq x} a(n) = o(x) \qquad \text{and} \qquad \sum_{n \leq x} | a(n) | = O(x) ,$$

then

$$\sum_{n \leq x} a(n) B\left(\frac{x}{n}\right) = o(x) .$$

53. In Problem 52, let $B(x) = \rho(x^r)$, where $\rho(t) = t - [t]$, and apply the theorem to the following cases:
(i) $r = 1, \quad a(n) = \mu(n)$,
(ii) $r = 1, \quad a(n) = \psi(n) - \psi(n-1) - 1 = \Lambda(n) - 1$,
(iii) $r = h, \quad a(n) = \mu(n)$.
What conclusions may be drawn?

54. In Problem 52, let $a(n) = \mu(n)$ and apply the theorem to the following:

(i) $$B(x) = x \sum_{m \leq x} \frac{1}{m} - [x] \log x - \gamma[x] ,$$

(ii) $$B(x) = x \sum_{m \leq x} \frac{1}{m} - x \log x - \gamma[x] ,$$

(iii) $$B(x) = (x - [x]) \log x ,$$

where γ is Euler's constant. What deductions follow?

55. If

$$G(x) = \sum_{n \leqq x} F\left(\frac{x}{n}\right) \log x ,$$

then

$$F(x) \log x + \sum_{n \leqq x} G\left(\frac{x}{n}\right) \Lambda(n) = \sum_{n \leqq x} \mu(n) G\left(\frac{x}{n}\right) .$$

Show that

$$\sum_{n \leqq x} \psi\left(\frac{x}{n}\right) = x \log x - x + O(\log x)$$

(see Problem 8), and then apply the above with

$$F(x) = \psi(x) - x + \gamma + 1 ,$$

and deduce

$$\psi(x) \log x + \sum_{n \leqq x} \Lambda(n) \psi\left(\frac{x}{n}\right) = 2x \log x + O(x) .$$

This is one form of the fundamental Selberg lemma from which an elementary proof of the prime number theorem is derived.

56. From Problems 35 and 46 and using complex integration, show that

$$\sum_{n \leqq x} d^2(n) \sim \alpha x \log^3 x$$

$$\sum_{n \leqq x} d_k(n) \sim \beta x \log^{k-1} x ,$$

and determine the value of the constants α and β.

57. Show that

$$\log \zeta(s) = \sum_{n=1}^{\infty} \frac{\Lambda_1(n)}{n^s}$$

converges for $s = 1 + it$, $t \neq 0$.

58. Prove that the series

$$\sum_{n=1}^{\infty} \frac{\Lambda(n)}{n^s} = -\frac{\zeta'(s)}{\zeta(s)}$$

converges for $s = 1 + it$ $(t \neq 0)$.

59. Show that

$$\sum_{p} \frac{1}{p^s}$$

converges for $s = 1 + it$, $t \neq 0$.

60. Let $\pi_2(x)$ be the number of integers $\leqq x$ which are the product of two distinct primes. Show that

$$\pi_2(x) = \sum_{pq \le x} 1 = \sum_{p \le x} \pi\left(\frac{x}{p}\right) - \pi(\sqrt{x}) .$$

Use the prime number theorem and Problem 7 to show that

$$\pi_2(x) \sim \frac{x \log \log x}{\log x} .$$

Notes to Chapter II

1. The quotation on page 37 is from Euler's memoir *Décourverte d'une loi tout extraordinaire des nombres par rapport à la somme des diviseurs* reprinted in his Collected Works, Vol. 2, p. 241. The formula Euler had found was based on his pentagonal number theorem (see Chapter III) and is the following

$$\sigma(n) - \sigma(n-1) - \sigma(n-2) + \sigma(n-5) + \sigma(n-7) - \sigma(n-12) - \sigma(n-15) + \cdots = 0 ,$$

where the numbers 1, 2, 5, 7, 12, 15, $\cdots$, are pentagonal numbers i.e., numbers of the form $n = (3k^2 - k)/2$ $(k = \pm 1, \pm 2, \cdots)$.

The formula for $\pi(x)$ given by Legendre appears in the *Essai sur la théorie des nombres*, 2nd ed., 1808, *D'une loi remarkable observée dans l'énumeration des nombres premiers.* It holds with remarkable accuracy for $x < 1{,}000{,}000$. The subsequent theorems of the chapter imply, however, that the best value for the constant is 1. Gauss's statement appears in a letter to Encke following his *Tafel der Frequenz der Primzahlen*, Werke, Vol. 2. Gauss conjectured on purely empirical grounds that $\pi(x) < \operatorname{li} x$ and this statement is correct as far as the tables of primes go. Littlewood showed, however, that the conjecture is false and Skewes established the existence of $x > 10^{10^{10^{34}}}$ for which $\pi(x) > \operatorname{li} x$. The following table taken from Gauss's calculations gives a comparison between $\pi(x)$, Legendre's function and li x.

x	$\operatorname{li} x - \pi(x)$	$\left(\frac{x}{\log x - 1.08} - \pi(x)\right)$	$\pi(x)$
500,000	50.4	− 23.3	41,556
1,000,000	126.5	42.2	78,501
1,500,000	151.1	68.1	114,112
2,000,000	171.8	92.8	148,883
2,500,000	229.0	159.1	183,316

Although no formula of the type Euler discovered for $\sigma(n)$ is known, the following have been given

(1) $$\pi(x) = 1 + \sum_{2 \le n \le x} \left\{1 + \lim_{m \to \infty} \left[1 - \prod_{k=2}^{n-1} \left(\sin \frac{\pi n}{k}\right)^{2}\right]^{m}\right\} .$$

Sierpiński, *Eléments de mathématiques*, Vol. 8, 1953.

(2) If $\alpha = \sum_{n=1}^{\infty} p_n 10^{-2^n}$ then

$$p_n = [10^{2^n}\alpha] - 10^{2^{n-1}}[10^{2^{n-1}}\alpha] .$$

Sierpiński, *Sur une formule donnant tous les nombres premiers*, C.R. Acad.

Sci. Paris **235** (1952), 1078–1079.

(3) There exists α_0, such that if $\alpha_{n+1} = 2^{\alpha_n}$, then

$$[2^{\alpha_0}], [2^{\alpha_1}], \cdots, [2^{\alpha_n}], \cdots$$

all represent prime numbers.

E.M. Wright, *A prime representing function*, Amer. Math. Monthly **58** (1951), 616–618.

(4) There exists a real number A such that

$$[A^{3^n}] \quad (n = 1, 2, \cdots)$$

represents primes only. W. H. Mills, *A prime representing function*, Bull. Amer. Math. Soc. **53** (1947), 604.

Though these formulae are interesting, they do not provide any deep insight into the theory of prime numbers.

2. Theorem 2.1 was first stated and partially proved by Euler and Legendre; formula (3) is Legendre's. Tchebycheff's Theorem 2.6 as well as his other contributions first appeared in the Journal de Mathématiques **17** (1852), *Sur la formule qui détermine la totalité des nombres premiers inférieurs à une limite donnée*. It may be of interest to record values of the constants A and B for which equation (26) is valid. Recent work of J.B. Rosser and L. Schoenfeld gives for $x \geqq 17$, $A = 1$, $B = 1.25506$.

Riemann's celebrated memoir first appeared in the Monatsbericht der Akademie der Wissenschaften, 1859, *Über die Anzahl der Primzahlen unter einer gegebener Grösse*. The memoir is rather fragmentary and many statements are made without proof. All of his statements have subsequently been verified with one exception—the famous Riemann hypothesis. There is a reproduction of his paper in his collected works and there is a more detailed account in Mathew's *Theory of numbers* where Riemann's analysis is described as "peculiar and difficult"!

The proofs of J. Hadamard and C. de la Vallée Poussin appeared respectively in Bull. Soc. Math. France **24** (1896), *Sur la distribution de la fonction $\zeta(s)$ et ses conséquences arithmétiques* and Ann. Soc. Sci. Bruxelles **20** (1896), *Recherches analytiques sur la théorie des nombres*. It is worthwhile noting that Hadamard based his proof on that given by E. Cahen *Sur la fonction $\zeta(s)$ de Riemann et sur les fonctions analogues*, Ann. École Normale Supérieure **11** (1894). Cahen assumes the truth of the Riemann hypothesis and ascribes the ideas of his proof to Halphen.

Landau's proof first appeared in 1903, *Neuer Beweis des Primzahlsatzes und Beweis des Primideal satzes*, Math. Ann. **56**. Here he uses an average and absolutely convergent integrals. The proof using nonabsolutely convergent integrals appeared in 1912 *Bedingt konvergente Integrale in der Primzahltheorie*, Math. Ann. **71**.

3. There are several proofs known of Theorem 4.4. In addition to those mentioned there is one due to A.E. Ingham which is outlined in Problem 38.

4. The difference $\pi(x) - \operatorname{li} x = R(x)$ has been the object of much study. As noted, the Riemann hypothesis implies that $R(x) = O(x^{1/2} \log x)$ and Littlewood

has shown that there exist values of x as large as we please for which $R(x) > cx^{1/2} \log\log\log x/\log x$ and values for which $R(x) < -cx^{1/2} \log\log\log x/\log x$. About the best value of $R(x)$ known to date without any assumptions is that

$$R(x) = (xe^{-\lambda(x)}), \qquad \text{where} \qquad \lambda(x) = c \log^{3/5} x\,.$$

There has been a succession of improvements in the value of $\lambda(x)$ given among others, by Tatuzawa, who obtained better estimates for $\zeta(s)$ based on the work of Tchudakoff, Vinogradoff, and Hua. These estimates are based on the so-called approximate functional equation of the zeta function together with refined estimates for trigonometric sums. See e.g., Titchmarsh, *Theory of the Riemann zeta function.*

5. The result $\lambda(x) = c \log^{1/2} x$ is due to de la Vallée Poussin in the above cited work.

The Hardy-Littlewood proof appears in Acta Math. **41**, *Contributions to the theory of the Riemann zeta function and the theory of the distribution of primes.* In addition to this proof, other interesting results are proved. They verify, for example, on the assumption of the Riemann hypothesis, the conjecture of Tchebycheff that

$$f(y) = \sum_{p>2} (-1)^{(p+1)/2} e^{-py} \to \infty \qquad \text{as } y \to 0\,.$$

This implies that in a certain sense, there are "more" primes of the form $4k+3$ than there are of the form $4k+1$.

Wiener's proof was a consequence of his general Tauberian theorems and was originally applied to Lambert series. The proof given here is Landau's version *Über den Wienerschen neuen Weg zum Primzahlsatz,* S.-B. Preuss. Akad. Wiss. **32/33** (1932), 514–521. It is based on S. Ikehara's work *An extension of Landau's theorem in the analytic theory of numbers,* J. Math. Phys. **10** (1931), 1–12.

The "elementary" proof referred to, appeared in two separate communications (a) A. Selberg, *An elementary proof of the prime number theorem,* Ann. of Math. (2) **50** (1949), 305–313 and (b) P. Erdös, *On a new method in elementary number theory which leads to an elementary proof of the prime number theorem,* Proc. Nat. Acad. Sci. U.S.A. **35** (1949), 374–384. Both versions start from the fundamental Selberg lemma given in Problem 54.

6. The result

$$\sum_{n=1}^{\infty} \frac{\mu(n)}{n} = 0$$

was first stated by Euler but with insufficient proof. His argument assumes that the series converges—a fact which is by no means obvious and which, as we have seen, is equivalent to the prime number theorem. The equivalence was first proved by E. Landau, *Über die Equivalenz zweier Hauptsätze der analytische Zahlentheorie,* S.-B. Akad. Wiss. Wien Nat. Kl. **120**.

Theorem 7.8 is due to Dirichlet. If we set $\Delta(x) = \sum_{n\le x} d(n) - x\log x - (2\gamma-1)x$, then the precise order of magnitude of $\Delta(x)$ is as yet undetermined. It can be shown that $\Delta(x)$ cannot have smaller order of magnitude than $x^{1/4}$ whereas, on the other hand, about the best that is known, using some deep results concerning the zeta function, is that $\Delta(x) = O(x^{27/82})$. See Titchmarsh, *Zeta function.*

By the same argument given in this section, it can be shown that if

$$P(x) = \sum_{n \leqq x} \lambda(n) \quad (\lambda(n) = (-1)^{a_1 + \cdots + a_r} \text{ when } n = p_1^{a_1} p_2^{a_2} \cdots p_r^{a_r})$$

then $P(x) = O(x^{1/2+\varepsilon})$ is equivalent to the Riemann hypothesis. There is an interesting argument which suggests the truth of this. If $\varepsilon_1, \varepsilon_2, \cdots, \varepsilon_n$, is an arbitrary sequence of ± 1, there being $N = 2^n$ of these, and $A(n, r)$ is the number of sets satisfying $| \sum_{i=1}^{n} \varepsilon_i | < r$ then

$$\lim_{n \to \infty} \frac{A(n, n^a)}{N} \to \begin{cases} 1 & \text{if } \frac{1}{2} < a < 1, \\ 0 & \text{if } 0 < a < \frac{1}{2}. \end{cases}$$

Thus for a sequence $\varepsilon_1, \cdots, \varepsilon_n$ chosen at random, the probability that

$$\left| \sum_{i=1}^{n} \varepsilon_i \right| \leqq n^a \qquad \text{for } a > \frac{1}{2},$$

is 1. $\lambda(n)$ is an ε sequence and if it were "random," then with probability 1,

$$P(x) = O(x^a) \qquad \text{for any } a > \tfrac{1}{2}.$$

Axer's theorem first appeared in Prace matematyczne-fizyczne **21**, *Beitrag zur Kenntnis der Zahlentheoretischen Funktionen.* See also Landau, *Über einige neuere Grenzwertsätze,* Rend. Circ. Mat. Palermo **34**.

In the following, we introduce some notations which can serve to simplify the statements of some of the results of § 7.

Let A denote the set of arithmetic functions. If f and g belong to A, we define the convolution of f and g as follows

$$(f * g) = \sum_{d \mid n} f(d) g\left(\frac{n}{d}\right).$$

It is easy to verify the following

(i) $f * g = g * f$.

(ii) If C is a constant

$$C(f * g) = Cf * g.$$

(iii) $f * (g * h) = (f * g) * h$.

(iv) $f * (g + h) = f * g + f * h$.

(v) If

$$E(n) = \begin{cases} 1 & \text{for } n = 1, \\ 0 & \text{for } n > 1, \end{cases}$$

then $f * E = f$. E thus serves as an identity.

(vi) If $f(1) \neq 0$, then there exists g, which is unique, such that

$$f * g = E.$$

We denote g by f^{-1}.

(vii) If $i(n) = 1$ for all n, then $\mu * i = E$ and indeed $\mu(n)$, the Möbius function, may be defined by this relation.

(viii) If $L(n) = \log n$, then

$$\Lambda = \mu * L .$$

(ix) The Möbius inversion formula is easily proved. For if $g = i * f$ then $(g * \mu) = (\mu * i) * f = E * f = f$.

(x) If f is multiplicative then

$$f(g * h) = fg * fh .$$

Let M be the linear space of complex valued functions defined and bounded for $x \geqq 1$ and A the set of arithmetic functions. To every g in A, we associate a linear transformation S_g of M as follows

$$(S_g f)x = \sum_{n \leqq x} g(n) f\left(\frac{x}{n}\right) .$$

The following are easily proved:

(i) $S_g + S_h = S_{g+h}$.

(ii) $S_g = S_h$ if and only if $g = h$.

(iii) $cS_g = S_{cg}$ for c a constant and g in A.

(iv) $S_g S_h = S_k$ where $k = g * h$.

(v) $S_E f = f$ i.e., S_E is the identity transformation $S_E S_g = S_g$.

(vi) For g in A, S_g^{-1} exists if and only if $g(1) \neq 0$. By (iv) $S_g^{-1} = S_{g^{-1}}$ where g^{-1} is the inverse of g with respect to $*$.

(vii) If g is multiplicative, then

$$S_{(h * k) g} = S_{hg * kg} = S_{hg} \cdot S_{kg} .$$

(viii) $S_i f = g$ if and only if $S_\mu g = f$.

(ix) $LS_h = S_h L + S_{h \cdot \log x}$.

We define, in addition, the transformation $I_g = S_{gx^{-1}}$, that is,

$$(I_g f)x = \sum_{n \leqq x} \frac{g(n)}{n} f\left(\frac{x}{n}\right) .$$

I has essentially all the properties of S.

If $\Lambda_2 = \mu * \log^2 x$, the following can be verified.

(i) $I_{\Lambda_2} = I_E^{-1} I_{\log^2 x}$;

(ii) $I_1 L I_\mu = L - I_\Lambda$;

(iii) $I_\mu L I_1 = L + I_\Lambda$;

(iv) $I_{\Lambda_2} = I_{\Lambda \log x} + I_\Lambda^2$.

In this notation, we can formulate some of the results we have proved.

(i) $M(x) = (S_\mu 1) = o(x)$,

(ii) $\psi(x) = (S_\Lambda \cdot 1) = O(x)$,

(iii) $(S_i \log) x = x + O(\log x)$,

(iv) $(S_\Lambda e)x = x \log x + O(x)$,

where $e(x) = x$. Let us prove using this notation that

$$\psi(x) = O(x) .$$

We have

$$\psi(x) = (S_\Lambda \cdot 1)x = (S_\mu \cdot S_L \cdot 1)x = S_\mu \log [x]! \,.$$
$$= S_\mu(x \log x - x + O(\log x)) = S_\mu(x \log x) + O(x) \,.$$

But $S_i ex = x \sum_{n \leq x} 1/n = x \log x + \gamma x + O(1)$, we have

$$x = S_E ex = S_{\mu * i} ex = S_\mu S_i ex = S_\mu(x \log x + \gamma x + O(1))$$
$$= S_\mu(x \log x) + O(x) \,.$$

$S_\mu(x \log x) = O(x)$ and therefore

$$\psi(x) = O(x) \,.$$

For further details and results, the reader may consult

(i) K. Yamamoto, J. Math. Soc. Japan **7** (1955), 424–434;

(ii) S. A. Amitsur, J. Analyse Math. **5** (1956), 273–314.

CHAPTER III

The Theory of Partitions

1. The generating function and elementary results. The prime numbers owe their importance primarily to their multiplicative properties. There are nevertheless important problems of an "additive" character and we consider two such questions in this and the next chapters.

Among the many additive problems are those which consider the decomposition of an integer into integers of a prescribed type

$$n = a_1 + a_2 + \cdots + a_r ;$$

the nature of the a_i being specified. For example, if the a_i are restricted to be squares, then we have the classical problem of the decomposition of an integer into a sum of squares. In addition to existence theorems, we are frequently interested in quantitative theorems. Thus the classical theorem of Euler-Lagrange on the existence of a decomposition of any integer into a sum of at most 4 squares is supplemented by the theorem of Jacobi on the number of such representations.

If the a_i are restricted to be primes, then we have the celebrated Goldbach problem. If the a_i are required to be kth powers, we have the famous Waring problem which is treated in detail in the next chapter.

While it would be highly interesting to find precise formulae for the number of representations of an integer into a prescribed decomposition, such formulae are generally speaking beyond the present resources of mathematics. We shall be content to derive asymptotic formulae from which, nevertheless, much interesting information can be inferred.

In this chapter we place no restriction on the a's and such an unrestricted decomposition is called a partition. The question we study in detail concerns the number $p(n)$ of unrestricted partitions of n. There are naturally many ramifications of this question. For example, we may ask about the number of partitions into odd summands; the number of partitions into a fixed number of summands, and so on. Our discussion is confined to the number of unrestricted partitions, though the methods are applicable to a large class of similar problems.

Let $p(n)$ denote the number of partitions of n. For example, since

$$\begin{aligned} 5 &= 1+1+1+1+1 = 2+1+1+1 = 2+2+1 \\ &= 3+1+1 = 3+2 = 4+1 , \end{aligned}$$

then it follows that $p(5) = 7$. In a similar manner, we can enumerate $p(n)$ for various values of n.

We denote by $p_k(n)$ the number of partitions of n into at most k parts. For example, since

$$9 = 8 + 1 = 7 + 2 = 7 + 1 + 1 = 6 + 3 = 6 + 2 + 1 = 5 + 4$$
$$= 5 + 3 + 1 = 5 + 2 + 2 = 4 + 4 + 1 = 4 + 3 + 2\,,$$

it follows that $p_3(9) = 11$.

The first substantial contributions to the theory of partitions were made by Euler. These properties by and large were deduced from the so-called generating function. To derive this function we make a few preliminary observations.

We have seen that the product of two Dirichlet series is a Dirichlet series whose coefficients were related to the original coefficients in a multiplicative way. Dirichlet series proved to be the natural tool for problems of a multiplicative nature. For problems of an additive character, however, it is natural to expect power series to play a fundamental role for the following reasons: If we multiply the power series

$$\text{(i)}\ \sum_{n=0}^{\infty} a(n)x^n\,, \qquad \text{(ii)}\ \sum_{n=0}^{\infty} b(n)x^n$$

together (ignoring for the moment any questions of convergence), we get

$$\sum_{n=0}^{\infty} a(n)x^n \sum_{m=0}^{\infty} b(m)x^m = \sum_{m,n=0}^{\infty} a(n)b(m)x^{n+m}\,;$$

and if we put $n + m = k$, this reduces to

$$\sum_{m,n=0}^{\infty} a(n)b(m)x^{m+n} = \sum_{k=0}^{\infty} c(k)x^k\,,$$

where

$$c(k) = \sum_{m+n=k} a(n)b(m)\,,$$

the summation being over all indices m, n whose sum is k. This is the familiar Cauchy product.

The coefficient $c(k)$ thus depends on the additive properties of k.

In particular, if for fixed λ, μ, we put

$$a(n) = \begin{cases} 1 & \text{for } n = \lambda r\,, \\ 0 & \text{otherwise}\,, \end{cases}$$

$$b(m) = \begin{cases} 1 & \text{for } m = \mu s\,, \\ 0 & \text{otherwise}\,, \end{cases}$$

then with $a(0) = b(0) = 1$,

$$\sum_{n=0}^{\infty} a(n)x^n = \sum_{r=0}^{\infty} x^{\lambda r} = \frac{1}{1 - x^{\lambda}}\,,$$

$$\sum_{m=0}^{\infty} b(m)x^m = \sum_{s=0}^{\infty} x^{\mu s} = \frac{1}{1 - x^{\mu}}\,.$$

Accordingly,

(1) $$\frac{1}{1-x^\lambda}\cdot\frac{1}{1-x^\mu}=\sum_{k=0}^{\infty}c(k)x^k\,,$$

where

$$c(k)=\sum_{r\lambda+s\mu=k}1=\text{number of solutions}$$

of the equation $k=r\lambda+s\mu$ for fixed λ,μ. We shall use these observations shortly.

We wish to derive the generating function for $p(n)$, that is, to express

$$\sum_{n=0}^{\infty}p(n)x^n \qquad (p(0)=1),$$

in simpler terms if possible. To do so, we make the partition

(2) $$n=a_1+a_2+\cdots+a_m$$

more systematic. Let k_1 be the number of 1's, k_2 the number of 2's, etc., $\cdots, k_r$ the number of r's in the partition (2). Then

(3) $$n=k_1+2k_2+\cdots+rk_r\,.$$

Thus $p(n)$ is the number of solutions of (3). This in conjunction with (1) leads us to consider the power series

$$\sum_{k_1=0}^{\infty}x^{k_1},\ \sum_{k_2=0}^{\infty}x^{2k_2},\cdots,\sum_{k_r=0}^{\infty}x^{rk_r}\,.$$

We have for $|x|<1$,

$$\sum_{k_i=0}^{\infty}x^{ik_i}=\frac{1}{1-x^i}\,,$$

and therefore

$$\frac{1}{1-x}\cdot\frac{1}{1-x^2}\cdots\frac{1}{1-x^r}=\sum_{k_1=0}^{\infty}x^{k_1}\cdots\sum_{k_r=0}^{\infty}x^{rk_r}=\sum_{n=0}^{\infty}c(n)x^n\,,$$

where $c(n)$ is the number of solutions of (3). In other words, letting $r\to\infty$, we conclude that formally,

(4) $$\sum_{n=0}^{\infty}p(n)x^n=\prod_{k=1}^{\infty}(1-x^k)^{-1}\,.$$

A proof of this relation is the object of the next theorem.

THEOREM 1.1. *For* $0\leqq x<1$,

(5) $$F(x)=\prod_{k=1}^{\infty}(1-x^k)^{-1}=\sum_{n=0}^{\infty}p(n)x^n\,.$$

PROOF. To begin with,

$$\prod_{k=1}^{\infty}(1-x^k)^{-1}=\prod_{k=1}^{\infty}\left(1+\frac{x^k}{1-x^k}\right)$$

and therefore the product converges when $0\leqq x<1$. What we wish to prove is that

$$\lim_{m\to\infty} \prod_{k=1}^{m} (1 - x^k)^{-1} = \sum_{n=0}^{\infty} p(n)x^n .$$

Let

(6) $$F_m(x) = \prod_{k=1}^{m} (1 - x^k)^{-1} ;$$

then since the series

$$\sum_{i=0}^{\infty} x^{ki} \qquad (k = 1, 2, \cdots, m)$$

all converge absolutely for $0 \leqq x < 1$, and therefore can be multiplied together and rearranged, it follows that the coefficient $p_m(k)$ in the expansion of $F_m(x)$ is the number of solutions of the equation

$$k = k_1 + 2k_2 + \cdots + mk_m .$$

This number, however, is the number of partitions of k into parts not exceeding m. If $m > k$, then $p_m(k) = p(k)$ since all the terms in a partition of k are evidently $\leqq k$. In any event,

(7) $$p_m(k) \leqq p(k) ,$$

and for every k,

(8) $$\lim_{m\to\infty} p_m(k) = p(k) .$$

On the other hand, from (6),

(9) $$F_m(x) = \sum_{n=0}^{m} p(n)x^n + \sum_{n=m+1}^{\infty} p_m(n)x^n .$$

Moreover, since $0 \leqq x < 1$,

$$F_m(x) \leqq F(x)$$

and

$$\lim_{m\to\infty} F_m(x) = F(x) ;$$

and therefore from (9),

$$\sum_{n=0}^{m} p(n)x^n \leqq F_m(x) \leqq F(x) .$$

This implies, however, that

$$\sum_{n=0}^{\infty} p(n)x^n$$

converges, and from (7), it follows that for fixed x satisfying $0 \leqq x < 1$,

$$\sum_{n=0}^{\infty} p_m(n)x^n$$

converges uniformly for all m. Therefore, from (8) and (9),

$$\sum_{n=0}^{\infty} p(n)x^n = \lim_{m\to\infty} \sum_{n=0}^{\infty} p_m(n)x^n = \lim_{m\to\infty} F_m(x) = F(x) ,$$

as was to be shown.

COROLLARY 1. *If x is a complex variable, then the relation*

$$\prod_{k=1}^{\infty} (1 - x^k)^{-1} = \sum_{n=0}^{\infty} p(n)x^n$$

holds inside the unit circle $|x| < 1$.

From the relation (5), there follows a number of interesting consequences. These can be deduced by the formal manipulation of power series. To derive several of the more interesting ones, we shall assume known the Euler pentagonal number theorem.

THEOREM 1.2.

$$\prod_{k=1}^{\infty} (1 - x^k) = \sum_{n=-\infty}^{\infty} (-1)^n x^{n(3n-1)/2} . \tag{10}$$

The numbers $n(3n - 1)/2$ ($n = 0, \pm 1, \pm 2, \cdots$) are the pentagonal numbers, so-called because of their geometric relation to the pentagon. A proof may be found in Hardy and Wright, *Theory of numbers*, Theorem 353. The reader may supply an inductive proof by induction on the number of factors on the left-hand side; see Problem 26.

We put for simplicity

$$\omega_n = \frac{n(3n-1)}{2} , \tag{11}$$

and then prove

THEOREM 1.3.

$$p(n) = \sum_{0<\omega_k\leqq n} (-1)^{k-1} p(n - \omega_k) , \tag{12}$$

where the summation is over those pentagonal numbers $\omega_k \leqq n$.

PROOF. The proof is a direct consequence of (5) and (10). In fact,

$$1 = \sum_{n=0}^{\infty} p(n)x^n \sum_{n=-\infty}^{\infty} (-1)^n x^{\omega_n} ,$$

and the statement of the theorem follows directly on equating coefficients of like powers.

This formula may be used to calculate $p(n)$ inductively for relatively small values of n since the number of terms is comparatively small. This number may be determined approximately as follows. For $k > 0$,

$$\frac{3k^2}{2} - \frac{k}{2} < n ,$$

and for large k, the term $k/2$ may be neglected, thus giving

$$k < \sqrt{\frac{2n}{3}}\,;$$

a similar estimate holding for $k < 0$, we have altogether approximately

$$2\sqrt{\frac{2n}{3}}$$

terms in the formula (12).

We remark parenthetically that formula (10) may be used to prove a remarkable formula due again to Euler. This is the formula involving $\sigma(n)$ alluded to in Chapter II, §1.

THEOREM 1.4. *If $\sigma(n)$ denotes the sum of the divisors of n, then*

$$\sigma(n) + \sum_{0<\omega_k\leqq n} (-1)^{k-1}\sigma(n-\omega_k) = \begin{cases} 0 & \text{if } n \neq \omega_m\,, \\ (-1)^m\omega_m & \text{if } n = \omega_m\,, \end{cases}$$

ω_k being once again a pentagonal number.

PROOF. The operations we perform on the power series can all be easily justified analytically. These questions are arithmetically not really relevant. We start by logarithmic differentiation of (10),

$$\sum_{n=1}^{\infty} \frac{-nx^{n-1}}{1-x^n} = \frac{\sum_{n=-\infty}^{\infty} (-1)^n\omega_n x^{\omega_n-1}}{\sum_{n=-\infty}^{\infty} (-1)^n x^{\omega_n}}\,,$$

from which it follows that

$$\sum_{n=-\infty}^{\infty} (-1)^n x^{\omega_n} \sum_{n=1}^{\infty} \frac{-nx^n}{1-x^n} = \sum_{n=-\infty}^{\infty} (-1)^n\omega_n x^{\omega_n}\,. \tag{13}$$

On the other hand,

$$\begin{aligned} \sum_{n=1}^{\infty} \frac{nx^n}{1-x^n} &= \sum_{n=1}^{\infty} nx^n \sum_{m=0}^{\infty} x^{mn} \\ &= \sum_{n=1}^{\infty} n \sum_{m=0}^{\infty} x^{(m+1)n} \\ &= \sum_{n=1}^{\infty} n \sum_{m=1}^{\infty} x^{mn}\,. \end{aligned} \tag{14}$$

If we put $mn = k$, what is the coefficient of x^k? This is evidently $\sigma(k) = \sum_{n\mid k} n$. Therefore, from (13) and (14), we conclude

$$\sum_{k=1}^{\infty} \sigma(k)x^k \sum_{n=-\infty}^{\infty} (-1)^n\omega_n = \sum_{n=-\infty}^{\infty} (-1)^{n-1}\omega_n x^{\omega_n}\,.$$

On equating coefficients of like powers, the relation enunciated follows.

Many further highly interesting algebraic relations concerning $p(n)$ may be proved. For further details, the reader is referred to the book of Hardy and Wright.

We are mainly concerned here with the magnitude of $p(n)$ as a function

of n. To gain some insight into this question, we can argue as follows.
If the power series

$$f(x) = \sum_{n=0}^{\infty} a_n x^n$$

has non-negative coefficients and radius of convergence 1, then according to Theorem 6.13, of Chapter II, the order of magnitude of a_n will determine the behavior of $f(x)$ in the neighborhood of $x = 1$ and conversely, the behavior as $x \to 1$ yields information concerning a_n. Let us start by determining roughly the behavior of

$$F(x) = \prod_{n=1}^{\infty} (1 - x^n)^{-1}$$

in the neighborhood of $x = 1$:

$$\begin{aligned} \log F(x) &= \sum_{n=1}^{\infty} \log \frac{1}{1 - x^n} = \sum_{n=1}^{\infty} \sum_{m=1}^{\infty} \frac{x^{mn}}{m} \\ &= \sum_{m=1}^{\infty} \frac{x^m}{m(1 - x^m)}, \end{aligned} \tag{15}$$

the interchange of summation being evidently justified. Since for real x, such that $0 < x < 1$, $mx^{m-1} < 1 + x + \cdots + x^{m-1} < m$, then

$$mx^{m-1}(1 - x) < 1 - x^m < m(1 - x),$$

and we get from (15)

$$\frac{1}{1 - x} \sum_{m=1}^{\infty} \frac{x^m}{m^2} < \log F(x) < \frac{1}{1 - x} \sum_{m=1}^{\infty} \frac{x}{m^2}. \tag{16}$$

On the other hand, $\zeta(2) = \pi^2/6$:

$$\lim_{x \to 1} \sum_{m=1}^{\infty} \frac{x^m}{m^2} = \zeta(2) = \frac{\pi^2}{6},$$

by Abel's Theorem. Therefore as $x \to 1$, by (16),

$$\log F(x) \sim \frac{\pi^2}{6(1 - x)};$$

accordingly,

$$F(x) = \exp\left\{\frac{\pi^2/6 + o(1)}{1 - x}\right\}. \tag{17}$$

Having determined a first approximation to $F(x)$, we ask about the magnitude of $p(n)$. What can it be? We try various possibilities. If $p(n) = n^\alpha$, then for $x = e^{-y}$,

$$F(x) = \sum_{n=1}^{\infty} n^\alpha x^n = \sum_{n=1}^{\infty} n^\alpha e^{-ny} \sim \int_0^\infty t^\alpha e^{-ty} dt = \frac{\Gamma(\alpha + 1)}{y^{\alpha+1}} \sim \frac{\Gamma(\alpha + 1)}{(1 - x)^{\alpha+1}}$$

as $x \to 1$ since $y = -\log x \sim (1 - x)$ as $x \to 1$.
This, however, is in contradiction to (17) and we conclude that n^α is too small.

On the other hand, if $p(n) = e^{cn}$ for some constant c, then there exists $\rho = \rho(c)$, $0 < \rho < 1$, for which

$$\sum_{n=0}^{\infty} e^{cn} \rho^n$$

diverges and this is a contradiction to the fact that

$$\sum_{n=0}^{\infty} p(n) x^n$$

converges for $|x| < 1$. Consequently e^{cn} is too large and a reasonable guess is that for some constants a and b $(0 < b < 1)$, $\exp(an^b)$ is just right. We have yet to guess at the values of a and b. If $x = e^{-y}$, then the series

$$\sum_{n=0}^{\infty} p(n) x^n = \sum_{n=0}^{\infty} e^{an^b - ny}$$

has as its order of magnitude that of its largest term since the series on the right is exponential. The largest term occurs when

$$abn^{b-1} - y = 0 ,$$

and in that event, solving for n, the largest term is

$$\exp(an^b - ny) = \exp[ay^{b/(b-1)} a^{-b/(b-1)} b^{-b/(b-1)} - y(y(ab)^{-1})^{1/(b-1)}] .$$

Since $y = -\log x \sim 1 - x$ as $x \to 1$, then a simple calculation shows that

$$F(x) \sim e^{an^b - ny} = \exp[y^{b/(b-1)} a^{1/(1-b)} b^{b/(1-b)} (1 - b)] \sim \exp[c(1 - x)^{-b/(1-b)}] , \tag{18}$$

where

$$c = a^{1/(1-b)} b^{b/(1-b)} (1 - b) .$$

Now we choose a and b so that (18) agrees with (17). This can be done by putting $b = \frac{1}{2}$ and $a^2 = 2\pi^2/3$, for then

$$c = \frac{2}{3} \pi^2 \cdot \frac{1}{2} \cdot \frac{1}{2} = \frac{\pi^2}{6} .$$

Accordingly, we can expect that $p(n)$ is about

$$\exp(an^{1/2}) , \tag{19}$$

where

$$a = \pi \sqrt{\frac{2}{3}} . \tag{20}$$

Actually, it is the case that

$$\log p(n) \sim \pi \sqrt{\frac{2}{3}} n^{1/2} . \tag{21}$$

This, however, does not give us very precise information about $p(n)$ itself. A logarithmic asymptotic relation is sometimes not very revealing since we get the same logarithmic relation whether

$$p(n) \sim n^{1000} \exp (an^{1/2})$$

or

$$p(n) \sim n^{-1000} \exp (an^{1/2}) .$$

Clearly there is a vast difference between these two, although

$$\log p(n) \sim an^{1/2}$$

is true in either case. We start by proving (21), and in order to do so use a simple but interesting lemma.

THEOREM 1.5. *If $p(n)$ is the number of partitions of n, then*

$$np(n) = \sum_{h=1}^{n} h \sum_{hk \leqq n;\ k \geqq 1} p(n - hk) . \tag{22}$$

PROOF. Let $p(n)$ be the number of partitions of n. We add together these partitions in two ways. On the one hand, we get directly that the sum is $np(n)$, since each partition adds up to n. On the other hand, we focus our attention on a fixed integer h and count how often h appears in the partitions of n. If h does occur in a partition, then on removing h, we are left with an unrestricted partition of $n - h$. Consequently the number of partitions of n having at least one h is precisely $p(n - h)$; having at least 2 parts equal to h is $p(n - 2h)$, and so on. The number of partitions having exactly one h is therefore $p(n - h) - p(n - 2h)$; the number having exactly two h's is $p(n - 2h) - p(n - 3h)$; and in general the number of partitions having exactly k parts equal to h is $p(n - kh) - p(n - (k + 1)h)$. Therefore the contribution of h to the sum of all the partitions is

$$h[p(n-h) - p(n-2h)] + 2h[p(n-2h) - p(n-3h)] + \cdots$$
$$= h(p(n-h) + p(n-2h) + \cdots) = \sum_{hk \leqq n;\ k \geqq 1} p(n - hk) .$$

Adding over all h, we get the relation (22).

THEOREM 1.6. *If*

$$a = \pi \sqrt{\frac{2}{3}} ,$$

then

$$\log p(n) \sim an^{1/2} , \tag{23}$$

PROOF. We prove two inequalities: (i)

$$p(n) < \exp (an^{1/2}) \tag{24}$$

and (ii) for every $\varepsilon > 0$, there exists a constant A_ε such that

$$p(n) > \frac{1}{A_\varepsilon} \exp [(a - \varepsilon)n^{1/2}] . \tag{25}$$

Relation (23) is a consequence of these two inequalities, for together they imply that

$$-\log A_\varepsilon + (a-\varepsilon)n^{1/2} < \log p(n) < an^{1/2}$$

or that

$$1 - \frac{\varepsilon}{a} \leqq \lim_{n\to\infty} \frac{\log p(n)}{an^{1/2}} \leqq 1 ,$$

and this implies (23).

We restrict our attention to (24); (25) is proved in exactly the same way. The proof of (24) is by induction on n and uses (22). We have evidently $p(1) < e^a$, and suppose that for all $m < n$, $p(m) < e^{am^{1/2}}$. Then from (22), defining for $r > 0$, $p(-r) = 0$:

$$\text{(26)} \qquad \begin{aligned} np(n) &= \sum_{\substack{h=1\\ hk\leqq n}}^{n} \sum_{k=1}^{n} hp(n-hk) \\ &< \sum_{h=1}^{n} \sum_{k=1}^{n} he^{a(n-hk)^{1/2}} . \end{aligned}$$

If we use the inequality, $(1-x)^\alpha \leqq 1 - \alpha x$, we get from (26),

$$\text{(27)} \qquad \begin{aligned} np(n) &< \sum_{h=1}^{n} \sum_{k=1}^{n} he^{an^{1/2} - akh/2n^{1/2}} \\ &< e^{an^{1/2}} \sum_{k=1}^{n} \sum_{h=1}^{\infty} he^{-(ak/2n^{1/2})h} . \end{aligned}$$

However, an easy argument shows that for $x > 0$,

$$\text{(28)} \qquad \sum_{m=1}^{\infty} me^{-mx} = \frac{1}{4\sinh^2 \dfrac{x}{2}} < \frac{1}{x^2}$$

since $\sinh x > x$. Therefore, from (27) and (28),

$$np(n) < \exp(an^{1/2}) \sum_{k=1}^{\infty} \frac{4n}{a^2k^2} < \exp(an^{1/2}) \frac{4n}{a^2} \frac{\pi^2}{6} = n \exp(an^{1/2}) .$$

This completes the proof of (24). The proof of (25) is essentially the same.

Our primary objective is, however, not $\log p(n)$ but $p(n)$ itself. We have made the reasonable hypothesis that $p(n)$ is about $\exp(an^{1/2})$; the object of the next section is to derive the precise statement that

$$p(n) \sim \frac{1}{4\sqrt{3}\,n} \exp(an^{1/2}) .$$

Actually we prove considerably more, as we shall see.

2. The asymptotic formula for $p(n)$. Several proofs of an asymptotic formula for $p(n)$ are known but no known proof is simple. In this section, we give a proof, due essentially to J. V. Uspensky, which uses Cauchy's theorem coupled with a result from the theory of modular forms which we prove in the next section.

The application of Cauchy's theorem arises in a natural way from equation (5) of § 1. From

$$F(x) = \prod_{n=1}^{\infty}(1 - x^n)^{-1} = \sum_{k=0}^{\infty} p(k)x^k , \tag{1}$$

we get

$$\frac{F(x)}{x^{n+1}} = \sum_{k=0}^{\infty} p(k)x^{k-n-1} .$$

$p(n)$ is thus the residue at $x = 0$ of the function $F(x)/x^{n+1}$ and by Cauchy's theorem, we get the basic relation

$$p(n) = \frac{1}{2\pi i}\int_{\mathscr{C}} \frac{F(x)}{x^{n+1}} dx , \tag{2}$$

where $\mathscr{C}$ is a simple closed contour lying inside the unit circle and enclosing the origin. The function $F(x)$ has a singularity whenever $x^n = 1$; thus any root of unity is a singularity of $F(x)$, that is, $x = e^{2\pi ih/k}$ for every rational number h/k is a singularity of $F(x)$. Since these points are dense on the unit circle, it follows that every point of the unit circle is a singularity. This fact appears as a formidable barrier to further progress and the situation is in contrast to the analogous integral for the function $\psi(x)$ which we studied in Chapter II. There the principal function involved viz. $\zeta(s)$ was regular in the entire plane with the exception of a simple pole with residue 1 at $s=1$ —a singularity of the simplest possible character. The evaluation of the integral was effected by moving the path of integration across the singularity and obtaining the dominant term from the contribution of the pole. The remainder of the argument consisted in estimating the integrand for large t. This involved substantial difficulty owing to the zeros of $\zeta(s)$ and the complex behavior of $\zeta(s)$ at ∞.

In the case at hand, the unit circle is a natural boundary, and there is no possibility of integrating across the singularities. Further pursuit of the question looks fruitless, but to quote G. H. Hardy, "For all that, there are strong consolations. $F(x)$ belongs to a class of functions called elliptic modular functions whose properties have been intensively studied and whose behavior is well known." In particular, $F(x)$ is very nearly the reciprocal of an important modular function studied by Riemann, Dedekind and others. The function is defined by

$$\eta(\tau) = e^{\pi i\tau/12}\prod_{n=1}^{\infty}(1 - e^{2\pi in\tau}) , \tag{3}$$

where to ensure convergence we choose $\mathscr{I}(\tau) > 0$. If we put $x = e^{2\pi i\tau}$ in (1), then

$$F(x) = F(e^{2\pi i\tau}) = e^{\pi i\tau/12}/\eta(\tau) . \tag{4}$$

Thus the properties of $\eta(\tau)$ are reflected in those of $F(x)$ and some of the properties of $\eta(\tau)$ have indeed been studied. Let us look at the integral and try to infer what properties would be of interest to us.

Since we cannot move across the singularities, we try to move close to them. From the definition of $F(x)$, we see that every factor in the denominator vanishes when $x = 1$, every second when $x = -1$, every third when $x = e^{2\pi i/3}$, and in general every kth when $x = e^{2\pi ih/k}$, $(h, k) = 1$. Thus, to put the matter crudely, we might expect that most of the contribution to the integral will come from the point $x = 1$. In fact, if $g(n)$ is the contribution to $p(n)$ from the point $x = 1$, we might expect the contribution from $x = -1$ to be $O(g(n)^{1/2})$ and so on. That this rough argument leads to a conclusion which is very nearly that of the actual state of affairs is surprising.

To a first approximation, then, we should like to select for the contour $\mathscr{C}$, a circle whose radius tends to 1 as $n \to \infty$ and such that the main contribution will come from some suitable neighborhood of $x = 1$. We should therefore like to find a function $\psi(x)$ whose behavior in some suitable neighborhood of 1 is the same as that of $f(x)$ in the sense that for x in a well-defined neighborhood of $x = 1$, the order of magnitude of $F(x) - \psi(x)$ is readily determined.

The existence of such a function may be inferred from the so-called functional equation for $\eta(\tau)$. In the next section, we shall derive the following important relation for $F(x)$: If $\mathscr{R}(\tau) > 0$,

$$F(x) = F(e^{-2\pi\tau}) = \sqrt{\tau}\exp\left[\frac{\pi}{12}\left(\frac{1}{\tau} - \tau\right)\right]F(e^{-2\pi/\tau}) = \psi(\tau)F(e^{-2\pi/\tau}), \tag{5}$$

where

$$\psi(\tau) = \sqrt{\tau}\exp\left[\frac{\pi}{12}\left(\frac{1}{\tau} - \tau\right)\right].$$

Now

$$F(e^{-2\pi/\tau}) = \sum_{n=0}^{\infty} p(n)e^{-2\pi n/\tau} \qquad (p(0) = 1)$$

and when $\tau \to 0$, $e^{-2\pi\tau} \to 1$, and $e^{-2\pi/\tau} \to 0$. Thus $F(e^{-2\pi/\tau})$ tends very rapidly to 1 when $\tau \to 0$. Hence for x close to 1 which is to say τ close to 0, $F(e^{-2\pi\tau})$ is nearly $\sqrt{\tau}\exp[(\pi/12)(1/\tau - \tau)]$. We may therefore expect that as $\tau \to 0$, $F(e^{-2\pi\tau})$ is closely approximated by $\psi(\tau) = \sqrt{\tau}\exp[(\pi/12)(1/\tau - \tau)]$.

There are formulae similar to (5) for other points of the unit circle, but we shall discuss these in detail later on.

We can expect then, that the main contribution to the integral (2) will come from the integral of $\psi(\tau)$, a function which is reasonably simple. We shall make all this reasoning precise and prove the important result of Hardy and Ramanujan.

Theorem 2.1. *If $a = \pi\sqrt{\frac{2}{3}}$, then*

$$p(n) \sim \frac{1}{4n\sqrt{3}}\exp(an^{1/2}). \tag{6}$$

More precisely, if

$$\lambda_n = \left(n - \frac{1}{24}\right)^{1/2},$$

then

$$p(n) = \frac{1}{2\pi\sqrt{2}} \frac{d}{dn} \frac{e^{a\lambda_n}}{\lambda_n} + O(e^{5a\lambda_n/8}) . \tag{7}$$

PROOF. It is easy to see that (6) follows from (7). For if we carry out the differentiation in (7), we get

$$\begin{aligned} p(n) &= \frac{1}{2\pi\sqrt{2}} \left\{ \frac{e^{a\lambda_n}\left(\frac{a}{2}\right) - e^{a\lambda_n}\left(\frac{1}{2}\right)\lambda_n^{-1}}{\lambda_n^2} \right\} + O(e^{5a\lambda_n/8}) \\ &= \frac{a}{4\pi\sqrt{2}} \frac{e^{a\lambda_n}}{\lambda_n^2}\left(1 - \frac{1}{a\lambda_n}\right) + O(e^{5a\lambda_n/8}) \\ &= \frac{1}{4\sqrt{3}} \frac{e^{a\lambda_n}}{n - \frac{1}{24}}\left(1 - \frac{1}{a\lambda_n}\right) + O(e^{5a\lambda_n/8}) . \end{aligned}$$

Since the term 1/24 is of no significance, it follows that

$$p(n) \sim \frac{1}{4n\sqrt{3}} \exp(an^{1/2}) .$$

The proof of (7) is not simple and takes place in three steps.

(i) We determine a neighborhood in which $F(e^{-2\pi\tau})$ is approximated by $\psi(\tau)$.

(ii) In the integral for $p(n)$, we replace $F(e^{-2\pi\tau})$ by $\psi(\tau)$ and calculate the error.

(iii) We evaluate the integral of $\psi(\tau)$.

We have

$$p(n) = \frac{1}{2\pi i} \int_{\mathscr{C}} \frac{F(x)}{x^{n+1}} dx ,$$

where $\mathscr{C}$ is a circle whose radius is < 1. We put

$$x = re^{2\pi i\varphi} ,$$

and for convenience of writing, we let

$$r = e^{-2\pi\alpha} ,$$

with $\alpha = \alpha(n) > 0$. Note that we shall ultimately choose α so that $\alpha \to 0$ as $n \to \infty$; the O processes refer to $n \to \infty$. Then

$$x = e^{-2\pi(\alpha - i\varphi)} , \tag{8}$$

and we put for abbreviation,

$$\tau = \alpha - i\varphi ; \tag{9}$$

that is, $x = e^{-2\pi\tau}$, $dx = e^{-2\pi\tau}2\pi i d\varphi$. Because the integrand is periodic with period 1 in φ we can integrate over any interval of length 1. We choose the symmetric interval $(-\frac{1}{2}, \frac{1}{2})$:

$$p(n) = \int_{-1/2}^{1/2} F(e^{-2\pi\tau})e^{2\pi n\tau}d\varphi .$$

Now we replace $F(e^{-2\pi\tau})$ by $\psi(\tau)$, where $\psi(\tau) = \sqrt{\tau}\, e^{\pi(\tau^{-1}-\tau)/12}$; then

$$p(n) = \int_{-1/2}^{1/2} \psi(\tau)e^{2\pi n\tau}d\varphi + \int_{-1/2}^{1/2} (F(e^{-2\pi\tau}) - \psi(\tau))e^{2\pi n\tau}d\varphi . \tag{10}$$

The first integral will contribute the principal term. To estimate the second integral, we break the interval of integration into three parts; a neighborhood of the origin, say $-\varphi_0 \leqq \varphi \leqq \varphi_0$, and the remaining two segments from $-\frac{1}{2}$ to $-\varphi_0$ and φ_0 to $\frac{1}{2}$. The specific choice of φ_0 will be made shortly; its value will be chosen at our convenience.

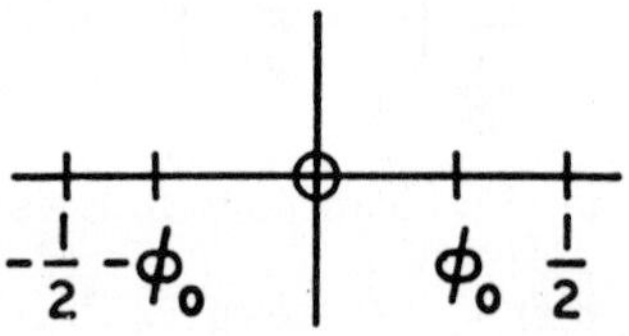

In the interval $|\varphi| \leqq \varphi_0$, we estimate the difference $F(e^{-2\pi\tau}) - \psi(\tau)$. In fact, since $1/\tau = (\alpha + i\varphi)/(\alpha^2 + \varphi^2)$, we get, using (5),

$$\begin{aligned} F(e^{-2\pi\tau}) - \psi(\tau) &= \psi(\tau)(F(e^{-2\pi/\tau}) - 1) \\ &= O\left(|\sqrt{\tau}|\left|\exp\left[\frac{\pi}{12}\left(\frac{1}{\tau} - \tau\right)\right]\right|\left|\sum_{m=1}^{\infty} p(m)e^{-2\pi m/\tau}\right|\right) \\ &= O\left((\alpha^2 + \varphi^2)^{1/2}e^{-\pi\alpha/12}e^{\pi\alpha/(12(\alpha^2+\varphi^2))}\sum_{m=1}^{\infty} p(m)\exp\left(-2\pi m\frac{\alpha}{\alpha^2 + \varphi^2}\right)\right) \qquad (11) \\ &= O\left((\alpha^2 + \varphi_0^2)^{1/2}e^{-\pi\alpha/12}\sum_{m=1}^{\infty} p(m)\exp\left[\frac{-2\pi\alpha}{\alpha^2 + \varphi^2}\left(m - \frac{1}{24}\right)\right]\right) \\ &= O\left((\alpha^2 + \varphi_0^2)^{1/2}\sum_{m=1}^{\infty} p(m)\exp\left[\frac{-2\pi\alpha}{\alpha^2 + \varphi_0^2}\left(m - \frac{1}{24}\right)\right]\right), \end{aligned}$$

since for $m \geqq 1$, $m - 1/24 > 0$, $|\varphi| \leqq \varphi_0$, $e^{-\pi\alpha/12} < 1$. To make this expression homogeneous in α we put

$$\varphi_0 = \lambda\alpha , \tag{12}$$

where λ will be chosen shortly. Then

$$F(e^{-2\pi\tau}) - \psi(\tau) = O\left(\alpha(1 + \lambda^2)^{1/2}\sum_{m=1}^{\infty} p(m)\exp\left[-\frac{2\pi}{\alpha(1 + \lambda^2)}\left(m - \frac{1}{24}\right)\right]\right).$$

Now we choose λ so that

$$2\pi = \alpha(1 + \lambda^2) \,, \tag{13}$$

and then because

$$\sum_{m=1}^{\infty} p(m) e^{-(m-1/24)}$$

converges, we conclude from (11) that

$$F(e^{-2\pi\tau}) - \psi(\tau) = O(\sqrt{\alpha}) = O(1) \,. \tag{14}$$

This inequality holds for $|\varphi| \leqq \varphi_0$, where now from (12) and (13)

$$\varphi_0 = \alpha\lambda = \alpha\left(\frac{2\pi}{\alpha} - 1\right)^{1/2} = (2\pi\alpha - \alpha^2)^{1/2} \,.$$

We have thus found a neighborhood of the origin depending on α, where the difference $F(e^{-2\pi\tau}) - \psi(\tau)$ remains bounded. The value of α is still at our disposal and will be fixed when we evaluate the first integral. It will turn out that the most convenient value of α is $O(1/\sqrt{n})$.

Now we obtain estimates in the interval $\varphi_0 \leqq \varphi \leqq \frac{1}{2}$. Here, we have

$$\begin{aligned}
\psi(\tau) &= O\left((\alpha^2 + \varphi^2)^{1/2} \left| \exp\left[\frac{\pi}{12}\left(\frac{1}{\tau} - \tau\right)\right]\right|\right) \\
&= O\left(\left(\alpha^2 + \frac{1}{4}\right)^{1/2} \exp\left[\frac{\pi}{12}\,\frac{\alpha}{\alpha^2 + \varphi^2}\right] e^{-\pi\alpha/12}\right) \\
&= O\left(\left(\alpha^2 + \frac{1}{4}\right)^{1/2} \exp\left[\frac{\pi}{12}\,\frac{\alpha}{\alpha^2 + \varphi_0^2}\right]\right) \\
&= O\left(\left(\alpha^2 + \frac{1}{4}\right)^{1/2} e^{\pi/(12(1+\lambda^2))}\right) = O(1) \,.
\end{aligned} \tag{15}$$

For the function $F(e^{-2\pi\tau})$, we have in the interval $\varphi_0 \leqq \varphi \leqq \frac{1}{2}$,

$$\begin{aligned}
F(e^{-2\pi\tau}) &= \psi(\tau) F(e^{-2\pi/\tau}) \\
&= O\left(F\left(\exp\left[\frac{-2\pi\alpha}{\alpha^2 + \varphi^2}\right]\right)\right) \\
&= O\left(F\left(\exp\left[\frac{-2\pi\alpha}{\alpha^2 + \frac{1}{4}}\right]\right)\right) ,
\end{aligned} \tag{16}$$

because $F(x)$ is an increasing function. Now as $\alpha \to 0$, $\alpha/(\alpha^2 + \frac{1}{4}) \to 0$, $\exp[-2\pi\alpha/(\alpha^2 + \frac{1}{4})] \to 1$, and $F(\exp[-2\pi\alpha/(\alpha^2 + \frac{1}{4})]) \to \infty$. On the other hand,

$$\left(\frac{\alpha}{\alpha^2 + \frac{1}{4}}\right)^{-1} = \frac{\alpha^2 + \frac{1}{4}}{\alpha} = \alpha + \frac{1}{4\alpha} \to \infty, \quad \text{as} \quad \alpha \to 0 \,;$$

hence

$$\exp\left[-2\pi\left(\frac{\alpha^2 + \frac{1}{4}}{\alpha}\right)\right] \to 0 \,,$$

and then

$$F\left(\exp\left[-2\pi\frac{\alpha^2 + \frac{1}{4}}{\alpha}\right]\right) \to 1 \,.$$

These observations lead us to apply the functional equation again to the right-hand side of (16):

$$F\left(\exp\left[-\frac{2\pi\alpha}{\alpha^2+\frac{1}{4}}\right]\right)=\psi\left(\frac{\alpha}{\alpha^2+\frac{1}{4}}\right)F\left(\exp\left[-2\pi\frac{\alpha^2+\frac{1}{4}}{\alpha}\right]\right). \tag{17}$$

The minimum value of $\alpha+1/4\alpha$ occurs when $\alpha=\frac{1}{2}$; consequently

$$e^{-2\pi(\alpha+1/4\alpha)}<e^{-2\pi}<1\,,$$

and

$$F(e^{-2\pi(\alpha+1/4\alpha)})<F(e^{-2\pi})=O(1)\,.$$

Therefore, from (17),

$$\begin{aligned}F\left(\exp\left[-2\pi\frac{\alpha}{\alpha^2+\frac{1}{4}}\right]\right)&=O\left(\left(\frac{\alpha}{\alpha^2+\frac{1}{4}}\right)^{1/2}\exp\left[\frac{\pi}{12}\left(\alpha+\frac{1}{4\alpha}-\frac{\alpha}{\alpha^2+\frac{1}{4}}\right)\right]\right)\\&=O(e^{\pi/(48\alpha)})\,.\end{aligned} \tag{18}$$

Accordingly, from (15), (16) and (18) for $\varphi_0\leqq\varphi\leqq\frac{1}{2}$,

$$F(e^{-2\pi\tau})=O(e^{\pi/(48\alpha)})\,,$$

and therefore in the same interval,

$$F(e^{-2\pi\tau})-\psi(\tau)=O(e^{\pi/(48\alpha)})\,. \tag{19}$$

Inequalities (14) and (19) are now used to estimate the second integral in (10):

$$\begin{aligned}\int_{-1/2}^{1/2}(F(e^{-2\pi\tau})-\psi(\tau))e^{2\pi n\tau}d\varphi&=\left(\int_{-1/2}^{-\varphi_0}+\int_{-\varphi_0}^{\varphi_0}+\int_{\varphi_0}^{1/2}\right)(F(e^{-2\pi\tau})-\psi(\tau))e^{2\pi n\tau}d\varphi\\&=I_1+I_2+I_3\,.\end{aligned}$$

From (14),

$$I_2=O\left(\int_{-\varphi_0}^{\varphi_0}|e^{2\pi n\tau}|\,d\varphi\right)=O(e^{2\pi n\alpha})\,, \tag{20}$$

whereas from (19),

$$I_3=O(e^{2\pi n\alpha+\pi/(48\alpha)})\,; \tag{21}$$

and exactly the same estimate holds for I_1. We have therefore proved that

$$p(n)=\int_{-1/2}^{1/2}\psi(\tau)e^{2\pi n\tau}d\varphi+O(e^{2\pi n\alpha+\pi/(48\alpha)})\,. \tag{22}$$

We denote the integral by J; it remains to evaluate J. In fact,

$$\begin{aligned}J&=\int_{-1/2}^{1/2}(\alpha-i\varphi)^{1/2}\exp[\pi\{1/(\alpha-i\varphi)-(\alpha-i\varphi)\}/12+2\pi n(\alpha-i\varphi)]d\varphi\\&=\int_{-1/2}^{1/2}(\alpha-i\varphi)^{1/2}\exp[\pi/12(\alpha-i\varphi)+2\pi\alpha(n-1/24)-2\pi i\varphi(n-1/24)]d\varphi\,.\end{aligned}$$

If, for convenience, we put $m=2\pi(n-1/24)=2\pi\lambda_n^2$, where

$$\lambda_n=\left(n-\frac{1}{24}\right)^{1/2}, \tag{23}$$

and to make the integrand homogeneous $\varphi = \alpha u$, we get

$$J = \alpha^{3/2}\int_{-1/2\alpha}^{1/2\alpha}(1-iu)^{1/2}\exp[\pi/12\alpha(1-iu)+m\alpha(1-iu)]du\,. \tag{24}$$

We recognize the integrand as that belonging to a Bessel function if the coefficients of $1/(1-iu)$ and $1-iu$ were equal. We set these equal and this fixes the value of α. If

$$\frac{\pi}{12\alpha} = m\alpha = \sigma \quad \text{(say)}\,,$$

then

$$\alpha = \sqrt{\frac{\pi}{12m}}\,, \qquad \sigma = \sqrt{\frac{\pi m}{12}}\,. \tag{25}$$

Consequently,

$$J = \alpha^{3/2}\int_{-1/2\alpha}^{1/2\alpha}(1-iu)^{1/2}\exp\left[\sigma\left(\frac{1}{1-iu}+1-iu\right)\right]du\,. \tag{26}$$

We could replace the path of integration by a loop and evaluate J as a Bessel function. In this particular case, however, we can proceed directly. (In the more general case that we encounter later, we perform a loop integration.) Transforming the exponent in (26), we have

$$\frac{1}{1-iu}+1-iu = 2-\frac{u^2}{1-iu} = 2-g(u)\,,$$

where

$$g(u) = \frac{u^2}{1-iu}\,.$$

If we make the abbreviation

$$u_0 = \frac{1}{2\alpha}\,, \tag{27}$$

then

$$J = \alpha^{3/2}e^{2\sigma}\int_{-u_0}^{u_0}(1-iu)^{1/2}e^{-\sigma g(u)}du\,. \tag{28}$$

To evaluate this integral, we put

$$v = \frac{u}{(1-iu)^{1/2}}\,, \tag{29}$$

so that $g(u) = v^2$, where that branch of the square root is chosen which is $+1$ when $u = 0$. As u varies from $-u_0$ to u_0, v ranges over a curve Γ with end points

$$v_0 = \frac{-u_0}{(1+iu_0)^{1/2}} \quad \text{and} \quad v_1 = \frac{u_0}{(1-iu_0)^{1/2}}\,, \tag{30}$$

and Γ passes through the origin. Moreover,

$$\mathscr{R}(v_0) = -\mathscr{R}(v_1) = H \quad \text{(say)} . \tag{31}$$

If we drop perpendiculars from v_0 and v_1 to the real axis and label the points A, B, C, D as shown in the diagram, then because the integrand is regular,

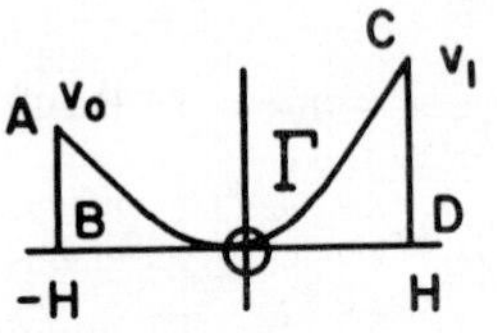

the integral along Γ is the sum of the integrals along AB, BD, CD. Call the integrals along these segments J_1, J_2 and J_3, respectively. We study J_2 first. Because by (29)

$$(1-iu)^{1/2} = \frac{u}{v} = \left(1-\frac{v^2}{4}\right)^{1/2} - \frac{iv}{2} ,$$

then

$$\begin{aligned} J_2 &= \int_{-H}^{H} e^{-\sigma v^2}\left(1 - v^2 + i\frac{v^3-3v}{2(1-v^2/4)^{1/2}}\right)dv \\ &= \int_{-H}^{H} e^{-\sigma v^2}(1-v^2)dv + i\int_{-H}^{H} \frac{v^3-3v}{2(1-v^2/4)^{1/2}}e^{-\sigma v^2}dv \\ &= J_2' + iJ_2'' . \end{aligned} \tag{32}$$

In J_2'' the points $v = \pm 2$ are points of discontinuity; we therefore divide the interval of integration into 4 parts:

$$J_2'' = \left(\int_0^2 + \int_2^H + \int_{-H}^{-2} + \int_{-2}^{0}\right) \frac{v^3-3v}{2\,(1-v^2/4)^{1/2}}\, e^{-\sigma v^2} dv . \tag{33}$$

If $|v| \leqq 2$, the integrand is an odd function of v and therefore

$$\int_{-2}^{2} \frac{v^3-3v}{2(1-v^2/4)^{1/2}} e^{-\sigma v^2} dv = 0 .$$

When $v^2 > 4$, we consider two possibilities:

(i) $v > 2$; in this case the above determination of the square root requires us to choose

$$\left(1-\frac{v^2}{4}\right)^{1/2} = -i\left(\frac{v^2}{4}-1\right)^{1/2} ;$$

(ii) $v < -2$ in which case

$$\left(1-\frac{v^2}{4}\right)^{1/2} = i\left(\frac{v^2}{4}-1\right)^{1/2} .$$

These determinations permit us to combine the two middle integrals in (33):

$$J_2 = \int_{-H}^{H} e^{-\sigma v^2}(1-v^2)dv + \int_2^H \frac{v^3-3v}{(v^2/4-1)^{1/2}} e^{-\sigma v^2} dv\,. \tag{34}$$

Because $v^2 > 4$, then $\sigma v^2 > \sigma v^2/2 + 2\sigma$, and

$$\begin{aligned}\int_2^H \frac{v^3-3v}{\left(\frac{v^2}{4}-1\right)^{1/2}} e^{-\sigma v^2} dv &= O\left(e^{-2\sigma}\int_2^\infty \frac{v^3-3v}{\left(\frac{v^2}{4}-1\right)^{1/2}} e^{-\sigma v^2/2} dv\right)\\ &= O\left(e^{-2\sigma}\int_2^\infty \frac{v^3-3v}{\left(\frac{v^2}{4}-1\right)^{1/2}} e^{-v^2/2} dv\right)\\ &= O(e^{-2\sigma})\,,\end{aligned} \tag{35}$$

if $\sigma > 2$.

Moreover,

$$\begin{aligned}\int_{-H}^{H} e^{-\sigma v^2}(1-v^2)dv &= \int_{-\infty}^{\infty} e^{-\sigma v^2}(1-v^2)dv + O\left(\int_H^\infty e^{-\sigma v^2}(1-v^2)dv\right)\\ &= \int_{-\infty}^{\infty} e^{-\sigma v^2}(1-v^2)dv + O(e^{-\sigma})\,,\end{aligned} \tag{36}$$

since

$$H = \frac{u_0}{(1+u_0^2)^{1/2}}\left(\frac{(1+u_0^2)^{1/2}+1}{2}\right)^{1/2} = O(u_0^{1/4}) = O(\sigma^{1/4})\,,$$

by (30) and (31).

The integral on the right of (36) is well known (see Appendix A on the Γ function), and its value is

$$\frac{1}{\sqrt{\sigma}}\Gamma\left(\frac{1}{2}\right) - \frac{1}{\sigma^{3/2}}\Gamma\left(\frac{3}{2}\right) = \frac{\sqrt{\pi}}{\sqrt{\sigma}}\left(1-\frac{1}{2\sigma}\right).$$

Consequently by (34), (35), (36),

$$J_2 = \frac{\sqrt{\pi}}{\sqrt{\sigma}}\left(1-\frac{1}{2\sigma}\right) + O(e^{-2\sigma}) + O(e^{-\sigma})\,. \tag{37}$$

To estimate J_1, we notice that

$$|v_0| = \frac{u_0}{(1+u_0^2)^{1/4}} = O(\sigma^{1/2})\,,$$

and therefore the length of AB is $O(\sigma^{1/2})$. Moreover,

$$1 - v^2 + i\frac{v^3-3v}{2\left(1-\frac{v^2}{4}\right)^{1/2}} = O(v_0^2) = O(\sigma)\,. \tag{38}$$

In addition, on AB

$$e^{-\sigma v^2} = O\left(\exp\left[-\sigma\mathscr{R}\left(\frac{u_0^2}{1-iu_0}\right)\right]\right) = O\left(\exp\left[-\sigma\frac{u_0^2}{1+u_0^2}\right]\right)$$

(39)
$$= O\left(\exp\left[-\sigma\frac{1}{1+\frac{1}{u_0^2}}\right]\right) = O(e^{-\sigma}) .$$

From (38), (39),

(40)
$$J_1 = O(\sigma^{3/2}e^{-\sigma}) ,$$

and by exactly the same argument,

(41)
$$J_3 = O(\sigma^{3/2}e^{-\sigma}) .$$

Accordingly, by (28), (32), (37), (40), and (41),

(42)
$$J = \int_{-1/2}^{1/2} \psi(\tau)e^{-2\pi n\tau}d\varphi$$
$$= \alpha^{3/2}e^{2\sigma}\left(\frac{\sqrt{\pi}}{\sqrt{\sigma}}\left(1-\frac{1}{2\sigma}\right) + O(\sigma^{3/2}e^{-\sigma}) + O(e^{-\sigma}) + O(e^{-2\sigma})\right),$$

where, from (25),

$$\alpha = \sqrt{\frac{\pi}{12m}}, \quad m = 2\pi\left(n-\frac{1}{24}\right) = 2\pi\lambda_n^2, \quad \sigma = \sqrt{\frac{\pi m}{12}};$$

that is,

$$\alpha = \frac{1}{2\sqrt{6}\lambda_n}, \quad \sigma = \frac{\pi\lambda_n}{\sqrt{6}}, \quad 2\sigma = \pi\sqrt{\frac{2}{3}}\lambda_n = a\lambda_n ,$$

and

$$\alpha^{3/2}\frac{\sqrt{\pi}}{\sqrt{\sigma}} = \frac{1}{4\sqrt{3}\lambda_n^2}, \quad \alpha\sigma = O(1) .$$

These calculations give, from (42),

(43)
$$J = \frac{1}{4\sqrt{3}\lambda_n^2}e^{a\lambda_n}\left(1-\frac{1}{a\lambda_n}\right) + O(e^{\sigma})$$
$$= \frac{1}{2\pi\sqrt{2}}\frac{d}{dn}\left(\frac{e^{a\lambda_n}}{\lambda_n}\right) + O(e^{a\lambda_n/2}) .$$

Combining this with (23), we get, with $a = \pi(\frac{2}{3})^{1/2}$,

$$p(n) = J + O(e^{2\pi n\alpha + \pi/48\alpha})$$
$$= \frac{1}{2\pi\sqrt{2}}\frac{d}{dn}\left(\frac{e^{a\lambda_n}}{\lambda_n}\right) + O(e^{a\lambda_n/2}) + O(e^{5a\lambda_n/8})$$
$$= \frac{1}{2\pi\sqrt{2}}\frac{d}{dn}\left(\frac{e^{a\lambda_n}}{\lambda_n}\right) + O(e^{5a\lambda_n/8}) ,$$

since $2\pi n\alpha + \pi/48\alpha = \pi n/\sqrt{6}\lambda_n + \pi\lambda_n/4\sqrt{6}$, and

$$O(e^{2\pi n\alpha+\pi/48\alpha}) = O(e^{5\pi\lambda_n/4\sqrt{6}}) = O(e^{5a\lambda_n/8}) .$$

This completes the proof. With additional care and analysis, we could replace the term $O(e^{5a\lambda_n/8})$ by $O(e^{a\lambda_n/2})$.

3. The behavior of $\eta(\tau)$ under modular transformation. In this section we prove formula 2.5, which was assumed to hold in § 2. We shall then derive a more general formula valid for a so-called modular transformation. We work with the Dedekind function $\eta(\tau)$.

Let

$$q = e^{2\pi i\tau}, \tag{1}$$

and

$$\eta(\tau) = q^{1/24} \prod_{m=1}^{\infty} (1 - q^m), \tag{2}$$

with $\mathscr{I}(\tau) > 0$, in order to assure convergence. We prove

THEOREM 3.1.

$$\eta\left(\frac{-1}{\tau}\right) = \sqrt{\frac{\tau}{i}}\,\eta(\tau); \tag{3}$$

the branch of the square root is that for which the value is $+1$ *when* $\tau = +i$.

PROOF. We suppose to begin with that τ is purely imaginary, $\tau = it$, $t > 0$. We prove that (3) holds for this τ and then the relation will hold by analytic continuation for all complex τ with $\mathscr{I}(\tau) > 0$. The simple proof we give is due to C. L. Siegel; other proofs are known, however.

We begin by taking logarithms in (2):

$$\begin{aligned} \log \eta(\tau) &= \frac{\pi i\tau}{12} + \sum_{m=1}^{\infty} \log(1 - q^m) \\ &= \frac{\pi i\tau}{12} - \sum_{m=1}^{\infty}\sum_{k=1}^{\infty} \frac{q^{mk}}{k} \\ &= \frac{\pi i\tau}{12} - \sum_{k=1}^{\infty} \frac{1}{k} \sum_{m=1}^{\infty} q^{mk} \\ &= \frac{\pi i\tau}{12} - \sum_{k=1}^{\infty} \frac{1}{k(q^{-k} - 1)} \\ &= \frac{\pi i\tau}{12} - \sum_{k=1}^{\infty} \frac{1}{k(e^{-2\pi ik\tau} - 1)}. \end{aligned} \tag{4}$$

It follows on replacing τ by $-1/\tau$ in (4), that

$$\log \eta\left(-\frac{1}{\tau}\right) = \frac{-\pi i}{12\tau} - \sum_{k=1}^{\infty} \frac{1}{k(e^{2\pi ik/\tau} - 1)}. \tag{5}$$

From (4) and (5) we conclude that the statement of the theorem is equivalent to the relation

$$\frac{\pi i}{12}(\tau + \tau^{-1}) + \frac{1}{2}\log\frac{\tau}{i} = \sum_{k=1}^{\infty} \frac{1}{k}\left(\frac{1}{e^{-2\pi ik\tau} - 1} - \frac{1}{e^{2\pi ik/\tau} - 1}\right). \tag{6}$$

Our objective then will be the summation of the series on the right and a natural recourse here is Cauchy's theorem and the calculus of residues.

We notice first that

$$\text{(7)} \qquad \frac{i}{2}\cot x = \frac{1}{2} + \frac{1}{e^{-2ix} - 1} = -\frac{1}{2} - \frac{1}{e^{2ix} - 1}$$

which for $x = \pi k\tau$ and $x = \pi k/\tau$ closely resembles the terms in the right-hand side of (6). This remark leads us to consider the function

$$g(z) = \cot \pi z \cot \frac{\pi z}{\tau}$$

and to construct the meromorphic function

$$G_N(z) = \frac{g(Nz)}{z},$$

where $N = n + \frac{1}{2}$ and n is a non-negative integer. $G_N(z)$ has simple poles at $z = \pm k/N$ and $z = \pm k\tau/N$ for $k = 1, 2, 3, \cdots$. The residues at these simple poles are respectively $(1/\pi k)\cot \pi k/\tau$ and $(1/\pi k)\cot \pi k\tau$.

In addition, however, $G_N(z)$ has a pole of order 3 at $z = 0$. Since

$$\cot x = \frac{1}{x}\left(1 - \frac{x^2}{3} - \frac{x^4}{45} - \cdots\right),$$

we find the residue at $z = 0$ from the expansion of $G_N(z)$ about $z = 0$. Indeed,

$$\text{(8)} \qquad G_N(z) = \frac{1}{z}\cdot\frac{1}{\pi Nz}\cdot\frac{\tau}{\pi Nz}\left(1 - \frac{(\pi Nz)^2}{3} - \frac{(\pi Nz)^4}{45} - \cdots\right) \times \left(1 - \frac{(\pi Nz)^2}{3\tau^2} - \frac{(\pi Nz)^4}{45\tau^4} - \cdots\right)$$

and therefore from (8), the residue is

$$\text{(9)} \qquad \frac{-\tau}{(\pi N)^2}\left(\frac{(\pi N)^2}{3} + \frac{(\pi N)^2}{3\tau^2}\right) = -\frac{1}{3}(\tau + \tau^{-1}).$$

Let $\mathscr{C}$ be the contour in the z-plane formed by the rhombus with vertices at ± 1, $\pm\tau$. Then from the residue theorem,

$$\text{(10)} \qquad \int_{\mathscr{C}} G_N(z)dz = -\frac{2\pi i}{3}(\tau + \tau^{-1}) + 4i\sum_{k=1}^{h(n)}\frac{1}{k}(\cot \pi k\tau + \cot \pi k/\tau),$$

since $\cot x$ is an odd function of x, where $h(n)$ is determined such that $k\tau/N \leqq 1$ and $k/N \leqq 1$, and therefore as $n \to \infty$, $h(n) \to \infty$. From (10), we therefore get

$$\text{(11)} \qquad \frac{\pi i}{12}(\tau + \tau^{-1}) + \frac{1}{8}\int_{\mathscr{C}} G_N(z)dz = \frac{i}{2}\sum_{k \leqq h(n)}\frac{1}{k}(\cot \pi k\tau + \cot \pi k/\tau).$$

But from (7), the parenthesis on the right-hand side of (11) is

$$\frac{i}{2}(\cot \pi k\tau + \cot \pi k/\tau) = \left(\frac{1}{2} + \frac{1}{e^{-2\pi ik\tau} - 1} - \frac{1}{2} - \frac{1}{e^{2\pi ik/\tau} - 1}\right),$$

and therefore

$$\frac{\pi i}{12}(\tau + \tau^{-1}) + \frac{1}{8}\int_{\mathscr{C}} G_N(z)dz = \sum_{k \leq h(n)} \frac{1}{k}\left(\frac{1}{e^{-2\pi ik\tau} - 1} - \frac{1}{e^{2\pi ik/\tau} - 1}\right). \tag{12}$$

Now we let $n \to \infty$ and calculate the limit of $g(Nz)$. We shall show that on the sides joining 1 to τ and -1 to $-\tau$, $g(Nz) \to +1$, whereas on the sides joining -1 to τ and $-\tau$ to 1, $g(Nz) \to -1$, these limits holding if the points ± 1, $\pm \tau$ are excluded. Moreover the convergence is bounded, and we shall therefore be justified in interchanging the processes of limit and integration.

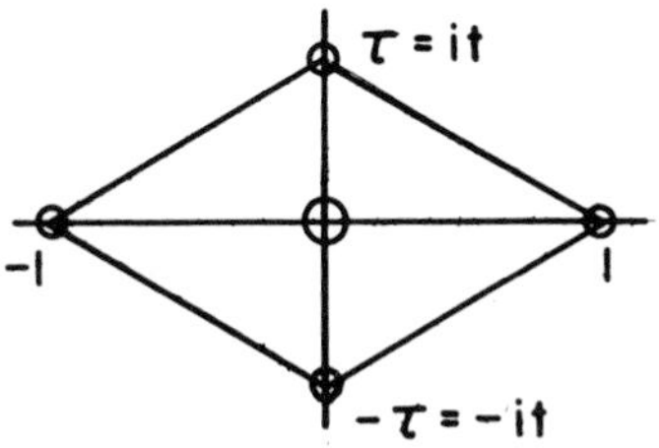

We shall then get

$$\begin{aligned} \lim_{n\to\infty}\int_{\mathscr{C}} \frac{G_N(z)}{8}dz &= \lim_{n\to\infty}\left(\int_1^\tau + \int_\tau^{-1} + \int_{-1}^{-\tau} + \int_{-\tau}^{1}\right)\frac{g(Nz)}{8z}dz \\ &= \frac{1}{8}\left(\int_1^\tau - \int_\tau^{-1} + \int_{-1}^{-\tau} - \int_{-\tau}^{1}\right)\frac{dz}{z} \\ &= \frac{1}{2}\log\frac{\tau}{i}. \end{aligned} \tag{13}$$

This together with (6) and (12) will complete the proof of the theorem. It thus remains only to verify the bounded convergence stated above. Indeed on the side joining 1 to τ, $z = x + iy = x + it(1 - x)$, where to exclude the points 1 and τ, we require that $0 < x < 1$. Therefore since $N = n + \frac{1}{2}$, using (7),

$$g(Nz) = -\left(1 + \frac{2}{e^{2\pi iN(x+it(1-x))} - 1}\right)\left(1 + \frac{2}{e^{2\pi iN(x/it+1-x)} - 1}\right) \to 1,$$

since we have avoided the points corresponding to $x = 0$, $x = 1$. That the convergence is bounded is easily seen since

$$2\pi iN(x + it(1 - x)) = (2n + 1)\pi ix - (2n + 1)\pi t(1 - x)$$

avoids an even multiple of πi by a safe margin.

The relation (3) which we proved valid for $\tau = it$ holds by analytic continuation for all τ for which $\mathscr{I}(\tau) > 0$ and we choose that branch of $\sqrt{(\tau/i)}$ which is $+1$ for $\tau = i$. If $\tau = \sigma + it$, $\tau > 0$, then the determination we have made of the square root requires us to choose

$$\left(\frac{\tau}{i}\right)^{1/2} = e^{-\pi i/4}\sqrt{\tau} \,,$$

where $\sqrt{\tau}$ is now the principal branch of $(\tau)^{1/2}$. Thus

$$\eta\left(-\frac{1}{\tau}\right) = e^{-\pi i/4}\sqrt{\tau}\eta(\tau) \,. \tag{14}$$

The relationship 2.5 involving $F(x)$ now follows as a simple corollary.

THEOREM 3.2. *If*

$$F(x) = \prod_{m=1}^{\infty}(1 - x^m)^{-1} \,, \tag{15}$$

then if $x = e^{-2\pi\tau}$, *with* $\mathscr{R}(\tau) > 0$,

$$F(e^{-2\pi\tau}) = \sqrt{\tau}e^{(\pi/12)(1/\tau - \tau)}F(e^{-2\pi/\tau}) \,. \tag{16}$$

PROOF. In (15), we put

$$x = e^{2\pi i\xi} \,, \qquad \mathscr{I}(\xi) > 0 \,;$$

then by Theorem 3.1,

$$\begin{aligned} F(e^{2\pi i\xi}) &= \prod_{m=1}^{\infty}(1 - e^{2\pi i m\xi})^{-1} \\ &= e^{\pi i\xi/12}/\eta(\xi) \\ &= e^{\pi i\xi/12}\sqrt{\frac{\xi}{i}}\Big/\eta\left(-\frac{1}{\xi}\right) \\ &= e^{\pi i\xi/12}\sqrt{\frac{\xi}{i}}e^{-\pi i/12\xi}F(e^{-2\pi i/\xi}) \\ &= e^{\pi(i\xi - i/\xi)/12}\sqrt{\frac{\xi}{i}}F(e^{-2\pi i/\xi}) \,. \end{aligned} \tag{17}$$

If now we replace $i\xi$ by $-\tau$, then $\mathscr{R}(\tau) = \mathscr{R}(-i\xi) = \mathscr{I}(\xi) > 0$ and the result (17) becomes

$$F(e^{-2\pi\tau}) = e^{\pi(1/\tau - \tau)/12}\sqrt{\tau}F(e^{-2\pi/\tau}) \,,$$

as required.

We have seen how the formula

$$\eta\left(-\frac{1}{\tau}\right) = \sqrt{\frac{\tau}{i}}\eta(\tau), \quad \text{for } \mathscr{I}(\tau) > 0 \tag{18}$$

had important consequences to $F(x)$. We make one more observation:

(19) $$\eta(\tau+1)=e^{\pi i(\tau+1)/12}\prod_{m=1}^{\infty}(1-e^{2\pi i m(\tau+1)})=e^{\pi i/12}e^{\pi i\tau/12}\prod_{m=1}^{\infty}(1-e^{2\pi i m\tau})=e^{\pi i/12}\eta(\tau)\,.$$

Thus the fact that $e^{2\pi i x}$ is a periodic function with period 1 reflects itself in the transformation (19).

One of the most interesting and important types of general transformations which incorporate transformations of the kind given by (18) and (19) is the so-called modular transformation. This is simply a bilinear transformation with a restriction placed on the coefficients:

(20) $$\tau'=\frac{a\tau+b}{c\tau+d}\,,$$

where a, b, c, d are rational integers with

$$ad-bc=1\,.$$

Notice that the transformation given by (18) is

(21) $$\tau'=\frac{0\tau-1}{\tau+0}\,,$$

and by (19) is

(22) $$\tau'=\frac{\tau+1}{0\tau+1}\,.$$

It is a surprising fact that any modular transformation can be obtained as a combination of the transformations (21) and (22). Let us first show that the product of two modular transformations is again modular.

THEOREM 3.3. *If*

(23) $$\tau''=\frac{a'\tau'+b'}{c'\tau'+d'}\,,\qquad \tau'=\frac{a\tau+b}{c\tau+d}\,,$$

with $a', b', c', d', a, b, c, d$ *integers for which*

$$a'd'-b'c'=1\,,\qquad ad-bc=1\,,$$

then

(24) $$\tau''=\frac{A\tau+B}{C\tau+D}\,,$$

where A, B, C, D *are integers for which* $AD-BC=1$.

PROOF. The proof is a matter of straightforward verification. From (23),

(25) $$\tau''=\frac{a'\dfrac{a\tau+b}{c\tau+d}+b'}{c'\dfrac{a\tau+b}{c\tau+d}+d'}=\frac{(aa'+b'c)\tau+(a'b+b'd)}{(ac'+cd')\tau+(bc'+dd')}$$
$$=\frac{A\tau+B}{C\tau+D}\,,$$

and

$$AD - BC = (aa' + b'c)(bc' + dd') - (a'b + b'd)(ac' + cd')$$
$$= (ad - bc)(a'd' - b'c') = 1\ .$$

THEOREM 3.4. *The modular transformations form a group.*

PROOF. Theorem 3.3 verified the closure. The transformation $\tau' = \tau = (\tau + 0)/(0\tau + 1)$ is the identity. The associative law clearly holds and the inverse of the transformation

$$\tau' = \frac{a\tau + b}{c\tau + d}$$

is

$$\tau'' = \frac{d\tau' - b}{-c\tau' + a}\ ,$$

for then

$$\tau'' = \frac{d\left(\dfrac{a\tau + b}{c\tau + d}\right) - b}{-c\left(\dfrac{a\tau + b}{c\tau + d}\right) + a} = \frac{\tau}{1} = \tau\ .$$

The rule of composition (25) leads us, for simplicity, to associate with the modular transformation

$$\tau' = \frac{a\tau + b}{c\tau + d}\ ,$$

the matrix

$$\begin{pmatrix} a & b \\ c & d \end{pmatrix}.$$

Because

$$\tau' = \frac{-a\tau - b}{-c\tau - d} = \frac{a\tau + b}{c\tau + d}\ ,$$

the matrices

$$\begin{pmatrix} a & b \\ c & d \end{pmatrix} \text{ and } \begin{pmatrix} -a & -b \\ -c & -d \end{pmatrix}$$

lead to the same modular transformation. The set of matrices

$$\begin{pmatrix} a & b \\ c & d \end{pmatrix}$$

with a, b, c, d integers, and $ad - bc = 1$, forms a group under multiplication. We shall show that this group is generated by

$$A=\begin{pmatrix}1 & 1\\ 0 & 1\end{pmatrix}, \qquad B=\begin{pmatrix}0 & -1\\ 1 & 0\end{pmatrix}.$$

Notice that A corresponds to the transformation (19), and B, to the transformation (18). Because

$$B^2=\begin{pmatrix}-1 & 0\\ 0 & -1\end{pmatrix}, \tag{26}$$

multiplying the matrix

$$\begin{pmatrix}a & b\\ c & d\end{pmatrix}$$

by B^2 has only the effect of changing it to

$$\begin{pmatrix}-a & -b\\ -c & -d\end{pmatrix}.$$

It will therefore follow that the group of modular transformations has A and B as generators.

To illustrate the procedure, we consider a particular example. We shall factor the transformation

$$\tau' = \frac{3\tau+4}{2\tau+3}.$$

We observe first that

$$A^{-1}=\begin{pmatrix}1 & -1\\ 0 & 1\end{pmatrix}$$

and therefore that

$$A^h=\begin{pmatrix}1 & h\\ 0 & 1\end{pmatrix}$$

for $h=0, \pm 1, \pm 2, \cdots$. We have

$$\tau' = \frac{3\tau+4}{2\tau+3} = 1+\frac{\tau+1}{2\tau+3} = 1+\tau_1 .$$

On the other hand,

$$\tau_1 = \frac{\tau+1}{2\tau+3} = \frac{-1}{-\dfrac{2\tau+3}{\tau+1}} = -\frac{1}{\tau_2},$$

$$\tau_2 = -\frac{2\tau+3}{\tau+1} = -2-\frac{1}{\tau+1} = -2+\tau_3 ,$$

$$\tau_3 = -\frac{1}{\tau+1} = \frac{-1}{\tau_4}; \quad \tau_4 = 1+\tau .$$

Each of these steps is obtained by one or the other of the transformations (18) or (19). In matrix notation,

$$\begin{pmatrix}3&4\\2&3\end{pmatrix}=\begin{pmatrix}1&1\\0&1\end{pmatrix}\begin{pmatrix}1&1\\2&3\end{pmatrix}=\begin{pmatrix}1&1\\0&1\end{pmatrix}\begin{pmatrix}0&-1\\1&0\end{pmatrix}\begin{pmatrix}2&3\\-1&-1\end{pmatrix}$$
$$=\begin{pmatrix}1&1\\0&1\end{pmatrix}\begin{pmatrix}0&-1\\1&0\end{pmatrix}\begin{pmatrix}1&-2\\0&1\end{pmatrix}\begin{pmatrix}0&1\\-1&-1\end{pmatrix}$$
$$=\begin{pmatrix}1&1\\0&1\end{pmatrix}\begin{pmatrix}0&-1\\1&0\end{pmatrix}\begin{pmatrix}1&-2\\0&1\end{pmatrix}\begin{pmatrix}0&-1\\1&0\end{pmatrix}\begin{pmatrix}-1&-1\\0&-1\end{pmatrix}$$
$$=\begin{pmatrix}1&1\\0&1\end{pmatrix}\begin{pmatrix}0&-1\\1&0\end{pmatrix}\begin{pmatrix}1&-2\\0&1\end{pmatrix}\begin{pmatrix}0&-1\\1&0\end{pmatrix}\begin{pmatrix}1&1\\0&1\end{pmatrix}\begin{pmatrix}-1&0\\0&-1\end{pmatrix}$$
$$=\begin{pmatrix}1&1\\0&1\end{pmatrix}\begin{pmatrix}0&-1\\1&0\end{pmatrix}\begin{pmatrix}1&-2\\0&1\end{pmatrix}\begin{pmatrix}0&-1\\1&0\end{pmatrix}\begin{pmatrix}1&1\\0&1\end{pmatrix}\begin{pmatrix}0&-1\\1&0\end{pmatrix}\begin{pmatrix}0&-1\\1&0\end{pmatrix}$$
$$=ABA^{-2}BAB^2 .$$

The idea of the above decomposition was to replace a by a value a_1 such that $|a_1|<|a|$ and then a_1 by a value a_2 such that $|a_2|<|a_1|$, etc. Since $|a|$ is bounded, we are led ultimately to $a_n=0$, and a matrix

$$\begin{pmatrix}0&b_n\\c_n&d_n\end{pmatrix}.$$

The determinant is still 1 and therefore $b_nc_n=-1$. We can choose, without loss of generality, $b_n=-1$, $c_n=1$; otherwise we multiply by

$$B^2=\begin{pmatrix}-1&0\\0&-1\end{pmatrix}.$$

We now prove the result in the form of

THEOREM 3.5 *The group of matrices of the form*

$$M=\begin{pmatrix}a&b\\c&d\end{pmatrix},$$

with a, b, c, d integers for which $ad-bc=1$, is generated by

$$A=\begin{pmatrix}1&1\\0&1\end{pmatrix} \quad \textit{and} \quad B=\begin{pmatrix}0&-1\\1&0\end{pmatrix}. \tag{27}$$

PROOF. The proof is most conveniently effected by induction on $m=|a|$. If $m=0$, then

$$M=\begin{pmatrix}0&b\\c&d\end{pmatrix},$$

and in that case $bc=-1$; assume without loss in generality that $b=+1$, $c=-1$. In that event

$$M=\begin{pmatrix}0&1\\-1&d\end{pmatrix}=\begin{pmatrix}0&-1\\1&0\end{pmatrix}\begin{pmatrix}-1&d\\0&-1\end{pmatrix}$$
$$=\begin{pmatrix}0&-1\\1&0\end{pmatrix}\begin{pmatrix}1&-d\\0&1\end{pmatrix}\begin{pmatrix}-1&0\\0&-1\end{pmatrix}=BA^{-d}B^2 .$$

Suppose then that the theorem is true for $0, 1, 2, \cdots, m-1$. Suppose, moreover, that $c > 0$; if $c = 0$, then $ad = 1$ and

$$M = \begin{pmatrix} a & b \\ 0 & d \end{pmatrix} = \begin{pmatrix} 1 & b \\ 0 & 1 \end{pmatrix} = A^b ,$$

or

$$M = \begin{pmatrix} -1 & b \\ 0 & -1 \end{pmatrix} = A^b \begin{pmatrix} -1 & 0 \\ 0 & -1 \end{pmatrix} = A^b B^2 .$$

If $c < 0$, then we replace M by $B^2 M$ which changes the signs of all the elements. Suppose, furthermore, that $|a| > c$; if $|a| < c$, then

$$M = \begin{pmatrix} 0 & -1 \\ 1 & 0 \end{pmatrix} \begin{pmatrix} c & d \\ -a & -b \end{pmatrix} = B \begin{pmatrix} c & d \\ -a & -b \end{pmatrix} ,$$

and M is replaced by a matrix in which $|a| > c$. Our object is to replace M by a matrix

$$M_1 = \begin{pmatrix} a_1 & b_1 \\ c_1 & d_1 \end{pmatrix} ,$$

in which $|a_1| < |a|$. In fact, for any h,

$$A^{-h} M = \begin{pmatrix} a - ch & b - dh \\ c & d - ch \end{pmatrix} . \tag{28}$$

We choose h such that

$$a = ch + r ,$$

where $h > 0$ if $a > 0$ and $h < 0$ if $a < 0$ and in any event,

$$|a - ch| = |r| < c < |a| .$$

Thus the induction hypothesis applies to $A^{-h} M$ and it follows that $A^{-h} M =$ product of A's and B's $= \prod (A, B)$, say, and therefore, that

$$M = A^h \prod (A, B) .$$

As a further arithmetical illustration, let us calculate $\eta(\tau')$ where

$$\tau' = \frac{5\tau + 4}{6\tau + 5} .$$

Since $5 < 6$, we apply B:

$$\eta(\tau') = \eta\left(-\frac{1}{-\dfrac{6\tau - 5}{5\tau + 4}} \right) = \eta\left(-\frac{1}{\tau_1} \right) = \sqrt{\frac{\tau_1}{i}}\, \eta(\tau_1) ,$$

where

$$\tau_1 = -\frac{6\tau + 5}{5\tau + 4} = -1 - \frac{\tau + 1}{5\tau + 4} = -1 - \tau_2 ;$$

$$\tau_2 = -\frac{\tau+1}{5\tau+4}, \qquad \eta(\tau_1) = e^{-\pi i/12}\eta(-\tau_2),$$

$$\eta(-\tau_2) = \eta\left(-\frac{\tau+1}{5\tau+4}\right) = \eta\left(\frac{\frac{-1}{5\tau+4}}{\tau+1}\right) = \eta\left(-\frac{1}{\tau_3}\right),$$

where

$$\tau_3 = \frac{5\tau+4}{\tau+1}; \qquad \eta\left(-\frac{1}{\tau_3}\right) = \sqrt{\frac{\tau_3}{i}}\eta(\tau_3),$$

$$\eta(\tau_3) = \eta\left(\frac{5\tau+4}{\tau+1}\right) = \eta\left(5 + \frac{-1}{\tau+1}\right) = \eta(5+\tau_4),$$

$$\tau_4 = -\frac{1}{\tau+1}, \qquad \eta(5+\tau_4) = e^{5\pi i/12}\eta(\tau_4),$$

$$\eta(\tau_4) = \eta\left(-\frac{1}{\tau+1}\right) = \sqrt{\frac{\tau+1}{i}}\eta(\tau+1) = e^{\pi i/12}\sqrt{\frac{\tau+1}{i}}\eta(\tau).$$

Consequently,

$$\begin{aligned}\eta\left(\frac{5\tau+4}{6\tau+5}\right) &= \left(\frac{-6\tau-5}{5\tau+4}\frac{1}{i}\right)^{1/2}\left(\frac{5\tau+4}{\tau+1}\frac{1}{i}\right)^{1/2}\left(\frac{\tau+1}{i}\right)^{1/2} e^{-\pi i/12}e^{5\pi i/12}e^{\pi i/12}\eta(\tau)\\ &= \left(\frac{6\tau+5}{i}\right)^{1/2} e^{5\pi i/12}\eta(\tau)\\ &= e^{-\pi i/4}e^{5\pi i/12}(6\tau+5)^{1/2}\eta(\tau)\\ &= e^{\pi i/6}(6\tau+5)^{1/2}\eta(\tau).\end{aligned} \tag{29}$$

The principle we have used in this specific example enables us to enunciate and prove

THEOREM 3.6. *If*

$$\tau' = \frac{a\tau+b}{c\tau+d}, \quad ad - bc = 1, \tag{30}$$

then

$$\eta(\tau') = \varepsilon(c\tau+d)^{1/2}\eta(\tau), \tag{31}$$

where ε *is a 24th root of unity, i.e.,* $\varepsilon^{24} = 1$.

PROOF. Suppose that the theorem is true for a particular set of values a, b, c, d; then we need only show that if we apply to τ' the fundamental substitutions corresponding to A and B of equation (27), then the functional relation (31) is preserved. In fact, if (31) holds,

$$\begin{aligned}\eta\left(-\frac{c\tau+d}{a\tau+b}\right) = \eta\left(-\frac{1}{\tau'}\right) &= e^{-\pi i/4}(\tau')^{1/2}\eta(\tau')\\ &= e^{-\pi i/4}\left(\frac{a\tau+b}{c\tau+d}\right)^{1/2}\varepsilon(c\tau+d)^{1/2}\eta(\tau)\\ &= (\varepsilon e^{-\pi i/4})(a\tau+b)^{1/2}\eta(\tau),\end{aligned}$$

and

$$\varepsilon_1^{24} = (\varepsilon e^{-\pi i/4})^{24} = 1 .$$

Also,

$$\eta\left(\frac{(a+c)\tau + (b+d)}{c\tau + d}\right) = \eta(\tau' + 1) = e^{\pi i/12}\eta(\tau')$$
$$= e^{\pi i/12}\varepsilon(c\tau + d)^{1/2}\eta(\tau)$$

and $(e^{\pi i/12}\varepsilon)^{24} = 1$.

By Theorem 3.5, then, the functional relation (31) holds for any modular substitution and this completes the proof.

The behavior of $\eta(\tau)$ under a modular substitution is completely determined therefore with one provision—the precise determination of the factor ε. To exhibit the factor ε as a function of the constants a, b, c, d of the substitution is not a simple matter. We saw above how it could be evaluated in a specific case by the decomposition of the transformation into a product of the elementary transformations and then a successive application of the functional relation for each of these. Its determination in general is, however, rather complicated.

We intend to deduce from the behavior of $\eta(\tau)$ some information about $F(x)$; in particular, we are interested in the behavior of $F(x)$ in the neighborhood of a rational point of the unit circle. This being the case, we should like to infer a litte more about the nature of those modular substitutions which interest us.

Let $x = e^{2\pi i\tau}$, $\mathscr{I}(\tau) > 0$ and

$$F(x) = F(e^{2\pi i\tau}) .$$

By Euler's relation

$$F(e^{2\pi i\tau}) = \sum_{n=0}^{\infty} p(n)e^{2\pi in\tau} ,$$

and therefore as $\tau \to i\infty$, $e^{2\pi in\tau} \to 0$, and as a result

$$F(e^{2\pi i\tau}) \to 1 .$$

Moreover, Theorem 3.6, together with Theorem 3.2, leads us to expect a relation for $F(x)$ of the following type

$$F(e^{2\pi i\tau'}) = \varphi(\tau)F(e^{2\pi i\tau}) ,$$

and we are interested in the behavior as $\tau \to h/k$, $(h, k) = 1$. Accordingly, we focus our attention on those substitutions for which $\tau' \to i\infty$, as $\tau \to h/k$ (not necessarily through real values). The most obvious choice is to put

$$\tau' = \frac{a\tau + b}{k\tau - h} , \tag{32}$$

and then to evaluate a, b in accordance with the restriction

(33) $$-ah - bk = 1\,.$$

This implies the congruence condition

$$ah \equiv -1 \pmod{k}\,,$$

which congruence is solvable since $(h, k) = 1$. We call the solution h',

(34) $$hh' \equiv -1 \pmod{k}\,.$$

In that event

$$-hh' - bk = 1\,,$$

and therefore

(35) $$b = -\frac{hh' + 1}{k}\,.$$

b is of course an integer since we guaranteed it by (34). Hence we study the transformation given by

(36) $$\tau' = \frac{h'\tau - \dfrac{1 + hh'}{k}}{k\tau - h}\,.$$

In the neighborhood of the point $e^{2\pi i h/k}$, it is convenient to exhibit x so as to bring this point into focus. We write therefore

(37) $$x = e^{2\pi i h/k - 2\pi z/k} = e^{2\pi i(h/k + iz/k)}\,,$$

and the behavior of $F(x)$ in the neighborhood of $e^{2\pi i h/k}$ is equivalent to a determination of the behavior of $F(x)$ as $z \to 0$. In the representation (37),

$$\tau = \frac{h}{k} + \frac{iz}{k}\,,$$

and therefore from (36),

(38) $$\tau' = \frac{h'\left(\dfrac{h}{k} + \dfrac{iz}{k}\right) - \dfrac{1 + hh'}{k}}{k\left(\dfrac{h}{k} + \dfrac{iz}{k}\right) - h} = \frac{h'}{k} + \frac{i}{kz}\,.$$

With this choice of τ', Theorem 3.6 gives

(39) $$\eta\left(\frac{h'}{k} + \frac{i}{zk}\right) = \varepsilon\sqrt{z}\,\eta\left(\frac{h}{k} + \frac{iz}{k}\right),$$

and this leads to

THEOREM 3.7. *If $\mathscr{R}(z) > 0$, $(h, k) = 1$, then*

$$F(e^{2\pi i(h/k + iz/k)}) = \omega_{h,k}\sqrt{z}\,e^{\pi(1/kz - z/k)/12}F(e^{2\pi i(h'/k + i/kz)})\,,$$

where $hh' \equiv -1 \pmod{k}$, and $\omega_{h,k}$ is a 24kth root of unity.

PROOF. Since for $\mathscr{I}(\tau) < 0$, $F(e^{2\pi i\tau}) = e^{\pi i\tau/12}/\eta(\tau)$, by § 2, (4) then

(40)
$$F(e^{2\pi i(h/k+iz/k)}) = e^{\pi i(h/k+iz/k)/12}/\eta\left(\frac{h}{k}+\frac{iz}{k}\right)$$
$$= e^{\pi i(h/k+iz/k)/12}/z^{-1/2}\eta\left(\frac{h'}{k}+\frac{i}{kz}\right)\varepsilon^{-1},$$

by (39). But
$$\left\{\eta\left(\frac{h'}{k}+\frac{i}{kz}\right)\right\}^{-1} = e^{-\pi i(h'/k+i/kz)/12}F(e^{2\pi i(h'/k+i/kz)}),$$

and therefore by (40),
$$F(e^{2\pi i(h/k+iz/k)}) = \varepsilon\sqrt{z}e^{\pi i(h/k+iz/k)/12-\pi i(h'/k+i/kz)/12}F(e^{2\pi i(h'/k+1/kz)})$$
$$= \varepsilon\sqrt{z}e^{\pi i(h/k-h'/k)/12}e^{\pi(1/kz-z/k)/12}F(e^{2\pi i(h'/k+1/kz)}).$$

On the other hand, if
$$\omega_{h,k} = \varepsilon e^{\pi i(h/k-h'/k)/12},$$

then
$$\omega_{h,k}^{24k} = 1,$$

and this completes the proof.

Our ultimate aim is to prove that if

(i)
$$A_k(n) = \sum_{1\leq h\leq k;(h,k)=1} \omega_{h,k}e^{-2\pi inh/k},$$

(ii)
$$c = \pi\left(\frac{2}{3}\right)^{1/2}, \qquad \lambda_n = \left(n-\frac{1}{24}\right)^{1/2},$$

then
$$p(n) = \frac{1}{\pi\sqrt{2}}\sum_{k=1}^{\infty} A_k(n)\sqrt{k}\frac{d}{dn}\frac{\sinh c\lambda_n/k}{\lambda_n}.$$

This series converges very rapidly and the precise calculation of $p(n)$ requires a knowledge of $\omega_{h,k}$.

We turn our attention to this problem.

4. Further study of $\eta(\tau)$. Rademacher has shown that Siegel's argument given in § 3, which was applicable to the transformation $\tau' = -1/\tau$, can be extended to cover the case of a more general modular substitution. We consider the behavior of $\eta(\tau)$ and then derive results concerning $F(x)$. Our primary object is to prove the fundamental

THEOREM 4.1. *If* $(h, k) = 1$,

(1)
$$\tau = \frac{h+iz}{k}, \qquad \tau' = \frac{h'+iz^{-1}}{k},$$

where $k > 0$, $\mathscr{R}(z) > 0$,

(2)
$$hh' \equiv -1 \pmod{k},$$

(3) $$\eta(\tau)=e^{\pi i\tau/12}\prod_{m=1}^{\infty}(1-e^{2\pi i m\tau}),$$

then

(4) $$\log\eta(\tau')=\log\eta(\tau)+\frac{1}{2}\log z+\frac{\pi i}{12k}(h'-h)+\pi i S(h,k),$$

where

(5) $$S(h,k)=\sum_{\mu=1}^{k-1}\left(\left(\frac{h\mu}{k}\right)\right)\left(\left(\frac{\mu}{k}\right)\right),$$

(6) $$((x))=\begin{cases}x-[x]-\frac{1}{2} & \textit{if } x \textit{ is not an integer},\\ 0 & \textit{otherwise}.\end{cases}$$

PROOF. The sums $S(h,k)$ are called "Dedekind" sums and the manner in which they arise and some of their properties will be seen shortly. We start out as we did in Theorem 3.1 by simplifying somewhat the expression for $\log\eta(\tau)$. In fact

(7) $$\begin{aligned}\log\eta(\tau)&=\log\eta\left(\frac{h+iz}{k}\right)\\&=\frac{\pi i}{12k}(h+iz)+\sum_{m=1}^{\infty}\log\left(1-e^{2\pi i m h/k}e^{-2\pi z m/k}\right).\end{aligned}$$

In the series on the right we expand the logarithm and break the summation on m into residue classes modulo k. To this end, we put

$$m=qk+\mu,$$

and from (7), we get

(8) $$\begin{aligned}\log\eta(\tau)&=\frac{\pi i}{12k}(h+iz)\\&\quad-\sum_{q=0}^{\infty}\sum_{\mu=1}^{k}\sum_{r=1}^{\infty}\frac{1}{r}e^{2\pi i h r\mu/k}e^{-2\pi z\mu r/k}e^{-2\pi z q r}.\end{aligned}$$

We move the summation on q inside and on summing the geometric series, we get

(9) $$\begin{aligned}\log\eta(\tau)&=\frac{\pi i h}{12k}-\frac{\pi z}{12k}\\&\quad-\sum_{\mu=1}^{k}\sum_{r=1}^{\infty}\frac{1}{r}e^{2\pi i h r\mu/k}\frac{e^{-2\pi z\mu r/k}}{1-e^{-2\pi r z}}.\end{aligned}$$

The assertion (4) of the theorem is therefore equivalent to proving that

(10) $$\begin{aligned}&\sum_{\nu=1}^{k}\sum_{r=1}^{\infty}e^{2\pi i h' r\nu/k}\frac{e^{-2\pi\nu r/kz}}{1-e^{-2\pi r/z}}-\sum_{\mu=1}^{k}\sum_{r=1}^{\infty}\frac{1}{r}e^{2\pi i h r\mu/k}\frac{e^{-2\pi\mu r z/k}}{1-e^{-2\pi r z}}\\&\quad-\frac{\pi}{12k}\left(z-\frac{1}{z}\right)+\pi i S(h,k)=-\frac{1}{2}\log z.\end{aligned}$$

Again as in the proof of Theorem 3.1, we construct a function $G_n(x)$ which will have as residues the terms on the left-hand side of (10). Evaluating the integral of $G_n(x)$ over an appropriate contour in another way will result in the right-hand side. The function used by Rademacher is the following

(11)
$$G_n(x) = -\frac{1}{4ix} \coth \pi Nx \cot \frac{\pi Nx}{z} + \sum_{\mu=1}^{k-1} \frac{1}{x} \frac{e^{2\pi\mu Nx/k}}{1-e^{2\pi Nx}} \cdot \frac{e^{-2\pi i\mu^* Nx/kz}}{1-e^{-2\pi iNx/z}},$$

where

(12)
$$N = n + \tfrac{1}{2},$$

n an integer, and in order to ensure convergence at one point, μ^* is defined by the conditions

(13)
$$h\mu \equiv \mu^* \pmod{k}, \qquad 0 \leqq \mu^* \leqq k-1.$$

In the x plane, we consider the parallelogram C with vertices at $\pm i$, $\pm z$. We have drawn the case with $\mathscr{I}(z) > 0$. Within C, the function $G_n(z)$ has

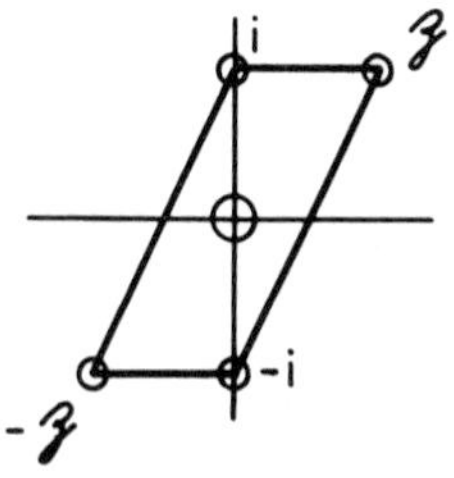

a pole of third order at $x = 0$. In addition there are simple poles at the points $x = ir/N$, $-zr/N$ ($r = \pm 1, \pm 2, \cdots, \pm n$). From Cauchy's theorem, we get

(14)
$$\frac{1}{2\pi i}\int_C G_n(x)dx = \sum \text{residues of } G_n(x) \text{ in } C.$$

We first calculate the residues and then evaluate the integral on the left by allowing $n \to \infty$. In the first place,

(15)
$$\frac{1}{e^t - 1} = \frac{1}{t}\left(1 - \frac{t}{2} + \frac{t^2}{12} + \cdots\right),$$

(16)
$$\frac{e^t+1}{e^t-1} = \frac{1}{t}\left(2 + \frac{t^2}{6} + \cdots\right),$$

(17)
$$\coth t = \frac{e^{2t}+1}{e^{2t}-1}, \quad \cot t = i\frac{e^{2it}+1}{e^{2it}-1}.$$

Accordingly, the residue at $x = 0$ of the first term in $G_n(x)$ is calculated as follows:

$$-\frac{1}{4ix}\coth\pi Nx\cot\frac{\pi Nx}{z}$$
$$=-\frac{1}{4x}\frac{e^{2\pi Nx}+1}{e^{2\pi Nx}-1}\cdot\frac{e^{2\pi iNx/z}+1}{e^{2\pi iNx/z}-1}$$
$$=-\frac{1}{4x}\left\{\frac{1}{2\pi Nx}\left(2+\frac{(2\pi Nx)^2}{6}+\cdots\right)\frac{z}{2\pi iNx}\left(2+\frac{(2\pi iNx)^2}{6z^2}+\cdots\right)\right\}$$
$$=-\frac{1}{4x}\frac{z}{(2\pi N)^2ix^2}\left(2+\frac{(2\pi Nx)^2}{6}+\cdots\right)\left(2+\frac{(2\pi iNx)^2}{6z^2}+\cdots\right)$$
$$=-\frac{z}{4x^3i(2\pi N)^2}\left\{4+\frac{(2\pi N)^2}{3}\left(1-\frac{1}{z^2}\right)x^2+\cdots\right\},$$

where we have used (16) and (17). The residue is therefore

$$-\frac{z}{4i}\cdot\frac{1}{3}\left(1-\frac{1}{z^2}\right)=-\frac{1}{12i}\left(z-\frac{1}{z}\right). \tag{18}$$

For the second term of $G_n(x)$, the residue at $x=0$ is computed as follows. In the first place,

$$\frac{1}{x}\frac{e^{2\pi\mu Nx/k}}{1-e^{2\pi Nx}}\cdot\frac{e^{-2\pi i\mu^*Nx/kz}}{1-e^{-2\pi iNx/z}}$$
$$=\frac{1}{x}\left\{\frac{1}{2\pi Nx}\frac{-z}{2\pi iNx}\left(1-\frac{2\pi Nx}{2}+\frac{(2\pi Nx)^2}{12}+\cdots\right)\left(1+\frac{2\pi\mu Nx}{k}+\frac{(2\pi\mu Nx)^2}{2k^2}+\cdots\right)\right.$$
$$\left.\cdot\left(1+\frac{2\pi iNx}{2z}+\frac{(2\pi iNx)^2}{12z^2}+\cdots\right)\left(1-\frac{2\pi i\mu^*Nx}{kz}+\frac{(2\pi i\mu^*Nx)^2}{2k^2z^2}+\cdots\right)\right\}$$
$$=\frac{-z}{(2\pi N)^2x^3i}\left\{\left[1+\left(\frac{2\pi N\mu}{k}-\frac{2\pi N}{2}\right)x+\left(\frac{(2\pi N)^2}{12}+\frac{(2\pi\mu N)^2}{2k^2}-\frac{(2\pi N)^2\mu}{2k}\right)x^2+\cdots\right]\right.$$
$$\cdot\left[1+\left(\frac{2\pi iN}{2z}-\frac{2\pi i\mu^*N}{kz}\right)x\right.$$
$$\left.\left.+\left(\frac{(2\pi iN)^2}{12z^2}+\frac{(2\pi iN)^2\mu^{*2}}{2k^2z^2}-\frac{(2\pi iN)^2\mu^*}{2kz^2}\right)x^2+\cdots\right]\right\}$$

where we have used (15).

The residue at $x=0$ of this single term of the sum in (11) is therefore

$$-\frac{z}{i}\left\{\left(\frac{1}{12}+\frac{\mu^2}{2k^2}-\frac{\mu}{2k}\right)-\left(\frac{1}{12z^2}+\frac{\mu^{*2}}{2k^2z^2}-\frac{\mu^*}{2kz^2}\right)+i\left(\frac{1}{2z}-\frac{\mu^*}{kz}\right)\left(\frac{\mu}{k}-\frac{1}{2}\right)\right\}$$
$$=\left(\frac{\mu^*}{k}-\frac{1}{2}\right)\left(\frac{\mu}{k}-\frac{1}{2}\right)+iz\left(\frac{1}{12}+\frac{\mu^2}{2k^2}-\frac{\mu}{2k}\right)+\frac{1}{iz}\left(\frac{1}{12}+\frac{\mu^{*2}}{2k^2}-\frac{\mu^*}{2k}\right).$$

On the other hand,

$$\frac{\mu^*}{k}=\frac{h\mu}{k}-\left[\frac{h\mu}{k}\right],$$

and therefore the residue at $x=0$ of the second term in $G_n(x)$ is

$$\sum_{\mu=1}^{k-1}\left(\frac{h\mu}{k}-\left[\frac{h\mu}{k}\right]-\frac{1}{2}\right)\left(\frac{\mu}{k}-\left[\frac{\mu}{k}\right]-\frac{1}{2}\right)$$

$$+iz\left(\frac{k-1}{12}+\frac{1}{2k^2}\frac{k(k-1)(2k-1)}{6}-\frac{k(k-1)}{4k}\right) \tag{19}$$

$$+\frac{1}{iz}\left(\frac{k-1}{12}+\frac{1}{2k^2}\frac{k(k-1)(2k-1)}{6}-\frac{k(k-1)}{4k}\right)$$

$$=S(h,k)+\frac{1}{12k}\left(iz+\frac{1}{iz}\right)-\frac{1}{12}\left(iz+\frac{1}{iz}\right).$$

Combining this with (18), we see that $G_n(x)$ has residue

$$S(h,k)+\left(\frac{1}{12k}\right)\left(iz+\frac{1}{iz}\right)$$

at $x=0$. The points ir/N are simple poles of $G_n(x)$ and the residues at these points are simple to calculate. In fact, the residue at ir/N is

$$\lim_{x\to ir/N}\left(x-\frac{ir}{N}\right)\left(-\frac{1}{4ix}\coth \pi Nx \cot \pi Nx/z\right)$$

$$+\lim_{x\to ir/N}\left(x-\frac{ir}{N}\right)\sum_{\mu=1}^{k-1}\frac{1}{x}\frac{e^{2\pi\mu Nx/k}}{1-e^{2\pi Nx}}\cdot\frac{e^{-2\pi i\mu^* Nx/kz}}{1-e^{-2\pi iNx/z}}$$

$$=\frac{1}{4\pi r}\cot\frac{\pi ir}{z}-\frac{1}{2\pi i}\sum_{\mu=1}^{k-1}\frac{1}{r}e^{2\pi i\mu r/k}\frac{e^{2\pi\mu^* r/kz}}{1-e^{2\pi r/z}}.$$

Because by (13) $h'\mu^*\equiv hh'\mu\equiv-\mu \pmod k$ and $\cot i\theta=(1/i)\coth\theta$, this becomes

$$\frac{1}{4\pi ri}\coth\frac{\pi r}{z}-\frac{1}{2\pi i}\sum_{\mu^*=1}^{k-1}\frac{1}{r}e^{-2\pi ih'\mu^* r/k}\frac{e^{2\pi\mu^* r/kz}}{1-e^{2\pi r/z}}.$$

As a result, the sum of the residues from the poles at ir/N ($r=\pm1,\cdots,\pm n$) is

$$\frac{1}{4\pi i}\sum_{r=1}^{n}\frac{1}{r}\coth\frac{\pi r}{z}-\frac{1}{2\pi i}\sum_{\mu^*=1}^{k-1}\sum_{r=1}^{n}\frac{1}{r}e^{-2\pi ih'\mu^* r/k}\frac{e^{2\pi\mu^* r/kz}}{1-e^{2\pi r/z}}$$

$$-\frac{1}{4\pi i}\sum_{r=1}^{n}\frac{1}{r}\coth\frac{-\pi r}{z}+\frac{1}{2\pi i}\sum_{\mu^*=1}^{k-1}\sum_{r=1}^{n}\frac{1}{r}e^{2\pi ih'\mu^* r/k}\frac{e^{-2\pi\mu^* r/kz}}{1-e^{-2\pi r/z}} \tag{20}$$

$$=S_1+S_2+S_3+S_4.$$

The first and third sums combine to give

$$S_1+S_3=\frac{1}{2\pi i}\sum_{r=1}^{n}\frac{1}{r}\left(\frac{e^{2\pi r/z}+1}{e^{2\pi r/z}-1}\right) \tag{21}$$

$$=\frac{1}{2\pi i}\sum_{r=1}^{n}\frac{1}{r}\left(\frac{2e^{-2\pi r/z}}{1-e^{-2\pi r/z}}+1\right).$$

The second sum can be written as

$$S_2=-\frac{1}{2\pi i}\sum_{\mu^*=1}^{k-1}\sum_{r=1}^{n}\frac{1}{r}e^{(2\pi ih'r/k)(k-\mu^*)}\frac{e^{(-2\pi r/kz)(k-\mu^*)}}{e^{-2\pi r/z}-1}.$$

As μ^* goes from 1 to $k-1$, so does $k-\mu^*$ and we therefore get

$$S_2 = \frac{1}{2\pi i}\sum_{\nu=1}^{k-1}\sum_{r=1}^{n}\frac{1}{r}e^{2\pi i h' r\nu/k}\frac{e^{-2\pi r\nu/kz}}{1-e^{-2\pi r/z}}. \tag{22}$$

Consequently, the sum of the residues at the poles ir/N ($r = \pm 1, \cdots, \pm n$) is, from (20), (21) and (22) (because S_2 and S_4 are now the same),

$$\begin{aligned} &\frac{1}{2\pi i}\sum_{r=1}^{n}\frac{1}{r}\left(\frac{2e^{-2\pi r/z}}{1-e^{-2\pi r/z}}+1\right)+\frac{1}{\pi i}\sum_{\nu=1}^{k-1}\sum_{r=1}^{n}\frac{1}{r}e^{2\pi i h' r\nu/k}\frac{e^{-2\pi r\nu/kz}}{1-e^{-2\pi r/z}} \\ &\quad = \frac{1}{2\pi i}\sum_{r=1}^{n}\frac{1}{r}+\frac{1}{\pi i}\sum_{\nu=1}^{k}\sum_{r=1}^{n}\frac{1}{r}e^{2\pi i h' r\nu/k}\frac{e^{-2\pi r\nu/kz}}{1-e^{-2\pi r/z}}, \end{aligned} \tag{23}$$

where we have taken the exponential term in the first sum and incorporated it into the second sum. By a similar argument, the sum of the residues at the poles, $x = -zr/N$ ($r = \pm 1, \cdots, \pm n$), is

$$\frac{i}{2\pi}\sum_{r=1}^{n}\frac{1}{r}+\frac{i}{\pi}\sum_{\mu=1}^{k}\sum_{r=1}^{n}e^{2\pi i h\mu r/k}\cdot\frac{e^{-2\pi\mu rz/k}}{1-e^{-2\pi rz}}.$$

Combining (19) and (23), we conclude that the sum of the residues of $G_n(x)$ inside C is

$$\begin{aligned} &\frac{1}{12ki}\left(\frac{1}{z}-z\right)+S(h,k)+\frac{1}{\pi i}\sum_{\nu=1}^{k}\sum_{r=1}^{n}\frac{1}{r}e^{2\pi i h'\nu r/k}\frac{e^{-2\pi r\nu/kz}}{1-e^{-2\pi r/z}} \\ &\quad -\frac{1}{\pi i}\sum_{\mu=1}^{k}\sum_{r=1}^{n}\frac{1}{r}e^{2\pi i h\mu r/k}\frac{e^{-2\pi\mu rz/k}}{1-e^{-2\pi rz}}. \end{aligned} \tag{24}$$

If we now let $n\to\infty$ in (24), we get precisely the left-hand side of (10) except for the factor πi. It therefore remains to show that

$$\lim_{n\to\infty}\int_C G_n(x)dx = \int_C \lim_{n\to\infty} G_n(x)dx = -\log z. \tag{25}$$

The truth of (25) depends on showing that as $n\to\infty$

$$xG_n(x)\to\begin{cases} \frac{1}{4} \text{ on the sides joining } i \text{ to } z \text{ and } -i \text{ to } -z, \\ -\frac{1}{4} \text{ on the sides joining } i \text{ to } -z \text{ and } -i \text{ to } z, \end{cases}$$

with the exception of the points $x = \pm i, \pm z$.

As in Theorem 3.1, the interchange of the limiting and integration processes will be proved justified in virtue of the fact that the convergence is bounded, the limit function being clearly integrable.

Indeed suppose that x lies on the side joining i to z, then $x = ai + bz$ where $a + b = 1$ and to avoid the points i and z, we restrict a and b to be > 0.

Accordingly, if we return to the definition (11) of $G_n(x)$, we have for the terms of the summation

$$\frac{1}{ai+bz}\,\frac{e^{2\pi\mu N(ai+bz)/k}}{1-e^{2\pi N(ai+bz)}}\,\frac{e^{-2\pi i\mu^* N(ai/z+b)/k}}{1-e^{2\pi N(a/z+b/i)}}. \tag{26}$$

As $N\to\infty$, since $ab\neq 0$, $\mu/k<1$, $\mu^*/k<1$, this term tends to 0.

For the behavior of the first term of $G_n(x)$, we have

(27)
$$\frac{1}{4i}\coth \pi Nx \cot \frac{\pi Nx}{z} = \frac{1}{4}\frac{e^{2\pi Nx}+1}{e^{2\pi Nx}-1}\cdot\frac{e^{2\pi i Nx/z}+1}{e^{2\pi i Nx/z}-1}$$
$$=\frac{1}{4}\frac{e^{2\pi N(ai+bz)}+1}{e^{2\pi N(ai+bz)}-1}\cdot\frac{e^{2\pi i N(ai/z+b)}+1}{e^{2\pi i N(ai/z+b)}-1}\,.$$

Since $ab\neq 0$, this term converges to $\frac{1}{4}$ as $N\to\infty$.

To show that the convergence is bounded, we shall show that the denominators are bounded away from 0 in absolute value. In fact suppose that

$$\lambda = 2\pi N(ai+bz) = (2n+1)\pi(ai+bz)\,.$$

Then it is enough to show that λ is bounded away from a multiple of $2\pi i$. Now λ is a point on the line segment joining the points $(2n+1)\pi i$ and $(2n+1)\pi z$ and since e^{λ} has period $2\pi i$, it follows that the distance between λ and an even multiple of πi is $\geqq |\pi(ai+bz)2K\pi i|$ for some fixed K and this is uniform in n. Though it is easy to determine specifically a lower bound for $|1-e^{\lambda}|$, we shall avoid the calculation.

The behavior of the denominator of the second factor is examined in the same way and we therefore see that the convergence on the segment joining i to z is bounded.

Exactly the same argument holds for the remaining sides. Consequently, using (27) and the analogue for the remaining sides,

(25)
$$\lim_{n\to\infty}\int_C G_n(x)dx = \frac{1}{4}\left\{-\int_{-i}^{z}\frac{dx}{x}+\int_{z}^{i}\frac{dx}{x}-\int_{i}^{-z}\frac{dx}{x}+\int_{-z}^{-i}\frac{dx}{x}\right\}$$
$$=\frac{1}{2}\left\{-\int_{-i}^{z}\frac{dx}{x}+\int_{z}^{i}\frac{dx}{x}\right\}$$
$$=\frac{1}{2}\left\{-\left(\log z+\frac{\pi i}{2}\right)+\left(\frac{\pi i}{2}-\log z\right)\right\}$$
$$=-\log z\,,$$

where the principal branch of the logarithm is chosen. This completes the proof.

As a corollary, we prove

THEOREM 4.2. *If* $F(x)=\prod_{m=1}^{\infty}(1-x^m)^{-1}$,

(29)
$$\tau=\frac{h+iz}{k}\,,\qquad \tau'=\frac{h'+iz^{-1}}{k}\,,\qquad \mathscr{R}(z)>0\,,$$

(30)
$$\psi_k(z)=\sqrt{z}e^{(\pi/12k)(1/z-z)}\,,$$

then

(31)
$$F(e^{2\pi i\tau})=\omega_{h,k}\psi_k(z)F(e^{2\pi i\tau'})\,,$$

where

(32)
$$\omega_{h,k}=e^{\pi i S(h,k)}\,,$$

and

$$hh' \equiv -1 \pmod{k}.$$

PROOF. Using Theorem 4.1 on the function $\eta(\tau)$, we have

$$\begin{aligned} F(e^{2\pi i\tau'}) &= e^{\pi i\tau'/12}/\eta(\tau') \\ &= e^{\pi i\tau'/12}/\eta(\tau)\sqrt{z}e^{\pi i(h'-h)/12k}e^{\pi iS(h,k)} \\ &= \frac{e^{\pi i\tau'/12}}{\sqrt{z}}e^{-\pi i(h'-h)/12k}e^{-\pi iS(h,k)}e^{-\pi i\tau/12}F(e^{2\pi i\tau}) \\ &= \frac{1}{\sqrt{z}}e^{\pi(z-1/z)/12k}e^{-\pi iS(h,k)}F(e^{2\pi i\tau}). \end{aligned}$$

On multiplying across, the conclusion of the theorem follows.

This result is the main theorem concerning $F(x)$ which we use in our further discussion of partitions. We may however, draw some further conclusions from Theorem 4.1. In fact, we determine the behavior of $\eta(\tau)$ under a general modular substitution:

$$\tau' = \frac{a\tau + b}{c\tau + d}.$$

Notice first that if

$$\tau = \frac{h + iz}{k}, \qquad \tau' = \frac{h' + iz^{-1}}{k},$$

then

$$z = -i(\tau k - h), \qquad z^{-1} = -i(\tau' k - h'), \tag{33}$$

and hence from (33)

$$(k\tau' - h')(k\tau - h) = -1,$$

$$\begin{aligned} \tau' &= \frac{h'\tau - \dfrac{hh' + 1}{k}}{k\tau - h} \\ &= \frac{a\tau + b}{c\tau + d}, \end{aligned} \tag{34}$$

where, because $hh' \equiv -1 \pmod{k}$, a, b, c, d are integers, and $ad - bc = 1$. This is therefore a modular substitution.

On the other hand, if $c > 0$, then we showed that the modular substitution

$$\tau' = \frac{a\tau + b}{c\tau + d}$$

could be written in the form

$$\tau = \frac{h + iz}{k}, \qquad \tau' = \frac{h' + iz^{-1}}{k}.$$

As a consequence, we prove

THEOREM 4.3. *If* $c > 0$,

(35) $$\tau' = \frac{a\tau + b}{c\tau + d},$$

with $ad - bc = 1$, *then*

(36) $$\log \eta(\tau') = \log \eta(\tau) + \frac{1}{2} \log (c\tau + d) - \frac{\pi i}{4} + \pi i \frac{(a + d)}{12c} - \pi i S(a, c).$$

PROOF. From (4),

(37) $$\log \eta(\tau') = \log \eta(\tau) + \frac{1}{2} \log z + \frac{\pi i}{12k}(h' - h) + \pi i S(h, k),$$

but $a = h'$, $b = -(hh' + 1)/k$, $c = k$, $d = -h$, and

(38) $$z = \frac{\tau k - h}{i} = \frac{c\tau + d}{i},$$

and therefore by (36), (37) and (38),

(39) $$\begin{aligned} \log \eta(\tau') = \log \eta(\tau) &= \frac{1}{2} \log \left(\frac{c\tau + d}{i} \right) + \frac{\pi i}{12c}(a + d) + \pi i S(-d, c) \\ &= \log \eta(\tau) + \frac{1}{2} \log (c\tau + d) - \frac{\pi i}{4} + \frac{\pi i (a + d)}{12c} + \pi i S(-d, c). \end{aligned}$$

We have yet to show that

$$S(-d, c) = -S(a, c),$$

and this is a consequence of Theorem 4.5, which we prove shortly.

We complete the discussion by considering the cases $c < 0$ and $c = 0$. If $c < 0$, then

$$\tau' = \frac{-a\tau - b}{-c\tau - d} = \frac{a_1\tau + b_1}{c_1\tau + d_1} \quad \text{with } c_1 > 0,$$

and from (39),

(40) $$\begin{aligned} \log \eta(\tau') &= \log \eta(\tau) + \frac{1}{2} \log (c_1\tau + d_1) - \frac{\pi i}{4} + \frac{\pi i}{12c_1}(a_1 + d_1) - \pi i S(a_1, c_1) \\ &= \log \eta(\tau) + \frac{1}{2} \log (c\tau + d) + \frac{\pi i}{4} + \frac{\pi i (a + d)}{12c} - \pi i S(-a, -c). \end{aligned}$$

If $c = 0$, then

$$\tau' = \frac{a\tau + b}{d}$$

and $ad = 1$, $a = \pm 1$, $d = \pm 1$, $a/d = 1$; hence

$$\tau' = \tau + \frac{b}{d}.$$

This is a translation by $\pm b$ and therefore

$$\log \eta(\tau') = \log \eta(\tau) + \frac{\pi i b}{12d} . \tag{41}$$

Equations (39), (40), and (41) give us a complete characterization of the root of unity involved. In fact, we have

THEOREM 4.4. *If*

$$\tau' = \frac{a\tau + b}{c\tau + d} ,$$

then

$$\eta(\tau') = \omega_{a,c}(c\tau + d)^{1/2}\eta(\tau) , \tag{42}$$

where

$$\omega_{a,c} = \exp\left[-\frac{\pi i}{4} + \pi i\frac{a+d}{12c} - \pi i S(a, c)\right], \qquad c > 0$$

$$\omega_{a,c} = \exp\left[\frac{\pi i}{4} + \pi i\frac{a+d}{12c} - \pi i S(-a, -c)\right], \qquad c < 0 \tag{43}$$

$$\omega_{a,c} = \exp\left[\frac{\pi i b}{12d}\right] \qquad c = 0 .$$

To pursue the subject further, we shall have to investigate the properties of $S(h, k)$ more carefully. It will be of interest to prove several theorems. In the first place, we notice that

$$((x_1)) = ((x_2)) \quad \text{if } x_1 - x_2 \text{ is an integer} ,$$

and therefore

$$\left(\left(\frac{h_1}{k}\right)\right) = \left(\left(\frac{h_2}{k}\right)\right) \quad \text{if } h_1 \equiv h_2 \pmod{k} . \tag{44}$$

This means that

$$S(h_1, k) = S(h_2, k) \quad \text{if } h_1 \equiv h_2 \pmod{k} . \tag{45}$$

THEOREM 4.5. *If* $hh' \equiv -1 \pmod{k}$, *then*

$$S(h', k) = - S(h, k) . \tag{46}$$

PROOF. By the remark (44),

$$S(h, k) = \sum_{\mu \bmod k} \left(\left(\frac{\mu}{k}\right)\right)\left(\left(\frac{h\mu}{k}\right)\right) = \sum_{\mu \bmod k} \left(\left(\frac{h'\mu}{k}\right)\right)\left(\left(\frac{hh'\mu}{k}\right)\right)$$

$$= \sum_{\mu \bmod k} \left(\left(\frac{h'\mu}{k}\right)\right)\left(\left(-\frac{\mu}{k}\right)\right) = - \sum_{\mu \bmod k} \left(\left(\frac{\mu}{k}\right)\right)\left(\left(\frac{h'\mu}{k}\right)\right) = - S(h', k) .$$

The next theorem is the remarkable reciprocity law for $S(h,k)$, first proved by Dedekind. Though many proofs are known, we shall prove the theorem with the help of Theorem 4.4.

THEOREM 4.6.

$$12S(c, d) + 12S(d, c) = -3 + \frac{c}{d} + \frac{d}{c} + \frac{1}{cd} \, . \tag{47}$$

PROOF. We suppose for simplicity that $c > 0$, $d > 0$. Then by Theorem 4.4,

$$\log \eta\left(\frac{a\tau + b}{c\tau + d}\right) = \log \eta(\tau) - \frac{\pi i}{4} + \frac{1}{2} \log (c\tau + d) + \frac{\pi i(a + d)}{12c} - \pi i S(d, c) \, , \tag{48}$$

since $ad \equiv 1 \pmod c$. Accordingly, if we replace τ by $-1/\tau$, in (48), we find

$$\log \eta\left(\frac{b\tau - a}{d\tau - c}\right) = \log \eta\left(-\frac{1}{\tau}\right) - \frac{\pi i}{4} + \frac{1}{2} \log \left(-\frac{c}{\tau} + d\right) + \frac{\pi i(a + d)}{12c} - \pi i S(d, c) \, . \tag{49}$$

On the other hand, by Theorem 4.4 again

$$\log \eta\left(\frac{b\tau - a}{d\tau - c}\right) = \log \eta(\tau) - \frac{\pi i}{4} + \frac{1}{2} \log (d\tau - c) + \frac{\pi i(b - c)}{12d} - \pi i S(-c, d) \, ,$$

and $\log \eta(-1/\tau) = \log \eta(\tau) + \frac{1}{2} \log \tau - \pi i/4$ by Theorem 3.1. Inserting these values in (49), we find

$$\log \eta(\tau) - \frac{\pi i}{4} + \frac{1}{2} \log (d\tau - c) + \frac{\pi i(b - c)}{12d} - \pi i S(-c, d)$$
$$= \log \eta(\tau) + \frac{1}{2} \log \tau - \frac{\pi i}{4} - \frac{\pi i}{4} + \frac{1}{2} \log \frac{d\tau - c}{\tau} + \frac{\pi i(a + d)}{12c} - \pi i S(d, c) \, .$$

This means that

$$\frac{\pi i(b - c)}{12d} + \pi i S(c, d) = -\frac{\pi i}{4} + \frac{\pi i(a + d)}{12c} - \pi i S(d, c) \, ,$$

which is equivalent to (47). The other possibilities $c < 0$, $d < 0$ are treated in the same way.

To illustrate the effectiveness of this reciprocity law, we shall calculate the value of the root of unity arising from the substitution in § 3, equation (29). We had computed it, so to speak, by hand. The transformation in question was

$$\tau' = \frac{5\tau + 4}{6\tau + 5} \, ,$$

in which case

$$\omega_{a,c} = \exp\left[-\frac{\pi i}{4} + \frac{10\pi i}{72} - \pi i S(5, 6)\right] .$$

But

$$12S(5, 6) + 12S(6, 5) = \frac{5}{6} + \frac{6}{5} + \frac{1}{30} - 3 \, ,$$

and since $12S(6,5) = 12S(1,5)$, by (45)

$$12S(1,5) + 12S(5,1) = \frac{1}{5} + 5 + \frac{1}{5} - 3\,,$$

we get altogether,

$$12S(5,6) = \frac{5}{6} + \frac{6}{5} + \frac{1}{30} - \frac{1}{5} - 5 - \frac{1}{5} = -\frac{10}{3}\,.$$

Consequently,

$$\omega_{a,c} = \exp\left[\pi i\left(-\frac{1}{4} + \frac{5}{36} + \frac{5}{18}\right)\right] = e^{\pi i/6}$$

As another illustration of the effectiveness of Theorem 4.6, we shall show that the function $(h' - h)/12k + S(h,k)$ in (4) leads to a 24th root of unity. Indeed by definition $2h^2S(k,h)$ is an integer. Therefore since by Theorem 4.6

$$12h^2kS(h,k) + 12h^2kS(k,h) = -3h^2k + h^3 + hk^2 + h\,,$$

it follows that

$$12h^2kS(h,k) \equiv h^3 + h \equiv h^2(h - h') \pmod{k}\,.$$

This shows that $(h' - h)/k + 12S(h,k)$ is an integer, and this is what we set out to prove.

5. Farey series and the Farey dissection. In obtaining the asymptotic formula for $p(n)$, we found a neighborhood of the origin where $F(x)$ behaved essentially like $\psi(\tau)$. We also remarked that each rational point could be treated in the same way. The problem is to find suitable neighborhoods of these rational points. This is provided by the so-called Farey dissection.

By a Farey series $\mathscr{F}_n$ of order n, we mean the set of all fractions h/k with $0 \leqq h \leqq k$, $(h,k) = 1$, $1 \leqq k \leqq n$, and arranged in ascending order of magnitude. For example $\mathscr{F}_5$ is

$$\frac{0}{1},\ \frac{1}{5},\ \frac{1}{4},\ \frac{1}{3},\ \frac{2}{5},\ \frac{1}{2},\ \frac{3}{5},\ \frac{2}{3},\ \frac{3}{4},\ \frac{4}{5},\ \frac{1}{1}\,.$$

These series have many remarkable properties, some of which we require and prove.

The first results are some simple lemmas.

Lemma 5.1. *If h/k and h'/k' are two successive fractions in a Farey series of order n, then $k + k' > n$.*

Proof. Obviously

$$\frac{h}{k} < \frac{h+h'}{k+k'} < \frac{h'}{k'}\,;$$

it follows that $k + k' > n$ since h/k and h'/k' are successive.

Lemma 5.2. *If h/k and h'/k' are successive fractions in $\mathscr{F}_n$, $n \neq 1$, then $k \neq k'$.*

PROOF. Suppose that $k = k'$; then $h < k - 1$ and

$$\frac{h}{k} < \frac{h}{k-1} < \frac{h+1}{k} \leqq \frac{h'}{k'} .$$

This means that $h/(k-1)$ separates h/k and h'/k' which is not allowed by hypothesis.

With the help of these results, we prove the highly interesting

THEOREM 5.1. *If h/k and h'/k' are two successive fractions in $\mathscr{F}_n$, then*

(1) $$kh' - hk' = 1 .$$

PROOF. We prove the theorem by induction on n. The theorem holding trivially for $n = 1$, we assume it true for $n - 1$.

If h/k and h'/k' are successive in $\mathscr{F}_{n-1}$, then the theorem holds by the inductive hypothesis. Suppose that one of these fractions, say h'/k', belongs to $\mathscr{F}_n$ but not to $\mathscr{F}_{n-1}$; that is $k' = n$. Let h''/k'' be the successor to h'/k' in $\mathscr{F}_n$; then h''/k'' belongs to $\mathscr{F}_{n-1}$ by Lemma 5.2 and h/k, h''/k'' are neighbors in $\mathscr{F}_{n-1}$ to which the inductive hypothesis therefore applies. We consider now

(2) $$kh' - hk' = r, \qquad k'h'' - h'k'' = s .$$

Both r and s are positive; our object is to prove that $r = s = 1$.

From (2), solving for h' and k' and using the inductive hypothesis on $hk'' - kh''$, we get

(3) $$h' = rh'' + sh , \qquad k' = rk'' + sk' .$$

As a consequence, r and s are relatively prime by (3) for if $d = (r, s)$, then $d \mid h'$, $d \mid k'$, $d \mid (h', k') = 1$. Consider now the set of fractions

$$\frac{H}{K} = \frac{\lambda h + \mu h''}{\lambda k + \mu k''} ,$$

for $\lambda, \mu > 0$, and $(\lambda, \mu) = 1$. It is easy to see that $h/k < H/K < h''/k''$. Moreover, $(H, K) = 1$; for if $d = (H, K)$, then using the inductive assumption,

$$d \mid k(\lambda h + \mu h'') - h(\lambda k + \mu k'') = \mu ,$$
$$d \mid h''(\lambda k + \mu k'') - k''(\lambda h + \mu h'') = \lambda .$$

Thus $d = 1$ since by assumption $(\lambda, \mu) = 1$. This means that H/K must appear in some Farey series. Its first appearance is when K is least, that is when $\lambda = \mu = 1$. Since H/K separates h/k and h''/k'', it follows that

$$\frac{h}{k} < \frac{h+h''}{k+k''} < \frac{h''}{k''} ,$$

and therefore $r = s = 1$, and furthermore $h' = h + h''$, $k' = k + k''$. The proof is therefore complete.

We are now in a position to describe the Farey dissection. Let $\mathscr{F}_n$ be a Farey series of order n and let h/k, h'/k' be successive fractions in $\mathscr{F}_n$. We define the mediant μ of these two fractions

(4) $$\mu = \frac{h + h'}{k + k'} .$$

Clearly

$$\frac{h}{k} < \mu < \frac{h'}{k'} ;$$

the first mediant being $1/(n+1)$ and the last $n/(n+1)$. We mark off these values on the unit interval and let P_μ denote the point corresponding to μ. For example, when $n = 5$ we get this picture:

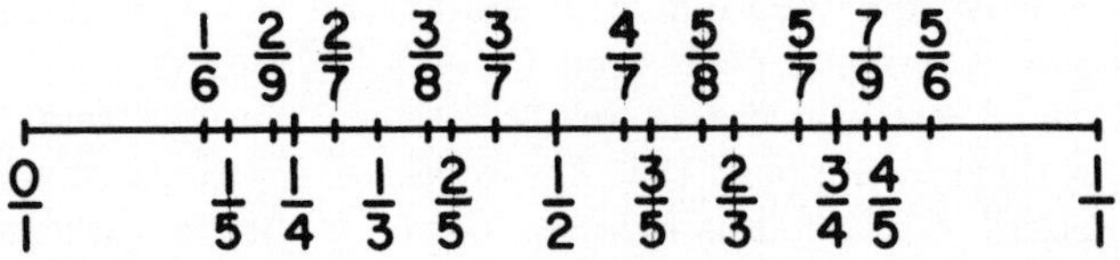

where the Farey fractions are written below the line and the mediants above. The unit interval is subdivided into intervals $I_{h,k}$ whose endpoints are P_μ and containing the fraction h/k. If h'/k', h/k, h''/k'' are three successive Farey fractions, then

(5) $$I_{h,k} = \left(\frac{h + h'}{k + k'} , \frac{h + h''}{k + k''} \right) .$$

The exceptions to this rule are the intervals corresponding to $1/n$ and $(n-1)/n$. That is, we define

$$I_{0,n} = \left(0, \frac{1}{n+1} \right)$$

and

$$I_{1,1} = \left(\frac{n}{n+1} , 1 \right) .$$

We prove the basic property of these intervals which we shall use:

THEOREM 5.2. *If h'/k', h/k, h''/k'' are three successive fractions in a Farey series of order n,*

$$L_1 = \frac{h + h''}{k + k''} - \frac{h}{k}$$

and

$$L_2 = \frac{h}{k} - \frac{h' + h}{k' + k} ,$$

then

(6) $$\frac{1}{k(2n-1)} \leqq L_i \leqq \frac{1}{k(n+1)} \qquad (i = 1, 2) .$$

PROOF. By Theorem 5.1

$$\frac{h}{k}-\frac{h'+h}{k'+k}=\frac{hk'-kh'}{k(k'+k)}=\frac{1}{k(k'+k)}\,.$$

On the other hand, by Lemma 5.1, $k'+k>n$ and quite clearly, by Lemma 5.2, $k'+k<2n$. Therefore

$$\frac{1}{k(2n-1)}\leqq L_2\leqq\frac{1}{k(n+1)}\,.$$

Exactly the same argument holds for L_1. We have shown incidentally that

$$\mu_1=\frac{h+h'}{k+k'}=\frac{h}{k}-\frac{1}{k(k+k')}\,,\qquad \mu_2=\frac{h+h''}{k+k''}=\frac{h}{k}+\frac{1}{k(k+k'')}\,.$$

Consequently from (5)

$$I_{h,k}=\left(\frac{h}{k}-\frac{1}{k(k+k')},\ \frac{h}{k}+\frac{1}{k(k+k'')}\right).$$

This interesting theorem will be of great importance to us. It implies that however irregularly the Farey fractions may be distributed, the lengths of the Farey intervals $I_{h,k}$ have a certain measure of uniformity. It is to this fact that this dissection owes its importance. We transform this dissection to a circular path in the complex plane.

Let C be a circle of radius r,

$$|x|=r\,,$$

and put

$$x=re^{2\pi i\theta}\,.$$

As θ ranges over the unit interval x describes the circle C. The Farey arcs $\xi_{h,k}$ of C are the arcs of this circle described when θ ranges over the interval $I_{h,k}$. The exception is again when $h=0$, and $h/k=1/1$. We agree to amalgamate the arcs corresponding to $I_{0,1}$, $I_{1,1}$ into a single arc $\xi_{0,1}$. Thus the point $(r,0)$ is interior to the arc $\xi_{0,1}$.

6. Rademacher's convergent series for $p(n)$. The original analysis of Hardy and Ramanujan which led to an asymptotic formula for $p(n)$ was simplified and perfected by Rademacher. We shall derive a convergent series for $p(n)$.

The starting point is equation (2) of §2,

$$p(n)=\frac{1}{2\pi i}\int_C\frac{F(x)}{x^{n+1}}dx\,,\tag{1}$$

where C is a simple closed contour contained in the unit circle and enclosing the origin. We choose C to be a circle of radius

$$r=|x|=e^{-2\pi/N^2}\,,$$

for a fixed N. Ultimately we let $N \to \infty$ and the circle "tends" to the unit circle. Henceforth, therefore, the O's refer to $N \to \infty$.

The derivation of the series takes place in three steps:

(i) We break C into Farey arcs $\xi_{h,k}$ of order N. The integral in (1) is therefore broken into a sum of integrals over these arcs.

(ii) On each arc $\xi_{h,k}$, we approximate $F(x)$ with the help of the transformation formula

$$F(x) = \psi_k(x)F(x'),$$

where $F(x') \to 1$ very rapidly as $N \to \infty$. In virtue of the simple relation

$$F(x) = \psi_k(x) + \psi_k(x)(F(x') - 1),$$

this allows us to replace the integral of $F(x)$ by that of $\psi_k(x)$.

(iii) We evaluate the integral of $\psi_k(x)$.

Step (i). Breaking the circle into Farey arcs of order N, we get

$$p(n) = \frac{1}{2\pi i} \sum_{\substack{0 \leqq h < k \leqq N \\ (h,k)=1}} \int_{\xi_{h,k}} \frac{F(x)}{x^{n+1}} dx, \tag{2}$$

with the understanding that when $k = 1$, the only value of h chosen is 0. On $\xi_{h,k}$, we put

$$x = r[\exp(2\pi i\theta)] = \exp\left(-\frac{2\pi}{N^2} + 2\pi i\theta\right),$$

and let

$$\theta = \frac{h}{k} + \varphi.$$

This substitution brings into evidence the rational point $e^{2\pi ih/k}$. As a result, we get

$$\begin{aligned} x &= \exp\left[-\frac{2\pi}{N^2} + 2\pi i\left(\frac{h}{k} + \varphi\right)\right] \\ &= \exp\left[2\pi i\frac{h}{k} - \frac{2\pi z}{k}\right] = \exp\left[2\pi i\left(\frac{h}{k} + \frac{iz}{k}\right)\right] \end{aligned} \tag{3}$$

where

$$z = k\left(\frac{1}{N^2} - i\varphi\right), \tag{4}$$

and x is now of the form given in Theorem 4.2. The value $\varphi = 0$ corresponds to the Farey point of the arc $\xi_{h,k}$. On $\xi_{h,k}$, φ ranges from $-\theta'_{h,k}$ to $\theta''_{h,k}$, where $\theta'_{h,k}$ and $\theta''_{h,k}$ are the same as L_2 and L_1 of Theorem 5.2 and we have shown there that

$$\frac{1}{2kN} \leqq \theta'_{h,k} < \frac{1}{kN}, \quad \frac{1}{2kN} \leqq \theta''_{h,k} < \frac{1}{kN}. \tag{5}$$

Making the substitution (3) in the integral (2), we get with $\theta' = \theta'_{h,k}$, $\theta'' = \theta''_{h,k}$:

$$p(n) = e^{2\pi N^{-2}n} \sum_{\substack{0 \leq h < k \leq N \\ (h,k)=1}} e^{-2\pi inh/k} \int_{-\theta'}^{\theta''} F(x) e^{-2\pi in\varphi} d\varphi \,, \tag{6}$$

where x is given by (3).

Step (ii). From Theorem 4.2, with

$$\begin{aligned} x' &= \exp\left[2\pi i \frac{h'}{k} - \frac{2\pi}{kz}\right] = \exp\left[2\pi i\left(\frac{h'}{k} + \frac{i}{kz}\right)\right], \\ F(x) &= e^{\pi i S(h,k)} \psi_k(z) F(x') = \omega_{h,k} \psi_k(z) F(x') \,, \end{aligned} \tag{7}$$

where

$$\psi_k(z) = \sqrt{z}\; e^{\pi(1/z - z)/12k} \,. \tag{8}$$

We substitute (7) in the integral of (6); the object is to replace $F(x)$ by $F(x')$ which tends very rapidly to 1 as $N \to \infty$:

$$p(n) = e^{2\pi N^{-2}n} \sum_{\substack{0 \leq h < k \leq N \\ (h,k)=1}} e^{-2\pi inh/k} \omega_{h,k} \int_{-\theta'}^{\theta''} \psi_k(z) F(x') e^{-2\pi in\varphi} d\varphi \,. \tag{9}$$

Let

$$j_{h,k} = \int_{-\theta'}^{\theta''} \psi_k(z) F(x') e^{-2\pi in\varphi} d\varphi \,.$$

Since $F(x') \to 1$, we replace $F(x')$ in $j_{h,k}$ by 1 and calculate the error made:

$$j_{h,k} = \int_{-\theta'}^{\theta''} \psi_k(z) e^{-2\pi in\varphi} d\varphi + \int_{-\theta'}^{\theta''} \psi_k(z) \{F(x') - 1\} e^{-2\pi in\varphi} d\varphi = j'_{h,k} + j''_{h,k} \,. \tag{10}$$

We first estimate the integrand in $j''_{h,k}$:

$$\begin{aligned} &\psi_k(z)\left\{F\left(\exp\left(\frac{2\pi ih'}{k} - \frac{2\pi}{kz}\right)\right) - 1\right\} \\ &= z^{1/2} \exp\left[\frac{\pi}{12k}\left(\frac{1}{z} - z\right)\right] \sum_{m=1}^{\infty} p(m) \exp\left[\left(\frac{2\pi ih'}{k} - \frac{2\pi}{kz}\right)m\right] \\ &= O\left(|z|^{1/2} \exp\left[\frac{\pi}{12k} \mathscr{R}\left(\frac{1}{z} - z\right)\right] \sum_{m=1}^{\infty} p(m) \exp\left[-\frac{2\pi m}{k} \mathscr{R}\left(\frac{1}{z}\right)\right]\right) \\ &= O\left(|z|^{1/2} \exp\left[-\frac{\pi}{12k} \mathscr{R}(z)\right] \sum_{m=1}^{\infty} p(m) \exp\left[-\frac{2\pi}{k} \mathscr{R}\left(\frac{1}{z}\right)\left(m - \frac{1}{24}\right)\right]\right). \end{aligned} \tag{11}$$

Because $m \geqq 1$ in the summation, $m - 1/24 > 0$; moreover, by (4),

$$\frac{1}{z} = \frac{1}{k(N^{-2} - i\varphi)} = \frac{N^{-2} + i\varphi}{k(N^{-4} + \varphi^2)} \,,$$

and from (5),

$$\varphi < \frac{1}{kN} \,,$$

and therefore

$$\frac{1}{k}\mathscr{R}\left(\frac{1}{z}\right)=\frac{N^{-2}}{k^2(N^{-4}+\varphi^2)}>\frac{N^{-2}}{k^2(N^{-4}+k^{-2}N^{-2})} \tag{12}$$

$$=\frac{1}{k^2N^{-2}+1}\geqq\frac{1}{2}\,.$$

In addition, we have

$$\begin{aligned}|z|^{1/2}&=|(N^{-2}-i\varphi)^{1/2}|k^{1/2}=O(k^{1/2}(N^{-4}+\varphi^2)^{1/4})\\&=O(k^{1/2}(N^{-4}+k^{-2}N^{-2})^{1/4})=O(N^{-1/2}(k^2N^{-2}+1)^{1/4})=O(N^{-1/2})\,.\end{aligned} \tag{13}$$

Consequently, from (11), (12) and (13),

$$\psi_k(z)\{F(x')-1\}=O(N^{-1/2}e^{-\pi kN^{-2}/12k}\sum_{m=1}^{\infty}p(m)e^{-\pi(m-1/24)})\,. \tag{14}$$

Since $e^{-\pi(m-1/24)}<1$, the series converges, i. e.,

$$\sum_{m=1}^{\infty}p(m)e^{-\pi(m-1/24)}=O(1)\,, \tag{15}$$

and therefore, by (14) and (15),

$$\psi_k(z)\{F(x')-1\}=O(N^{-1/2})\,. \tag{16}$$

Accordingly, by (5), (11) and (16),

$$j''_{h,k}=O(N^{-1/2})\int_{-\theta'}^{\theta''}d\varphi=O(N^{-3/2}k^{-1})\,.$$

Therefore, estimating the second term of (9) as it arises from (10), we get

$$e^{2\pi N^{-2}n}\sum_{\substack{0\leqq h<k\leqq N\\(h,k)=1}}\omega_{h,k}e^{-2\pi inh/k}j''_{h,k}=O\left(e^{-2\pi N^{-2}n}\sum_{h,k}\frac{N^{-3/2}}{k}\right)$$

$$=O\left(e^{-2\pi N^{-2}n}\sum_{k\leqq N}N^{-3/2}\right)=O(N^{-1/2})\,.$$

Thus as $N\to\infty$, the contribution to $p(n)$ arising from $F(x')-1$ tends to 0, and therefore from (9) and (10),

$$p(n)=\lim_{N\to\infty}e^{2\pi N^{-2}n}\sum_{h,k}\omega_{h,k}e^{-2\pi inh/k}j'_{h,k}\,.$$

We have therefore completed parts (i) and (ii) of the program.

Step (iii). It remains to evaluate

$$j'_{h,k}=\int_{-\theta'}^{\theta''}(k(N^{-2}-i\varphi))^{1/2}\exp\left[\frac{\pi}{12k}\left(\frac{1}{k(N^{-2}-i\varphi)}-k(N^{-2}-i\varphi)\right)\right]e^{-2\pi in\varphi}d\varphi\,.$$

To this end, we introduce a new variable:

$$w=N^{-2}-i\varphi\,;$$

then

$$J_{h,k} = e^{2\pi N^{-2}n} j'_{h,k} = \frac{\sqrt{k}}{i}\int_{N^{-2}-i\theta''}^{N^{-2}+i\theta'} \sqrt{w}\, e^{\pi(1/kw - kw)/12k} e^{2\pi n w}\, dw \tag{17}$$
$$= \frac{\sqrt{k}}{i}\int_{N^{-2}-i\theta''}^{N^{-2}+i\theta'} \sqrt{w}\, e^{\pi/12k^2 w} e^{2\pi\lambda_n^2 w}\, dw\,,$$

where

$$\lambda_n^2 = n - \frac{1}{24}\,. \tag{18}$$

The integrand is suggestive of that belonging to a Bessel function and its evaluation is best effected if we view it in this light. We replace the segment $N^{-2} - i\theta''$, $N^{-2} + i\theta'$ by a loop as follows: Consider a contour which starts at $-\infty$, circles the origin in a counterclockwise direction and returns

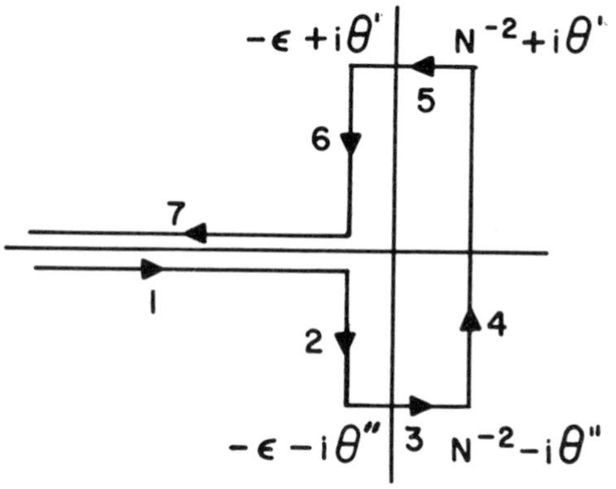

to $-\infty$. It consists of seven segments as noted in the figure and we are interested in segment 4. We note that as $N \to \infty$, θ', $\theta'' \to 0$ and we choose $\varepsilon > 0$ but $\varepsilon < N^{-2}$ and ultimately, we let $\varepsilon \to 0$. By Cauchy's theorem, we infer that

$$\int_{-\infty}^{(+0)} = \int_{-\infty}^{-\varepsilon} + \int_{-\varepsilon}^{-\varepsilon - i\theta''} + \int_{-\varepsilon - i\theta''}^{N^{-2}-i\theta''} + \int_{N^{-2}-i\theta''}^{N^{-2}+i\theta'} + \int_{N^{-2}+i\theta'}^{-\varepsilon + i\theta'} + \int_{-\varepsilon+i\theta'}^{-\varepsilon} + \int_{-\varepsilon}^{-\infty}\,.$$

It follows that

$$J_{h,k} = \frac{\sqrt{k}}{i}\int_{-\infty}^{(0+)} \sqrt{w}\, e^{\pi/12k^2 w} e^{2\pi\lambda_n^2 w}\, dw + i\sqrt{k}\left(\int_{-\infty}^{-\varepsilon} + \int_{-\varepsilon}^{-\varepsilon - i\theta''} + \int_{-\varepsilon - i\theta''}^{N^{-2}-i\theta''}\right.$$
$$\left. + \int_{N^{-2}+i\theta'}^{-\varepsilon + i\theta'} + \int_{-\varepsilon+i\theta'}^{-\varepsilon} + \int_{-\varepsilon}^{-\infty}\right) \sqrt{w}\, e^{\pi/12k^2 w} e^{2\pi\lambda_n^2 w}\, dw \tag{19}$$
$$= \frac{\sqrt{k}}{i} U_k + i\sqrt{k}(I_1 + I_2 + I_3 + I_5 + I_6 + I_7)\,,$$

where U_k denotes the loop integral which starts at $-\infty$, circles the origin counterclockwise and returns to $-\infty$.

We evaluate I_1 and I_7; they contribute one essential term to the final formula. In I_1, $\arg(-w) = -\pi$, whereas in I_7, $\arg(-w) = \pi$. Consequently,

$$I_1 = \int_{-\infty}^{-\varepsilon} \sqrt{|w|}\, e^{-\pi i/2} e^{\pi/12k^2 w} e^{2\pi\lambda_n^2 w} dw ,$$

$$I_7 = \int_{-\varepsilon}^{-\infty} \sqrt{|w|}\, e^{\pi i/2} e^{\pi/12k^2 w} e^{2\pi\lambda_n^2 w} dw ,$$

and therefore

$$I_1 + I_7 = -2i \int_{\varepsilon}^{\infty} w^{1/2} e^{-\pi/12k^2 w} e^{-2\pi\lambda_n^2 w} dw . \tag{20}$$

We continue by estimating the remaining integrals:

$$I_2 = O\left| \int_{-\varepsilon}^{-\varepsilon - i\theta''} w^{1/2} e^{\pi/12k^2 w} e^{2\pi\lambda_n^2 w} dw \right| .$$

In the integral, we change variables by putting

$$v = -i(w + \varepsilon) , \qquad w = iv - \varepsilon ,$$

and then

$$I_2 = O\left(\int_0^{-\theta''} (\varepsilon^2 + v^2)^{1/4} e^{-2\pi\lambda_n^2 \varepsilon} \exp\left[\frac{\pi}{12k^2} \mathscr{R}\left(\frac{1}{iv - \varepsilon} \right) \right] dv \right) .$$

But

$$\mathscr{R}\left(\frac{1}{iv - \varepsilon} \right) = -\frac{\varepsilon}{v^2 + \varepsilon^2} ,$$

and therefore

$$\begin{aligned} I_2 &= O\left(\int_0^{\theta''} (\varepsilon^2 + v^2)^{1/4} \exp[-2\pi\lambda_n^2 \varepsilon] \exp\left[-\frac{\pi}{12k^2} \frac{\varepsilon}{v^2 + \varepsilon^2} \right] dv \right) \\ &= O((\varepsilon^2 + \theta''^2)^{1/4} \theta'') = O((\varepsilon^2 + N^{-2}k^{-2})^{1/4} N^{-1} k^{-1}) , \end{aligned} \tag{21}$$

where we have used (5). The analogue I_6 of I_2 yields in the same way

$$I_6 = O((\varepsilon^2 + N^{-2}k^{-2})^{1/4} N^{-1} k^{-1}) . \tag{22}$$

In I_3, we make the substitution

$$w = v - i\theta'' ,$$

and then

$$I_3 = O\left(\int_{-\varepsilon}^{N^{-2}} (v^2 + \theta''^2)^{1/4} \exp\left[\frac{\pi}{12k^2} \mathscr{R}\left(\frac{1}{v - i\theta''} \right) \right] e^{2\pi\lambda_n^2 v} dv \right) .$$

In this case

$$\begin{aligned} \frac{1}{k^2} \mathscr{R}\left(\frac{1}{v - i\theta''} \right) &= \frac{v}{k^2(v^2 + \theta''^2)} \leqq \frac{N^{-2}}{k^2 \theta''^2} \\ &\leqq \frac{N^{-2}}{k^2 (2kN)^{-2}} = 4 ; \end{aligned}$$

hence

$$
\begin{aligned}
I_3 &= O\left(\int_{-\varepsilon}^{N^{-2}} (N^{-4} + \theta'^2)^{1/4} e^{2\pi\lambda_n^2 N^{-2}} dv\right) \\
&= O((N^{-2} + \varepsilon)(N^{-4} + \theta'^2)^{1/4} e^{2\pi\lambda_n^2 N^{-2}}) \\
&= O((N^{-2} + \varepsilon)(N^{-4} + k^{-2}N^{-2})^{1/4} e^{2\pi\lambda_n^2 N^{-2}}) \qquad (23) \\
&= O((N^{-2})(N^{-1/2})(N^{-2} + k^{-2})^{1/4} e^{2\pi\lambda_n^2 N^{-2}}) \\
&= O(k^{-1/2} N^{-5/2} e^{2\pi\lambda_n^2 N^{-2}}) .
\end{aligned}
$$

For I_5, we get the same estimate. From (19), (20), (21), (22), and (23), we conclude that

$$
\begin{aligned}
J_{h,k} = \frac{\sqrt{k}}{i} U_k &+ 2\sqrt{k}\int_{\varepsilon}^{\infty} w^{1/2} e^{-\pi/12k^2 w} e^{-2\pi\lambda_n^2 w} dw \\
&+ O(k^{1/2}(\varepsilon^2 + k^{-2}N^{-2})^{1/4} k^{-1}N^{-1}) \\
&+ O(k^{1/2}k^{-1/2}N^{-5/2} e^{2\pi\lambda_n^2 N^{-2}}) .
\end{aligned}
$$

We now let $\varepsilon \to 0$; the integral tends to

$$V_k = \int_0^{\infty} w^{1/2} e^{-\pi/12k^2 w} e^{-2\pi\lambda_n^2 w} dw .$$

As a consequence,

$$J_{h,k} = \frac{\sqrt{k}}{i} U_k + 2\sqrt{k} V_k + O(k^{-1}N^{-3/2}) + O(N^{-5/2}) . \tag{24}$$

Let

$$W_k = \frac{\sqrt{k}}{i} U_k + 2\sqrt{k} V_k ; \tag{25}$$

then from (24), (10) and (17),

$$p(n) = \sum_{h,k} \omega_{h,k} e^{-2\pi inh/k} W_k(n) + O\left(\sum_{h\ k} N^{-3/2}k^{-1}\right) + O\left(\sum_{h\ k} N^{-5/2}\right) + O(N^{-1/2}) . \tag{26}$$

On the other hand,

$$\sum_{h\ k} N^{-3/2}k^{-1} = O\left(N^{-3/2}\sum_{k \leqq N} 1\right) = O(N^{-3/2}N) = O(N^{-1/2})$$

and

$$\sum_{h,k} N^{-5/2} = O(N^{-1/2}) ,$$

and therefore from (26),

$$
\begin{aligned}
p(n) &= \sum_{0 \leqq h < k \leqq N;\ (h,k)=1} \omega_{h,k} e^{-2\pi inh/k} W_k(n) + O(N^{-1/2}) \\
&= \sum_{1 \leqq k \leqq N} \left(\sum_{0 \leqq h < k;\ (h,k)=1} \omega_{h,k} e^{-2\pi inh/k}\right) W_k(n) + O(N^{-1/2}) \\
&= \sum_{k=1}^{N} A_k(n) W_k(n) + O(N^{-1/2}) ,
\end{aligned}
$$

where

(28) $$A_k(n) = \sum_{0 \leq h < k;\ (h\ k)=1} \omega_{h,k} e^{-2\pi i n h/k},$$

only the value $h = 0$ being taken when $k = 1$. As $N \to \infty$, we conclude from (27) that

(29) $$p(n) = \sum_{k=1}^{\infty} A_k(n) W_k(n).$$

Thus in principle, the argument is complete. We have only to evaluate

$$W_k(n) = \frac{\sqrt{k}}{i} \int_{-\infty}^{(0+)} w^{1/2} e^{\pi/12k^2 w} e^{2\pi \lambda_n^2 w} dw + 2\sqrt{k} \int_0^{\infty} w^{1/2} e^{-\pi/12k^2 w} e^{-2\pi \lambda_n^2 w} dw.$$

We evaluate U_k first:

$$\frac{1}{i} U_k = \frac{1}{i} \int_{-\infty}^{(0+)} w^{1/2} \sum_{m=0}^{\infty} \frac{1}{m!} \left(\frac{\pi}{12k^2 w} \right)^m e^{2\pi \lambda_n^2 w} dw$$
$$= \frac{1}{i} \sum_{m=0}^{\infty} \frac{1}{m!} \left(\frac{\pi}{12k^2} \right)^m \int_{-\infty}^{(0+)} w^{-m+1/2} e^{2\pi \lambda_n^2 w} dw.$$

Interchanging the summation and integration processes raises no problem. To change the integral so as to bring it in the form of a Γ function, we put

$$2\pi \lambda_n^2 w = -z,$$

and then

$$\frac{1}{i} U_k = 2\pi \sum_{m=0}^{\infty} \frac{1}{m!} \left(\frac{\pi}{12k^2} \right)^m (2\pi \lambda_n^2)^{m-3/2} \frac{1}{2\pi i} \int_{\infty}^{(0+)} (-z)^{-m+1/2} e^{-z} dz$$

(30) $$= 2\pi \sum_{m=0}^{\infty} \frac{1}{m!} \left(\frac{\pi}{12k^2} \right)^m (2\pi \lambda_n^2)^{m-3/2} \frac{1}{\Gamma(m - \frac{1}{2})}$$
$$= \frac{1}{\sqrt{(2\pi)}} \lambda_n^{-3} \sum_{m=0}^{\infty} \frac{1}{m!} \left(\frac{\pi^2 \lambda_n^2}{6k^2} \right)^m \frac{1}{\Gamma(m - \frac{1}{2})}.$$

We have used here Theorem A.4 of Appendix A. On the other hand, using the functional relation for $\Gamma(z)$, we find

$$\Gamma(m - \tfrac{1}{2}) = 2^{-(m-1)} \Gamma(\tfrac{1}{2}) 1 \cdot 3 \cdot 5 \cdots (2m-3) = \sqrt{\pi} 2^{-(m-1)} \cdot 1 \cdot 3 \cdot 5 \cdots (2m-3).$$

With this in mind, we look at the series in (30). Let

$$X = \frac{\pi^2 \lambda_n^2}{6k^2},$$

then

$$\sum_{m=0}^{\infty} \frac{1}{m!} \left(\frac{\pi^2 \lambda_n^2}{6k^2} \right)^m \frac{1}{\Gamma(m - \frac{1}{2})} = \frac{1}{\sqrt{\pi}} \sum_{m=1}^{\infty} \frac{1}{m!} \frac{X^m 2^{m-1}}{1 \cdot 3 \cdot 5 \cdots (2m-3)} - \frac{1}{2\sqrt{\pi}}$$
$$= \frac{1}{\sqrt{\pi}} \sum_{m=1}^{\infty} \frac{X^m \cdot 2^{m-1} \cdot (2m-1) \cdot 2^m}{(2m)!} - \frac{1}{2\sqrt{\pi}}$$
$$= \frac{1}{2\sqrt{\pi}} \left[\sum_{m=1}^{\infty} \frac{(4X)^m \cdot (2m-1)}{(2m)!} - 1 \right].$$

In this expression, we put $(4X) = Y^2$ and then

$$\frac{1}{2\sqrt{\pi}}\left[\sum_{m=0}^{\infty}\frac{(4X)^m(2m-1)}{(2m)!}-1\right]=\frac{1}{2\sqrt{\pi}}\left(-1+\sum_{m=1}^{\infty}\frac{Y^{2m}(2m-1)}{(2m)!}\right)$$
$$=\frac{1}{2\sqrt{\pi}}\left(-1+Y^2\sum_{m=1}^{\infty}\frac{Y^{2m-2}(2m-1)}{(2m)!}\right)$$
$$=\frac{1}{2\sqrt{\pi}}\left(-1+Y^2\cdot\frac{d}{dY}\sum_{m=1}^{\infty}\frac{Y^{2m-1}}{(2m)!}\right)$$
$$=\frac{1}{2\sqrt{\pi}}\left(-1+Y^2\frac{d}{dY}\left(\frac{\cosh Y-1}{Y}\right)\right)$$
$$=\frac{1}{2\sqrt{\pi}}\left(Y^2\frac{d}{dY}\frac{\cosh Y}{Y}\right).$$

In our particular case,

$$X=\frac{1}{4}Y^2=\frac{\pi^2\lambda_n^2}{6k^2},$$

or

$$Y=\sqrt{\frac{2}{3}}\frac{\pi\lambda_n}{k}=\frac{c\lambda_n}{k},$$

where

$$c=\pi\sqrt{\frac{2}{3}}.$$

Moreover,

$$\frac{d}{dn}\frac{\cosh Y}{Y}=\frac{d}{dY}\frac{\cosh Y}{Y}\cdot\frac{dY}{dn}=\frac{d}{dY}\frac{\cosh Y}{Y}\cdot\frac{c}{2k\lambda_n}.$$

Consequently, from (30), and using the result we have just derived,

$$\frac{1}{i}U_k=\frac{1}{(2\pi)^{1/2}}\lambda_n^{-3}\frac{1}{2\sqrt{\pi}}\frac{c^2\lambda_n^2}{k^2}\cdot\frac{2k\lambda_n}{c}\frac{d}{dn}\frac{\cosh Y}{Y}$$

(31)
$$=\frac{1}{\pi\sqrt{2}}\frac{c}{k}\frac{d}{dn}\left(\frac{\cosh\dfrac{c\lambda_n}{k}}{\dfrac{c\lambda_n}{k}}\right)$$
$$=\frac{1}{\pi\sqrt{2}}\frac{d}{dn}\left(\frac{\cosh\dfrac{c\lambda_n}{k}}{\lambda_n}\right).$$

To evaluate

$$V_k=\int_0^{\infty}w^{1/2}e^{-\pi/12k^2w}e^{-2\pi\lambda_n^2w}dw=\int_0^{\infty}w^{1/2}e^{-a^2w^{-1}-b^2w}dw,$$

where $a=(\pi/12k^2)^{1/2}$, $b=(2\pi\lambda_n^2)^{1/2}$, and $ab>0$, we notice that

(32)
$$V_k=-\frac{1}{2b}\frac{d}{db}\int_0^{\infty}w^{-1/2}e^{-a^2w^{-1}-b^2w}dw=-\frac{1}{2b}\frac{d}{db}J.$$

In J we put $w = u^2$, and find

$$
\begin{aligned}
J &= 2\int_0^\infty e^{-a^2u^{-2}-b^2u^2}du = \frac{1}{b}\int_0^\infty e^{-a^2u^{-2}-b^2u^2}d\left(bu+\frac{a}{u}+bu-\frac{a}{u}\right)\\
&= \frac{1}{b}\int_0^\infty e^{-a^2u^{-2}-b^2u^2}d\left(bu+\frac{a}{u}\right)+\frac{1}{b}\int_0^\infty e^{-a^2u^{-2}-b^2u^2}d\left(bu-\frac{a}{u}\right)\\
&= \frac{e^{2ab}}{b}\int_0^\infty e^{-(bu+a/u)^2}d\left(bu+\frac{a}{u}\right)+\frac{e^{-2ab}}{b}\int_0^\infty e^{-(bu-a/u)^2}d\left(bu-\frac{a}{u}\right)\\
&= \frac{e^{2ab}}{b}J_1+\frac{e^{-2ab}}{b}J_2 .
\end{aligned}
\tag{33}
$$

On the other hand,

$$
J_1 = \int_0^{(a/b)^{1/2}} e^{-(bu+a/u)^2}d\left(bu+\frac{a}{u}\right)+\int_{(a/b)^{1/2}}^\infty e^{-(bu+a/u)^2}d\left(bu+\frac{a}{u}\right),
$$

and if we put

$$
v = bu+\frac{a}{u},
$$

then

$$
J_1 = \int_\infty^{(2ab)^{1/2}} e^{-v^2}dv+\int_{(2ab)^{1/2}}^\infty e^{-v^2}dv = 0 . \tag{34}
$$

In J_2, we put

$$
v = bu-\frac{a}{u},
$$

and get

$$
J_2 = \int_{-\infty}^\infty e^{-v^2}dv = \sqrt{\pi} . \tag{35}
$$

Therefore from (33), (34) and (35),

$$
J = \frac{\sqrt{\pi}e^{-2ab}}{b},
$$

and hence

$$
\begin{aligned}
V_k &= -\frac{\sqrt{\pi}}{2b}\frac{d}{db}\left(\frac{e^{-2ab}}{b}\right) = -\frac{\sqrt{\pi}}{2(2\pi)^{1/2}\lambda_n}\frac{d}{db}\left(\frac{e^{-c\lambda_n/k}}{(2\pi)^{1/2}\lambda_n}\right)\\
&= -\frac{1}{4\sqrt{\pi}\lambda_n}\frac{d}{db}\left(\frac{e^{-c\lambda_n/k}}{\lambda_n}\right) = -\frac{1}{4\sqrt{\pi}\lambda_n}\frac{d}{dn}\left(\frac{e^{-c\lambda_n/k}}{\lambda_n}\right)\cdot\frac{2\lambda_n}{(2\pi)^{1/2}}\\
&= -\frac{1}{2\sqrt{2}\pi}\frac{d}{dn}\left(\frac{e^{-c\lambda_n/k}}{\lambda_n}\right).
\end{aligned}
$$

Combining this with (31), we get from (25),

$$W_k = k^{1/2}\frac{1}{\pi\sqrt{2}}\frac{d}{dn}\left(\frac{\cosh\frac{c\lambda_n}{k}}{\lambda_n} - \frac{e^{-c\lambda_n/k}}{\lambda_n}\right)$$

$$= k^{1/2}\frac{1}{\pi\sqrt{2}}\frac{d}{dn}\left(\frac{\sinh\frac{c\lambda_n}{k}}{\lambda_n}\right).$$

This means, however, that

$$p(n) = \frac{1}{\pi\sqrt{2}}\sum_{k=1}^{\infty} A_k(n)k^{1/2}\frac{d}{dn}\left(\frac{\sinh\frac{c\lambda_n}{k}}{\lambda_n}\right),$$

and this completes the derivation. We state our result in the form of

THEOREM 6.1. *If*

$$c = \pi\left(\frac{2}{3}\right)^{1/2}, \qquad \lambda_n = \left(n - \frac{1}{24}\right)^{1/2},$$

$$A_k(n) = \sum_{h \bmod k, (h,k)=1} \omega_{h,k} e^{-2\pi i n h/k},$$

$$\omega_{h,k} = e^{\pi i S(h,k)},$$

where

$$S(h, k) = \sum_{\mu=1}^{k-1}\left(\frac{h\mu}{k} - \left[\frac{h\mu}{k}\right] - \frac{1}{2}\right)\left(\frac{\mu}{k} - \frac{1}{2}\right)$$

then

$$p(n) = \frac{1}{\pi\sqrt{2}}\sum_{k=1}^{\infty} A_k(n)\sqrt{k}\frac{d}{dn}\frac{\sinh\frac{c\lambda_n}{k}}{\lambda_n}.$$

There is another derivation, due to Rademacher, of the series for the partition function which brings into evidence a little more clearly the contribution of the various rational points. The essential difference is to replace the path along the circle by one which goes from i to $1 + i$ along arcs of certain circles. The nature of the path is explained in the problems following this section.

It may be of interest finally to comment on the rapidity with which the series for $p(n)$ converges. We have from Theorem 6.1

$$p(n) = \frac{1}{\pi\sqrt{2}}\sum_{k=1}^{M} A_k(n)\sqrt{k}\frac{d}{dn}\left(\frac{\sinh\frac{c\lambda_n}{k}}{\lambda_n}\right) + R_n(M).$$

We shall estimate the remainder $R_n(M)$. Since $|A_k(n)| \leqq k$, we have

$$|R_n(M)| \leqq \frac{1}{\pi\sqrt{2}} \sum_{k=M+1}^{\infty} k^{3/2} \frac{d}{dn} \sum_{l=0}^{\infty} \frac{\left(\frac{c}{k}\right)^{2l+1} \lambda_n^{2l}}{(2l+1)!} = \frac{1}{\pi\sqrt{2}} \sum_{k=M+1}^{\infty} k^{3/2} \sum_{l=1}^{\infty} \frac{\left(\frac{c}{k}\right)^{2l+1} l \cdot \lambda_n^{2l-2}}{(2l+1)!}$$
$$\leqq \frac{1}{\pi\sqrt{2}} \sum_{l=1}^{\infty} \frac{c^{2l+1}\lambda_n^{2l-2} l}{(2l+1)!} \sum_{k=N+1}^{\infty} \frac{1}{k^{2l-1/2}} \leqq \frac{1}{\pi\sqrt{2}} \sum_{l=1}^{\infty} \frac{c^{2l+1}\lambda_n^{2l-2} l}{(2l+1)!} \int_M^{\infty} \frac{dX}{X^{2l-1/2}}$$
$$= \frac{1}{\pi\sqrt{2}} \sum_{l=1}^{\infty} \frac{c^{2l+1}\lambda_n^{2l-2} l}{(2l+1)!\left(2l-\frac{3}{2}\right) M^{2l-3/2}}$$
$$= \frac{c^2 M^{1/2}}{\pi\sqrt{2}\lambda_n} \left\{ \frac{c}{3} \frac{\lambda_n}{M} + \sum_{l=2}^{\infty} \frac{\left(\frac{c\lambda_n}{M}\right)^{2l-1}}{(2l-1)!(2l+1)(4l-3)} \right\}$$
$$< \frac{c^2 M^{1/2}}{\pi\sqrt{2}\lambda_n} \left\{ \frac{c\lambda_n}{3M} + \frac{1}{5^2} \sum_{l=2}^{\infty} \frac{\left(\frac{c\lambda_n}{M}\right)^{2l-1}}{(2l-1)!} \right\}$$
$$= \frac{c^2 M^{1/2}}{\pi\sqrt{2}\lambda_n} \left\{ \left(\frac{1}{3} - \frac{1}{25}\right) \frac{c\lambda_n}{M} + \frac{1}{25} \sinh\left(\frac{c\lambda_n}{M}\right) \right\}.$$

In the first sum of $p(n)$, we replace $\sinh c\lambda_n/k$ by $e^{c\lambda_n/k}$ and calculate the error. It is

$$\left| \frac{1}{2\pi\sqrt{2}} \sum_{k=1}^{M} A_k(n) k^{1/2} \frac{d}{dn} \left(\frac{e^{-c\lambda_n/k}}{\lambda_n} \right) \right|$$
$$\leqq \frac{1}{2\pi\sqrt{2}} \sum_{k=1}^{M} k^{3/2} \left(\frac{c}{k} \frac{e^{-c\lambda_n/k}}{2\lambda_n^2} + \frac{e^{-c\lambda_n/k}}{2\lambda_n^3} \right)$$
$$= \frac{c}{4\pi\sqrt{2}\lambda_n^2} \sum_{k=1}^{M} k^{1/2} e^{-c\lambda_n/k} + \frac{1}{4\pi\sqrt{2}\lambda_n^3} \sum_{k=1}^{M} k^{3/2} e^{-c\lambda_n/k}$$
$$< \frac{c}{4\pi\sqrt{2}\lambda_n^2} e^{-c\lambda_n/M} \int_1^{M+1} x^{1/2} dx + \frac{1}{4\pi\sqrt{2}\lambda_n^3} e^{-c\lambda_n/M} \int_1^{M+1} x^{3/2} dx$$
$$< \frac{1}{2\sqrt{3}} \frac{(M+1)^{3/2}}{\lambda_n^2} e^{-c\lambda_n/M} \left\{ \frac{1}{3} + \frac{\sqrt{3}}{5\pi\sqrt{2}} \frac{M+1}{\lambda_n} \right\},$$

on putting in the value $c = \pi(\frac{2}{3})^{1/2}$. Replacing λ_n by $(n-1)^{1/2}$ or $n^{1/2}$ depending on its position, we may therefore write

$$p(n) = \frac{1}{2\pi\sqrt{2}} \sum_{k=1}^{M} A_k(n) k^{1/2} \frac{d}{dn} \frac{e^{c\lambda_n/k}}{\lambda_n}$$
$$+ \theta \left\{ \frac{44\pi^2}{225\sqrt{3}} M^{-1/2} + \frac{\pi\sqrt{2}}{75} \left(\frac{M}{n-1} \right)^{1/2} \sinh \frac{c\sqrt{n}}{M} \right.$$
$$\left. + \frac{1}{2\sqrt{3}} \frac{(M+1)^{3/2}}{n-1} e^{-c(n-1)^{1/2}/M} \left(\frac{1}{3} + \frac{\sqrt{3}}{5\pi\sqrt{2}} \frac{(M+1)}{(n-1)^{1/2}} \right) \right\},$$

where θ is some real number such that $|\theta| < 1$. This contrasts with the formula of Hardy and Ramanujan

$$p(n) = \frac{1}{2\pi\sqrt{2}} \sum_{k \leq \alpha\sqrt{n}} A_k(n) k^{1/2} \frac{d}{dn} \frac{e^{c\lambda_n/k}}{\lambda_n} + O(n^{-1/4}),$$

where α is arbitrary but where the constant implied by the O was not given explicitly.

As numerical examples Rademacher gave the following calculations which were initiated by D. H. Lehmer. For $n = 599$, $M = 18$,

$$p(n) = 4353,\ 50207,\ 84031,\ 73482,\ 70000$$

with an error at most 0.43123 and for $n = 721$, $M = 21$,

$$p(n) = 16,\ 10617,\ 55750,\ 27947,\ 76355,\ 34762,$$

with an error at most .37819.

Thus 18 and 21 terms respectively of the series for $p(n)$ suffice to determine precisely $p(599)$ and $p(721)$ which have respectively 24 and 27 digits.

Problems

In the following problems, let

$$p(n, R_1, R_2)$$

denote the number of partitions of n into parts in which R_1 denotes a property of the *number* of parts and R_2 a property of the parts themselves. Similarly for

$$q(n, R_1, R_2)$$

except that $q(n, R_1, R_2)$ has the additional property that no two parts are equal.

In every case $*$ means that there is no condition or restriction.

EXAMPLES. $p(n, k, q)$ = number of partitions into k parts of which the greatest is q. $p(n, *, *) = p(n)$ the number of unrestricted partitions. $p(n, k, \leqq m)$ = number of partitions of n into k parts no one of which exceeds m.

Derive the following generating functions assuming that $p(0, R_1, R_2) = q(0, R_1, R_2) = 1$.

1. $\prod_{r=1}^{\infty} (1 + x^r) = \sum_{n=0}^{\infty} q(n, *, \leqq m)x^n$.
2. $\prod_{r=1}^{\infty} (1 + zx^r) = \sum_{n,m}^{0,\infty} q(n, m, *)z^m x^n$.
3. $\prod_{r=1}^{m} (1 + x^r) = \sum_{n=0}^{\infty} q(n, *, *)x^n$.
4. $\prod_{r=1}^{m} (1 - zx^r)^{-1} = \sum_{n,l}^{0,\infty} p(n, l, \leqq m)z^l x^n$.
5. $\prod_{r=0}^{m} (1 - zx^r)^{-1} = \sum_{n,l}^{0,\infty} p(n, \leqq l, \leqq m)z^l x^n$.
6. $\prod_{r=1}^{m} (1 - x^r)^{-1} = \sum_{n=0}^{\infty} p(n, *, \leqq m)x^n$.
7. $\prod_{r=1}^{\infty} (1 - zx^r)^{-1} = \sum_{n,l}^{0,\infty} p(n, l, *)z^l x^n$.
8. $\prod_{r=1}^{\infty} (1 - zx^r)^{-1} = \sum_{n,l}^{0,\infty} p(n, \leqq l, *)z^l x^n$.
9. $\prod_{r=1}^{m} (1 - zx^r)(1 - z)^{-1} = \sum_{n,l}^{0,\infty} q(n, \leqq l, \leqq m)z^l x^n$.
10. $\prod_{r=0}^{\infty} (1 - x^{2r+1})^{-1} = \sum_{n=0}^{\infty} p(n, *, \text{odd})x^n$.
11. $\prod_{r=1}^{\infty} (1 - x^{2r})^{-1} = \sum_{n=0}^{\infty} p(n, *, \text{even})x^n$.
12. $\prod_{r=0}^{\infty} (1 + x^{2r+1}) = \sum_{n=0}^{\infty} q(n, *, \text{odd})x^n$.

Using the above generating functions, or otherwise, prove as follows.

13. $p(n, *, \text{odd}) = q(n, *, *)$.

14. $p(n, *, \leqq m) = p(n, *, \leqq m-1) + p(n-m, *, \leqq m)$ if $n \geqq m$,
$= p(n, *, \leqq m-1)$ if $n < m$.
15. $p(n, m, *) = p(n-m, *, \leqq m)$.
16. $q(n, m, *) = p(n - \frac{1}{2}m(m+1), *, \leqq m)$.
17. $p(n, m, r) = p(n-r, m-1, \leqq r)$.
18. $p(n, *, m) = p(n-m, *, \leqq m)$.
19. $p(n, \leqq m, \leqq r) = p(n, \leqq r, \leqq m)$.
20. $p(n, m, r) = p(n, r, m)$.
21. $p(n, m, \leqq r) = p(n, \leqq r, m)$.
22. $q(n, m, *) = p(n - \frac{1}{2}m(m-1), m, *)$.
23. $p(n, m, *) = q(n + \frac{1}{2}m(m-1), m, *)$.
24. $p(n, m, *) = p(n-1, m-1, *) + p(n-m, m, *)$.

Give some of the preceding an interpretation.

25. Let

$$F(a) = F(a, x) = \prod_{k=0}^{\infty}(1 + ax^{2k+1}) = \sum_{m=0}^{\infty} c_m a^m ,$$

where $c_m = c_m(x)$ is independent of a.

Show that $F(a) = (1+ax)F(ax^2)$, and hence that

$$c_m = \frac{x^{2m-1}}{1-x^{2m}} c_{m-1} = \frac{x^{1+3+\cdots+2m-1}}{(1-x^2)(1-x^4)\cdots(1-x^{2m})} .$$

Deduce that

$$\prod_{m=0}^{\infty}(1+x^{2m+1}) = \sum_{m=1}^{\infty} \frac{x^{m2}}{(1-x^2)(1-x^4)\cdots(1-x^{2m})} + 1 .$$

26. Prove Euler's pentagonal number theorem as follows. Prove that

$$\begin{aligned} f(x) = \prod_{n=1}^{M}(1-x^n) &= (1-x) - x^2(1-x) - x^3(1-x)(1-x^2) \\ &\quad - x^4(1-x)(1-x^2)(1-x^3) - \cdots \\ &= 1 - x - x^2 f_1^{(M)}(x) , \end{aligned} \tag{1}$$

where

$$\begin{aligned} f_1^{(M)}(x) &= (1-x) + x(1-x)(1-x^2) + x^2(1-x)(1-x^2)(1-x^3) + \cdots \\ &\quad + x^{M-2}(1-x)(1-x^2)\cdots(1-x^{M-1}) . \end{aligned}$$

If $f_i^{(M)}(x) = (1-x^i) + x^i(1-x^i)(1-x^{i+1}) + x^{2i}(1-x^i)(1-x^{i+1})(1-x^{i+2}) + \cdots$, then show that

$$f_i^{(M)}(x) = 1 - x^{2i+1} - x^{3i+2} f_{i+1}^{(M-1)} .$$

Deduce from (1) that

$$f(x) = 1 - x - x^2(1-x^3) + x^{2+5}(1-x^5) - x^{2+5+8}(1-x^7) + \cdots .$$

Allow $M \to \infty$, and conclude that

$$\prod_{n=1}^{\infty}(1-x^n) = \sum_{i=1}^{\infty}(-1)^i(1-x^{2i+1})x^{2+5+8+\cdots+(3i-1)} + 1 - x .$$

27. Prove that

$$\prod_{n=1}^{\infty}(1-x^n)^3=\sum_{i=0}^{\infty}(-1)^i(2i+1)x^{(i^2+i)/2},$$

as follows:

Let $f(x,a)=\prod_{n=1}^{\infty}(1+ax^n)$, and put $f_1(x,a)=f(x,a^{-1})$, $a\neq 0$.

Prove:

(i) If $f\cdot f_1=\sum_{m=-\infty}^{\infty}g_m(x)a^m$, then

$$g_m=g_{-m}\,.$$

(ii) $(1+a)(1+ax)^{-1}f(x,a)f_1(x,a)=f(x,ax)f_1(x,ax)$.

(iii) Therefore

$$G_m\equiv g_m+g_{m-1}=x^{m-1}(g_{m-1}+g_{m-2})=x^{m-1}G_{m-1}\,.$$

(iv) Hence

$$G_m=x^{1+2+\cdots+m-1}G_1\,.$$

(v) $(1+a)f(x,a)f_1(x,a)=G_1(x)\sum_{m=-\infty}^{\infty}x^{m(m-1)/2}a^m$.

(vi) $(1+a)f(x^3,a)f_1(x^3,a)=G_1(x^3)\ \sum_{m=-\infty}^{\infty}x^{3m(m-1)/2}a^m$.

(vii) Putting $a=-x$,

$$(1-x)f(x^3,a)f_1(x^3,a)=G_1(x^3)\sum_{m=-\infty}^{\infty}(-1)^m x^{m(3m-1)/2}$$

$$=G_1(x^3)\prod_{m=1}^{\infty}(1-x^m)\,.$$

(viii) $G_1(x^3)=\prod_{m=1}^{\infty}(1-x^{3m})^{-1}$, $G_1(x)=\prod_{m=1}^{\infty}(1-x^m)^{-1}$.

(ix) From (v) and (viii), deduce the result.

28. The same general argument may be used to prove the following general theorem of Jacobi: If $z\neq 0$ and $|q|<1$, then

$$\prod_{k=1}^{\infty}(1-q^{2k})(1-q^{2k-1}z^2)(1-q^{2k-1}z^{-2})=\sum_{k=-\infty}^{\infty}(-1)^k z^{2k}q^{k^2}\,.$$

Let

$$\varphi(z)=\prod_{1}^{n}(1-q^{2k-1}z^2)(1-q^{2k-1}z^{-2})\,;$$

show that

(*) $$\varphi(qz)(q^{2n}-qz^2)=\varphi(z)(1-q^{2n+1}z^2)\,.$$

If

$$\varphi(z)=c_0+c_1(z^2+z^{-2})+\cdots+c_n(z^{2n}+z^{-2n})\,,$$

then

$$c_n=q^{n^2}$$

and by equating coefficients of like powers in (*) deduce that

$$c_k = c_{k-1}\frac{q^{2k-1}(1-q^{2n-2k+2})}{1-q^{2n+2k}}$$

$$= \frac{(-1)^k q^{k^2}}{(1-q^2)\cdots(1-q^{2n})}\prod_{n+1}^{n+k}(1-q^{2\nu})^{-1}\prod_{\nu=n-k+1}^{2n}(1-q^{2\nu})$$

$$\to \frac{(-1)^k q^{k2}}{\prod_{\nu=1}^{\infty}(1-q^{2\nu})}, \qquad \text{as } n\to\infty .$$

29. Let $f(x)$ and $g(x)$ be power series in x with integer coefficients. The notation

$$f(x) \equiv g(x) \pmod n$$

means that the coefficients of $f(x) - g(x)$ are all divisible by n. Prove the following theorem of Ramanujan,

$$p(5n+4) \equiv 0 \pmod 5$$

as follows:

(i)
$$\frac{1}{(1-q)^5} \equiv \frac{1}{1-q^5} \pmod 5 .$$

(ii) Write

$$\frac{q(1-q^5)(1-q^{10})\cdots}{(1-q)(1-q^2)\cdots} = q\{(1-q)(1-q^2)\cdots\}\{(1-q)(1-q^2)\cdots\}^3\frac{(1-q^5)(1-q^{10})\cdots}{\{(1-q)(1-q^2)\cdots\}^5} .$$

Using Problems 26, 27, the right-hand side is

$$= \sum_{\mu=-\infty}^{\infty}\sum_{\nu=-\infty}^{\infty}(-1)^{\mu+\nu}(2\nu+1)q^{1+\mu(3\mu+1)/2+\nu(\nu+1)/2}\frac{(1-q^5)(1-q^{10})\cdots}{\{(1-q)(1-q^2)\cdots\}^5} .$$

(iii) In the series, if the exponent of q is divisible by 5,

$$2(\mu+1)^2 + (2\nu+1)^2 = 8(1+\tfrac{1}{2}\mu(3\mu+1)+\tfrac{1}{2}\nu(\nu+1)) - 10\mu^2 - 5 \equiv 0(5) ,$$

and therefore $2\nu+1 \equiv 0(5)$.

(iv) It follows by (i), that the coefficient of q^{5m+5} on the right is $\equiv 0 (\text{mod } 5)$. But the coefficient of q^{5m+5} on the left is $p(5m+4)$.

30. Let

$$\varphi(x) = \prod_{n=1}^{\infty}(1+x^n) = \sum_{m=0}^{\infty} q(m)x^m , \qquad q(0) = 1 .$$

$q(m)$ is the number of partitions of m into unequal parts. Show that $\varphi(x) = F(x)/F(x^2)$, where $F(x) = \prod_{n=1}^{\infty}(1-x^n)^{-1}$, and

$$q(m) = \frac{1}{2\pi i}\int_C \frac{\varphi(x)dx}{x^{m+1}} ,$$

where C is a simple closed contour in the unit circle enclosing the origin. Evaluate the integral by the methods of § 2, and show that

$$q(m) \sim \frac{e^{\pi\lambda_m\sqrt{3}}}{4\sqrt[4]{3}\,\lambda_m^{3/2}}, \qquad \lambda_m = \left(m - \frac{1}{24}\right)^{1/2}.$$

31. If

$$\psi(x) = \prod_{k=0}^{\infty}(1 + x^{2k+1}) = \sum_{m=0}^{\infty} r(m)x^m, \qquad r(0) = 1,$$

where $r(m)$ = number of partitions of m into odd distinct parts, and

$$\psi(x) = \frac{F(x)F(x^4)}{(F(x^2))^2},$$

then

$$r(m) \sim \frac{e^{\pi\lambda_m}}{2\sqrt[4]{24}\,\lambda_m^{3/2}}, \qquad \text{where } \lambda_m = \left(m - \frac{1}{24}\right)^{1/2},$$

32. Use the fact that

$$\log F(x) < \frac{\pi^2}{6}\frac{x}{1-x}$$

to show that

$$p(N) < e^{\sqrt{(2/3)}\,\pi\sqrt{N}}$$

as follows:

$$p(N)x^N < F(x),$$

$$\log p(N) < \frac{\pi^2}{6}\frac{x}{1-x} + N\log\frac{1}{x} < \frac{\pi^2}{6}\cdot\frac{1}{u} + Nu,$$

where $u = (1-x)/x$, and hence

$$\log p(N) < \sqrt{\frac{2}{3}}\,\pi\sqrt{N}.$$

33. Let $p_3(n)$ be the number of partitions of n into at most 3 parts:

$$\sum_{n=0}^{\infty} p_3(n)x^n = \frac{1}{(1-x)(1-x^2)(1-x^3)} = f(x).$$

Decompose the right-hand side into partial fractions

$$f(x) = \frac{1}{6(1-x)^3} + \frac{1}{4(1-x)^2} + \frac{12}{72}\frac{1}{(1-x)} + \frac{1}{8(1+x)} + \frac{1}{9(1-\rho x)} + \frac{1}{9(1-\rho^2 x)},$$

where ρ is a primitive cube root of unity. Expand each term in a power series and equate coefficients, then

$$p_3(n) = \frac{(n+3)^2}{12} - \frac{7}{72} + \frac{1}{8}(-1)^n + \frac{1}{9}(\rho^n + \rho^{2n}) = \frac{(n+3)^2}{12} + b_n.$$

Show that $|b_n| < \frac{1}{2}$, and conclude that

$$p_3(n) = \text{nearest integer to } \frac{(n+3)^2}{12} .$$

34. Use the pentagonal number theorem to prove the following result: If n is not of the form $k(3k-1)/2$, then the number of partitions of n into an even number of distinct parts is the same as the number of partitions into an odd number of distinct parts. If $n = k(3k-1)/2$, then there is one more "even" partition than "odd" partition or vice versa, according as k is even or odd.

35. Show that

$$p(7n+5) \equiv 0 \pmod 7$$

by observing that

$$\frac{x^2}{\prod_{n=1}^{\infty}(1-x^n)} \prod_{n=1}^{\infty}(1-x^{7n}) \equiv x^2\left\{\prod_{n=1}^{\infty}(1-x^n)^3\right\}^2 \pmod 7 .$$

Expand the inner brace bracket by Problem 27.

36. Let

$$n = q_1^{\alpha_1} q_2^{\alpha_2} \cdots q_r^{\alpha_r}$$

be the canonical decomposition of the integer n. Using the fundamental theorem on abelian groups, show that if $a(n)$ is the number of abelian groups of order n, then

$$a(n) = \prod_{i=1}^{r} p(\alpha_i) ,$$

where $p(\alpha_i)$ is the number of partitions of α_i. Show that $a(n)$ is multiplicative, i. e.,

$$a(mn) = a(m)a(n) \qquad (m, n) = 1 .$$

Hence if q is a prime,

$$\sum_{\lambda=0}^{\infty} \frac{a(q^\lambda)}{q^{\lambda s}} = \prod_{\nu=1}^{\infty} (1 - q^{-\nu s})^{-1}$$

and

$$\sum_{n=1}^{\infty} \frac{a(n)}{n^s} = \prod_{\nu=1}^{\infty} \zeta(\nu s) .$$

It can then be shown, by the methods of Chapter II, that if

$$A(x) = \sum_{n \leq x} a(n) ,$$

then

$$A(x) = \alpha x - \beta x^{1/2} + O(x^{1/3} \log x) ,$$

where

$$\alpha = \prod_{n=2}^{\infty} \zeta(n) = 2.29485 \cdots .$$

37. Show that

$$\prod_{m=0}^{\infty} (1 + x^{2^m}) = \sum_{n=0}^{\infty} x^n$$

and deduce that the binary representation of an integer is unique.

38. Show that

$$\prod_{m=0}^{\infty} (x^{-3^m} + 1 + x^{3^m}) = \sum_{n=0}^{\infty} x^n + \sum_{n=0}^{\infty} x^{-n}$$

and deduce that the ternary expansion is unique.

39. Show that the number of permutations of n letters each having i inversions is the coefficient of t^i in

$$(1 + t)(1 + t + t^2) \cdots (1 + t + \cdots + t^{n-1}) = (1 - t)^{-n} P ,$$

where

$$P = (1 - t)(1 - t^2) \cdots (1 - t^n) .$$

40. If $n = x + 2y + 3z + \cdots$ is an unrestricted partition of n, then

(a) $$\sum (1 - x + xy - xyz + \cdots) = 0 ,$$

(b) $$\sum (x - 2xy + 3xyz - \cdots) = d(n) ,$$

where the summation is over all partions of n.

41. Since

$$\log (1 + x + \cdots + x^n + \cdots) = - \log (1 - x) = \sum_{n=1}^{\infty} \frac{x^n}{n} ,$$

then

$$\sum_{n=1}^{\infty} x^n = \prod_{n=1}^{\infty} e^{x^n/n} .$$

Expanding and equating coefficients, show that

$$\sum \frac{1}{2^b 3^c 4^d \cdots a! b! c! \cdots} = 1 ,$$

where the summation is over all solutions of

$$a + 2b + 3c + \cdots = n ;$$

i. e., over all partitions of n.

42. Show that the set

$$\begin{pmatrix} a & b \\ c & d \end{pmatrix}$$

of modular substitutions for which

$$\begin{pmatrix} a & b \\ c & d \end{pmatrix} \equiv \begin{pmatrix} 1 & 0 \\ 0 & 1 \end{pmatrix} \bmod n$$

forms a subgroup of the group of all substitutions.

43. Let

$$f(\tau) = \frac{e^{-\pi i/24}\eta\left(\dfrac{\tau+1}{2}\right)}{\eta(\tau)} .$$

Show that $f(-1/\tau) = f(\tau)$. Find $f(\tau+1)$. Suppose that

$$f_1(\tau) = \frac{\eta\left(\dfrac{\tau}{2}\right)}{\eta(\tau)} ,$$

$$f_2(\tau) = \sqrt{2}\frac{\eta(2\tau)}{\eta(\tau)} .$$

Show that $f_1(-1/\tau) = f_2(\tau)$ and $f_2(-1/\tau) = f_1(\tau)$. In addition, find $f_1(\tau+1)$, $f_2(\tau+1)$.

44. Let

$$\theta(\tau) = \frac{\eta^2\left(\dfrac{\tau+1}{2}\right)}{\eta(\tau+1)} .$$

Show that

$$\theta\left(-\frac{1}{\tau}\right) = \frac{1}{\sqrt{\tau}}\theta(\tau) ,$$

$$\theta(\tau+2) = \theta(\tau) .$$

$\theta(\tau)$ is the familiar $\sum_{n=-\infty}^{\infty} e^{-\pi n^2 \tau}$.

Show that if $(h, k) = 1$,

45. $\sum_{\mu=1}^{k} ((\mu/k)) = \sum_{\mu \bmod k} ((\mu/k)) = 0$;

46. $\sum_{\mu \bmod k} ((h\mu/k)) = 0$;

47. $\sum_{\mu \bmod k} (((\mu + x)/k)) = ((x))$.

[The difference has period 1, and is independent of x for $0 \leqq x < 1$; has value 0 at $x = 0$.]

48. $S(h, k) = S(h', k)$ if $hh' \equiv 1 \pmod{k}$.

49. $S(qh, qk) = S(h, k)$.

50. If p is prime

$$\sum_{m=0}^{p-1}\left(\left(y + \frac{\mu m}{p}\right)\right) = \begin{cases} ((py)) & \text{if } p \nmid \mu , \\ p((y)) & \text{if } p \mid \mu , \end{cases}$$

and hence

$$S(ph, k) + \sum_{m=0}^{p-1} S(h + mk, pk) = (p+1)S(h, k) .$$

51. Let

$$c_q = \sum_{1 \leq a \leq q;\ (a,q)=1} e^{2\pi i a/q} .$$

Show that

$$\sum_{d|q} c_d = \sum_{d|q} \sum_{(a,d)=1\ 1 \leq a \leq d} e^{2\pi i a/d} = \sum_{h=1}^{q} e^{2\pi i h/q} = \begin{cases} 0 & \text{if } q \neq 1 \\ 1 & \text{if } q = 1 . \end{cases}$$

Deduce that $c_q = \mu(q)$, the Möbius function.

If N is an integer,

$$M(N) = \sum_{n \leq N} \mu(n) = \sum_{n \leq N} \sum_{1 \leq a \leq N;\ (a,n)=1} e^{2\pi i a/n} = \sum_{r_\nu} e^{2\pi i r_\nu}$$

where the summation is over all Farey fractions r_ν of order N. If

$$\delta_\nu = r_\nu - \frac{\nu}{A} ,$$

where A is the number of terms in a Farey series of order N, then it can be shown that the Riemann hypothesis is equivalent to the assertion that

$$\sum_\nu \delta_\nu^2 = O\left(\frac{1}{N^{1-\varepsilon}}\right)$$

for every $\varepsilon > 0$.

52. Let h/k be a Farey fraction of order N. Consider the complex τ plane and suppose that there is drawn a circle $C_{h,k}$ in the τ plane with center at the point

$$\sigma_{h,k} = \frac{h}{k} + \frac{i}{2k^2}$$

and radius $1/2k^2$. Such a circle is called a Ford circle.

Prove the following:

(i) These circles are tangent to the real axis.

(ii) No two circles intersect.

(iii) Two circles $C_{h,k}$ and $C_{h',k'}$ are tangent if and only if h/k and h'/k' are neighbors in a Farey series of the same order.

53. Let $h_2/k_2 < h/k < h_1/k_1$ be three successive Farey fractions of order N and C_{h_1,k_1}, $C_{h,k}$, C_{h_2,k_2}, the corresponding Ford circles. $C_{h,k}$ is tangent to each of the circles C_{h_1,k_1} and C_{h_2,k_2} by Problem 52. Let $\gamma_{h,k}$ be the upper arc of $C_{h,k}$ determined by the points of tangency. Show that the end points of $\gamma_{h,k}$ are

$$\frac{h}{k} + \left(\frac{+k_1}{k(k^2+k_1^2)} + \frac{i}{k^2+k_1^2}\right) = \frac{h}{k} + \rho'_{h,k} ,$$

$$\frac{h}{k} + \left(\frac{-k_2}{k(k^2+k_2^2)} + \frac{i}{k^2+k_2^2}\right) = \frac{h}{k} + \rho''_{h,k} ,$$

and that

$$\frac{1}{2N^2} \leq \begin{cases} \mathscr{I}(\rho'_{h,k}) \\ \mathscr{I}(\rho''_{h,k}) \end{cases} \leq \frac{2}{(N+1)^2} .$$

54. Let P_N consist of all the upper arcs $\gamma_{h,k}$ of the circles $C_{h,k}$ belonging to Farey fractions of order N. The arc of $C_{0,1}$ to the left of the imaginary axis being replaced by the arc of $\gamma_{1,1}$, to the left of the line $\mathscr{R}(\tau)=1$.

Show that

(i) $$p(n)=\int_i^{i+1} f(e^{2\pi i\tau})e^{-2\pi in\tau}d\tau\,,$$

where the path from i to $i+1$ is the path P_N.

(ii) $$p(n)=\sum_{0\leq h<k\leq N}\int_{\gamma_{h,k}} f(e^{2\pi i\tau})e^{-2\pi in\tau}d\tau\,.$$

(iii) $$p(n)=\sum_{0\leq h<k\leq N}\int_{\rho'}^{\rho''} f\left(e^{2\pi i(h/k+\rho)}\right)e^{-2\pi in(h/k+\rho)}d\rho\,,$$

where ρ runs from ρ' to ρ'' on the arc of a circle of radius $1/2k^2$ about the point $i/2k^2$.

55. Making the substitution $\rho = iz/k^2$ show that

$$p(n)=\sum_{0\leq h<k\leq N}\frac{i}{k^2}e^{-2\pi inh/k}\int_{z'}^{z''} f\left(e^{2\pi ih/k-2\pi z/k^2}\right)e^{2\pi nz/k^2}dz\,,$$

where now z runs over an arc of the circle K of radius $\frac{1}{2}$ about the point $\frac{1}{2}$. Find the ends z' and z'' of this arc.

56. Apply the functional equation to $f(x)$,

$$f(x)=\omega_{h,k}\psi_k(z)f(x')\,,$$

and let

$$I_{h,k}=\int_{z'}^{z''}\psi_k(z)e^{2\pi nz/k^2}dz\,.$$

$$I^*_{h,k}=\int_{z'}^{z''}\psi_k(z)\{f(x')-1\}e^{2\pi nz/k^2}dz\,.$$

Replacing the arc z' to z'' by the chord, show that

(i) $$|I^*_{h,k}|<c_1k^{3/2}N^{-3/2}\,.$$

Let

$$I_{h,k}=\int_K-\int_0^{z'}-\int_0^{z''}\psi_k(z)e^{2\pi nz/k^2}dz\,,$$

where K is described in a clockwise direction. Show that

(ii) $$\left|\int_0^{z'}\psi_k(z)e^{2\pi nz/k^2}dz\right|\leq c_2e^{2\pi n}k^{3/2}N^{-3/2}\,;$$

(iii) $$\left|\int_0^{z''}\psi_k(z)e^{2\pi nz/k^2}dz\right|\leq c_3e^{2\pi n}k^{3/2}N^{-3/2}\,,$$

and, letting $N\to\infty$, deduce that

$$p(n) = i \sum_{k=1}^{\infty} A_k(n) k^{-3/2} \int_K z^{1/2} e^{\pi/12z + 2\pi z \lambda_n^2/k^2} dz .$$

It remains only to evaluate the integral.

Notes to Chapter III

1. Most of the algebraic properties of partitions in this section were discovered by Euler and communicated in two memoirs *De partitione numerorum*, 1750, and *Observationes analyticae variae de combinationibus*, 1741, *Collected works*, Vol. 2. The pentagonal number theorem is the subject of the memoir *Evoluti producti infiniti* $\prod(1 - x^n)$ *in seriem simplicem, Collected works*, Vol. 3. The relation involving the sum of the divisors has already been referred to in Chapter II.

A large number of algebraic properties of partitions had subsequently been discovered and a fairly complete summary up to the time of its writing may be found in Sylvester's *Collected works*, Vol. 2 or Proc. London Math. Soc. **28**.

The first formula of an asymptotic character is the one of Theorem 1.6. It is proved in Hardy and Ramanujan's pioneering article in Proc. London Math. Soc. **17** (1918): *Asymptotic formulae in combinatory analysis.* This article contains the basic idea underlying what has since been called the "circle method." This method and its several adaptations have been astoundingly successful in the solution of problems of additive number theory.

The argument given by Hardy and Ramanujan for Theorem 1.6 is based on a refinement of the Tauberian theorem of Chapter II, Theorem 6.13 viz. If $g(z) = \sum a(n)z^n$ is a power series with positive coefficients and

$$\log g(z) \sim \frac{A}{1-z}$$

as $z \to 1$, then

$$\log S(n) = \log \sum_{k \leq n} a(k) \sim 2(An)^{1/2} ;$$

this theorem is then applied to

$$g(x) = (1 - x)F(x) = \sum (p(n) - p(n-1))x^n .$$

2. The proof we have given of Theorem 2.1, is due to J. V. Uspensky and appeared in Bull. Acad. Sci. URSS **14**. Of the several proofs of this result, Uspensky's is in some ways the simplest.

The methods of these sections may be applied to a number of variations; for example, to the determination of an asymptotic formula for the number of partitions into squares, kth powers, primes, etc., as well as the determination of the asymptotic behavior of the coefficients of certain modular functions.

As an example we note that the number of partitions of n into primes is asymptotically $\exp[2\pi(n/\log n)^{1/2}/\sqrt{3}]$.

3. The function $\eta(\tau)$ is a particular example of a wide class of functions

called modular functions and occupies a central position in that theory. It was studied by Hermite, Riemann and Dedekind. Of the various known proofs of Theorem 3.1, we have selected the extremely elegant proof of C. L. Siegel in Mathematika **1** (1954), 4. The underlying idea is based on the calculus of residues but the use of Cauchy's theorem is especially effective here.

A detailed account of modular functions may be found in the work of Klein Fricke *Elliptische Modulfunktionen,* in L. R. Ford's *Automorphic functions* and in J. Lehner's forthcoming book on automorphic functions.

4. The 24th root of unity which appears in the transformation formula has two forms. The one we have given and one involving Legendre's symbol. Rademacher has shown the equivalence of the two forms. Dedekind's derivation may be found in the *Erlauterungen zu den Fragmenten über die Grenzfalle der elliptischer Modulfunktionen* in Riemann's *Collected works.*

There are numerous proofs of the reciprocity law given by Theorem 6.6. These are obtained independently of the origin of the sums. One such proof may be found in *Theorems on Dedekind sums* by H. Rademacher and A. Whiteman in Amer. J. Math. **63** (1941), 377–407.

The proof of Theorem 4.1 which we have given is one of two by Rademacher. The other is in Crelle's Journal **167**. The Dedekind sums arise much more naturally in the proof we have given.

Farey series are another instance of incomplete assignment of credit for mathematical discovery. The fundamental property of "Farey" fractions was stated by Farey in 1816. Farey was primarily a geologist and did not supply a proof. This was done by Cauchy. On the other hand, the series and their properties were first studied in 1802 by the mathematician Naros.

There are numerous proofs known of the fundamental property of Farey fractions. See for example Hardy and Wright, *The theory of numbers,* Chapter 3.

The asymptotic formula of Hardy and Ramanujan originally took the form:

$$P(n) = \sum_{k=1}^{[\alpha\sqrt{n}]} A_k(n)\Phi_k(n) + O(n^{-1/4}) ,$$

where α is any constant, $A_k(n)$ has the same meaning as that given by (28), and

$$\Phi_k(n) = \frac{\sqrt{k}}{2\pi\sqrt{2}} \frac{d}{dn}\left(\frac{e^{c\lambda_n/k}}{\lambda_n}\right) .$$

Their analysis left open the question of the convergence of the series

$$\sum_{k=1}^{\infty} A_k(n)\Phi_k(n) .$$

This was decided in the negative by D. H. Lehmer in *The Hardy-Ramanujan series for the partition function,* J. London Math. Soc. **12** (1937), 171–176. In addition Lehmer proved that $A_k(n)$ is multiplicative.

The analysis of Rademacher was published in the Proc. London Math. Soc. (2) **43** (1937), 241–254. In a later publication, Rademacher made use of the

Ford circles (as outlined in the problems) to derive the convergent series anew. See Ann. of Math. (2) **44** (1943), 416–422.

A highly interesting form for the function $A_k(n)$ has been given by A. Selberg.

Ramanujan proved several additional congruence properties for $p(n)$; e.g.,

$$p(25m+24) \equiv 0 \pmod{5^2} .$$

There are similar congruence properties for moduli 5^2, 7^2, 11^2, etc.

For arithmetic calculations relating to $p(n)$, we may refer the reader to the above cited works of Rademacher and Lehmer.

CHAPTER IV

Waring's Problem

1. Introduction Among the additive problems of number theory, the so-called Waring's problem (and its many variants and ramifications) occupies a central position.

The name stems from the assertion made by the mathematician Waring in 1792 to the effect that every integer is a sum of four squares, nine cubes, 17 biquadrates, etc. His implication is that for any given integer k, there exists an integer $s = s(k)$, depending only on k such that every integer n is a sum of at most s kth powers. That is to say, to every k there exists s depending only on k so that the diophantine equation,

$$n = n_1^k + n_2^k + \cdots + n_s^k \,, \tag{1}$$

has at least one solution in integers $n_i \geqq 0$ $(i = 1, \cdots, s)$.

Researches into this problem have been carried out for many years and the relevant mathematical contributions have grown to formidable proportions. We treat here only a relatively restricted aspect of the problem but the mathematical techniques involved are basic to most of the variant problems.

The solution of the problem is by no means obvious. Indeed, even the case $k = 2$ presented to Euler and Lagrange some unexpected difficulties. Subsequent to Waring's assertion, many specific cases of his conjecture had been solved, but it was not until 1909 that Hilbert gave the first complete solution for every k. The method he used was an inductive one and is based on the proof of the existence of an identity of the type

$$N(y_1^2 + \cdots + y_4^2)^k = \sum_{l=1}^{M} (d_{l_1} y_1 + \cdots + d_{l_4} y_4)^{2k} \,,$$

where $M, N > 0$, and $d_{l_i} \geqq 0$ are integers depending on k. The proof of the existence of such a relation is rather intricate and depends on a wholesale use of volumes in a 5-dimensional space.

The next complete proof was given by Hardy and Littlewood in a series of contributions entitled *Partitio Numerorum*. It is the Vinogradoff modification and improvement of this method which we present here, since it has the great advantage over Hilbert's proof in that it admits of extensive application to other problems of additive number theory.

The answer to a question concerning the additive properties of integers is generally speaking not in the least obvious. The decomposition of an integer into a sum of integers of a prescribed type is often nonexistent owing to a variety of reasons. For instance, simple congruence considerations may preclude certain possibilities. This is the basis, for example, of the observation that there are infinitely many integers which are not a sum of three squares for a sum of three squares is easily seen to exclude the residue class

7 modulo 8. Sometimes the reason is a little more subtle. In Waring's problem, the critical feature is that s must depend only on k and not on n, the integer represented. We give an example of an additive problem in which the number of summands does depend on n.

To this end, suppose we seek to decompose an integer into a sum of powers of 2. It is an elementary fact that the dyadic (or binary) expansion of an integer is unique. If we consider the specific sequence

$$n_k = 2^k - 1 = 2^{k-1} + 2^{k-2} + \cdots + 1\,,$$

we find that the number of summands is precisely k. That is, $s = k$. On the other hand, as $k \to \infty$, $n_k \to \infty$ and s is unbounded.

To facilitate our later discussion, it is worthwhile at this stage to introduce two functions which we denote by $g(k)$ and $G(k)$. Suppose that (1) has a solution for every n and some fixed s. Then it clearly has a solution for any $t \geqq s$. Hence if there exists one s for which (1) is always solvable, then there exists a least s. We call this least value $g(k)$. We know that $g(2) = 4$ since as implied above, every integer of the form $8m + 7$ is not a sum of three squares, these integers being excluded by congruence conditions. There is, however, another number closely allied to $g(k)$ with which we shall be primarily concerned. To illustrate, we take the case $k = 3$. It can be shown that every integer is a sum of nine cubes. On the other hand, it can be further shown that with only finitely many exceptions, every integer is a sum of seven cubes. For example, exceptions to seven cubes are 23 and 239. These require nine cubes. It is therefore natural to define $G(k)$ as the least integer for which (1) is solvable with at most finitely many exceptions. Expressed otherwise, there exists n_0 such that (1) is solvable for every $n \geqq n_0$ and $s \geqq G(k)$. Thus $G(3) \leqq 7$; the point being that relatively small integers have accidental peculiarities which conceal to some extent the fundamental issue.

The theorems we prove in this chapter all concern $G(k)$; this is partly because $G(k)$ is fundamentally more interesting than $g(k)$ and partly because the analysis leads naturally to results concerning $G(k)$.

2. The analytic setting and outline of proof. The Hardy-Littlewood treatment of the Waring problem follows the basic idea inherent in the Hardy-Ramanujan treatment of the partition problem. The analytic starting point is once again Cauchy's theorem but, as Vinogradoff has shown, it is technically simpler to work with finite sums.

Let

$$f(x) = \sum_{n=0}^{\infty} x^{n^k}\,. \tag{1}$$

The series on the right converges when $|x| < 1$ and so represents an analytic function within the unit circle. The boundary of the unit circle is a natural one; every point is a singularity. This is not difficult to prove, but we shall not need this fact. We take the Cauchy product of s copies of $f(x)$:

(2)
$$f^s(x) = \sum_{n_1=0}^{\infty} x^{n_1^k} \sum_{n_2=0}^{\infty} x^{n_2^k} \cdots \sum_{n_s=0}^{\infty} x^{n_s^k} = \sum_{n_1, n_2, \cdots, n_s} x^{n_1^k + \cdots + n_s^k} .$$

If we put in (2)

(3)
$$n = n_1^k + \cdots + n_s^k ,$$

we find

(4)
$$f^s(x) = \sum_{n=0}^{\infty} r_1(n) x^n ,$$

where $r_1(n)$ is the number of solutions of (3).

The solution of Waring's problem is therefore equivalent to showing that for some value of s, $r_1(n) > 0$ for every n (or at any rate for n sufficiently large). This is the same as saying that for some s, (3) has at least one solution.

We apply Cauchy's theorem to (4). This yields,

$$r_1(n) = \frac{1}{2\pi i} \int_C \frac{f^s(x)}{x^{n+1}} dx ,$$

where C is a closed contour lying in the unit circle and enclosing the origin.

Since the unit circle is a natural boundary, we cannot take the contour C far away from the origin nor indeed are we in this case in possession of a functional equation as we were in the case of the partition function. Nevertheless, many of the principles used in the partition problem are applicable here. We can still obtain an approximation to $f(x)$ in the neighborhood of a rational point of the unit circle, though unfortunately the approximation is not as precise as in the problem of partitions. Moreover, we can expect that the principal contribution will come from points $e^{2\pi ih/k}$ with relatively small k. The complete details can be carried out and indeed were by Hardy and Littlewood.

In the absence of a functional equation for $f(x)$—indeed of any significant analytic properties—there is no particularly compelling reason to work with $f(x)$. The largest value which can be assumed by any n_i in (3) is

(5)
$$P = [n^{1/k}] ,$$

and it occurred to Vinogradoff that the discussion of Hardy-Littlewood becomes technically much simpler if the infinite series $f(x)$ is replaced by a truncated series extending to P. Indeed, let

$$h(z) = \sum_{m=1}^{P} z^{m^k} .$$

Since this is a finite sum, we avoid in the first place questions of convergence. Moreover, we can extend the contour C of integration up to the unit circle. In fact, we put

(6)
$$z = e^{2\pi i x}$$

and consider

$$g(x) = \sum_{m=1}^{P} e^{2\pi i m^k x} . \tag{7}$$

We no longer need Cauchy's theorem but prove directly

THEOREM 2.1. *If $r(n)$ is the number of solutions of the equation*

$$n = n_1^k + n_2^k + \cdots + n_s^k \qquad (n_i \geqq 1), \tag{8}$$

then

$$r(n) = \int_0^1 g^s(x) e^{-2\pi i n x} \, dx .$$

PROOF. The integrand is

$$g^s(x) e^{-2\pi i n x} = \sum_{n_1=1}^{P} \cdots \sum_{n_s=1}^{P} e^{2\pi i (n_1^k + \cdots + n_s^k - n) x} .$$

We now use the simple fact that

$$\int_0^1 e^{2\pi i m x} \, dx = \begin{cases} 0 & \text{if } m \neq 0 , \\ 1 & \text{if } m = 0 . \end{cases} \tag{9}$$

Further,

$$J = \int_0^1 g^s(x) e^{-2\pi i n x} \, dx = \sum_{n_1, n_2, \cdots, n_s}^{1, P} \int_0^1 e^{2\pi i (n_1^k + \cdots + n_s^k - n) x} \, dx .$$

By (9), the integral contributes 1 to the sum whenever

$$n_1^k + \cdots + n_s^k = n ,$$

that is, whenever (8) has a solution. Consequently, $J = \sum^{1,P}_{n_1, n_2, \cdots, n_s ; n_1^k + \cdots + n_s^k = n} 1$ = number of solutions of (8) with n_i in the range 1 to P. But this comprises all the solutions of (8) and the theorem is proved.

We notice that the integrand is a function with period 1 and so the value of the integral is the same if we integrate over any interval of length 1. We shift the origin to the left by τ^{-1} where τ will later be chosen conveniently, and deduce

COROLLARY.

$$I = \int_{-\tau^{-1}}^{1-\tau^{-1}} g^s(x) e^{-2\pi i n x} \, dx = r(n) . \tag{10}$$

Our objective in this chapter is the proof of two principal theorems:

A. *We prove that there exists n_0 such that if $s \geqq 2^k + 1$, then $r(n) > 0$ for $n > n_0$, and at the same time derive an asymptotic formula for $r(n)$. We infer that $G(k) \leqq 2^k + 1$.*

B. *We prove that there exists n_0 such that if $s \geqq [6k \log k] + 10k + 3$, then $r(n) > 0$ for $n > n_0$, but do not derive an asymptotic formula valid for this s.*

That is, $G(k) \leqq [6k \log k] + 10k + 3$.

It will be noticed that for small values of k, A yields a smaller bound for $G(k)$, but for large values, B is vastly superior.

We fix our attention first on A; our objective here is to evaluate the integral in (10) and we sketch briefly the steps:

Step 1. We first divide the interval of integration into Farey intervals of order N for some suitable N. We divide the points into two categories in accordance with the observation that Farey intervals with (a) relatively small denominators yield the main contribution to the integral and (b) those with relatively large denominators yield a term of lower order of magnitude. The arcs corresponding to (a) were called "major arcs" by Hardy and Littlewood and the intervals were called "basic intervals" by Vinogradoff. Those in category (b) were called "minor arcs" and "supplementary intervals," respectively. We shall adhere to the terminology of Hardy and Littlewood, even though the path of integration is no longer an arc. We shall determine later on precisely what "relatively small" and "relatively large" mean. We are led in this way to a sum

$$I = I_1 + I_2 , \tag{11}$$

where I_1 is the sum of integrals over major arcs and I_2 the integral over the minor arcs.

Step 2. We approximate I_1 by approximating to $g(x)$ on a major arc. We put

$$x = \frac{a}{q} + y , \qquad (a, q) = 1 \tag{12}$$

and then

$$g(x) = \sum_{m=1}^{P} e^{2\pi i m^k x} = \sum_{m=1}^{P} e^{2\pi i m^k (a/q+y)} . \tag{13}$$

We break the summation into residue classes mod q and find

$$g(x) = \sum_{r=1}^{q} e^{2\pi i r^k a/q} \sum_{l=0}^{[(P-r)/q]} e^{2\pi i (lq+r)^k y} . \tag{14}$$

The inner sum is replaced by an integral and this leads us to

$$g(x) = \frac{1}{q} \sum_{r=1}^{q} e^{2\pi i r^k a/q} \int_0^P e^{2\pi i u^k y}\, du + \text{error} . \tag{15}$$

We put

$$S(a, q) = \sum_{r=0}^{q-1} e^{2\pi i r^k a/q} , \tag{16}$$

and on raising $g(x)$ to the sth power, we find after suitable estimates

$$I_1 = \gamma(s, k) \sum_{q \leq P} \sum_{\substack{a=1 \\ (a,q)=1}}^{q-1} q^{-s} S^s(a, q) e^{-2\pi i n a/q} P^{s-k} + \text{error} , \tag{17}$$

where $\gamma(s, k)$ is a constant depending only on s and k and which is explicitly evaluated.

For convenience, we make the abbreviation

$$A(q) = q^{-s} \sum_{a=1;\ (a,q)=1}^{q-1} S^s(a, q) e^{-2\pi i n a/q} \tag{18}$$

and

$$\mathfrak{S}(n) = \sum_{q=1}^{\infty} A(q) . \tag{19}$$

$\mathfrak{S}(n)$ is the so-called "singular series." Then

$$I_1 = \gamma(s, k) n^{s/k-1} \mathfrak{S}(n) + \text{error} . \tag{20}$$

Step 3. In order that we may derive meaningful consequences, the error must be

$$o(n^{s/k-1}) \qquad \text{or} \qquad o(P^{s-k}) ,$$

since $P = [n^{1/k}]$. This requirement determines to some extent the choice of the major arcs. We then must show that for some suitable choice of s,

$$I_2 = o(n^{s/k-1}) . \tag{21}$$

To see in part what this involves, we notice that the crudest approximation for $g(x)$ is given by

$$g(x) = O(P) ,$$

and this leads to

$$I_2 = O(P^s) = O(n^{s/k}) .$$

To achieve our goal, we must gain a factor slightly more than n. This would be the case if we could show that on a minor arc,

$$g(x) = o(P^{1-k/s}) , \tag{22}$$

for some suitable choice of s.

This is unfortunately a comparatively difficult step. The proof we shall give is based on a method due to H. Weyl. The nature of this proof inevitably leads to a comparatively large value of s for which (22) is valid.

Vinogradoff has invented a new method for dealing with trigonometric sums which avoids the iterations inherent in Weyl's method. This brilliant method is characterized by great intricacy and supreme ingenuity. Because the details often overshadow the underlying ideal, we prefer in this elementary account to restrict ourselves to the method of H. Weyl. A complete account of Vinogradoff's method is given in the excellent book of Vinogradoff which has been translated and carefully annotated by K. F. Roth and Ann Davenport.

Having proved that

$$I_2 = o(n^{s/k-1}) ,$$

we find

$$r(n) = \gamma(s, k)\mathfrak{S}(n)n^{s/k-1} + o(n^{s/k-1}) . \tag{23}$$

This asymptotic formula will be proved valid for $s \geqq 2^k + 1$, and will allow us to conclude that $r(n) > 0$ for n sufficiently large, provided that

$$\mathfrak{S}(n) \geqq c > 0 , \tag{24}$$

for some constant c. The last part of the chapter will be devoted to a proof of (24).

3. The Farey dissection. We start by putting

$$P = [n^{1/k}] , \tag{1}$$

$$\tau = 2kP^{k-1} \tag{2}$$

and consider the Farey fractions of order τ. Let a/q be such a Farey fraction and a'/q', a''/q'' be its immediate left and right neighbors. We consider the interval $[(a' + a)/(q' + q),\ (a'' + a)/(q'' + q)]$ whose end points are the mediants.

If x is in this interval, then

$$x = \frac{a}{q} + y ,$$

where

$$-\frac{1}{q'(q + q')} = \frac{a' + a}{q' + q} - \frac{a}{q} \leqq y \leqq \frac{a'' + a}{q'' + q} - \frac{a}{q} = \frac{1}{q(q + q'')} .$$

We have used Theorem 5.1 of Chapter III and observed that by Theorem 5.2

$$| y | \leqq \frac{1}{q\tau} . \tag{3}$$

The Farey interval defined by the fraction a/q is not symmetric about the point a/q. It is convenient therefore to enlarge the interval to achieve symmetry. We thus define

$$M = M(a, q) = \text{set of points } x \text{ of the form } x = a/q + y , \tag{4}$$

where

$$| y | \leqq \frac{1}{q\tau} .$$

If we take the set of all $M(a, q)$ for all Farey fractions of order τ, then they will in general overlap. They will not overlap if we restrict q. Let δ be any real number satisfying

$$\frac{1}{k} \leqq \delta \leqq \frac{3}{4} \tag{5}$$

and let

(6) $$q \leqq P^{1-\delta}.$$

We prove

THEOREM 3.1. *If $M(a, q)$ is the set of points x of the form*

$$x = \frac{a}{q} + y, \qquad |y| \leqq \frac{1}{q\tau},\ q \leqq P^{1-\delta},$$

then no two such intervals corresponding to different fractions overlap.

PROOF. The idea of the proof is that the condition (6) guarantees that the $M(a, q)$ are far apart even though the set $M(a, q)$ has incorporated a Farey interval.

Indeed if $M(a, q)$, $M(a_1, q_1)$ have a point in common, then for some y, y_1,

$$\frac{a}{q} + y = \frac{a_1}{q_1} + y_1, \qquad \frac{a_1}{q_1} \neq \frac{a}{q},\ 1 \leqq q < q_1 \leqq P^{1-\delta}$$

and therefore

$$\frac{1}{qq_1} \leqq \frac{|aq_1 - a_1 q|}{qq_1} \leqq |y| + |y_1| \leqq \frac{1}{q\tau} + \frac{1}{q_1\tau} \leqq \frac{2}{q\tau}.$$

In other words, by (2) and (6),

$$kP^{k-1} = \frac{\tau}{2} \leqq q_1 \leqq P^{1-\delta}$$

and this is impossible if $k \geqq 2$.

If $q = 1$, then $a = 1$ or 0 and $M(0, 1)$ is the set of points, $x = 0 + y$, $|y| \leqq 1/\tau$ and $M(1, 1)$ is the set of points $x = 1 + y$, $|y| \leqq 1/\tau$. That is $M(0, 1)$ is the interval $(-1/\tau, 1/\tau)$ and $M(1, 1)$ is the interval $(1 - 1/\tau, 1 + 1/\tau)$. All other $M(a, q)$ are interior to $(0, 1)$. This remark suggests that we choose as the interval of integration in § 2, (10), the interval $(-1/\tau, 1 - 1/\tau)$. We shall call the intervals $M(a, q)$ determined by the conditions (4) and (6) "major arcs." The points which remain in the interval $(-1/\tau, 1 - 1/\tau)$ after the removal of the major arcs will be called points on "minor arcs." We shall characterize points on minor arcs more precisely. To do this we first prove

THEOREM 3.2. *To every real number x and integer m, there corresponds an irreducible fraction a/q such that $0 < q \leqq m$ and*

$$\left| x - \frac{a}{q} \right| \leqq \frac{1}{q(m+1)}.$$

PROOF. This is a well-known theorem on the approximation of real numbers by rational numbers. We shall use Farey series to establish the property. We start with Farey series of order m and since we may suppose that $0 < x < 1$, then we may suppose that x lies in a Farey interval

$$\left(\frac{a + a'}{q + q'},\ \frac{a + a''}{q + q''} \right)$$

belonging to the fraction a/q. We have supposed that the immediate left- and right-hand fractions are a'/q', a''/q'' respectively. Then by Theorem 5.2

$$\left|x-\frac{a}{q}\right| \leqq \max\left\{\frac{a+a''}{q+q''}-\frac{a}{q}, \frac{a}{q}-\frac{a+a'}{q+q'}\right\} \leqq \frac{1}{q(m+1)}$$

as required.

In particular, to every real x, there corresponds a rational number a/q $(a, q)=1$ such that

$$\left|x-\frac{a}{q}\right| \leqq \frac{1}{q\tau}, \qquad q \leqq \tau .$$

With this result we characterize points on minor arcs.

THEOREM 3.3. *If x is a point on a minor arc, there exist a rational number a/q, $(a, q)=1$, such that*

$$x=\frac{a}{q}+y, \qquad |y| \leqq \frac{1}{q\tau},$$

$$P^{1-\delta} < q \leqq \tau = 2kP^{k-1} . \tag{7}$$

PROOF. The important condition is (7). By the previous theorem, to every x, we can find a rational number a/q $(a, q)=1$, such that

$$x=\frac{a}{q}+y, \qquad |y| \leqq \frac{1}{q\tau}, \quad q \leqq \tau .$$

But if $q \leqq P^{1-\delta}$, then x is on a major arc, and this is a contradiction.

It should be pointed out that it is possible to vary the construction of these major and minor arcs to suit the convenience of later calculations.

The essential feature can be described roughly as follows: Most of the contribution to the integral I for $r(n)$ in § 2, (11), will come from major arcs; that is from neighborhoods of rational points with relatively small denominators. On the other hand, rational points with relatively large denominators are, so to speak, more nearly irrational. We can therefore say, broadly speaking, that the less we put into the major arcs, the easier is I_1 to estimate but the more difficult is I_2 to estimate since the relatively smaller order of $g(x)$ in I_2 has its origin in the "irrationality" of x on the minor arc. However, if we put a large proportion of the unit interval in the major arcs, then I_1 becomes more difficult to manage. Thus the choice of the major arcs is, as it were, a compromise to balance the relative ease with which I_1 and I_2 can be estimated.

As a consequence of the Farey dissection, we can write (10) of the preceding section (§2) as

$$r(n)=\sum \int_{M(a,q)} g^s(x)e^{-2\pi inx}\,dx+\int_{\mathfrak{m}} g^s(x)e^{-2\pi inx}\,dx , \tag{8}$$

where $\mathfrak{m}$ denotes the set of points not on any major arc and the summation is over all major arcs.

4. The contribution of the major arcs. We start out by approximating $g(x)$ on major arcs. Let $M(a, q)$ be a major arc belonging to the fraction a/q. Then if x is in $M(a, q)$,

$$x = \frac{a}{q} + y, \qquad |y| \leqq \frac{1}{q\tau}, \quad q \leqq P^{1-\delta}.$$

Putting this value of x in $g(x)$, we find

$$g(x) = \sum_{m=1}^{P} e^{2\pi i m^k (a/q+y)}. \tag{1}$$

Because of the denominator q, we break the summation into residue classes mod q and to this end, put

$$m = jq + r.$$

Then from (1),

$$\begin{aligned} g(x) &= \sum_{r=1}^{q} \sum_{j=0}^{[(P-r)/q]} e^{2\pi i (jq+r)^k (a/q+y)} \\ &= \sum_{r=1}^{q} \sum_{j=0}^{[(P-r)/q]} e^{2\pi i (jq+r)^k a/q} \cdot e^{2\pi i (jq+r)^k y} \\ &= \sum_{r=1}^{q} e^{2\pi i r^k a/q} \sum_{j=0}^{[(P-r)/q]} e^{2\pi i (jq+r)^k y}. \end{aligned} \tag{2}$$

We wish to replace the inner sum by an integral and our natural recourse is to use the Euler-MacLaurin formula. The error we should thus obtain, however, is not sufficient for our purposes, and we refine it according to the method of van der Corput.

THEOREM 4.1. *Let $f(x)$ be a real valued function which is twice differentiable and suppose that*

$$|f'(x)| \leqq \theta < 1, \tag{3}$$

and $f'(x)$ is monotone. Then

$$\sum_{a<n\leqq b} e^{2\pi i f(n)} = \int_a^b e^{2\pi i f(x)}\, dx + O(1). \tag{4}$$

PROOF. The proof begins with the Euler-MacLaurin formula, but treats the error more carefully. We have in fact

$$\sum_{a<n\leqq b} e^{2\pi i f(n)} = \int_a^b e^{2\pi i f(x)}\, dx + O(1) + 2\pi i \int_a^b \left(x - [x] - \frac{1}{2}\right) f'(x) e^{2\pi i f(x)}\, dx. \tag{5}$$

Our object is to show that the second integral is $O(1)$ and to this end, we expand the periodic function $x - [x] - \frac{1}{2}$ in its Fourier series. The function $x - [x] - \frac{1}{2}$ is of bounded variation, has period 1 and is an odd function. Therefore, if x is not an integer,

$$x - [x] - \frac{1}{2} = -\frac{1}{\pi} \sum_{n=1}^{\infty} \frac{\sin 2\pi n x}{n}. \tag{6}$$

The reader who is not acquainted with Fourier series may start with the relation

$$-\log(1-z)=\sum_{n=1}^{\infty}\frac{z^n}{n}$$

where $z=re^{2\pi ix}$, $0\leqq r\leqq 1$, $0<x<1$. Next show that the series on the right converges for r in this interval, apply Abel's theorem and then separate real and imaginary parts. The expansion (6) follows by periodicity.

We insert this series in the second integral of (5). The series in (6) is boundedly convergent and is uniformly convergent in any interval which excludes the points of discontinuity of the function $x-[x]-\frac{1}{2}$. Hence we may interchange the order of summation and integration, and find for the second integral of (5),

$$\begin{aligned}2\pi i\int_a^b\left(x-[x]-\frac{1}{2}\right)f'(x)e^{2\pi if(x)}\,dx&=-2i\sum_{n=1}^{\infty}\frac{1}{n}\int_a^b\sin 2\pi nx\,e^{2\pi if(x)}f'(x)\,dx\\&=\sum_{n=1}^{\infty}\frac{1}{n}\int_a^b(e^{-2\pi inx}-e^{2\pi inx})e^{2\pi if(x)}f'(x)\,dx\\&=\frac{1}{2\pi i}\sum_{n=1}^{\infty}\frac{1}{n}\int_a^b\frac{f'(x)}{f'(x)-n}d(e^{2\pi i(f(x)-nx)})\\&\quad-\frac{1}{2\pi i}\sum_{n=1}^{\infty}\frac{1}{n}\int_a^b\frac{f'(x)}{f'(x)+n}d(e^{2\pi i(f(x)+nx)})\\&=S_1+S_2\,.\end{aligned}\tag{7}$$

These steps are justified in virtue of the hypothesis on $f'(x)$. We consider the second sum S_2 first. Suppose that $f''(x)\geqq 0$ (the case $f''(x)\leqq 0$ is treated in the same way), then

$$\frac{d}{dx}\frac{f'(x)}{f'(x)+n}=\frac{nf''(x)}{(f'(x)+n)^2}\geqq 0\,.\tag{8}$$

The function $f'(x)/(f'(x)+n)$ is monotone increasing and we can therefore apply the second mean value theorem to the integral in the second sum:

$$\begin{aligned}&\int_a^b\frac{f'(x)}{f'(x)+n}d(e^{2\pi i(f(x)+nx)})\\&\qquad=\int_a^b\frac{f'(x)}{f'(x)+n}d(\cos 2\pi(f(x)+nx))+i\int_a^b\frac{f'(x)}{f'(x)+n}d(\sin 2\pi(f(x)+nx))\\&\qquad=\frac{f'(b)}{f'(b)+n}\{\cos 2\pi(f(b)+nb)-\cos 2\pi(f(\xi)+n\xi)\}\\&\qquad\quad+i\frac{f'(b)}{f'(b)+n}\{\sin 2\pi(f(b)+nb)-\sin 2\pi(f(\eta)+n\eta)\}\,,\end{aligned}$$

where $a\leqq\xi\leqq b$, $a\leqq\eta\leqq b$. As a consequence,

$$\int_a^b\frac{f'(x)}{f'(x)+n}d(e^{2\pi i(f(x)+nx)})=O\left(\frac{f'(b)}{f'(b)+n}\right)=O\left(\frac{1}{n-\theta}\right),\tag{9}$$

because of (3) and (8). From (9), it follows that

$$S_2 = \sum_{n=1}^{\infty} \frac{1}{n} \cdot \frac{1}{n-\theta} = O(1) .$$

By exactly the same argument,

$$S_1 = O(1) ,$$

and the proof of the theorem is therefore complete. This result helps us to approximate the inner sum in (2).

THEOREM 4.2. *If*

$$J = \int_0^P e^{2\pi i u^k y}\, du , \tag{10}$$

then

$$\sum_{j=0}^{[(P-r)/q]} e^{2\pi i (jq+r)^k y} = q^{-1} J + O(1) . \tag{11}$$

PROOF. If

$$f(x) = (qx+r)^k y ,$$

then

$$f'(x) = kq(qx+r)^{k-1} y ,$$

$$|f'(x)| = kq\,|y|\,P^{k-1} \leqq k\frac{1}{\tau}P^{k-1} \leqq \frac{1}{2} ,$$

$$f''(x) = k(k-1)q^2(qx+r)^{k-2} y .$$

Thus $f(x)$ satisfies the conditions of Theorem 4.1 and

$$\sum_{j=0}^{[(P-r)/q]} e^{2\pi i (jq+r)^k y} = \int_0^{(P-r)/q} e^{2\pi i (qx+r)^k y}\, dx + O(1) .$$

If we change variables in the integral, putting

$$u = qx + r ,$$

the conclusion follows.

This lemma allows us to draw a conclusion about $g(x)$.

THEOREM 4.3. *With J defined as in* (10), *and*

$$S(a, q) = \sum_{r=0}^{q-1} e^{2\pi i r^k a/q} , \tag{12}$$

then

$$g(x) = q^{-1} S(a, q) J + O(q) . \tag{13}$$

PROOF. The proof is an immediate consequence of (2) and (11).

The next step is to approximate $g^s(x)$ and for this purpose, we prove

LEMMA 4.1. *For any real or complex numbers a, b, and integer $s \geqq 0$, we have*

$$a^s - b^s = O\{|a - b|(\max(|a|, |b|))^{s-1}\} .$$

PROOF. The proof is indeed simple and is an obvious consequence of the relation

$$a^s - b^s = (a - b)(a^{s-1} + a^{s-2}b + \cdots + b^{s-1}) .$$

If $a = g(x)$ and $b = q^{-1}S(a, q)J$, then to apply the lemma we must have estimates for $g(x)$, $S(a, q)$ and J. We shall assume as will be proved in § 8, Theorem 8.8, that

$$S(a, q) = O(q^{1-1/k}) , \tag{14}$$

and to obtain an estimate for J, we prove

THEOREM 4.4. *If J is the integral defined by* (10), *then*

$$J = O(\min(P, |y|^{-1/k})) .$$

PROOF. We have

$$J = \int_0^P e^{2\pi i u^k y}\,du = O\left(\int_0^P du\right) = O(P) . \tag{15}$$

On the other hand, if we put $v = uy^{1/k}$ in J, we get

$$J = |y|^{-1/k} \int_0^{P|y|^{1/k}} e^{2\pi i v^k}\,dv . \tag{16}$$

The theorem follows if we show that

$$\int_0^\infty e^{2\pi i v^k}\,dv$$

converges. In fact

$$\begin{aligned}\int_0^\infty e^{2\pi i v^k}\,dv &= \int_0^1 e^{2\pi i v^k}\,dv + \int_1^\infty e^{2\pi i v^k}\,dv \\ &= O(1) + \int_1^\infty e^{2\pi i v^k}\,dv .\end{aligned} \tag{17}$$

Moreover,

$$\begin{aligned}\int_1^\infty e^{2\pi i v^k}\,dv &= \int_1^\infty (2\pi i k v^{k-1}) e^{2\pi i v^k} \frac{1}{2\pi i k v^{k-1}}\,dv \\ &= \frac{e^{2\pi i v^k}}{2\pi i k v^{k-1}}\Bigg]_1^\infty + \frac{k-1}{2\pi i k}\int_1^\infty \frac{e^{2\pi i v^k}}{v^k}\,dv .\end{aligned} \tag{18}$$

Since $k > 1$, the second integral of (18) converges and (18), together with (17), shows that

$$\int_0^\infty e^{2\pi i v^k}\,dv$$

converges. The proof of the theorem now follows from (15) and (16).

An estimate for $g(x)$ is given by

THEOREM 4.5. *On a major arc,*

(19) $$g(x) = O(q^{-1/k} \min(P, |y|^{-1/k})) .$$

PROOF. From (13), (14) and Theorem 4.4,

$$\begin{aligned} g(x) &= O(q^{-1}q^{1-1/k} \min(P, |y|^{-1/k})) + O(q) \\ &= O(q^{-1/k} \min(P, |y|^{-1/k})) + O(q) . \end{aligned}$$

It now remains to show that either possibility in the first parenthesis is larger than q in order of magnitude. Indeed, on a major arc $q \leqq P^{1-\delta}$, and

$$q^{-1/k}P > q^{-1/k} \cdot q^{1/(1-\delta)} = q^{1/(1-\delta)-1/k} .$$

By assumption $\delta \geqq 1/k$, and therefore

$$\frac{1}{1-\delta} - \frac{1}{k} > 1 ;$$

hence

$$q^{-1/k}P > q .$$

Furthermore,

$$\begin{aligned} q^{-1/k}|y|^{-1/k} &\geqq \tau^{1/k} = 2kP^{(k-1)/k} \geqq P^{1-1/k} \\ &\geqq q^{(k-1)/k(1-\delta)} \geqq q . \end{aligned}$$

We have used 3.2 and 3.3. This completes the proof.

The approximation to $g^s(x)$ now follows in the form of

THEOREM 4.6. *If*

(20) $$s \geqq 2k + 1 ,$$

then on $M(a, q)$

(21) $$g^s(x) = q^{-s}S^s(a, q)J^s + O(q^{-1} \min^{s-1}(P, |y|^{-1/k})) ,$$

where J *is defined by* (10).

PROOF. We have shown in Theorems 4.4 and 4.5, that if

$$a = g(x), \qquad b = q^{-1}S(a, q)J ,$$

then on a major arc,

$$\max(|a|, |b|) = O(q^{-1/k} \min(P, |y|^{-1/k})) .$$

If we apply Lemma 4.1 we infer, using (13) of Theorem 4.3, that

$$g^s(x) = q^{-s}S^s(a, q)J^s + O(qq^{-(s-1)/k} \min^{s-1}(P, |y|^{-1/k})) .$$

The conclusion of the theorem follows in virtue of the fact that

$$1 - \frac{s-1}{k} \leqq 1 - \frac{2k}{k} = -1 ,$$

by the assumption (20).

We have thus approximated $g^s(x)$ in the neighborhood of a rational point with small denominator. With the help of this approximation we determine the contribution from a single major arc.

THEOREM 4.7. *If*

$$H(a, q) = \int_{M(a,q)} g^s(x)e^{-2\pi inx}\,dx\,, \tag{22}$$

then

$$H(a, q) = e^{-2\pi ina/q}q^{-s}S^s(a, q)\int_{-(q\tau)^{-1}}^{(q\tau)^{-1}} J^s e^{-2\pi iny}\,dy + O(q^{-1}P^{s-k-1})\,, \tag{23}$$

where J is defined by (10).

PROOF. If x is on a major arc, then

$$x = \frac{a}{q} + y, \qquad |y| \leqq \frac{1}{q\tau},$$

and from (22), and Theorem 4.6,

$$\begin{aligned} H(a, q) &= \int_{-(q\tau)^{-1}}^{(q\tau)^{-1}} q^{-s}S^s(a, q)J^s e^{-2\pi in(a/q+y)}\,dy \\ &\quad + O\left(q^{-1}\int_{-(q\tau)^{-1}}^{(q\tau)^{-1}} \min{}^{s-1}(P, |y|^{-1/k})\,dy\right). \end{aligned} \tag{24}$$

We estimate the integral in the error term. We first replace the interval by an infinite one and then break the latter up into two parts:

$$\begin{aligned} \int_{-(q\tau)^{-1}}^{(q\tau)^{-1}} \min{}^{s-1}(P, |y|^{-1/k})\,dy &= O\left(\int_0^\infty \min{}^{s-1}(P, |y|^{-1/k})\,dy\right) \\ &= O\left(\int_0^{P^{-k}} + \int_{P^{-k}}^\infty \min{}^{s-1}(P, |y|^{-1/k})\,dy\right). \end{aligned}$$

In the first integral, $\min(P, |y|^{-1/k}) = P$, and in the second one, $\min(P, |y|^{-1/k}) = |y|^{-1/k}$. Accordingly,

$$\begin{aligned} \int_{-(q\tau)^{-1}}^{(q\tau)^{-1}} \min{}^{s-1}(P, |y|^{-1/k})\,dy &= O(P^{s-1-k}) + O\left(\int_{P^{-k}}^\infty y^{-(s-1)/k}\,dy\right) \\ &= O(P^{s-1-k}) + O(P^{s-k-1}) = O(P^{s-1-k})\,. \end{aligned} \tag{25}$$

The proof is complete using (24) and (25).

In equation (23), we should like to replace the integral by one more amenable to explicit calculation. Since most of the contribution comes from a neighborhood of a/q, we might expect that replacing the interval by the entire infinite line will not lead to too great an error. In fact, we prove

LEMMA 4.2.

$$\int_{-(q\tau)^{-1}}^{(q\tau)^{-1}} J^s e^{-2\pi iny}\,dy = \int_{-\infty}^{\infty} J^s e^{-2\pi iny}\,dy + O((q\tau)^{s/k-1})\,. \tag{26}$$

PROOF. The difference between the integrals in (26) is

$$O\left(\int_{(q\tau)^{-1}}^{\infty} |J|^s\, dy\right) = O\left(\int_{(q\tau)^{-1}}^{\infty} \min^s(P, y^{-1/k})\, dy\right).$$

On the other hand, if $y \geqq (q\tau)^{-1}$, then by §3, (3),

$$y^{-1/k} \leqq (q\tau)^{1/k} \leqq (2k)^{1/k} P\,;$$

hence $\min(P, y^{-1/k}) = O(y^{-1/k})$ in the given range. Consequently,

$$\int_{(q\tau)^{-1}}^{\infty} \min^s(P, |y|^{-1/k})\, dy = O\left(\int_{(q\tau)^{-1}}^{\infty} y^{-s/k}\, dy\right) = O((q\tau)^{s/k-1}),$$

as required. This observation leads directly to

THEOREM 4.8. *If* $s \geqq 2k+1$,

$$L = \int_{-\infty}^{\infty} J^s e^{-2\pi i n y}\, dy\,, \tag{27}$$

then

$$H(a, q) = e^{-2\pi i n a/q} q^{-s} S^s(a, q) L + O(q^{-1} P^{s-k-1})\,. \tag{28}$$

PROOF. From (23), applying (26), we get

$$H(a, q) = e^{-2\pi i n a/q} q^{-s} S^s(a, q) L + O(q^{-1} P^{s-k-1}) + O(q^{-s} |S^s(a, q)| (q\tau)^{s/k-1})\,.$$

On account of (14) and §3, (3), the second error term is

$$O(q^{-s} q^{s-s/k} \cdot q^{s/k-1} \tau^{s/k-1}) = O(q^{-1} \tau^{s/k-1}) = O(q^{-1} P^{s-k-1})\,.$$

In §6, we shall evaluate L explicitly (see Theorem 6.3) but in the meanwhile, let us assume that

$$L = O(P^{s-k})\,. \tag{29}$$

We shall determine the contribution from all the major arcs. Let

$$A(q) = q^{-s} \sum_{\substack{a=1 \\ (a,q)=1}}^{q} e^{-2\pi i n a/q} \cdot S^s(a, q), \qquad A(1) = 1 \tag{30}$$

and

$$\mathfrak{S}(n) = \mathfrak{S} = \sum_{q=1}^{\infty} A(q)\,. \tag{31}$$

It is clear that $A(q)$, and therefore the singular series $\mathfrak{S}$, is real.

THEOREM 4.9. *If* $1/k \leqq \delta \leqq \frac{3}{4}$, $s \geqq 2k+1$, $x = a/q + y$, $|y| \leqq 1/q\tau$, $\tau = 2kP^{k-1}$, $q \leqq P^{1-\delta}$, *then*

$$\sum_{1 \leqq q \leqq P^{1-\delta}} \sum_{\substack{1 \leqq a < q \\ (a,q)=1}} \int_{-(q\tau)^{-1}}^{(q\tau)^{-1}} g^s e^{-2\pi i n x}\, dy = L\mathfrak{S} + O(P^{s-k-(1-\delta)/k})\,.$$

PROOF. If $a = 0$, then $H(0, 1) = O(P^{s-k-1}) + L$, from (28). Starting from

(28), we first sum over a, and then over q, and get, because of (30),

$$\sum_{q\leq P^{1-\delta}}\sum_{\substack{a=1\\(a,q)=1}}^{q} H(a,q)=\sum_{q\leq P^{1-\delta}} A(q)L+O\Big(\sum_{q\leq P^{1-\delta}}\sum_{a=1}^{q} q^{-1}P^{s-k-1}\Big)$$
(32)
$$=L\sum_{q\leq P^{1-\delta}} A(q)+O(P^{s-k-\delta})\,.$$

On the other hand, by (14)

$$A(q)=\sum_{\substack{a=1\\(a,q)=1}}^{q} q^{-s}e^{-2\pi ina/q}\cdot S^{s}(a,q)$$
(33)
$$=O(q\cdot q^{-s}q^{s-s/k})=O(q^{1-s/k})=O(q^{-1-1/k})\,,$$

using the condition $s\geqq 2k+1$. It follows that the series

$$\sum_{q=1}^{\infty} A(q)=O\Big(\sum_{q=1}^{\infty} q^{-1-1/k}\Big)=O(1)\,,$$

and therefore converges absolutely when $s\geqq 2k+1$.

If in (32) we replace the finite sum by $\mathfrak{S}$, the error we make is, in virtue of (29) and (33),

$$O\Big(\sum_{q>P^{1-\delta}} A(q)L\Big)=O\Big(P^{s-k}\sum_{q>P^{1-\delta}} q^{1-s/k}\Big)$$
(34)
$$=O\Big(P^{s-k}\cdot\sum_{q>P^{1-\delta}} q^{-1-1/k}\Big)$$
$$=O(P^{s-k}\cdot P^{-(1-\delta)/k})\,.$$

We turn our attention now to the minor arcs.

5. Weyl's method for estimating trigonometric sums. The estimation of trigonometric or exponential sums plays a fundamental role in many problems of analytic number theory. A full account of the deepest methods, which are due in large measure to Vinogradoff, is somewhat beyond the scope of this chapter. In this section, we restrict our attention to the method of H. Weyl since many of the underlying ideas inherent in this method play some role in the deeper theory.

We start with some generalities and consider, to begin with, an exponential sum of a fairly general type:

(1) $$T(x,A,B)=\sum_{A\leq m\leq B} e^{2\pi i f(m)x}\,,$$

where $f(u)$ is a real valued function of u defined for integral values of u, and m ranges over some or all integers lying in the range (A,B).

If, for example, $f(u)=u^k$, $A=1$, $B=P$, and m ranges over all the integers in $(1,P)$, then T coincides with $g(x)$. If $A=0$, $B=q-1$, $x=a/q$, $f(u)=u^k$, then T coincides with $S(a,q)$.

Suppose that the number of values assumed by m in (1) is Q, then we observe that trivially

(2) $$T(x,A,B)=O(Q)\,,$$

since each term has absolute value 1. Our objective is to show that under certain circumstances, enough cancellation takes place among the terms that the order of magnitude can be reduced substantially. We write

$$T = O(Q)\gamma \ , \tag{3}$$

and following Vinogradoff, call γ the "factor of reduction." For a nontrivial estimate we wish to show that with restrictions placed on $f(u)$ and on the values assumed by m,

$$\gamma \to 0 \text{ as } Q \to \infty \ ,$$

and an important feature of the problem is to determine the rate at which $\gamma \to 0$. What are the restrictions on $f(u)$ or on the values assumed by m which allow a nontrivial factor of reduction? Only partial answers can be given and we begin by proving a simple result. Suppose that $f(u)$ is linear and that m takes all values between A and B. We prove

THEOREM 5.1. *If ax is not an integer, and*

$$T = T(x, A, B) = \sum_{A \leqq n \leqq B} e^{2\pi i(an+b)x} \ ,$$

then

$$T = O\left(\frac{1}{\| ax \|}\right), \tag{4}$$

where $\| u \|$ means the distance from u to the nearest integer. That is,

$$\| u \| = \min (u - [u], [u] + 1 - u).$$

PROOF. The problem here is simple, since it involves summing a geometric series. In fact,

$$\begin{aligned} T &= e^{2\pi ibx} \frac{e^{2\pi iax(B+1)} - e^{2\pi ixA}}{e^{2\pi iax} - 1} \\ &= O\left(\frac{1}{| e^{2\pi iax} - 1 |}\right) = O\left(\frac{1}{| e^{\pi iax} - e^{-\pi iax} |}\right) \\ &= O\left(\frac{1}{| \sin \pi ax |}\right). \end{aligned}$$

From elementary trigonometry, however,

$$\sin \pi\alpha \geqq 2\alpha \text{ if } 0 \leqq \alpha \leqq \tfrac{1}{2} \ ;$$

whereas, on the other hand, if $\alpha > \frac{1}{2}$, then either $\alpha - [\alpha] \leqq \frac{1}{2}$, or $[\alpha] + 1 - \alpha \leqq \frac{1}{2}$. Since

$$| \sin \pi\alpha | = | \sin \pi(\alpha - [\alpha]) | = | \sin \pi([\alpha] + 1 - \alpha) | \ ,$$

it follows that in every case

$$| \sin \pi\alpha | \geqq 2 \| \alpha \| \ ,$$

and this completes the proof.

This simple example illustrates the fact that when the values assumed by the function $f(u)$ have some measure of regularity, then we can expect a nontrivial factor of reduction. The precise meaning of "regularity" will depend to a large extent on the nature of the function. There is a regularity of a specific kind which plays an important role in the theory of diophantine approximation. It may be worthwhile to digress for a moment to relate this regularity to trigonometric sums.

Let $a_1, a_2, \cdots, a_n \cdots$ be any sequence of real numbers, and consider their "residues" modulo 1. By this is meant that to each real number a_i we associate the number $\alpha_i = a_i - [a_i]$. Clearly $0 \leqq \alpha_i < 1$. Let (a, b) be a subinterval of the unit interval and suppose that $A(n)$ is the number of elements of the set $a_1, \cdots, a_n$ for which the corresponding α_i lies in (a, b). Then we say that the sequence $\{a_n\}$ is uniformly distributed mod 1 if each subinterval of $(0, 1)$ has its rightful share of α_i. Precisely, if

$$\lim_{n\to\infty} \frac{A(n)}{n} = b - a \,, \tag{5}$$

for every subinterval (a, b). The relevance of this concept to the problem of exponential sums is seen as follows. We can show that if $f(x)$ is any Riemann integrable function which is periodic with period 1, then if $\{a_n\}$ is uniformly distributed,

$$\lim_{n\to\infty} \frac{1}{n} \sum_{m=1}^{n} f(a_m) = \int_0^1 f(x)dx \,. \tag{6}$$

This may be proved easily by first noting its validity for step functions, and observing that if $f(x)$ is a Riemann integrable function, then there exists for every $\varepsilon > 0$, step functions f_1 and f_2, $f_1 \leqq f \leqq f_2$ such that

$$\int_0^1 (f_2 - f_1)\, dx < \varepsilon \,, \qquad \int_0^1 (f - f_1)\, dx < \varepsilon \,.$$

In particular, $e^{2\pi imx}$ has period 1 for every integer m and we can deduce from (6) as a corollary, that if $\{a_n\}$ is uniformly distributed, then

$$\lim_{n\to\infty} \frac{1}{n} \sum_{k=1}^{n} e^{2\pi i a_k m} = \int_0^1 e^{2\pi imu}\, du = 0 \,. \tag{7}$$

This means that if the sequence a_n is uniformly distributed, then

$$\sum_{k=1}^{n} e^{2\pi i a_k m} = o(n) \,,$$

for every integer m. The interesting fact is that the converse holds: If for every integer m, we have

$$\sum_{k=1}^{n} e^{2\pi i a_k m} = o(n) \,,$$

then the sequence $\{a_n\}$ is uniformly distributed mod 1. A relatively simple proof may be constructed with the help of Fourier series.

We return now to

$$g(x) = \sum_{m=1}^{P} e^{2\pi i m^k x} . \tag{8}$$

What regularity, if any, is exhibited by the kth powers? Weyl observes that the $(k-1)$st differences of the kth powers are in arithmetic progression. To capitalize on this observation, we should like to introduce differences in the exponent of (8). To do this, we consider the following somewhat more general sum:

$$T = \sum_{h=0}^{Q} e^{2\pi i \varphi(h)} , \tag{9}$$

where $\varphi(h)$ is a polynomial of degree k,

$$\varphi(y) = \alpha y^k + \alpha_1 y^{k-1} + \cdots + \alpha_k ,$$

and α, α_i are real numbers.

Here then is Weyl's construction. We consider

$$\begin{aligned} |T|^2 = T\bar{T} &= \sum_{h_1=0}^{Q} e^{2\pi i \varphi(h_1)} \cdot \sum_{h_2=0}^{Q} e^{-2\pi i \varphi(h_2)} \\ &= \sum_{h_1=0}^{Q} \sum_{h_2=0}^{Q} e^{2\pi i (\varphi(h_1) - \varphi(h_2))} . \end{aligned}$$

In this double sum, we put $h_1 = h_2 + r_1$ and

$$\varphi(h_1) - \varphi(h_2) = r_1 \varphi(r_1 ; h_2) . \tag{10}$$

Since $r_1 = h_1 - h_2$ and h_1, h_2 range over all values of the interval $(0, Q)$, it follows that r_1 ranges over all values in the interval $-Q \leqq r_1 \leqq Q$, that is, $|r_1| \leqq Q$. For a given value of r_1, however, $h_2 = h_1 - r_1$ ranges over the values

(a) 0 to $Q - r_1$ if r_1 is positive, and

(b) $-r_1$ to Q if r_1 is negative.

In any case h_2 ranges over $Q - |r_1|$ *consecutive* values. That the values are consecutive is important. Hence

$$|T|^2 = \sum_{r_1} \sum_{h_2} e^{2\pi i r_1 \varphi(r_1 ; h_2)} .$$

Now we iterate the process:

$$|T|^4 = |T^2|^2 = \Big| \sum_{r_1} \sum_{h_2} e^{2\pi i r_1 \varphi(r_1 ; h_2)} \Big|^2 .$$

Using the Cauchy-Schwarz inequality, we get

$$\begin{aligned} |T|^4 &\leqq \Big(\sum_{r_1} 1 \Big) \sum_{r_1} \Big| \sum_{h_2} e^{2\pi i r_1 \varphi(r_1 ; h_2)} \Big|^2 \\ &\leqq q_1 \sum_{r_1} \sum_{h_2} \sum_{h_3} e^{2\pi i r_1 (\varphi(r_1 ; h_2) - \varphi(r_1 ; h_3))} , \end{aligned} \tag{11}$$

where q_1 is the number of solutions of the inequality $|r_1| \leqq Q$. We put again

$$h_2 = h_3 + r_2$$

and

(12) $$\varphi(r_1; h_3 + r_2) - \varphi(r_1; h_3) = r_2\varphi(r_1, r_2; h_3).$$

Then by (11)

$$|T|^4 \leqq q_1 \sum_{r_1} \sum_{r_2} \sum_{h_3} e^{2\pi i r_1 r_2 \varphi(r_1, r_2; h_3)},$$

with the ranges of summation obtained as follows:

Since

$$r_2 = h_2 - h_3,$$

then as h_2 and h_3 range over the set (a) or (b) of the preceding analysis, it is a simple calculation to verify that r_2 ranges over the set $-(Q - |r_1|)$ to $(Q - |r_1|)$. That is, the range in the first two summands is over the set of values of r_1 and r_2 satisfying

$$|r_1| + |r_2| \leqq Q.$$

For a given pair of values r_1 and r_2, h_3 ranges over the set 0 to $Q - |r_1| - r_2$ if $r_2 > 0$ and $-r_2$ to $Q - |r_1|$ if $r_2 < 0$. In any event, h_3 ranges over $Q - |r_1| - |r_2|$ consecutive values. If we repeat the process, we find

(13) $$\begin{aligned} |T|^{2^3} &\leqq \Big| q_1 \sum_{r_1, r_2} \sum_{h_3} e^{2\pi i r_1 r_2 \varphi(r_1, r_2; h_3)} \Big|^2 \\ &\leqq q_1^2 \Big(\sum_{r_1, r_2} 1 \Big) \sum_{r_1, r_2} \Big| \sum_{h_3} e^{2\pi i r_1 r_2 \varphi(r_1, r_2; h_3)} \Big|^2 \\ &\leqq q_1^2 q_2 \sum_{r_1, r_2} \sum_{h_3} \sum_{h_4} e^{2\pi i r_1 r_2 (\varphi(r_1, r_2; h_3) - \varphi(r_1, r_2; h_4))}, \end{aligned}$$

where q_2 is the number of solutions of the inequality

(14) $$|r_1| + |r_2| \leqq Q.$$

If in (13) we put $h_3 = h_4 + r_3$, and $\varphi(r_1, r_2; h_4 + r_3) - \varphi(r_1, r_2; h_4) = r_3\varphi(r_1, r_2, r_3; h_4)$, we find

$$|T|^{2^3} \leqq q_1^2 q_2 \sum_{r_1, r_2, r_3} \sum_{h_4} e^{2\pi i r_1 r_2 r_3 \varphi(r_1, r_2, r_3; h_4)},$$

where r_1, r_2, r_3 range over the set of values satisfying

$$|r_1| + |r_2| + |r_3| \leqq Q,$$

and h_4 ranges over $Q - |r_1| - |r_2| - |r_3|$ consecutive values. We prove then by induction

THEOREM 5.2. *If q_m is the number of solutions of the inequality $|r_1| + |r_2| + \cdots + |r_m| \leqq Q$, then*

(15) $$|T|^{2^{k-1}} \leqq q_1^{2^{k-3}} q_2^{2^{k-4}} \cdots q_{k-2} \sum_{r_1, \ldots, r_{k-1}} \sum_{h_k} e^{2\pi i r_1 \cdots r_{k-1} \varphi(r_1 \cdots r_{k-1}; h_k)},$$

where $r_1, \cdots, r_{k-1}$ range over the set defined by $|r_1| + \cdots + |r_{k-1}| \leqq Q$, h_k ranges over a set of $Q - |r_1| - \cdots - |r_{k-1}|$ consecutive integers.

Proof. The theorem being true for $k = 3$, we suppose that

$$| T |^{2^{k-2}} \leqq q_1^{2^{k-4}} q_2^{2^{k-5}} \cdots q_{k-3} \sum_{r_1, \cdots, r_{k-2}} \sum_{h_{k-1}} \exp[2\pi i r_1 \cdots r_{k-2} \varphi(r_1, \cdots, r_{k-2}; h_{k-1})] .$$

Then

$$\begin{aligned}
| T |^{2^{k-1}} &= | \, | T |^{2^{k-2}} |^2 \leqq (q_1^{2^{k-4}} q_2^{2^{k-5}} \cdots q_{k-3})^2 \\
&\quad \times \Big(\sum_{r_1 \cdots r_{k-2}} 1 \Big)^2 \sum_{r_1 \cdots r_{k-2}} \Big| \sum_{h_{k-1}} \exp[2\pi i r_1 r_2 \cdots r_{k-2} \varphi(r_1, \cdots, r_{k-2}; h_{k-1})] \Big|^2 \\
&\leqq q_1^{2^{k-3}} q_2^{2^{k-4}} \cdots q_{k-3}^2 q_{k-2} \\
&\quad \times \sum_{r_1 \cdots r_{k-2}} \sum_{h_{k-1}} \sum_{h_k} \exp[2\pi i r_1 \cdots r_{k-2} \{ \varphi(r_1, \cdots, r_{k-2}; h_{k-1}) \\
&\qquad\qquad - \varphi(r_1, \cdots, r_{k-2}; h_k) \}] .
\end{aligned} \tag{16}$$

If in (16), we put

$$h_{k-1} = r_{k-1} + h_k ,$$

and

$$\varphi(r_1, \cdots, r_{k-2}; h_{k-1}) - \varphi(r_1, \cdots, r_{k-2}; h_k) = r_{k-1} \varphi(r_1, \cdots, r_{k-1}; h_k) ,$$

we get

$$| T |^{2^{k-1}} \leqq q_1^{2^{k-3}} q_2^{2^{k-2}} \cdots q_{k-3}^2 q_{k-2} \sum_{r_1 \cdots r_{k-1}} \sum_{h_k} e^{2\pi i r_1 \cdots r_{k-1} \varphi(r_1 \cdots r_{k-1}; h_k)} ,$$

where the summation ranges are easily confirmed.

We find it convenient to make the abbreviation $h = h_k$. The function $\varphi(r_1, \cdots, r_{k-1}; h)$ is a $(k-1)$st difference; we evaluate it. In the first place,

$$\begin{aligned}
\varphi(r_1; h_2) &= \frac{1}{r_1} (\varphi(r_1 + h_2) - \varphi(h_2)) \\
&= \frac{1}{r_1} [(\alpha(r_1 + h_2)^k + \cdots + \alpha_k) - (\alpha h_2^k + \cdots + \alpha_k)] \\
&= \alpha k h_2^{k-1} + \text{lower powers of } h_2 .
\end{aligned}$$

Moreover,

$$\begin{aligned}
\varphi(r_1, r_2; h_3) &= \frac{1}{r_2} (\varphi(r_1; r_2 + h_3) - \varphi(r_1; h_3)) \\
&= \frac{1}{r_2} \{ \alpha k (r_2 + h_3)^{k-1} + \text{lower powers of } (r_2 + h_3) \\
&\qquad - (\alpha k h_3^{k-1} + \text{lower powers of } h_3) \} \\
&= \frac{1}{r_2} \{ \alpha k r_2 (k-1) h_3^{k-2} + \text{lower powers of } h_3 \} \\
&= \alpha k (k-1) h_3^{k-2} + \text{lower powers of } h_3 .
\end{aligned}$$

It is then easy to see that in general

$$\begin{aligned}
\varphi(r_1, r_2, \cdots, r_{k-1}; h) &= \alpha k! h + \text{constant term involving } r_1, \cdots, r_{k-1} \\
&= \alpha k! h + \mu ,
\end{aligned} \tag{17}$$

where μ involves only $r_1, r_2, \cdots, r_{k-1}$.

We put $N = q_1^{k-3} q_2^{k-4} \cdots q_{k-2}$, $R = r_1 \cdots r_{k-1}$, and we get from (17) and Theorem 5.2

THEOREM 5.3.

$$|T|^{2^{k-1}} \leqq N \sum_{r_1, \ldots, r_{k-1}} e^{2\pi i R\mu} \sum_h e^{2\pi i R\alpha k! h} . \tag{18}$$

We obtain now an upper bound for N. For this purpose, we note that since q_m is the number of solutions of

$$|r_1| + \cdots + |r_m| \leqq Q , \tag{19}$$

q_m is bounded above by the volume of the "octahedron" determined by (19). This volume, however, is easily seen to be

$$\frac{(2Q)^m}{m!} = O(Q^m) .$$

Hence

$$N = O(Q^l) ,$$

where

$$l = 1 \cdot 2^{k-3} + 2 \cdot 2^{k-4} + \cdots + (k-2)2^0 .$$

On the other hand,

$$2l = 2^{k-2} + 2 \cdot 2^{k-3} + 3 \cdot 2^{k-4} + \cdots + (k-2)2^1 .$$

Hence

$$l = 2^{k-2} + 2^{k-3} + \cdots + 2 - k + 2 = 2^{k-1} - k .$$

We have therefore proved

THEOREM 5.4.

$$N = q_1^{k-3} \cdot q_2^{k-4} \cdots q_{k-2} = O(Q^{2^{k-1}-k}) . \tag{20}$$

Returning to (18), we can now prove

THEOREM 5.5. *If* $R = r_1 r_2 \cdots r_{k-1}$, *then*

$$T^{2^{k-1}} = O(Q^{2^{k-1}-k}) \sum_{r_1, \ldots, r_{k-1}} \min\left(Q, \frac{1}{\|R\alpha k!\|}\right).$$

It should be observed that we interpret $\min(Q, 1/0)$ *to mean* Q.

PROOF. Suppose that $R\alpha k! h$ is not an integer, then Theorem 5.1 is applicable to the inner sum of (18) since h runs over a set of consecutive integers. On the other hand, if $R\alpha k! h$ is an integer, then $e^{2\pi i R\alpha k! h} = 1$ and

$$\left|\sum_h e^{2\pi i R\alpha k! h}\right| \leqq Q .$$

Consequently,

$$|T|^{2^{k-1}} \leqq N \sum_{r_1, \ldots, r_{k-1}} \min\left(Q, \frac{1}{\|R\alpha k!\|}\right),$$

and by Theorem 5.4, the result follows.

We continue and make one further reduction. Let

$$r = r_1 \cdots r_{k-1} k! = Rk! \,. \tag{21}$$

Then

$$|r| \leqq Q^{k-1} \cdot k! \,.$$

This leads to the validity of

THEOREM 5.6.

$$T^{2^{k-1}} = O\Big(Q^{2^{k-1}-k} \sum_r b_r \min\Big(Q, \frac{1}{\|r\alpha\|}\Big)\Big), \tag{22}$$

where b_r is the number of solutions of (21) *subject to the restriction*

$$|r_1| + \cdots + |r_{k-1}| \leqq Q \,. \tag{23}$$

To get an estimate for b_r, we require a lemma:

LEMMA 5.1. *If $d(n)$ denotes the number of divisors of n, then for every $\varepsilon > 0$,*

$$d(n) = O(n^{\varepsilon}) \,. \tag{24}$$

PROOF. If $n = \prod_{p|n} p^a$, then

$$\frac{d(n)}{n^{\varepsilon}} = \prod_{p|n} \frac{a+1}{p^{a\varepsilon}} = \prod_{p|n;\, p<2^{1/\varepsilon}} \frac{a+1}{p^{a\varepsilon}} \prod_{p|n;\, p\geqq 2^{1/\varepsilon}} \frac{a+1}{p^{a\varepsilon}} \,.$$

The second factor however is $\leqq 1$ for $p^{a\varepsilon} \geqq 2^a \geqq a+1$, and therefore

$$\begin{aligned} \frac{d(n)}{n^{\varepsilon}} &\leqq \prod_{p|n;\, p<2^{1/\varepsilon}} \frac{a+1}{p^{a\varepsilon}} \leqq \prod_{p|n;\, p<2^{1/\varepsilon}} \frac{a+1}{a\varepsilon \log 2} \\ &\leqq \prod_{p|n;\, p<2^{1/\varepsilon}} \frac{2}{\varepsilon \log 2} \leqq \prod_{p<2^{1/\varepsilon}} \frac{2}{\varepsilon \log 2} = C(\varepsilon) \,. \end{aligned}$$

Each of these steps may very easily be verified.

We now prove the basic

THEOREM 5.7. *For any $\varepsilon > 0$, we have*

$$T^{2^{k-1}} = O\left(Q^{2^{k-1}-1} + Q^{2^{k-1}-k+\varepsilon} \sum_{r=1}^{k!Q^{k-1}} \min\Big(Q, \frac{1}{\|r\alpha\|}\Big)\right). \tag{25}$$

PROOF. The proof hinges on the determination of an estimate for b_r where b_r is the number of solutions of (21) restricted by (23). Two cases arise:

Case (i). $r = 0$. In this case we can choose $r_i = 0$ and the remainder arbitrarily. Each r_i can be chosen in at most $2Q$ ways; hence

$$b_0 \leqq (k-1)(2Q)^{k-2} = O(Q^{k-2}) \,, \tag{26}$$

there being $k-1$ ways of choosing $r_i = 0$ and having done so there remain $k-2$ r's which can be chosen arbitrarily subject to $|r_i| < Q$.

Case (ii). $r \neq 0$. Here we prove that $b_r = O(r^{\varepsilon})$ for every $\varepsilon > 0$. In this case we are required to find the number of solutions of

$$r_1 \cdots r_{k-1} = \frac{r}{k!} = r_0 \text{ (say)} . \tag{27}$$

Since each r_i $(i = 1, \cdots, k-1)$ divides r_0, it follows that each r_i can have at most $2d(|r_0|)$ values. Thus the number of solutions of (27) is, by (24), at most

$$(2d(|r_0|))^{k-1} = O(r_0^\varepsilon) = O(r^\varepsilon) , \tag{28}$$

where the O in (28) depends on k and ε.

The sum on the right of (22) is then broken into three parts, $r = 0, r > 0, r < 0$. Since $||r\alpha|| = ||-r\alpha||$, it follows that the sum for $r < 0$ has the same character as that for $r > 0$. Consequently from (26) and (28),

$$\begin{aligned} T^{2^{k-1}} &= O\left(Q^{2^{k-1}-k} \sum_{|r| \leqq k!Q^{k-1}} b_r \min\left(Q, \frac{1}{||r\alpha||}\right)\right) \\ &= O\left(Q^{2^{k-1}-k+k-2+1} + Q^{2^{k-1}-k+\varepsilon} \sum_{r=1}^{k!Q^{k-1}} \min\left(Q, \frac{1}{||r\alpha||}\right)\right) \\ &= O\left(Q^{2^{k-1}-1} + Q^{2^{k-1}-k+\varepsilon} \sum_{r=1}^{k!Q^{k-1}} \min\left(Q, \frac{1}{||r\alpha||}\right)\right), \end{aligned}$$

and this completes the proof.

Clearly from (9) $|T| \leqq Q$ and therefore $T^{2^{k-1}} = O(Q^{2^{k-1}})$. We notice that if each term in the second sum of (25) has the value Q, then the second term will have as its order of magnitude $Q^{2^{k-1}+\varepsilon}$ and this would mean that after all our labor we arrive at a trivial estimate. Thus we should like to save one power of Q in the second term (additional saving is pointless since the first term has already order $Q^{2^{k-1}-1}$). To do this we must show that in about $O(Q)$ cases, $\min(Q, 1/||r\alpha||) \neq Q$. This means roughly that the integer nearest to $r\alpha$ is relatively far away. Before making this precise, we perform a further reduction on the sum in (25). Suppose that

$$\alpha = \frac{a}{q} + y, \qquad \text{where } |y| < \frac{1}{q^2} ;$$

then the nearest integer to $r\alpha$ will be determined, roughly speaking, by the residue of r modulo q. We therefore divide the sum

$$U = \sum_{r=1}^{k!Q^{k-1}} \min\left(Q, \frac{1}{||r\alpha||}\right) \tag{29}$$

into sums of q terms each. A typical sum has the form

$$U_m = \sum_{r=mq+1}^{(m+1)q} \min\left(Q, \frac{1}{||r\alpha||}\right) . \tag{30}$$

In U there are $[k!Q^{k-1}/q]$ sums of the form U_m; there may in addition be a possible last sum occurring, having fewer than q terms. The precise nature of this possible last sum is not important. Its value is at most qQ. If we translate the index of summation in (30), by putting

$$t = r - mq - 1\ ,$$

we find

$$U_m = \sum_{t=0}^{q-1} \min\left(Q, \frac{1}{\|\alpha(t+mq+1)\|}\right) = \sum_{t=0}^{q-1} \min\left(Q, \frac{1}{\|\alpha t + \beta\|}\right),$$

where we have put

$$\beta = \alpha(mq+1)\ .$$

We prove now

THEOREM 5.8. *If* $\alpha = a/q + y$, $|y| < 1/q^2$, *then*

$$\sum_{t=0}^{q-1} \min\left(Q, \frac{1}{\|\alpha t + \beta\|}\right) \leqq 5Q + 4q \log q\ . \tag{31}$$

PROOF. We wish to calculate

$$\|\alpha t + \beta\|\ .$$

Let M be the integer nearest to $q\beta$ (if $q\beta \equiv \frac{1}{2} (\mathrm{mod}\ 1)$, we choose either integer), then

$$|q\beta - M| \leqq \tfrac{1}{2}\ ,$$

and hence

$$\left|\beta - \frac{M}{q}\right| \leqq \frac{1}{2q}\ .$$

That is,

$$\beta = \frac{M}{q} + \frac{z}{q}\ ,$$

where

$$|z| \leqq \tfrac{1}{2}\ . \tag{32}$$

Moreover,

$$\left|\alpha t - \frac{at}{q}\right| = t\left|\alpha - \frac{a}{q}\right| < q \cdot \frac{1}{q^2} = \frac{1}{q}\ ;$$

consequently,

$$\alpha t = \frac{at}{q} + \frac{w}{q}\ , \tag{33}$$

where $|w| < 1$. It follows from (32) and (33) that

$$\alpha t + \beta = \frac{at}{q} + \frac{M}{q} + \frac{\theta(t)}{q} = \frac{at + M}{q} + \frac{\theta(t)}{q}\ , \tag{34}$$

where

$$|\theta(t)| < \frac{3}{2}\ . \tag{35}$$

Now, as t runs through the set $0, 1, \cdots, q-1$, $at + M$ runs through a complete residue system modulo q, since $(a, q) = 1$. Moreover, since $\|\gamma\| = \|\sigma\|$ if $\gamma \equiv \sigma (\mathrm{mod}\ 1)$, it follows that

$$\|\alpha t+\beta\| = \left\|\frac{\rho(t)}{q}+\frac{\theta(t)}{q}\right\|,$$

where $\rho(t)$ runs through a complete residue system modulo q wherever t does. Suppose we restrict $\rho(t)$ to be relatively far removed from the end points of $(0, q-1)$ (for close to the end points, $\rho(t)/q$ is nearly an integer). Specifically, let

$$3 \leqq \rho(t) \leqq q-3\,. \tag{36}$$

We shall account for the five remaining values shortly. Then from (34) and (35), we get

$$\rho(t)-\frac{3}{2} < \rho(t)+\theta(t) < \rho(t)+\frac{3}{2}\,;$$

and

$$\rho(t)+\theta(t) < q-3+\frac{3}{2} < q-\frac{3}{2}\,;$$

whence

$$\left[\frac{\rho(t)+\theta(t)}{q}\right]=0\,.$$

Therefore, since by definition $\|x\| = \min(x-[x], [x]+1-x)$, we get from (34),

$$\begin{aligned}
\|\alpha t+\beta\| = \left\|\frac{\rho(t)+\theta(t)}{q}\right\| &\geqq \min\left(\frac{\rho(t)+\theta(t)}{q}, 1-\frac{\rho(t)+\theta(t)}{q}\right)\\
&\geqq \min\left(\frac{\rho(t)-\frac{3}{2}}{q}, \frac{q-\rho(t)-\frac{3}{2}}{q}\right)\\
&\geqq \min\left(\frac{2\rho(t)-3}{2q}, \frac{2q-2\rho(t)-3}{2q}\right)\\
&\geqq \min\left(\frac{\rho(t)}{2q}, \frac{q-\rho(t)}{2q}\right),
\end{aligned} \tag{37}$$

where we have used, with the help of (36), the fact that

$$2\rho(t)-3 = \rho(t)+(\rho(t)-3) \geqq \rho(t)\,,$$

and

$$2q-2\rho(t)-3 = q-\rho(t)+(q-3-\rho(t)) \geqq q-\rho(t)\,.$$

We conclude from (37), taking account of the five values excepted from (36), that

$$\sum_{t=0}^{q-1}\min\left(Q, \frac{1}{\|\alpha t+\beta\|}\right) \leqq 5Q+2q\sum_{3\leqq\rho(t)\leqq q-3}\max\left(\frac{1}{\rho(t)}, \frac{1}{q-\rho(t)}\right).$$

But

$$\max\left(\frac{1}{\rho(t)}, \frac{1}{q-\rho(t)}\right) \leqq \frac{2}{\rho(t)},$$

and therefore

$$\begin{aligned}\sum_{t=0}^{q-1} \min\left(Q, \frac{1}{\|\alpha t+\beta\|}\right) &\leqq 5Q + 4q \sum_{3\leqq\rho(t)\leqq q-3} \frac{1}{\rho(t)} \\ &\leqq 5Q + 4q \sum_{2\leqq\rho(t)\leqq q} \frac{1}{\rho(t)} \\ &\leqq 5Q + 4q\log q,\end{aligned}$$

since

$$\sum_{2\leqq\rho(t)\leqq q} \frac{1}{\rho(t)} \leqq \int_1^q \frac{dx}{x} = \log q.$$

This completes the proof.

We now apply these results to

$$g(x) = \sum_{m=1}^{P} e^{2\pi i m^k x}.$$

We prove the fundamental

THEOREM 5.9. *If* $\sigma = 1/2^{k-1}$, *and* $x = a/q + y$, $|y| \leqq 1/q\tau$, $q \leqq \tau = 2kP^{k-1}$ *then,*

$$g(x) = O\left(P^{1+\varepsilon}\left(\frac{1}{q} + \frac{1}{P} + \frac{q}{P^k}\right)^{\sigma}\right). \tag{38}$$

PROOF. In Theorem 5.7, let $\varphi(y) = xy^k$, $Q = P$, and let a/q be a rational number for which

$$x = \frac{a}{q} + y, \qquad \text{with } |y| \leqq \frac{1}{q\tau} \leqq \frac{1}{q^2}.$$

The existence of a/q was established in Theorem 3.2. Then from Theorem 5.7, we have

$$g(x)^{2^{k-1}} = O(P^{2^{k-1}-1} + P^{2^{k-1}-k+\varepsilon}U) \tag{39}$$

where

$$U = \sum_{r=1}^{k!P^{k-1}} \min\left(P, \frac{1}{\|xr\|}\right).$$

We break U into at most

$$\frac{k!P^{k-1}}{q} + 1$$

sums of the type given in Theorem 5.8. It then follows, using the result of Theorem 5.8, that

$$U = O\left(\frac{k!P^{k-1}}{q} + 1\right)(5P + 4q\log q). \tag{40}$$

Since we restricted q in such a way that $q \leqq 2kP^{k-1}$, then $\log q = O(P^{\varepsilon})$ and hence from (40),

$$U = O\left(\frac{P^k}{q} + P + P^{k-1+\varepsilon} + P^{\varepsilon}q\right)$$

$$= O\left(P^{k+\varepsilon}\left(\frac{1}{q} + \frac{1}{P^{k-1}} + \frac{1}{P} + \frac{q}{P^k}\right)\right) \tag{41}$$

$$= O\left(P^{k+\varepsilon}\left(\frac{1}{q} + \frac{1}{P} + \frac{q}{P^k}\right)\right).$$

Putting this value in (39), we get

$$g(x)^{2^{k-1}} = O\left(P^{2^{k-1}-1} + P^{2^{k-1}+\varepsilon}\left(\frac{1}{q} + \frac{1}{P} + \frac{q}{P^k}\right)\right).$$

The first term on the right is smaller than the middle term of the parenthesis. Hence, taking the 2^{k-1}th root, we get

$$g(x) = O\left(P^{1+\varepsilon}\left(\frac{1}{q} + \frac{1}{P} + \frac{q}{P^k}\right)^{\sigma}\right),$$

as required.

Thus according to Theorem 3.3, if x is a point on a minor arc, then

$$x = \frac{a}{q} + y, \qquad \text{with } |y| \leqq \frac{1}{q\tau},$$

and

$$P^{1-\delta} < q \leqq \tau. \tag{42}$$

Consequently, we can deduce the very important

THEOREM 5.10. *If x is a point on a minor arc, that is*

$$x = \frac{a}{q} + y, \qquad |y| \leqq \frac{1}{q\tau}, \ \tau = 2kP^{k-1}, \ P^{1-\delta} < q \leqq \tau$$

and $\sigma = 2^{1-k}$, then

$$g(x) = O(P^{1-\sigma(1-\delta)+\varepsilon}).$$

PROOF. On a minor arc,

$$\frac{1}{q} < \frac{1}{P^{1-\delta}}$$

and

$$\frac{q}{P^k} \leqq \frac{\tau}{P^k} = \frac{2k}{P} < \frac{1}{P^{1-\delta}},$$

if P is sufficiently large. Therefore by Theorem 5.9,

$$g(x) = O\left(P^{1+\varepsilon}\left(\frac{1}{q} + \frac{1}{P} + \frac{q}{P^k}\right)^{\sigma}\right) = O(P^{1+\varepsilon}P^{-\sigma(1-\delta)})$$

as required.

On a minor arc, then, the factor of reduction is $O(P^{-\sigma(1-\delta)+\varepsilon})$ and though the constant $\sigma(1-\delta)$ is indeed very small for large k, it nevertheless enables us to deduce an asymptotic formula for $r(n)$.

6. Asymptotic formula for $r(n)$. The preceding discussion allows us to derive an asymptotic formula for $r(n)$ and as a consequence an upper bound for $G(k)$.

In § 4, we were able to calculate the contribution to $r(n)$ arising from the major arcs. The analysis of § 5 leads to an upper bound for the contribution from the minor arcs. Let $\mathfrak{m}$ denote the set of points not on any major arc; then the points of $\mathfrak{m}$ are on the minor arcs. We prove

THEOREM 6.1. *If*

$$s \geqq k2^k + 1 , \tag{1}$$

then

$$\int_{\mathfrak{m}} g^s(x)e^{-2\pi inx}\,dx = o(P^{s-k}) . \tag{2}$$

PROOF. The proof is a simple consequence of Theorem 5.10. Indeed,

$$\begin{aligned}\int_{\mathfrak{m}} g^s(x)e^{-2\pi inx}dx &= O\left(\int_{\mathfrak{m}} |\, g(x)\,|^s dx\right) \\ &= O(P^{(1-\sigma(1-\delta)+\varepsilon)s})\end{aligned} \tag{3}$$

where $\sigma = 1/2^{k-1}$. The estimate in (3) however is $o(P^{s-k})$ if

$$s(1-\sigma(1-\delta)+\varepsilon) < s-k ,$$

or

$$s\sigma(1-\delta) > k+\varepsilon$$

which is assured by (1).

The next step is to evaluate the integral L in § 4, (28) which arose in Theorems 4.8, and 4.9. The evaluation depends on two lemmas.

LEMMA 6.1. *If $\alpha_i > 0$, $i = 1, 2, \cdots, s$, then*

$$I = \int_{0\leq \sum_{i=1}^{s} t_i \leq 1; t_i \geq 0} \cdots \int t_s^{\alpha_s-1} \cdots t_1^{\alpha_1-1}\,dt_s \cdots dt_1 = \frac{\Gamma(\alpha_1)\cdots\Gamma(\alpha_s)}{\Gamma(\alpha_1+\cdots+\alpha_s+1)} . \tag{4}$$

PROOF. This is a classical result due to Dirichlet. We put

$$t_3 + t_4 + \cdots + t_s = u ,$$

then

$$I = \int_{0\leq u\leq 1} \cdots \int t_s^{\alpha_s-1} \cdots t_3^{\alpha_3-1} dt_s \cdots dt_3 \int_0^{1-u} \int_0^{1-u-t_2} t_2^{\alpha_2-1} t_1^{\alpha_1-1}\,dt_1 dt_2 .$$

The evaluation of I can be made to depend on a transformation of the inner integral. In fact, suppose that we prove that

$$\int_0^{1-u}\int_0^{1-u-t_2} t_2^{\alpha-1}t_1^{\beta-1}\,dt_1dt_2 = \frac{\Gamma(\alpha)\Gamma(\beta)}{\Gamma(\alpha+\beta)}\int_0^{1-u} t^{\alpha+\beta-1}\,dt\,. \tag{5}$$

Then

$$I = \frac{\Gamma(\alpha_1)\Gamma(\alpha_2)}{\Gamma(\alpha_1+\alpha_2)}\int_{0\leq u\leq 1}\cdots\int t_s^{\alpha_s-1}\cdots t_3^{\alpha_3-1}\,dt_s\cdots dt_3\int_0^{1-u} t^{\alpha_1+\alpha_2-1}\,dt\,. \tag{6}$$

Repeating the argument with t_3 and t, we find, putting

$$u_1 = t_4 + \cdots + t_s\,,$$

in the integral of (6),

$$\begin{aligned} I &= \frac{\Gamma(\alpha_1)\Gamma(\alpha_2)}{\Gamma(\alpha_1+\alpha_2)}\cdot\frac{\Gamma(\alpha_1+\alpha_2)\Gamma(\alpha_3)}{\Gamma(\alpha_1+\alpha_2+\alpha_3)}\int_{0\leq u_1\leq 1}\cdots\iint_0^{1-u_1} t^{\alpha_1+\alpha_2+\alpha_3-1}\,dt \\ &= \frac{\Gamma(\alpha_1)\Gamma(\alpha_2)\Gamma(\alpha_3)}{\Gamma(\alpha_1+\alpha_2+\alpha_3)}\int_{0\leq u_1\leq 1}\cdots\iint_0^{1-u_1} t^{\alpha_1+\alpha_2+\alpha_3-1}\,dt\,. \end{aligned}$$

In general, by induction, we infer that

$$\begin{aligned} I &= \frac{\Gamma(\alpha_1)\cdots\Gamma(\alpha_s)}{\Gamma(\alpha_1+\cdots+\alpha_s)}\int_0^1 t^{\alpha_1+\cdots+\alpha_s-1}\,dt \\ &= \frac{\Gamma(\alpha_1)\cdots\Gamma(\alpha_s)}{\Gamma(\alpha_1+\alpha_2+\cdots+\alpha_s+1)}\,, \end{aligned}$$

where we have used Theorem A.4, of Appendix A on the gamma function. It remains to prove (5). Let

$$J = \int_0^{1-u}\int_0^{1-u-t_2} t_2^{\beta-1}t_1^{\alpha-1}\,dt_1dt_2\,. \tag{7}$$

Then, putting $t_1 = t_2(1/v - 1)$, we get from (7)

$$J = \int_0^{1-u}\int_{v/(1-u)}^{1} (1-v)^{\alpha-1}v^{-\alpha-1}t_2^{\alpha+\beta-1}\,dv\,dt_2\,. \tag{8}$$

On changing the order of integration in (8) (which is reasonably easy to justify) and following this by the substitution $t_2 = vt$, we are led to

$$J = \int_0^{1-u}\int_0^1 (1-v)^{\alpha-1}v^{\beta-1}t^{\alpha+\beta-1}\,dv\,dt\,. \tag{9}$$

Using Theorem A.7, of Appendix A, we conclude from (9) after a simple calculation that

$$J = \frac{\Gamma(\alpha)\Gamma(\beta)}{\Gamma(\alpha+\beta)}\int_0^{1-u} t^{\alpha+\beta-1}\,dt\,,$$

as required.

The next result is well known; we sketch a proof.

LEMMA 6.2. *If* $\alpha \neq 0$,

$$\operatorname{sgn}\alpha = \frac{\alpha}{|\alpha|} = \begin{cases} 1 & \text{if } \alpha > 0 \\ -1 & \text{if } \alpha < 0 , \end{cases}$$

then

(10) $$\int_0^\infty \frac{\sin \alpha x}{x} dx = \frac{\pi}{2} \operatorname{sgn} \alpha .$$

PROOF. We show that the integral converges; indeed, using the mean value theorem, we get for some value c between a and b,

$$\left| \int_a^b \frac{\sin \alpha x}{x} dx \right| = \frac{1}{c} \int_a^b \sin \alpha x dx = O\left(\frac{1}{c}\right) = o(1) ,$$

as $a \to \infty$. If we define

(11) $$J(\sigma) = \int_0^\infty e^{-\sigma x} \frac{\sin \alpha x}{x} dx ,$$

then

(12) $$J'(\sigma) = -\int_0^\infty e^{-\sigma x} \sin \alpha x dx = -\frac{\alpha}{\sigma^2 + \alpha^2} .$$

Therefore by (12)

$$J(\sigma) = -\int \frac{\alpha d\sigma}{\sigma^2 + \alpha^2} + K = -\tan^{-1}\frac{\sigma}{\alpha} + K .$$

Moreover,

(13) $$K = J(0) = \int_0^\infty \frac{\sin \alpha x}{x} dx .$$

We let $\sigma \to \infty$, justify the interchange of the limiting processes and deduce that

$$J(0) = \frac{\pi}{2} \operatorname{sgn} \alpha .$$

The conclusion of the theorem follows by (13).

These lemmas are used in a proof of

THEOREM 6.2. *If* $0 < c \leqq 1$, *then for* $s \geqq k + 1$, *we have*

(14) $$\varphi(c) = \int_{-\infty}^\infty \left(\int_0^1 e^{2\pi i y u^k} du \right)^s e^{-2\pi i y c} dy = c^{s/k-1} \frac{\Gamma\left(1 + \frac{1}{k}\right)^s}{\Gamma\left(\frac{s}{k}\right)} .$$

PROOF. If $s \geqq k + 1$, the integral in $\varphi(c)$ converges absolutely. This follows by an argument similar to that used in Theorem 4.4. In fact,

$$\int_0^1 e^{2\pi i y u^k} du = O(|y|^{-1/k})$$

and for any $a > 0$,

$$\varphi(c) = O\left(\int_a^\infty y^{-s/k} dy\right) + O(1)$$
$$= O(1) + O\left(y^{-s/k+1}\Big]_a^\infty\right)$$
$$= O(1) \quad \text{if } -\frac{s}{k} < -1 ,$$

that is, if $s \geqq k+1$. This being proved, we have

$$\Phi(c) = \int_0^c \varphi(t)\,dt$$
(15)
$$= \int_{-\infty}^\infty \left(\int_0^1 e^{2\pi i y u^k} du\right)^s \frac{1 - e^{-2\pi i y c}}{2\pi i y} dy ,$$

the interchange of the order of integration being justified by absolute convergence. Then from (15)

(16) $$\Phi(c) = \int_0^1 \cdots \int_0^1 du_s du_{s-1} \cdots du_1 \int_{-\infty}^\infty \frac{e^{2\pi i y(u_1^k + \cdots + u_s^k)} - e^{2\pi i y(u_1^k + \cdots + u_s^k - c)}}{2\pi i y} dy .$$

We let $\lambda = u_1^k + \cdots + u_s^k$, and if we notice that the inner integral in (16) is real, we are led to

(17) $$\Phi(c) = \frac{1}{\pi} \int_0^1 \cdots \int_0^1 du_s \cdots du_1 \int_0^\infty \left(\frac{\sin 2\pi y\lambda}{y} - \frac{\sin 2\pi y(\lambda - c)}{y}\right) dy .$$

By Lemma 6.2, however, (17) is

(18) $$\Phi(c) = \frac{1}{2} \int_0^1 \cdots \int_0^1 (\operatorname{sgn} \lambda - \operatorname{sgn}(\lambda - c)) du_s \cdots du_1 .$$

Since $\lambda \geqq 0$, the integrand of (18) vanishes if $\lambda - c > 0$ and its value is 2 if $\lambda - c < 0$. Accordingly, from (18),

$$\Phi(c) = \int_{0\,\lambda - c \leqq 0 \leqq \lambda}^1 \cdots \int_0^1 du_s \cdots du_1$$
(19)
$$= \int_{0\,\lambda \leqq c}^1 \cdots \int_0^1 du_s \cdots du_1 .$$

We reduce this to the integral in Lemma 6.1 by putting $u_i = v_i^{1/k} c^{1/k} (i = 1, 2, \cdots, s)$ and then from (19), since $v_i \geqq 0$,

(20) $$\Phi(c) = k^{-s} c^{s/k} \int_{0\,\sum v_i \leqq 1}^{1/c} \cdots \int_0^{1/c} v_s^{1/k-1} \cdots v_1^{1/k-1} dv_s \cdots dv_1 .$$

On the other hand, by assumption $0 < c \leqq 1$, and therefore $\infty > 1/c \geqq 1$ and the range of integration in (20) is completely characterized by the condition $\sum v_i \leqq 1$. Since Lemma 6.1 is applicable, our conclusion is

$$\Phi(c) = k^{-s}c^{s/k}\,\frac{\Gamma^s\left(\frac{1}{k}\right)}{\Gamma\left(\frac{s}{k}+1\right)}\,. \tag{21}$$

Differentiating (21) with respect to c, we conclude that

$$\varphi(c) = k^{-s}\frac{s}{k}\,c^{s/k-1}\,\frac{\Gamma^s\left(\frac{1}{k}\right)}{\frac{s}{k}\Gamma\left(\frac{s}{k}\right)}\,.$$

This is the statement of the theorem if only we observe that

$$\frac{1}{k}\Gamma\left(\frac{1}{k}\right) = \Gamma\left(\frac{1}{k}+1\right).$$

As an important consequence, we evaluate L.

Theorem 6.3. *If $s \geqq 2k+1$, then*

$$\begin{aligned} L &= \int_{-\infty}^{\infty}\left(\int_0^P e^{2\pi i u^k y}du\right)^s e^{-2\pi i n y}dy \\ &= P^{s-k}\frac{\Gamma^s\left(1+\frac{1}{k}\right)}{\Gamma\left(\frac{s}{k}\right)} + O(P^{s-k-1})\,. \end{aligned} \tag{22}$$

Proof. The proof amounts to a reduction of L to an integral of the type given in Theorem 6.2. In L, we put $u = Pv$, and follow this by the substitution $P^k y = z$; then

$$L = P^{s-k}\int_{-\infty}^{\infty}\left(\int_0^1 e^{2\pi i v^k z}dv\right)^s e^{-2\pi i n P^{-k}z}dz\,. \tag{23}$$

This is nearly the same as the integral in Theorem 6.2 except that since $P = [n^{1/k}]$, we cannot assert that $nP^{-k} \leqq 1$. We can argue, however, as follows. If

$$a = nP^{-k}\,,$$

then

$$a = n([n^{1/k}])^{-k} = n(n^{1/k}+w)^{-k}\,, \tag{24}$$

where $w = O(1)$. Then

$$a = \left(1+\frac{w}{n^{1/k}}\right)^{-k} = \left(1+\frac{w_1}{P}\right),$$

where $w_1 = O(1)$. Hence, from (23) and (24),

$$\begin{aligned} L &= P^{s-k}\int_{-\infty}^{\infty}\left(\int_0^1 e^{2\pi i v^k z}dv\right)^s e^{-2\pi i a z}dz \\ &= P^{s-k}\int_{-\infty}^{\infty}\left(\int_0^1 e^{2\pi i v^k z}dv\right)^s e^{-2\pi i z(1+w_1/P)}dz\,. \end{aligned} \tag{25}$$

However,

$$e^{-2\pi iz(1+w_1/P)} = e^{-2\pi iz} + O\left(\frac{1}{P}\right) \tag{26}$$

and therefore from (25), using (26) and (14),

$$L = P^{s-k}\frac{\Gamma^s\left(1+\frac{1}{k}\right)}{\Gamma\left(\frac{s}{k}\right)} + O\left(P^{s-k-1}\right).$$

As a simple corollary, we have

THEOREM 6.4.

$$L = n^{s/k-1}\frac{\Gamma^s\left(1+\frac{1}{k}\right)}{\Gamma\left(\frac{s}{k}\right)} + O(P^{s-k-1}) = \gamma(s, k)n^{s/k-1} + O(P^{s-k-1}).$$

PROOF. We repeat the argument of (24) in a slightly different form. Since

$$\begin{aligned} P &= n^{1/k} + O(1), \\ P^{s-k} &= n^{s/k-1}\left(1 + O\left(\frac{1}{P}\right)\right)^{s-k} \\ &= n^{s/k-1}\left(1 + O\left(\frac{1}{P}\right)\right) \\ &= n^{s/k-1} + O(P^{s-k-1}), \end{aligned}$$

the theorem follows from (22) since the integral converges.

The asymptotic formula for $r(n)$ is finally merely a collection of what we have established.

THEOREM 6.5. *Let $r(n)$ be the number of solutions of the equation*

$$n = n_1^k + n_2^k + \cdots + n_s^k, \tag{27}$$

$$s \geqq k \cdot 2^k + 1, \tag{28}$$

$$\gamma(s, k) = \frac{\Gamma^s\left(1+\frac{1}{k}\right)}{\Gamma\left(\frac{s}{k}\right)}, \tag{29}$$

$$S(a, q) = \sum_{m=0}^{q-1} e^{2\pi i a m^k/q}, \tag{30}$$

$$A(q) = \sum_{1 \leqq a \leqq q; (a,q)=1} q^{-s} S(a, q) e^{-2\pi i n a/q}, \tag{31}$$

$$\mathfrak{S}(n) = \sum_{q=1}^{\infty} A(q); \tag{32}$$

then

(33) $$r(n) = \gamma(s, k)\mathfrak{S}(n)n^{s/k-1} + o(n^{s/k-1}) .$$

PROOF. From (3.7),

(34) $$r(n) = \sum_M \int_{M(a,q)} g^s(x)e^{-2\pi inx}dx + \int_{\mathfrak{m}} g^s(x)e^{-2\pi inx}dx .$$

By Theorem 4.9, the first sum is, for $1/k \leqq \delta \leqq \frac{3}{4}$ and $s \geqq 2k+1$,

$$\sum_M \int_{M(a,q)} g^s(x)e^{-2\pi inx}dx = L\mathfrak{S}(n) + O(P^{s-k-(1-\delta)/k}) ,$$

and in Theorem 6.4, L is specifically evaluated and therefore

$$\begin{aligned}\sum_M \int_{M(a,q)} g^s(x)e^{-2\pi inx}dx &= (n^{s/k-1}\gamma(s, k) + O(P^{s-k-1}))\mathfrak{S}(n) + O(P^{s-k-(1-\delta)/k}) \\ &= n^{s/k-1}\gamma(s, k)\mathfrak{S}(n) + O(P^{s-k-1}) + O(P^{s-k-(1-\delta)/k}) \\ &= n^{s/k-1}\gamma(s, k)\mathfrak{S}(n) + O(P^{s-k-1/4k}) \\ &= n^{s/k-1}\gamma(s, k)\mathfrak{S}(n) + o(n^{s/k-1}) .\end{aligned}$$

By Theorem 6.1, the second term in (34) is $o(n^{s/k-1})$ if $s \geqq k\cdot 2^k + 1$, and this completes the proof.

We can infer the existence of an upper bound for $G(k)$ from this asymptotic formula. Let us assume, as we shall prove in §8, that there exists a constant $c > 0$ so that for $s \geqq 4k$,

(35) $$\mathfrak{S}(n) \geqq c > 0$$

for all n. Then we prove

THEOREM 6.6.

(36) $$G(k) \leqq k\cdot 2^k + 1 .$$

PROOF. The proof depends on showing that there exists n_0 such that for $n \geqq n_0$, $r(n) > 0$, and this is a consequence of Theorem 6.5. In fact, by (33),

(37) $$\lim_{n\to\infty} \frac{r(n)}{n^{s/k-1}} = \mathfrak{S}(n)\gamma(s, k) .$$

Since we have assumed that $\mathfrak{S}(n) \geqq c > 0$, it follows that $\mathfrak{S}(n)\gamma(s, k) \geqq c_1 > 0$ and therefore from (37), $r(n) > 0$ for $n \geqq n_0$. This means that every sufficiently large integer is a sum of at most $k\cdot 2^k + 1$ kth powers. The statement of the theorem is thus proved.

In particular,

$$G(3) \leqq 25, \qquad G(4) \leqq 65, \text{ etc.}$$

We notice, however, that as k increases, the upper bound for $G(k)$ increases very rapidly because of the exponential factor 2^k. The presence of this factor is entirely a consequence of the imperfect estimate for $g(x)$ on the minor arcs. Using his deep theorems on the estimates of trigonometric sums, Vinogradoff has shown that (33) holds, provided $k \geqq 12$ and

$$s \geqq [10k^2 \log k] .$$

The analysis required to prove this, however, is rather long and intricate and we shall content ourselves with an improvement due to Hua. Hua's procedure establishes the validity of (33) for

$$s \geqq 2^k + 1 . \tag{38}$$

For small values of k, this leads to interesting consequences. It implies that

$$G(k) \leqq 2^k + 1 ,$$

and in particular that $G(3) \leqq 9$, $G(4) \leqq 17$, $G(5) \leqq 33$, etc. The best known result concerning $G(3)$ is that $G(3) \leqq 7$. This was proved by U. V. Linnik and G. L. Watson independently. For $G(4)$, it has been shown by an intricate analysis of H. Davenport that $G(4) = 16$.

We prove Hua's theorem from which (38) follows. The statement of the theorem is

THEOREM 6.7. *If $k \geqq 2$, $1 \leqq m \leqq k$, $\varepsilon > 0$, then*

$$\int_0^1 | g(x) |^{2^m} dx = O(P^{2^m - m + \varepsilon}) , \tag{39}$$

where the constant implied by the O depends only on k and ε.

Before proceeding with the proof, we make a few observations which indicate, in some way, the manner in which this theorem proves to be useful. On the minor arc,

$$\int_{\mathfrak{m}} | g(x) |^s dx = \int_{\mathfrak{m}} | g(x) |^{s-2} | g(x) |^2 dx . \tag{40}$$

By Theorem 5.10, on a minor arc,

$$g(x) = O(P^{1-\sigma(1-\delta)+\varepsilon}) ,$$

and therefore

$$\int_{\mathfrak{m}} | g(x) |^s dx = O(P^{(s-2)(1-\sigma(1-\delta)+\varepsilon)}) \int_0^1 | g(x) |^2 dx$$
$$= O\left(P^{(s-2)(1-\sigma(1-\delta)+\varepsilon)} \sum_{m_1, m_2}^{1,P} \int_0^1 e^{2\pi i (m_1^k - m_2^k) x} dx\right) .$$

The integral on the right, however, is 0 except when $m_1 = m_2$, in which case its value is 1. On the other hand, in the double sum, $m_1 = m_2$ occurs P times, and therefore

$$\sum_{m_1, m_2}^{1,P} \int_0^1 e^{2\pi i (m_1^k - m_2^k) x} dx = O(P) . \tag{41}$$

Thus by this artifice, we have proved that

$$\int_{\mathfrak{m}} | g(x) |^s dx = O(P^{s(1-\sigma(1-\delta))-1+2\sigma(1-\delta)+\varepsilon}) ,$$

whereas previously, a direct application of 5.10 gave us

$$\int_{\mathfrak{m}} | g(x) |^s dx = O(P^{s(1-\sigma(1-\delta))+\varepsilon}) .$$

We have therefore saved a factor $P^{1-2\sigma(1-\delta)+\varepsilon}$. By a k-fold repetition of the argument, we can hope to save substantially more—indeed, we shall show that we can economize by a factor $O(P^{k-2(1-\delta)+\varepsilon})$.

PROOF OF THE THEOREM. The proof is by induction on m. We first show that

$$\int_0^1 | g(x) |^{2^m} dx \leqq c(m, k, \varepsilon)P^{2^m-m+\varepsilon} ,$$

and having done so, we choose

(42) $$c(k, \varepsilon) = \max_{1 \leqq m \leqq k} c(m, k, \varepsilon) ,$$

and this is the value of the constant implied by the O in (39). For $m = 1$, (41) shows that

$$\int_0^1 | g(x) |^2 dx = O(P) = O(P^{2^1-1+\varepsilon}) .$$

Suppose that we have proved the theorem for $m - 1$, that is, suppose

$$\int_0^1 | g(x) |^{2^{m-1}} dx \leqq c(m-1, k, \varepsilon)P^{2^{m-1}-(m-1)+\varepsilon} .$$

In Theorems 5.2 and 5.4 in Weyl's method for estimating trigonometric sums, let $\varphi(y) = y^k$; then

$$| g(x) |^{2^{m-1}} = O(P^{2^{m-1}-m}) \sum_{r_1, r_2, \cdots, r_m} \sum_{h_m} \exp [2\pi i r_1 \cdots r_{m-1} \varphi(r_1, \cdots, r_{m-1}; h_m)x]$$

and $r_1, r_2, \cdots, r_{m-1}$ range over the set defined by $| r_1 | + \cdots + | r_{m-1} | \leqq P$. Furthermore, $\varphi(r_1, \cdots, r_{m-1}; h_m)$ is a polynomial in h_m of degree $k - m + 1$. If

(43) $$r_1 \cdots r_{m-1} \varphi(r_1, \cdots, r_{m-1}, h_m) = 0 ,$$

then the value of the exponential function is 1. We therefore seek an upper bound for the number of solutions of (43). One of the factors in (43) must be zero. If $r_i = 0$, then the value of each of the remaining r's may be selected arbitrarily, as may the values assumed by φ. Since there are at most $2P$ values which each r may have, and P values which φ may have, there are at most

(44) $$(m-1)(2P)^{m-2}P = O(P^{m-1})$$

solutions in which one $r_i = 0$.

On the other hand, $\varphi(r_1, \cdots, r_{m-1}; h_m)$ may be 0. The number of times this can occur is at most equal to the degree of φ in h_m; this degree is $k - m + 1$. When $\varphi = 0$, the r's may be selected arbitrarily. Thus the number of solutions of (43) with $\varphi = 0$ is at most

$$(k-m+1)(2P)^{m-1} = O(P^{m-1}) . \tag{45}$$

Altogether then, there are, by (44) and (45), $O(P^{m-1})$ solutions of (43).

Consequently,

$$\begin{aligned} | g(x) |^{2^{m-1}} &= O(P^{2^{m-1}-1}) \\ &+ O(P^{2^{m-1}-m}) \sum_{r_i} \sum_{h_m}^{*} \exp [2\pi i r_1 \cdots r_{m-1}\varphi(r_1, r_2, \cdots r_{m-1}; h_m)x , \end{aligned} \tag{46}$$

where the asterisk indicates that the values for which $r_1 \cdots r_{m-1}\varphi = 0$ are to be omitted. We multiply (46) by $| g(x) |^{2^{m-1}}$ and integrate between 0 and 1:

$$\begin{aligned} \int_0^1 | g(x) |^{2^m} dx &= O(P^{2^{m-1}-1}) \int_0^1 | g(x) |^{2^{m-1}} dx \\ &+ O(P^{2^{m-1}-m}) \int_0^1 \sum_{r_i} \sum_{h_m}^{*} e^{2\pi i r_1 \cdots r_{m-1}\varphi x} | g(x) |^{2^{m-1}} dx . \end{aligned} \tag{47}$$

By the induction hypothesis, the first term is

$$O(P^{2^{m-1}-1}) O(P^{2^{m-1}-(m-1)+\varepsilon}) = O(P^{2^m - m+\varepsilon}) .$$

It therefore remains to estimate the second term. For this purpose, we try to induce as much cancellation as possible:

$$\begin{aligned} | g(x) |^{2^{m-1}} &= (| g(x) |^2)^{2^{m-2}} = \left| \sum_{m_1, m_2}^{1,P} e^{2\pi i(-m_1^k + m_2^k)x} \right|^{2^{m-2}} = \cdots \\ &= \sum_{\substack{m_j=1 \\ j=1,2,3,\cdots,2^{m-1}}}^{P} \exp [-2\pi i(m_1^k - m_2^k + \cdots + m_{2^{m-1}-1}^k - m_{2^{m-1}}^k)x] . \end{aligned} \tag{48}$$

Inserting this in the second integral of (47), we get

$$\begin{aligned} I &= \int_0^1 \sum_{r_i} \sum_{h_m}^{*} \exp [2\pi i r_1 \cdots r_{m-1}\varphi(r_1, \cdots, r_{m-1}; h_m)x] \, | g(x) |^{2^{m-1}} dx \\ &= \sum_{r_i} \sum_{h_m}^{*} \sum_{m_j} \int_0^1 \exp [2\pi i \{ r_1 \cdots r_{m-1}\varphi(r_1 \cdots r_{m-1}, h_m) \\ &\qquad - (m_1^k - m_2^k + \cdots - m_{2^{m-1}}^k)\} x] dx . \end{aligned} \tag{49}$$

The integral in (49) is 0 except when the exponent vanishes, that is, except when

$$r_1 r_2 \cdots r_{m-1}\varphi(r_1, \cdots, r_{m-1}; h_m) = m_1^k - m_2^k + \cdots - m_{2^{m-1}}^k . \tag{50}$$

We find an upper bound to the number of solutions of (50) with the right-hand side $\neq 0$. For simplicity, we let

$$w = m_1^k - m_2^k + \cdots + m_{2^{m-1}-1}^k - m_{2^{m-1}}^k ,$$

and we calculate an upper bound to the number of solutions of

$$r_1 \cdots r_{m-1}\varphi(r_1, \cdots, r_{m-1}; h_m) = w \neq 0 . \tag{51}$$

Each $r_i \mid w$ and $\varphi \mid w$; but $\varphi \mid w$ occurs at most $k - m + 1$ times, since $\varphi = w/d = w_0$ has at most $k - m + 1$ solutions.

Thus for a given set $m_1, m_2, \cdots, m_{2^{m-1}}$, equation (51) has at most

$$O(d^{m-1}(w))$$

solutions, where $d(w)$ denotes the number of divisors of w. It therefore follows from (49) that

$$I = O(\sum_{m_i} d^{m-1}(m_1^k - m_2^k + \cdots - m_{2^{m-1}}^k)) . \tag{52}$$

To estimate this sum, let $k_1, k_2, \cdots, k_t$ be the values, equal or distinct, arranged in ascending order of magnitude, assumed by w as $m_1, m_2, \cdots$, range over their assigned values. Then from (52) and using Lemma 5.1,

$$I = O\Big(\sum_{j=1}^{t} d^{m-1}(k_j)\Big) = O\Big(\sum_{j=1}^{t} k_j^{\varepsilon}\Big) = O(tk_t^{\varepsilon}) . \tag{53}$$

Because each $m_i \leqq P$, it follows that $k_t \leqq 2^{m-1}P^k$, and $t \leqq P^{2^{m-1}}$ since the number of possible choices of sets of values $m_1, m_2, \cdots, m_{2^{m-1}}$ is at most $P^{2^{m-1}}$. Therefore from (53)

$$I = O(P^{\varepsilon} P^{2^{m-1}}) = O(P^{2^{m-1}+\varepsilon}) . \tag{54}$$

Accordingly, by (47) and (54),

$$\int_0^1 | g(x) |^{2^m} dx = O(P^{2^m - m+\varepsilon}) + O(P^{2^{m-1}+\varepsilon})(P^{2^{m-1}-m}) = O(P^{2^m-m+\varepsilon}) .$$

The constant implied by the O depends on k, m, ε, but we choose $c(k, \varepsilon)$ as in (42) and the theorem is completely proved. Note that the value of ε is not necessarily the same at each occurrence.

THEOREM 6.8. *The asymptotic formula* (33) *of Theorem* 6.5 *is valid for* $s \geqq 2^k + 1$.

PROOF. We have only to show that on the minor arc,

$$\int_{\mathfrak{m}} | g(x) |^s dx = o(P^{s-k}) .$$

In fact,

$$\int_{\mathfrak{m}} | g(x) |^s dx = O\left(\int_{\mathfrak{m}} | g(x) |^{s-2^k} | g(x) |^{2^k} dx\right) .$$

This, by Theorem 5.10, is

$$O\left(P^{(s-2^k)(1-\sigma(1-\delta)+\varepsilon)} \int_0^1 | g(x) |^{2^k} dx\right) = O(P^{(s-2^k)(1-\sigma(1-\delta)+\varepsilon)} P^{2^k-k+\varepsilon}) ,$$

by Theorem 6.7. On the other hand, this is $o(P^{s-k})$ provided

$$s\sigma(1-\delta) > 2(1-\delta) + \varepsilon$$

or, in other words, if

$$s \geqq 2^k + 1 .$$

THEOREM 6.9.

$$G(k) \leqq 2^k + 1 .$$

PROOF. The proof follows directly from the validity of (33) for $s \geqq 2^k + 1$.

7. Further investigation of $G(k)$. In the preceding sections, we derived an asymptotic formula for $r(n)$, the number of representations of n as a sum of s kth powers, and on the assumption of the positive character of the singular series, we inferred an upper bound for $G(k)$. Because of the iterations involved in the estimation for exponential sums, the asymptotic formula held only for $s \geqq 2^k + 1$, a function involving the exponential factor 2^k. If we are concerned primarily with $G(k)$ and not with an asymptotic formula, it is possible to alter the analysis in accordance with the ideas of Vinogradoff. Indeed, Vinogradoff has shown that

(1) $$G(k) \leqq 2k \log k + a(k) ,$$

where $a(k) = 4k \log \log k + 2k \log \log \log k + 13k$. Evidence from the singular series (as well as other sources) led Hardy and Littlewood to the belief that $G(k) \leqq 2k + 1$ except when k is a power of 2 in which case $G(k) \leqq 4k$. On the other hand, it is comparatively easy to show that $G(k) \geqq k + 1$ (see Problem 1).

This last fact, together with the conjecture of Hardy and Littlewood, leads to the conjecture that the order of magnitude of $G(k)$ is precisely k.

The significance of Vinogradoff's result (1) is thus easily seen since it fails only by a factor $\log k$ to confirm the conjecture. We shall obtain here less precise results than (1) and refer the reader to the book of Vinogradoff for a proof of a somewhat less precise form of (1).

Our object again is to prove that $r(n) > 0$ and to do so at a minimum cost in the number of summands. In the preceding sections, we took all possible representations of n as a sum of s kth powers. The present analysis depends on allowing a freedom of choice.

Let H_l denote the set of integers u of the form

$$u = x_1^k + x_2^k + \cdots + x_l^k , \qquad x_i \geqq 0 ,$$

for some fixed l. While it may be comparatively difficult to find a representation of n as a sum of relatively few kth powers, the problem becomes simpler if we try to represent $n - u$ for some choice of u in H_l. We allow ourselves some liberty in the choice of u, the only restriction being that it belong to H_l. Having found a representation of $n - u$ as a sum of relatively few kth powers, it will follow immediately that n itself will be a sum of kth powers, and by an appropriate choice of l, we may hope to make the number of summands relatively small. In other words, it is sufficient to show that

(2) $$\sum_u r(n - u) > 0 ,$$

for some values of s and l, where the summation is over an appropriate set of integers u belonging to H_l. In what follows, the letter u (with or without subscript) will denote a member of the set H_l. We shall later require a lower bound to the number of integers of H_l which are less than some constant Q. This is given by

THEOREM 7.1. *Let $H_l(Q)$ denote the number of integers u belonging to the set H_l for which $0 < u \leqq Q$. Then there exists a constant $c > 0$ and depending only on l and k, such that*

(3) $$H_l(Q) \geqq cQ^{1-(1-1/k)^l},$$

PROOF. The proof depends on restricting the x_i in such a way that all the resulting u are distinct. There are various ways of doing this; we proceed by induction on l. For $l = 1$, we have

$$H_1(Q) = [Q^{1/k}] > \tfrac{1}{2}Q^{1/k} = c_1 Q^{1-(1-1/k)} .$$

We assume that

(4) $$H_{l-1}(Q) \geqq c_2 Q^{1-(1-1/k)^{l-1}},$$

and construct the following numbers:

(5) $$u_1 = u + x_l^k ,$$

where u belongs to H_{l-1}, and

(6) $$u \leqq (\tfrac{1}{2}Q^{1/k})^{k-1} , \qquad \tfrac{1}{2}Q^{1/k} < x_l \leqq Q^{1/k} - 1 .$$

We shall show that these numbers are distinct and all belong to H_l, and moreover $u_1 \leqq Q$. That u_1 belongs to H_l is obvious, and $u_1 \leqq Q$ since by (6),

(7) $$x_l^k < u_1 = x_l^k + u \leqq x_l^k + x_l^{k-1} \leqq (x_l + 1)^k \leqq Q .$$

If two of the u_1 are equal

$$x_l^k + u = x_l'^k + u' ,$$

then (7) coupled with (6) leads to a contradiction. Consequently $H_l(Q)$ is greater than or equal to the number of u_1 satisfying (5) and (6). Using (4), we get

$$\begin{aligned} H_l(Q) &\geqq ((Q^{1/k} - 1) - \tfrac{1}{2}Q^{1/k} - 1)H_{l-1}(2^{-k+1}Q^{1-1/k}) \\ &\geqq c_2(\tfrac{1}{2}\, Q^{1/k} - 2)[2^{-k+1}Q^{1-1/k}]^{1-(1-1/k)^{l-1}} . \end{aligned}$$

If Q is sufficiently large, that is, $Q \geqq c(k)$, then

$$H_l(Q) \geqq c_3 Q^{1/k} \cdot Q^{(1-1/k)(1-(1-1/k)^{l-1})} = c_3 Q^{1-(1-1/k)^l} .$$

If $Q \leqq c(k)$, then

$$H_l(Q) \geqq 1 \geqq \frac{Q}{c(k)} \geqq c_4 Q^{1-(1-1/k)^l} ,$$

and this completes the proof with $c = \min(c_3, c_4)$.

To make the summation on u in (2) more precise, we let

(8) $$R(x) = \sum_{u \leqq P^k/4} e^{2\pi i u x} ,$$

where it is understood that u ranges in the set H_l, and we put

(9) $$A_R = \sum_{u \leqq P^k/4} 1 .$$

In other words, A_R is the number of terms in the summation (8), and

(10) $$A_R = H_l(\tfrac{1}{4}P^k)\ .$$

Consider the integral

(11) $$I(n) = \int_0^1 R^2(x)g^s(x)e^{-2\pi inx}\,dx\ .$$

This can be written as

$$I(n) = \sum_{u_1, u_2} \int_0^1 g^s(x)e^{-2\pi i(n-u_1-u_2)x}\,dx\ ,$$

or, if we put $N = n - u_1 - u_2$, it becomes

(12) $$I(n) = \sum_{u_1, u_2} r(N)\ ,$$

where $r(N)$ is the number of representations of N as a sum of s kth powers and u_1, u_2 belong to H_l, and $u_i \leqq \frac{1}{4}P^k (i = 1, 2)$. We shall choose s as economically as possible, viz.

(13) $$s = 4k\ ,$$

in order to use the estimates on the major arcs which we have already established.

We shall show that

$$\sum r(N) > 0\ ,$$

from which it will follow that for at least one choice of u_1 and u_2,

$$r(n - u_1 - u_2) > 0\ .$$

This means, however, that with the choice of s in (13),

$$n - u_1 - u_2 = m_1^k + \cdots + m_{4k}^k\ ,$$

and therefore there is at least one representation of n as a sum of kth powers. The number required is at most $4k + 2l$ and therefore

$$G(k) \leqq 4k + 2l\ .$$

We shall try to choose l as economically as possible.

As in §6, we let

$$P = [n^{1/k}]\ , \qquad \tau = 2kP^{k-1}\ ,$$

and consider the set of fractions a/q with $0 < q \leqq P^{1-\delta}$. The major arcs $M = M(a, q)$ are defined by the set of points x for which

$$x = \frac{a}{q} + y, \qquad |\, y \,| \leqq \frac{1}{q\tau}.$$

The remaining points of the interval $(-\tau^{-1}\cdot 1 - \tau^{-1})$ are on minor arcs. The integrand in (11) has period 1, and therefore we get

$$
(14)\qquad
\begin{aligned}
I(n) &= \int_{-\tau^{-1}}^{1-\tau^{-1}} R^2(x)g^s(x)e^{-2\pi i n x}\,dx \\
&= \sum_M \int_M R^2(x)g^s(x)e^{-2\pi i n x}\,dx \\
&\quad + \int_{\mathfrak{m}} R^2(x)g^s(x)e^{-2\pi i n x}\,dx \\
&= \sum_{u_1, u_2} \sum_M \int_M g^s(x)e^{-2\pi i N x}\,dx + I_1(n)\,,
\end{aligned}
$$

where $N = n - u_1 - u_2$. Because the N in (14) is not the same as the n which defines the major arcs, we start by proving a modified version of Theorem 4.9.

THEOREM 7.2. *If $0 < N \leqq P^k$, then*

$$
(15)\qquad
\begin{aligned}
\sum_M \int_M g^s(x)e^{-2\pi i N x}\,dx &= \gamma(s, k)\mathfrak{S}(N)N^{s/k-1} \\
&\quad + O(P^{s-k-\delta}) + O(P^{s-k-(1-\delta)/k})\,,
\end{aligned}
$$

where $\gamma(s, k)$ and $\mathfrak{S}(N)$ are as defined in Theorem 6.5 *and the summation is over all the major arcs.*

PROOF. This is proved by a slight modification of the argument of § 4. We had in fact, from Theorem 4.6 if $x = a/q + y$,

$$
(16)\qquad g^s(x) = q^{-s}S^s(a, q)\left(\int_0^P e^{2\pi i u^k y}\,du\right)^s + O(q^{-1}\min{}^{s-1}(P, |y|^{-1/k}))\,.
$$

Furthermore if $J(y)$ denotes the integral in (16), then putting $u = vP$ followed by $z = P^k y$, we get

$$
\int_{-\infty}^{\infty} J^s(y)e^{-2\pi i N y}\,dy = P^{s-k}\int_{-\infty}^{\infty}\left(\int_0^1 e^{2\pi i z v^k}\,dv\right)^s e^{-2\pi i z P^{-k}N}\,dz\,.
$$

But by assumption $0 < P^{-k}N \leqq 1$ and therefore applying Theorem 6.2 we get

$$
(17)\qquad \int_{-\infty}^{\infty} J^s(y)e^{-2\pi i N y}\,dy = \gamma(s, k)N^{s/k-1}\,.
$$

Therefore on M, we have, using (17) and Lemma 4.2,

$$
(18)\qquad
\begin{aligned}
\int_M J^s(y)e^{-2\pi i N y}\,dy &= \int_{-(q\tau)^{-1}}^{(q\tau)^{-1}} J^s(y)e^{-2\pi i N y}\,dy \\
&= \int_{-\infty}^{\infty} J^s(y)e^{-2\pi i N y}\,dy + O((q\tau)^{s/k-1}) \\
&= \gamma(s, k)N^{s/k-1} + O((q\tau)^{s/k-1})\,.
\end{aligned}
$$

Thus using (16), we get, with $H(a, q)$ defined as in Theorem 4.7, and taking special account of the term $H(0, 1)$,

$$\sum_{M}\int_{M} g^s(x)e^{-2\pi i N x}\,dx = \sum_{M} H(a, q)$$

$$= \sum_{q\leqq P^{1-\delta}}\ \sum_{(a,q)=1;1\leqq a\leqq q} e^{-2\pi i N a/q} q^{-s} S^s(a, q)\int_{-(q\tau)^{-1}}^{(q\tau)^{-1}} J^s(y)e^{-2\pi i N y}\,dy$$

$$+ O\left(\sum_{q\leqq P^{1-\delta}}\ \sum_{(a,q)=1;\ 1\leqq a\leqq q} q^{-1}\int_{0}^{(q\tau)^{-1}} \min{}^{s-1}(P, |y|^{-1/k})\,dy\right)$$

$$+ O(P^{s-k-1})\,.$$

The integral in the second term however, is by § 4, (25)

$$O(P^{s-k-1})\,.$$

Thus if

$$A(q) = q^{-s}\sum_{(a,q)=1,1\leqq a\leqq q} S^s(a, q)e^{-2\pi i N a/q}\,,$$

then using (18), we get

$$\sum_{M} H(a, q) = \gamma(s, k)\sum_{q\leqq P^{1-\delta}} A(q)N^{s/k-1} + O(P^{s-k-1})$$

$$+ O\left(\sum_{q\leqq P^{1-\delta}}\ \sum_{(a,q)=1;1\leqq a\leqq q} q^{-1}P^{s-k-1}\right)$$

$$+ O\left(\sum_{q\leqq P^{1-\delta}} q\cdot q^{-s}\,|\,S(a, q)\,|^s(q\tau)^{s/k-1}\right).$$

The last term is, by the assumption in § 4, (14), on the sum $S(a, q)$ which is proved in Theorem 8.8,

$$O\Big(\sum_{q\leqq P^{1-\delta}} q\cdot q^{-s}\cdot q^{s-s/k}(q\tau)^{s/k-1}\Big) = O\Big(\sum_{q\leqq P^{1-\delta}} P^{s-s/k-k+1}\Big)$$

$$= O(P^{s-s/k-k+1+1-\delta})\,.$$

Since $s \geqq 2k+1$, this is $O(P^{s-k-\delta})$. Thus

$$\sum_{M} H(a, q) = \gamma(s, k)N^{s/k-1}\sum_{q\leqq P^{1-\delta}} A(q) + O(P^{s-k-\delta})\,.$$

Using § 4, (34), we replace the finite sum by $\mathfrak{S}(N)$. The error is,

$$O\Big(N^{s/k-1}\sum_{q>P^{1-\delta}} A(q)\Big) = O\Big(N^{s/k-1}\cdot \sum_{q>P^{1-\delta}} q^{1-s/k}\Big) = O(P^{s-k-(1-\delta)/k})\,,$$

since $s \geqq 2k+1$ and the proof is therefore complete.

THEOREM 7.3. *If* $k \geqq 3$,

(19) $$G(k) \leqq 2[k^2\log 2] + 4k + 2\,.$$

PROOF. We start from (14) and estimate the contribution to $I_1(n)$ from the minor arc in equation (14). On $\mathfrak{m}$ by Theorem 5.10,

(20) $$g(x) = O(P^{1-\sigma(1-\delta)+\varepsilon})\,,$$

where $\sigma = 1/2^{k-1}$. Therefore

$$I_1(n) = O(P^{s(1-\sigma(1-\delta)+\varepsilon)}) \int_0^1 |R(x)|^2 dx$$

$$= O(P^{s(1-\sigma(1-\delta)+\varepsilon)}) \sum_{u_1, u_2} \int_0^1 e^{2\pi i(u_1-u_2)x} dx .$$

The integral is 0 unless $u_1 = u_2$ and this occurs as often as there are terms in the summation for R. That is,

(21) $$I_1(n) = O(A_R P^{s(1-\sigma(1-\delta)+\varepsilon)}) .$$

For the first term of the right-hand side of (14), we have, by Theorem 7.2

(22) $$\sum_{u_1, u_2} \sum_{M} \int g^s(x) e^{-2\pi i N x} dx = \sum_{u_1 u_2} \gamma(s, k) \mathfrak{S}(N) N^{s/k-1} + \sum_{u_1, u_2} (O(P^{s-k-\delta}) + O(P^{s-k-(1-\delta)/k}))$$

$$= \sum_{u_1, u_2} \gamma(s, k) \mathfrak{S}(N) N^{s/k-1} + O(A_R^2 \{P^{s-k-\delta} + P^{s-k-(1-\delta)/k}\}) .$$

Now $N = n - u_1 - u_2 \geqq P^k - \frac{1}{4}P^k - \frac{1}{4}P^k = \frac{1}{2}P^k$ and, moreover, since $s = 4k$, $\mathfrak{S}(N) \geqq c > 0$ by Theorem 8.15. Therefore, by (14) and (22),

(23) $$I(n) = \sum_{u_1, u_2} \gamma(s, k) \mathfrak{S}(N) N^{s/k-1} + O(A_R^2 P^{s-k-\delta}) + O(A_R^2 P^{s-k-(1-\delta)/k}) + O(A_R P^{s(1-\sigma(1-\delta)+\varepsilon)}) .$$

Since $\mathfrak{S}(N) \geqq c > 0$ the summation is

$$\sum_{u_1, u_2} \gamma(s, k) \mathfrak{S}(N) N^{s/k-1} > c_1 P^{s-k} \sum_{u_1, u_2} 1 = c_1 P^{s-k} A_R^2 .$$

In (23), the second and third terms are therefore smaller than the first, and to conclude that $I(n) > 0$, for n sufficiently large, we must show that the fourth term is $o(A_R^2 P^{s-k})$. In fact, by Theorem 7.1

$$A_R P^{s(1-\sigma(1-\delta)+\varepsilon)} = O(A_R^2 P^{s(1-\sigma(1-\delta)+\varepsilon)} P^{-k(1-(1-1/k)^l)}) .$$

This is $o(A_R^2 P^{s-k})$ provided

$$s(-\sigma(1-\delta) + \varepsilon) + k\left(1 - \frac{1}{k}\right)^l < 0 ,$$

or

$$4k(-\sigma(1-\delta) + \varepsilon) + k\left(1 - \frac{1}{k}\right)^l < 0 .$$

Let $l = rk$; then this inequality is satisfied if

$$4(-\sigma(1-\delta) + \varepsilon) + e^{-r} < 0 ,$$

that is if $e^{-r} < 4\sigma(1-\delta) - \varepsilon$ and this is assured if

$$e^{-r} < \frac{\sigma}{2} = 2^{-k} \qquad \text{i.e., } r > k \log 2 .$$

In other words, $I(n) > 0$, provided $s = 4k$ and

$$l \geqq k^2 \log 2 + 1 .$$

This means that $\sum_{u_1, u_2} r(n - u_1 - u_2) > 0$ if $s = 4k$ and $l \geqq k^2 \log 2 + 1$. That is $G(k) \leqq 4k + 2l$ and the proof of Theorem 7.3 is thus complete.

We shall show now that this upper bound can be further improved: To effect the reduction we allow ourselves additional liberty in the choice of the u in (2). Let

$$T(x) = \sum_{v \leqq P^{1/2k}/4} \sum_{u \leqq P^{k-1}/4} e^{2\pi i v^k u x} ,$$

where u again belongs to H_l. We consider, as above, the following integral:

$$I(n) = \int_0^1 T(x) R^2(x) g^s(x) e^{-2\pi i n x} \, dx .$$

On the one hand, this is

$$I(n) = \sum_{u_1, u_2, u_3, v} \int_0^1 g^s(x) e^{2\pi i (n - u_1 - u_2 - u_3 v^k) x} \, dx , \tag{24}$$

and if again we put

$$N = n - u_1 - u_2 - u_3 v^k ,$$

we get

$$I(n) = \sum_{u_1, u_2, u_3, v} r(N) , \tag{25}$$

where $r(N)$ is the number of representations of N as a sum of s kth powers. We choose s economically by requiring

$$s = 4k .$$

We shall show again that for n sufficiently large,

$$I(n) > 0 ,$$

in which case $r(N) > 0$ for some choice of u_1, u_2, u_3, v and then

$$n = u_1 + u_2 + u_3 v^k + m_1^k + \cdots + m_s^k .$$

It will follow that

$$G(k) \leqq 4k + 3l . \tag{26}$$

We shall choose l as small as possible.

We begin by proving a theorem which allows us to estimate $T(x)$ on the minor arc. We shall not require here an estimate for $g(x)$ on the minor arc.

THEOREM 7.4. *Let ξ range over α integers in an interval of length A and η over β integers in an interval of length B. If $x = a/q + y$, $|y| < 1/q^2$,*

$$f(x) = \sum_{\xi, \eta} e^{2\pi i \xi \eta x}$$

then

$$|f(x)|^2 = O\left(\alpha\beta AB \frac{\log q}{q}\left(1 + \frac{q}{A}\right)\left(1 + \frac{q}{B}\right)\right) . \tag{27}$$

PROOF. Using the Cauchy-Schwarz inequality, we have

$$\begin{aligned}|f(x)|^2 &= \Big|\sum_{\xi}\sum_{\eta} e^{2\pi i\xi\eta x}\Big|^2 \\ &\leqq \Big(\sum_{\xi} 1^2\Big)\Big(\sum_{\xi}\Big|\sum_{\eta} e^{2\pi i\xi\eta x}\Big|^2\Big) \\ &\leqq \alpha\sum_{\xi}\Big|\sum_{\eta} e^{2\pi i\xi\eta x}\Big|^2 .\end{aligned}$$

If we extend the range of ξ to its maximum possible values, then this becomes (where m is the start of the interval)

$$|f(x)|^2 \leqq \alpha \sum_{\xi_1=[m]+1}^{[m+A]-1} \sum_{\eta_1,\eta_2} e^{2\pi i\xi_1(\eta_1-\eta_2)x} \leqq \alpha \sum_{\eta_1,\eta_2}\sum_{\xi_1} e^{2\pi i\xi_1(\eta_1-\eta_2)x} .$$

By Theorem 5.1, it follows that

$$|f(x)|^2 = O\left(\alpha \sum_{\eta_1,\eta_2} \min\left(A, \frac{1}{\|(\eta_1-\eta_2)x\|}\right)\right).$$

If we put $\zeta = \eta_1 - \eta_2$, then if t is the start of the interval of length B,

$$\begin{aligned}\sum_{\eta_1,\eta_2} \min\left(A, \frac{1}{\|(\eta_1-\eta_2)x\|}\right) &= O\left(\beta \sum_{\zeta=[t]+1}^{[t+B]-1} \min\left(A, \frac{1}{\|\zeta x\|}\right)\right) \\ &= O\left(\beta\left(1+\frac{B}{q}\right)(5A + 4q\log q)\right),\end{aligned}$$

by Theorem 5.8. Therefore

$$|f(x)|^2 = O\left(\alpha\beta AB\frac{\log q}{q}\left(1+\frac{q}{A}\right)\left(1+\frac{q}{B}\right)\right).$$

COROLLARY. *If $B \leqq q \leqq A$, then*

$$|f(x)|^2 = O(\alpha\beta A\log q) . \tag{28}$$

THEOREM 7.5. *On a minor arc,*

$$|T(x)|^2 = O(A_T P^{k-1}\log P) ,$$

where

$$T(x) = \sum_{v\leqq P^{1/2k}/4}\ \sum_{u\leqq P^{k-1}/4} e^{2\pi i v^k u x}$$

and

$$A_T = \sum_{v\leqq P^{1/2k}/4}\ \sum_{u\leqq P^{k-1}/4} 1 .$$

PROOF. If x is a point on a minor arc,

$$x = \frac{a}{q} + y , \qquad |y| \leqq \frac{1}{q\tau},$$

and

$$P^{1-\delta} \leqq q \leqq 2kP^{k-1} .$$

In virtue of the assumption on δ, we can choose $A = 2kP^{k-1}$, $B = P^{1-\delta}$;

$$B \leqq q \leqq A ,$$

and Theorem 7.4, corollary, is applicable. In fact, since

$$A_T = \alpha\beta ,$$

we get

$$| T(x) |^2 = O(A_T P^{k-1} \log P) ,$$

as required. This completes the preliminaries to

THEOREM 7.6. $G(k) = O(k \log k)$. *More precisely,*

$$G(k) \leqq [6k \log k] + 10k + 3 .$$

PROOF. From (24) and (25)

$$\begin{aligned} I(n) &= \int_{\tau^{-1}}^{1-\tau^{-1}} T(x)R^2(x)g^s(x)e^{-2\pi inx}\,dx \\ &= \sum_{M} \int_{M} T(x)R^2(x)g^s(x)e^{-2\pi inx}\,dx \\ &\quad + \int_{\mathfrak{m}} R^2(x)T(x)g^s(x)e^{-2\pi inx}\,dx \\ &= \sum_{u_1} \sum_{u_2, u_3, v} \sum_{M} \int_{M} g^s(x)e^{-2\pi iNx}\,dx + I_1(n) . \end{aligned}$$

We estimate $I_1(n)$. Because $g(x) = O(P)$ trivially, we get from Theorem 7.5,

(29)
$$\begin{aligned} I_1(n) &= O(A_T^{1/2} P^{s+(k-1)/2} \log^{1/2} P) \int_0^1 | R(x) |^2\,dx \\ &= O(A_R A_T^{1/2} P^{s+(k-1)/2} \log^{1/2} P) . \end{aligned}$$

We have used the argument on $R(x)$ given in the proof of Theorem 7.3. We have

(30)
$$\begin{aligned} P^k &\geqq N = n - u_1 - u_2 - u_3 v^k \\ &\geqq P^k - \tfrac{1}{4} P^k - \tfrac{1}{4} P^k - \tfrac{1}{16} P^{k-1} P^{1/2} \geqq \tfrac{1}{4} P^k . \end{aligned}$$

Moreover, by Theorem 7.2,

$$\sum_{M} \int_{M} g^s(x)e^{-2\pi iNx}\,dx = \gamma(s, k)\mathfrak{S}(N)N^{s/k-1} + O(P^{s-k-\delta}) + O(P^{s-k-(1-\delta)/k})$$

and therefore

(31)
$$\begin{aligned} \sum_{u_1} \sum_{u_2} \sum_{u_3, v} \sum_{M} \int_{M} g^s(x)e^{-2\pi iNx}\,dx &= \gamma(s, k) \sum_{u_1, u_2, u_3, v} \mathfrak{S}(N)N^{s/k-1} \\ &\quad + O(A_R^2 A_T (P^{s-k-\delta} + P^{s-k-(1-\delta)/k})) . \end{aligned}$$

The sum on the right, however, is by (30)

$$\sum_{u_1, u_2, u_3, v} \mathfrak{S}(N)N^{s/k-1} > c_2 P^{s-k} \sum_{u_1, u_2, u_3, v} 1 = c_2 P^{s-k} A_R^2 A_T .$$

Consequently, by (29) and (31),

$$I(n) > c_2 P^{s-k} A_R^2 A_T + O(A_R^2 A_T (P^{s-k-\delta} + P^{s-k-(1-\delta)/k})) + O(A_R A_T^{1/2} P^{s+(k-1)/2} \log^{1/2} P) .$$

It follows that $I(n) > 0$ for n sufficiently large, provided the third term on the right is

$$o(P^{s-k} A_R^2 A_T) .$$

By Theorem 7.1,

$$A_R \geqq c_3 P^{k(1-(1-1/k)^l)}$$

and

$$A_T \geqq c_4 P^{1/2k} P^{(k-1)(1-(1-1/k)^l)} ,$$

and therefore

$$A_R A_T^{1/2} P^{s+(k-1)/2} \log^{1/2} P = O(A_R^2 A_T P^{s+(k-1)/2} P^{1/4k-(k+(k-1)/2)(1-(1-1/k)^l)} \log^{1/2} P)$$
$$= O(A_R^2 A_T P^{s-k} P^{-1/4k+(3k-1)(1-1/k)^l/2} \log^{1/2} P) .$$

This is $o(A_R^2 A_T P^{s-k})$ provided $(3k-1)(1-1/k)^l/2 < 1/4k$ or $(1-1/k)^l < 1/2k(3k-1)$. If $l = rk$, this inequality holds provided

$$e^{-r} < \frac{1}{2k(3k-1)} ,$$

and this is assured if

$$r > \log 2k(3k-1) ;$$

that is $l \geqq k[\log 6k^2] + 1$. From (26), this means that

$$G(k) \leqq 3k(2 \log k + \log 6) + 4k + 3 .$$

The proof of the theorem is thus complete.

We could investigate the inequality satisfied by r more precisely, but the significant factor

$$6k \log k$$

would not be changed. The main point is that

$$G(k) = O(k \log k) .$$

For small values of k, the inequality

$$G(k) \leqq 2^k + 1$$

is superior, and as far as specific values of $G(k)$ are concerned, the main attention focuses on the values for $k = 3, 4, 5$. The best known values of $G(k)$ for these values of k are given in the notes following the problems.

8. **The singular series.** In this section, we complete the discussion of Waring's problem by proving two statements which were assumed in the

preceding sections.

Let $(a, q) = 1$; then we defined

$$S(a, q) = \sum_{m=0}^{q-1} e^{2\pi i a m^k/q} , \tag{1}$$

$$A(q) = q^{-s} \sum_{a=1;\ (a, q)=1}^{q} S^s(a, q) e^{-2\pi i n a/q} , \tag{2}$$

and

$$\mathfrak{S}(n) = \sum_{q=1}^{\infty} A(q) . \tag{3}$$

Notice that in the definitions of $S(a, q)$ and $A(q)$, it does not matter if we change the index of summation so as to range over any complete, respectively reduced, residue system modulo q. Furthermore we recall that $A(q)$ and hence $\mathfrak{S}(n)$ are real. The statements we wish to prove are

$$S(a, q) = O(q^{1-1/k}) , \tag{I}$$

$$\mathfrak{S}(n) \geqq c > 0 , \tag{II}$$

where c is constant.

The proof of (I) depends on the reduction to the case when q is a power of a prime while the proof of (II) is achieved by reducing $\mathfrak{S}(n)$ to

$$\mathfrak{S}(n) = \prod_{p} \psi(p) , \tag{4}$$

where $\psi(p) = \sum_{r=0}^{\infty} A(p^r)$.

In the following discussion, we shall assume known the following results from elementary number theory. Moreover, we assume that $k \geqq 3$.

THEOREM 8.1. *If p is a prime and r is an arbitrary positive integer, then there exists a primitive root modulo p^r. Otherwise expressed, the group of reduced residues modulo p^r is cyclic of order $\varphi(p^r)$.*

This means that there exists an integer g such that g^b $(b = 1, 2, \cdots, \varphi(p^r))$ comprises all the reduced residues modulo p^r. If $(u, p) = 1$ and b is the least integer such that

$$u \equiv g^b \pmod{p^r} ,$$

then we call b the index of u and write $b = \operatorname{ind} u$.

The index obeys the following rule:

$$\operatorname{ind} uv \equiv \operatorname{ind} u + \operatorname{ind} v \pmod{\varphi(p^r)} .$$

THEOREM 8.2. *If p is a prime and $d = (k, p-1)$, then the congruence*

$$x^k \equiv a \pmod{p}$$

is solvable if and only if $d \mid \operatorname{ind} a$. When the congruence is solvable, the num-

ber of solutions is precisely d. Moreover, as a runs from 1 *to* $p-1$, *the index of a assumes all values modulo d equally often.*

Proofs of both these theorems may be found in books on elementary number theory. For example, Uspensky and Heaslet, Chapters 8, §§ 4 and 7.

The first theorem we prove shows that the evaluation of $S(a, q)$ for any q can be reduced to its evaluation when $q = p^{\alpha}$, p a prime.

THEOREM 8.3. *If*

$$q = p_1^{\alpha_1} p_2^{\alpha_2} \cdots p_r^{\alpha_r} ,$$

then there exist integers $a_1, a_2, \cdots, a_r$, *such that*

$$S(a, q) = S(a_1, p_1^{\alpha_1}) \cdots S(a_r, p_r^{\alpha_r}) .$$

PROOF. The proof uses essentially the Chinese remainder theorem. Let $M_i = q/p_i^{\alpha_i}$ $(i = 1, 2, \cdots, r)$, then $(M_i, M_j) = 1$, $i \neq j$. The congruence

$$a \equiv a_1 M_1 + \cdots + a_r M_r \pmod q \tag{5}$$

is therefore solvable for $a_1, \cdots, a_r$, and indeed as x_i runs through a system of residues modulo $p_i^{\alpha_i}$ $(i = 1, 2, \cdots, r)$ then the expression

$$x_1 M_1 + \cdots + x_r M_r$$

runs through a residue system modulo q.

Using (5), we have

$$\begin{aligned} S(a, q) &= \sum_{m=1}^{q} e^{2\pi i a m^k/q} = \sum_{m=1}^{q} \exp\left[\frac{2\pi i m^k (a_1 M_1 + \cdots + a_r M_r)}{q}\right] \\ &= \sum_{m_1=1}^{p_1^{\alpha_1}} \cdots \sum_{m_r=1}^{p_r^{\alpha_r}} \exp\left[2\pi i \left(\frac{a_1}{p_1^{\alpha_1}} + \cdots + \frac{a_r}{p_r^{\alpha_r}}\right)(m_1 M_1 + \cdots + m_r M_r)^k\right] \\ &= \sum_{m_1=1}^{p_1^{\alpha_1}} \cdots \sum_{m_r=1}^{p_r^{\alpha_r}} \exp\left[\frac{2\pi i}{p_1^{\alpha_1}} a_1 (m_1 M_1)^k\right] \exp\left[\frac{2\pi i}{p_2^{\alpha_2}} a_2 (m_2 M_2)^k\right] \cdots \exp\left[\frac{2\pi i}{p_r^{\alpha_r}} a_r (m_r M_r)^k\right] \\ &= S(a_1, p_1^{\alpha_1}) \cdots S(a_r, p_r^{\alpha_r}) . \end{aligned}$$

We have used the facts that $M_i \equiv 0 \pmod{p^{\alpha_j}}$ if $i \neq j$ and as the m_i runs through a complete residue system modulo $p_i^{\alpha_i}$, so does $m_i M_i$.

The next theorem shows that this multiplicative property is inherited by the $A(q)$.

THEOREM 8.4. *If* $q = p_1^{\alpha_1} \cdots p_r^{\alpha_r}$, *then*

$$A(q) = A(p_1^{\alpha_1}) \cdots A(p_r^{\alpha_r}) . \tag{6}$$

PROOF. We define M_i as above and solve the congruence (5) for $a_1, \cdots, a_r$. Then as a_i run through a reduced system modulo $p_i^{\alpha_i}$, $a = a_1 M_1 + \cdots + a_r M_r$ runs through a reduced system modulo q and conversely. We therefore have

$$A(q) = q^{-s} \sum_{a=1;\ (a,q)=1}^{q} S^s(a, q) e^{-2\pi i n a/q}$$

$$= (p_1^{\alpha_1} \cdots p_r^{\alpha_r})^{-s} \sum_{a_1=1;\ (a_1,p_1)=1}^{p_1^{\alpha_1}} \cdots \sum_{a_r=1;\ (a_r,p_r)=1}^{p_r^{\alpha_r}} S^s(a_1, p_1^{\alpha_1}) \cdots S^s(a_r, p_r^{\alpha_r}) \times \exp\left[\frac{-2\pi i n(a_1 M_1 + \cdots + a_r M_r)}{q}\right]$$

$$= (p_1^{\alpha_1} \cdots p_r^{\alpha_r})^{-s} \sum_{a_1=1;\ (a_1,p_1)=1}^{p_1^{\alpha_1}} S^s(a_1, p_1^{\alpha_1}) \exp\left[\frac{-2\pi i n a_1}{p_1^{\alpha_1}}\right] \cdots \sum_{a_r=1;\ (a_r,p_r)=1}^{p_r^{\alpha_r}} S^s(a_r, p_r^{\alpha_r}) \times \exp\left[\frac{-2\pi i n a_r}{p_r^{\alpha_r}}\right]$$

$$= A(p_1^{\alpha_1}) \cdots A(p_r^{\alpha_r}) .$$

To infer the validity of (4), we wish to show first that

$$\sum_{q=1}^{\infty} A(q)$$

converges absolutely. This will follow from an appropriate estimate for $A(q)$ which we derive from an estimate for $S(a, q)$. This latter estimate, we have seen, can be made to depend on an estimate for $S(a, p_i^{r_i})$ and even this can be further reduced.

We first require a lemma.

LEMMA 8.1. *If q is a positive integer and a is any integer, then*

$$S = \sum_{r=0}^{q-1} e^{2\pi i a r/q} = \begin{cases} q & \text{if } q \mid a , \\ 0 & \text{otherwise} . \end{cases}$$

PROOF. The proof is immediate since if $q \mid a$, then each term of S has value 1, whereas if $q \nmid a$, then $x = e^{2\pi i a/q} \neq 1$ and S is thus the sum of a geometric series. In fact,

$$S = \frac{x^q - 1}{x - 1} = 0 .$$

We start by considering the sum $S(a, p)$ for a prime p.

THEOREM 8.5. *If p is a prime, $(a, p) = 1$, $d = (k, p-1)$ and*

$$S(a, p) = \sum_{r=0}^{p-1} e^{2\pi i r^k a/p} ,$$

then

$$|S(a, p)| \leq (d-1)p^{1/2} . \tag{7}$$

PROOF. If $d = 1$, then by Theorem 8.2, the congruence

$$r^k \equiv m \pmod{p}$$

is solvable and has precisely one solution. Thus as r ranges from 0 to $p-1$, m also runs from 0 to $p-1$ in some order. Accordingly,

$$S(a, p) = \sum_{m=0}^{p-1} e^{2\pi i m a/p} ,$$

and this, by Lemma 8.1, is 0.

If $d \neq 1$, let g be a primitive root modulo p, and suppose that

$$r^k \equiv m \equiv g^b \pmod{p} . \tag{8}$$

As r ranges from 0 to $p-1$, only those residues $m \bmod p$ occur for which $d \mid b$ and these occur exactly d times by Theorem 8.2. Thus

$$S(a, p) = \sum_{r=0}^{p-1} e^{2\pi i r^k a/p} = \sum_{m=0}^{p-1} e^{2\pi i m a/p} \chi(m) ,$$

where

$$\chi(m) = \begin{cases} 0 & \text{if } d \nmid b \\ d & \text{if } d \mid b \end{cases} \qquad (\chi(0) = 1) .$$

On the other hand, by Lemma 8.1, we can write $\chi(m)$ as follows:

$$\chi(m) = \sum_{l=0}^{d-1} e^{2\pi i b l/d} ,$$

and therefore

$$S(a, p) = 1 + \sum_{m=1}^{p-1} \sum_{l=1}^{d-1} e^{2\pi i (ma/p + bl/d)} + \sum_{m=1}^{p-1} e^{2\pi i m a/p} .$$

The last sum is -1, and therefore

$$S(a, p) = \sum_{m=1}^{p-1} \sum_{l=1}^{d-1} e^{2\pi i (ma/p + bl/d)} . \tag{9}$$

Applying the Cauchy-Schwarz inequality, we get

$$\begin{aligned} | S(a, p) |^2 &\leqq (d-1) \sum_{l=1}^{d-1} \left| \sum_{m=1}^{p-1} e^{2\pi i (ma/p + bl/d)} \right|^2 \\ &\leqq (d-1) \sum_{l=1}^{d-1} \sum_{m_1=1}^{p-1} \sum_{m=1}^{p-1} \exp\left[2\pi i \left\{ \left(\frac{m_1 a}{p} - \frac{ma}{p} \right) + \left(\frac{b_1 l}{d} - \frac{bl}{d} \right) \right\} \right] , \end{aligned} \tag{10}$$

where $b_1 = \operatorname{ind} m_1$ and $b = \operatorname{ind} m$.

This means, however, that $b_1 - b$ is the index of m_1/m. Let t be determined by the conguence

$$m_1 \equiv mt \pmod{p} .$$

Then by (10)

$$| S(a, p) |^2 \leqq (d-1) \sum_{l=1}^{d-1} \sum_{t=1}^{p-1} \sum_{m=1}^{p-1} e^{2\pi i m (t-1)/p} e^{2\pi i b_t l/d} , \tag{11}$$

where $b_t = \operatorname{ind} t$. If we notice that

$$\sum_{m=1}^{p-1} e^{2\pi i m (t-1)/p} = -1 ,$$

then we get from (11),

$$| S(a, p) |^2 \leqq (d-1)\sum_{l=1}^{d-1}\left\{\sum_{m=1}^{p-1} e^{2\pi i l/d} + \sum_{t=2}^{p-1} e^{2\pi i b_t l/d}\sum_{m=1}^{p-1} e^{2\pi i m(t-1)/p}\right\}$$

$$\leqq (d-1)\sum_{l=1}^{d-1}\left\{(p-1)e^{2\pi i l/d} - \sum_{t=2}^{p-1} e^{2\pi i b_t l/d}\right\} \tag{12}$$

$$\leqq (d-1)\sum_{l=1}^{d-1}\left\{p - \sum_{t=1}^{p-1} e^{2\pi i b_t l/d}\right\} .$$

As t runs from 1 to $p-1$, ind t assumes all values modulo d equally often by Theorem 8.2. Therefore by Lemma 8.1,

$$\sum_{t=1}^{p-1} e^{2\pi i b_t l/d} = 0 ,$$

which we readily see by breaking the sum into $(p-1)/d$ parts. Consequently, by (12),

$$| S(a, p) |^2 \leqq (d-1)\sum_{l=1}^{d-1} p = (d-1)^2 p ,$$

and this is equivalent to the assertion of the theorem.

The next two theorems reduce the calculation of $S(a, p^\alpha)$ to simpler terms.

Theorem 8.6. *If m is any integer for which $1 < m \leqq k$, and $(p, k) = 1$, where p is a prime, then*

$$S(a, p^m) = p^{m-1} . \tag{13}$$

Proof. By definition,

$$S(a, p^m) = \sum_{r=0}^{p^m-1} e^{2\pi i r^k a/p^m} .$$

We break the summation as follows. Let

$$r = p^{m-1}t + u .$$

As t and u range independently over the values 0 to $p-1$ and 0 to $p^{m-1}-1$, respectively, r ranges from 0 to $p^m - 1$. Thus

$$S(a, p^m) = \sum_{t=0}^{p-1}\sum_{u=0}^{p^{m-1}-1} \exp\left[\frac{2\pi i a}{p^m}(p^{m-1}t + u)^k\right]. \tag{14}$$

On the other hand, since $2(m-1) \geqq m$,

$$(p^{m-1}t + u)^k \equiv u^k + ku^{k-1}p^{m-1}t \pmod{p^m} , \tag{15}$$

and therefore by (14) and (15),

$$S(a, p^m) = \sum_{u=0}^{p^{m-1}-1} e^{2\pi i u^k a/p^m}\sum_{t=0}^{p-1} e^{2\pi i k u^{k-1} a t/p} . \tag{16}$$

However, $(p, ka) = 1$, and therefore by Theorem 8.3, the inner sum is 0 except when $p \mid u$ in which case its value is p. There are altogether p^{m-2} terms in the outer sum for which $p \mid u$ and because $k \geqq m$, $e^{2\pi i u^k a/p^m} = 1$, and therefore from (16),

$$S(a, p^m) = \sum_{u=0\,;\,u|p}^{p^{m-1}-1} p = p^{m-1}\,.$$

The next case is $m > k$. If we attempt to use the idea of equation (15), we are led to introduce the following integer. Let α be the highest power of the prime p which enters into the decomposition of k i.e, $p^\alpha \| k$. For later use, we also introduce the integer γ. This is defined as follows:

$$\gamma = \begin{cases} \alpha + 1 & \text{if } p \neq 2 \\ \alpha + 2 & \text{if } p = 2 \end{cases}. \tag{17}$$

THEOREM 8.7. *If $m > k$, then*

$$S(a, p^m) = p^{k-1}S(a, p^{m-k})\,.$$

PROOF. We have

$$S(a, p^m) = \sum_{r=0}^{p^m-1} e^{2\pi i a r^k/p^m}\,. \tag{18}$$

Let α be the integer defined above and let

$$r = p^{m-\alpha-1}t + u\,,$$

where t ranges over the set from 0 to $p^{\alpha+1} - 1$ and u over the set from 0 to $p^{m-\alpha-1} - 1$. Then because $k \geqq 2^\alpha \geqq \alpha + 1$ and $m \geqq \alpha + 2$, we have

$$(u + p^{m-\alpha-1}t)^k \equiv u^k + ku^{k-1}p^{m-\alpha-1}t \pmod{p^m}\,. \tag{19}$$

Thus from (18) and (19),

$$\begin{aligned} S(a, p^m) &= \sum_{u=0}^{p^{m-\alpha-1}-1} \sum_{t=0}^{p^{\alpha+1}-1} \exp\left[\frac{2\pi i a u^k}{p^m} + \frac{2\pi i a k u^{k-1}t}{p^{\alpha+1}}\right] \\ &= \sum_{u=0}^{p^{m-\alpha-1}-1} e^{2\pi i a u^k/p^m} \sum_{t=0}^{p^{\alpha+1}-1} e^{2\pi i a k u^{k-1}t/p^{\alpha+1}}\,. \end{aligned} \tag{20}$$

The inner sum, however, is 0 unless $p^{\alpha+1} \mid u^{k-1}$, that is $p \mid u$ since $k - 1 \geqq \alpha + 1$, k being assumed $\geqq 3$. In this latter case, its value is $p^{\alpha+1}$. Therefore from (20),

$$\begin{aligned} S(a, p^m) &= p^{\alpha+1} \sum_{u=0;p|u}^{p^{m-\alpha-1}-1} e^{2\pi i a u^k/p^m} \\ &= p^{\alpha+1} \sum_{v=0}^{p^{m-\alpha-2}-1} e^{2\pi i a (pv)^k/p^m} \\ &= p^{\alpha+1} \sum_{l=0}^{p^{k-\alpha-2}-1} \sum_{v=lp^{m-k}}^{(l+1)p^{m-k}-1} e^{2\pi i v^k a/p^{m-k}} \\ &= p^{\alpha+1}p^{k-\alpha-2}S(a, p^{m-k}) \\ &= p^{k-1}S(a, p^{m-k})\,. \end{aligned}$$

We are now in a position to prove the important estimate I. This is given by

THEOREM 8.8.

$$S(a, q) = O(q^{1-1/k})\,,$$

where the constant implied by the O depends only on k.

PROOF. Let

$$T(a, q) = q^{-1+1/k} S(a, q) . \tag{21}$$

The assertion of the theorem is equivalent to

$$T(a, q) = O(1) .$$

Because $T(a, q)$ is multiplicative since $S(a, q)$ is, it is enough to show that for every $\beta \geqq 1$,

$$T(a, p^\beta) = O(1) .$$

We consider four cases:

Case (i). Suppose that $1 \leqq \beta \leqq k$ and that $p \mid k$. Then we have the trivial estimate

$$\begin{aligned} | T(a, p^\beta) | &= p^{-\beta(1-1/k)} \, | S(a, p^\beta) | \\ &\leqq p^{-\beta+\beta/k} p^\beta = p^{\beta/k} \leqq p \leqq k . \end{aligned} \tag{22}$$

Case (ii). If $\beta = 1$, and $(k, p) = 1$, then Theorem 8.5 is applicable and we get

$$| T(a, p^\beta) | \leqq (d-1) p^{-1+1/k} p^{1/2} \leqq k p^{-1/2+1/k} \leqq k p^{-1/6} \tag{23}$$

since by assumption $k \geqq 3$.

Case (iii). If $1 < \beta \leqq k$, $(k, p) = 1$, then Theorem 8.6 is applicable and we get

$$| T(a, p^\beta) | \leqq p^{-\beta+\beta/k+\beta-1} = p^{\beta/k-1} \leqq 1 . \tag{24}$$

Accordingly, if $1 \leqq \beta \leqq k$, then from (22), (23), (24), we get

$$| T(a, p^\beta) | \leqq \begin{cases} k & \text{if } p \leqq k^6 \\ 1 & \text{if } p > k^6 \end{cases} . \tag{25}$$

Case (iv). If $\beta > k$, then by Theorem 8.7, we get by induction,

$$T(a, p^\beta) = T(a, p^{\beta-\lambda k})$$

for integral λ. We choose λ such that $\beta - \lambda k \leqq k$ and then the inequalities in (25) hold for all β. Consequently

$$| T(a, q) | = \Big| \prod_{p|q;\, p \leqq k^6} T(a, p^\beta) \prod_{p|q;\, p > k^6} T(a, p^\beta) \Big| \leqq k^{k^6} .$$

This completes the proof.

An immediate consequence of this estimate is

THEOREM 8.9. *The singular series converges absolutely for $s \geqq 2k + 1$.*

PROOF. The estimate for $S(a, q)$ yields the following

$$\begin{aligned} A(q) &= q^{-s} \sum_{a=1;\ (a, q)=1}^{q} S^s(a, q) e^{-2\pi i n a/q} \\ &= O(q^{-s} q \cdot q^{s(1-1/k)}) = O(q^{1-s/k}) . \end{aligned}$$

This implies the assertion of the theorem. An important corollary is

THEOREM 8.10. *If p is a prime and*

$$\psi(p) = \sum_{r=0}^{\infty} A(p^r)\,,$$

then

$$\mathfrak{S}(n) = \prod_{p} \psi(p)\,.$$

PROOF. The proof is a consequence of Theorem 1.5 of Chapter I, and the absolute convergence of $\mathfrak{S}(n)$.

It remains to study $\psi(p)$. For this purpose, we look closely at $A(p^r)$. In fact, by definition,

$$(26)\qquad \begin{aligned} A(p^r) &= p^{-rs} \sum_{a=1;\,(a,p)=1}^{p^r} S^s(a, p^r) e^{-2\pi i n a/p^r} \\ &= p^{-rs} \sum_{m_1=0}^{p^r-1} \sum_{m_2=0}^{p^r-1} \cdots \sum_{m_s=0}^{p^r-1} \sum_{a=1;\,(a,p)=1}^{p^r} \exp\left[\frac{2\pi i}{p^r}(m_1^k + \cdots + m_s^k - n)a\right]. \end{aligned}$$

If the inner sum extended to all values of a, then its value would be 0 by Lemma 8.1, except in those cases when

$$(27)\qquad m_1^k + \cdots + m_s^k \equiv n \pmod{p^r}\,.$$

In these cases, its value is p^r. The inner sum, however, is restricted by the condition $(a, p) = 1$. Nevertheless, we can relate the value of $A(p^r)$ to the solvability of the congruence (27). To this end, let

$$M(n, s, m)$$

denote the number of solutions of the congruence

$$(28)\qquad m_1^k + \cdots + m_s^k \equiv n \pmod{m}.$$

Then we prove

THEOREM 8.11. *If m is any positive integer,*

$$\sum_{q\mid m} A(q) = m^{-(s-1)} M(n, s, m)\,.$$

PROOF. Indeed, by Lemma 8.1,

$$(29)\qquad mM(n, s, m) = \sum_{m_1=1}^{m} \cdots \sum_{m_s=1}^{m} \sum_{a=1}^{m} \exp\left[\frac{2\pi i}{m}(m_1^k + \cdots + m_s^k - n)a\right],$$

since the inner sum is 0 unless the congruence (28) is solvable, in which case its value is m. We break the inner summation as follows. Let $m = (a, m)q$ and put $a/m = b/q$ where $b = a/(a, m)$. Then $(b, q) = 1$. As a ranges over the set from 1 to m, q ranges over the divisors of m and b over the reduced residues molulo q. Therefore

$$(30)\qquad mM(n, s, m) = \sum_{q\mid m} \sum_{m_i=1}^{m} \sum_{b=1;(b,q)=1}^{q} \exp\left[\frac{2\pi i}{q}(m_1^k + \cdots + m_s^k - n)b\right].$$

On the other hand, since $q \mid m$, then

$$\sum_{m_i=1}^{m} e^{2\pi i m_i^k b/q} = \frac{m}{q} \sum_{m_i=1}^{q} e^{2\pi i m_i^k b/q} ,$$

and therefore from (30),

$$\begin{aligned} mM(n, s, m) &= \sum_{q \mid m} \sum_{(b,q)=1} \left(\frac{m}{q}\right)^s S^s(b, q) e^{-2\pi i n b/q} \\ &= m^s \sum_{q \mid m} A(q) . \end{aligned} \tag{31}$$

In particular, if m is a power of a prime, $m = p^r$, then

$$\sum_{q \mid p^r} A(q) = \sum_{j=0}^{r} A(p^j) = p^{-r(s-1)} M(n, s, p^r) . \tag{32}$$

It remains to study the solvability of the congruence (28).

THEOREM 8.12. *If γ is defined as in* (17) *and*

$$s \geqq 4k ,$$

then the congruence

$$m_1^k + \cdots + m_s^k \equiv n \pmod{p^\gamma} \tag{33}$$

is solvable with not all m_i divisible by p.

PROOF. It evidently suffices to show that the congruence

$$m_1^k + \cdots + m_t^k \equiv n \pmod{p^\gamma} , \tag{34}$$

with $t \leqq 4k - 1$, and $(n, p) = 1$ is solvable. For if $p \mid n$, then $p \nmid n - 1$ and we solve the congruence (33) by simply adding 1^k to a solution for $n - 1$.

If $p = 2$, then

$$n < p^\gamma = 2^{\alpha+2} \leqq 4k ,$$

and the congruence (34) is solvable with $t = n$ for we have only to choose $m_1 = m_2 = \cdots = m_t = 1$. If $p > 2$, we let $t = t(n)$ be the least value of t for which (34) is solvable. We suppose that $0 < n < p^\gamma$ and we say that n_1 is equivalent to n_2 ($n_1 \sim n_2$) if $t(n_1) = t(n_2)$. This is clearly an equivalence relation. If c denotes the number of equivalence classes, then we shall show that $c \leqq k$. For let g be a primitive root mod p^γ and let $b(n) = \operatorname{ind} n$, that is

$$n \equiv g^{b(n)} \pmod{p^\gamma} .$$

This is possible since $(p, n) = 1$. Furthermore let $b(n) \equiv v(n) \pmod{k}$. We prove that if, for two integers n and n_1, $v(n_1) = v(n)$, then $n \sim n_1$, that is $t(n) = t(n_1)$. Indeed, since $b(n) \equiv b(n_1) \pmod{k}$, there exists λ such that $0 \leqq \lambda < k$ for which

$$n_1 \equiv g^{b(n_1)} \equiv g^{b(n)+\lambda k} \pmod{p^\gamma} .$$

In that event,

$$n_1 \equiv n \cdot r^k \pmod{p^\gamma}$$

where $r = g^{\lambda}$.

Accordingly (34) becomes

$$(m_1 r)^k + \cdots + (m_t r)^k \equiv n_1 \pmod{p^{\gamma}} .$$

This means however that $t(n_1) \leqq t(n)$. By symmetry, $t(n) \leqq t(n_1)$ and therefore $t(n) = t(n_1)$. The number c of classes is therefore at most k.

We now take the least member of each class and arrange these in ascending order of magnitude, say

$$n_1 , n_2 , \cdots, n_c .$$

Clearly $n_1 = 1$ and therefore $t(n_1) = 1 = 2 - 1$. We prove by induction that

$$t(n_j) \leqq 2j - 1 \qquad \text{for } j = 1, 2, \cdots, c .$$

Suppose in fact that this inequality holds for $j < r$; then since n_r is the least member of its class, one of the numbers $n_r - 1$, $n_r - 2$, is not divisible by p (> 2). Then there exists $j < r$, such that either $n_r - 1$ or $n_r - 2$ belongs to the class whose representative is n_j. Therefore

$$t(n_r) \leqq 2j - 1 + 2 \leqq 2(r-1) - 1 + 2 = 2r - 1 .$$

In particular,

$$t(n_c) \leqq 2c - 1 \leqq 2k - 1 < 4k - 1 .$$

This means that the congruence (34) is solvable with $t \leqq 4k - 1$.

The next theorem allows us to infer the solvability of one binomial congruence from the solvability of another.

THEOREM 8.13. *If for any a there exists b, such that $p \nmid b$ and*

$$b^k \equiv a \pmod{p^{\gamma}} , \tag{35}$$

then the congruence

$$x^k \equiv a \pmod{p^{\beta}}$$

is solvable for any $\beta > \gamma$.

PROOF. The congruence

$$y b^k \equiv a \pmod{p^{\beta}}$$

is solvable for y since $(b, p) = 1$. Let g be a primitive root modulo p^{β}. Then there exists m so that

$$y \equiv g^m \pmod{p^{\beta}} , \tag{36}$$

that is,

$$g^m b^k \equiv a \pmod{p^{\beta}} . \tag{37}$$

We shall show that we can select the exponent of g to be a multiple of k. In fact by (35) and (37), it follows that

$$g^m \equiv 1 \pmod{p^{\gamma}}$$

and therefore $\varphi(p^\gamma) = p^{\gamma-1}(p-1) \mid m$. As a result, since $\gamma - 1 \geqq \alpha$ where, it will be recalled, α is the highest power of p dividing k, it follows that $m = p^\alpha(p-1)m_1$. From (37), we can write

$$g^{m+\lambda\varphi(p^\beta)} b^k \equiv a \pmod{p^\beta} \tag{38}$$

and

$$m + \lambda\varphi(p^\beta) = m + \lambda p^{\beta-1}(p-1) = p^\alpha(p-1)(m_1 + \lambda p^{\beta-\alpha-1}) .$$

Let $k = p^\alpha k_1$, so that $(k_1, p) = 1$; now choose λ so that

$$m_1 + \lambda p^{\beta-\alpha-1} \equiv 0 \pmod{k_1} .$$

Consequently $p^\alpha(p-1)(m_1 + \lambda p^{\beta-\alpha-1}) = p^\alpha(p-1)k_1\mu = k\nu$, where ν is an integer. We have therefore shown that we can select λ so that $m + \lambda\varphi(p^\beta) \equiv 0 \pmod k$ and this proves the theorem.

A simple consequence is the following lower bound for $M(n, s, p^\beta)$.

THEOREM 8.14. *Suppose that $\beta > \gamma$ and $s \geqq 4k$, then*

$$M(n, s, p^\beta) \geqq p^{(\beta-\gamma)(s-1)} . \tag{39}$$

PROOF. According to Theorem 8.12, we can find an integer m_1 not divisible by p and integers $m_2, m_3, \cdots, m_s$ so that

$$m_1^k \equiv n - m_2^k - \cdots - m_s^k \pmod{p^\gamma} .$$

By Theorem 8.13, however, this implies that the congruence

$$x^k \equiv n - n_2^k - \cdots - n_s^k \pmod{p^\beta} \tag{40}$$

is solvable if $n_i \equiv m_i \pmod{p^\gamma}$, $i = 2, 3, \cdots, s$. This means that the congruence

$$m_1^k + \cdots + m_s^k \equiv n \pmod{p^\beta}$$

has at least as many solutions as there are possible choices of n_i in (40). Modulo p^β, there are $p^{\beta-\gamma}$ choices of each n_i. Therefore

$$M(n, s, p^\beta) \geqq p^{(\beta-\gamma)(s-1)} ,$$

as required.

We turn now to $\mathfrak{S}(n)$.

THEOREM 8.15. *If $s \geqq 4k$, there exists a constant $c > 0$ so that for all n,*

$$\mathfrak{S}(n) \geqq c > 0 .$$

PROOF. By Theorem 8.10,

$$\mathfrak{S}(n) = \prod_p \psi(p) , \tag{41}$$

where $\psi(p) = \sum_{r=0}^\infty A(p^r)$. However, by the corollary to Theorem 8.11, equation (31), and Theorem 8.14 for $\beta > \gamma$,

$$\sum_{q \mid p^\beta} A(q) = p^{-\beta(s-1)} M(n, s, p^\beta) \geqq p^{-\beta(s-1)} p^{(\beta-\gamma)(s-1)} = p^{-\gamma(s-1)} .$$

Letting $\beta \to \infty$, we conclude that

(42) $$\psi(p) \geqq p^{-\gamma(s-1)} .$$

Moreover by Theorem 8.8,

$$\psi(p) - 1 = \sum_{r=1}^{\infty} A(p^r) = O\left(\sum_{r=1}^{\infty} p^{r(1-s/k)}\right)$$
$$= O\left(\sum_{r=1}^{\infty} p^{-3r}\right) = O(p^{-3}) .$$

Therefore if p is sufficiently large, say $p > K$, we can conclude that

(43) $$\psi(p) > 1 - p^{-2} .$$

Hence from (41), (42), (43),

$$\mathfrak{S}(n) = \prod_{p \leqq K} \psi(p) \prod_{p>K} \psi(p)$$
$$\geqq \prod_{p \leqq K} p^{-\gamma(s-1)} \prod_{p>K} \left(1 - \frac{1}{p^2}\right) = c > 0 ,$$

since $\prod (1 - p^{-2})$ converges.

The proof is thus complete.

PROBLEMS

1. Show that $G(k) \geqq k + 1$ $(k \geqq 2)$. If $n = \sum_{i=1}^{k} x_i^k$, $x_i \geqq 0$, $0 \leqq x_1 \leqq x_2 \cdots \leqq x_k$, $x_i \leqq n^{1/k}$. If $1 \leqq n \leqq m$, then $\sum_{i=1}^{k} x_i^k$ takes on at most $\prod_{r=1}^{k} ([m^{1/k}] + r)/k!$ $\leqq 3m/4$ values, if m is sufficiently large.

2. Assuming the theorem of Euler-Lagrange viz. $G(2) = g(2) = 4$, show that $g(4) \leqq 50$ as follows. Verify the identity

$$6\left(\sum_{i=1}^{4} x_i^2\right)^2 = \sum_{1 \leqq i < j \leqq 4} (x_i + x_j)^4 + \sum_{1 \leqq i < j \leqq 4} (x_i - x_j)^4 ,$$

and then suppose that $n = 6N + r$. Notice finally that

$$n = 6N + r = 6(\sum y_i^2)^2 + r ,$$

and use the above identity.

3. Prove that $G(3) \leqq 13$ as follows. Suppose that $z \equiv 1 \pmod 6$ and let I_z be the interval

$$(11z^9 + (z^3 + 1)^3 + (5z)^3, 14z^9) .$$

If z is sufficiently large, the intervals I_z overlap and every n sufficiently large lies in some I_z. The following identity holds:

$$\sum_{i=1}^{4} ((z^3 + x_i)^3 + (z^3 - x_i)^3) = 8z^9 + 6z^3\left(\sum_{i=1}^{4} x_i^2\right) .$$

If N is a number which can be written as a sum of 5 cubes, then show that every n in I_z can be written as

$$n = N + 8z^9 + 6mz^3 , \qquad 0 \leqq m \leqq z^6 .$$

In fact, if $n \equiv 6r \pmod{z^3}$, $n \equiv S + 4 \pmod 6$, choose $N = (r+1)^3 + (r-1)^3 + 2(z^3 - r)^3 + (Sz)^3$. Write m as a sum of 4 squares and use the above identity.

4. Verify the identity

$$60\left(\sum_{i=1}^{4} x_i^2\right)^3 = \sum_{i<j<k}^{1\ 4} (x_i \pm x_j \pm x_k)^6 + 2\sum_{i<j}^{1\ 4} (x_i - x_j)^6 + 36 \sum_{i=1}^{4} x_i^6 .$$

Deduce that $g(6) \leqq 2451$ assuming the bound for $G(3)$ (Problem 3) holds also for $g(3)$. Write $n = 60N + r$ and note that

$$60N = 60 \sum_{i=1}^{g(3)} N_i^3 = 60 \sum_{i=1}^{g(3)} (a_i^2 + b_i^2 + c_i^2 + d_i^2)^3 .$$

The method of this chapter may be used to treat the Goldbach problem.

5. Let

$$f(x) = f(x, n) = \sum_{p \leqq n} e^{2\pi i p x} ,$$

where the summation is over primes. Show that if $r(n)$ is the number of representations of n as a sum of 3 primes,

$$n = p_1 + p_2 + p_3 ,$$

then

$$r(n) = \int_0^1 f^3(x) e^{-2\pi i n x}\, dx ,$$

and since the integrand has period 1,

$$r(n) = \int_{-\tau^{-1}}^{1-\tau^{-1}} f^3(x) e^{-2\pi i n x}\, dx .$$

6. Let $(a, q) = 1$, $a \leqq q$, $q \leqq \log^c n$ and $\tau = n/\log^c n$, where c is some constant to be chosen. Define $M(a, q)$ as the set of points x such that

$$\left| x - \frac{a}{q} \right| \leqq \frac{1}{\tau} .$$

Show that no two $M(a, q)$ overlap.

7. Show that

$$f(x_1 + x_2, n) = e^{2\pi i n x_2} f(x_1, n) - 2\pi i x_2 \int_0^n e^{2\pi i u x_2} f(x_1, u)\, du .$$

Generalize to any sum of the form

$$\sum_{0 < m \leqq v} a_m e^{2\pi i m x} .$$

8. If $\pi(n, q, l) = \sum_{p \leqq n;\, p \equiv l \pmod q} 1$, then

$$\sum_{p \leqq n;\, p \nmid q} e^{2\pi i p a/q} = \sum_{0 < l \leqq q;\, (l, q) = 1} e^{2\pi i l a/q} \pi(n, q, l) .$$

9. Assume known the following theorem. *If* $q \leqq \log^c n$, *then*

$$\pi(n, q, l) = \frac{1}{\varphi(q)} \int_2^n \frac{dt}{\log t} + O\left(\frac{n}{\log^{c_1} n}\right)$$

for some constant c_1 and the constant implied by the O is independent of q. Moreover $\sum_{(l,q)=1;\, 0<l\leq q} e^{2\pi i l a/q} = \mu(q)$ (see Problem 51, Chapter III). Show that

(i) $$f\left(\frac{a}{q}\right) = \sum_{p\leq n;\, p\nmid q} e^{2\pi i a p/q} + O(q)\,;$$

(ii) $$f\left(\frac{a}{q}\right) = \frac{\mu(q)}{\varphi(q)} \int_2^n \frac{dt}{\log t} + O\left(\frac{n}{\log^{c_2} n}\right)$$

for some constant c_2.

10. Using Problem 7, show that

$$f\left(\frac{a}{q} + y\right) = \frac{\mu(q)}{\varphi(q)} \int_2^n \frac{e^{2\pi i y t}}{\log t} dt + O\left(\frac{n}{\log^{c_3} n}\right).$$

11. Show that

$$f^3\left(\frac{a}{q} + y\right) = \frac{\mu(q)}{\varphi^3(q)} \left(\int_2^n \frac{e^{2\pi i y t}}{\log t} dt\right)^3 + O\left(\frac{n^3}{\log^{c_4} n}\right).$$

12. Using the major arcs of Problem 6, and denoting the remaining points of the interval by $\mathfrak{m}$, show that

$$r(n) = \sum_{q\leq \log^c n} \sum_{a=0;\,(a,q)=1}^{q-1} \int_{M(a,q)} f^3(x) e^{-2\pi i n x} dx + \int_{\mathfrak{m}} f^3(x) e^{-2\pi i n x} dx\,.$$

Denote the second integral by $I_{\mathfrak{m}}$. Show then that

$$\begin{aligned} r(n) &= \sum_{q\leq \log^c n} \sum_{a=0;\,(a,q)=1}^{q-1} e^{-2\pi i n a/q} \int_{-\tau^{-1}}^{1-\tau^{-1}} f^3\left(\frac{a}{q} + y\right) e^{-2\pi i n y} dy + I_{\mathfrak{m}} \\ &= R(n) \sum_{q\leq \log^c n} \sum_{a=1;\,(a,q)=1}^{q} \frac{\mu(q)}{\varphi^3(q)} e^{-2\pi i n a/q} + I_{\mathfrak{m}} + O\left(\frac{n^2}{\log^{c_4} n}\right), \end{aligned}$$

where $R(n)$ is some function of n.

13. Let

$$\mathfrak{S}(n) = \sum_{q=1}^{\infty} C(q)\,,$$

where

$$C(q) = \sum_{a=1;\,(a,q)=1}^{q} \frac{\mu(q)}{\varphi^3(q)} e^{-2\pi i n a/q}\,.$$

Show that $\mathfrak{S}(n)$ converges and that

$$\sum_{q\leq \log^c n} C(q) = \mathfrak{S}(n) + O\left(\frac{1}{\log^{c_5} n}\right).$$

Show that $C(q)$ is multiplicative and that

$$\mathfrak{S}(n) = \prod_p \left(1 - \frac{c_p}{(p-1)^3}\right),$$

where

$$c_p = \sum_{a=1;\,(a,p)=1}^{p} e^{-2\pi i a n/p} .$$

Moreover,

$$\mathfrak{S}(n) = \prod_{p\nmid n}\left(1+\frac{1}{(p-1)^3}\right)\prod_{p\mid n}\left(1-\frac{1}{(p-1)^2}\right) .$$

Therefore if n is even, i.e., $2\mid n$, the second factor vanishes, that is $\mathfrak{S}(2k)=0$.

14. Assume that on $\mathfrak{m}$,

$$f(x) = O\left(\frac{n}{\log^3 n}\right)$$

and show that

$$\int_{\mathfrak{m}} f^3(x)e^{-2\pi i n x}\,dx = O\left(\frac{n^2}{\log^4 n}\right) .$$

Hence deduce that $r(n) > 0$ for sufficiently large odd n.

15. Suppose that the polynomial

$$\varphi(h) = \alpha h^k + \alpha_1 h^{k-1} + \cdots + \alpha_k$$

takes integral values for integral values of h. Let $r(n)$ denote the number of solutions of the equation

$$n = \varphi(h_1) + \cdots + \varphi(h_s) .$$

Let

$$S_\varphi(a, q) = \sum_{r=1}^{q} e^{2\pi i a\varphi(r)/q} \qquad (a, q) = 1,\ q > 0 ,$$

$$A_\varphi(q) = q^{-s} \sum_{a=1;\,(a,q)=1}^{q} S_\varphi^s(a, q)e^{-2\pi i a n/q} ,$$

$$\mathfrak{S}_\varphi(n) = \sum_{q=1}^{\infty} A(q) ,$$

then if $s \geqq k2^k + 1$,

$$(*) \qquad r(n) = \alpha^{-s/k}\frac{\Gamma^s\left(1+\dfrac{1}{k}\right)}{\Gamma\left(\dfrac{s}{k}\right)}\mathfrak{S}_\varphi(n)n^{s/k-1} + o(n^{s/k-1}) .$$

The proof follows exactly the discussion in the preceding chapter. Fill in the details of the following assertions. Use the same major and minor arcs and define

$$f(x) = \sum_{m\leqq P} e^{-2\pi i \varphi(m)x} .$$

(i) On a major arc,

$$f(x) = q^{-1}S_\varphi(a, q)\int_0^P e^{2\pi i \alpha y u^k}\,du + O(P^{1-\delta}q) .$$

(ii) $f^s(x) = q^{-s}S_\varphi^s(a, q)J^s + O(q^{-1}\min(P, |y|^{-1/k})^{s-1})$, where

$$J = \int_0^P e^{2\pi i\alpha y u^k}\, du\,.$$

(iii)
$$\int_{M(a,q)} f^s(x)e^{-2\pi i n x}\, dx = q^{-s}S_\varphi^s(a, q)e^{-2\pi i n a/q}\int_{-\infty}^{\infty} J^s e^{-2\pi i n y}\, dy + O(q^{-1}P^{s-k-1})\,.$$

(iv)
$$\sum_{q \le P^{1-\delta}} \sum_{a=0;\,(a,q)=1}^{q-1} \int_{M(a,q)} f^s(x)e^{-2\pi i n x}\, dx = \sum_{q\le P^{1-\delta}} A_\varphi(q)I + O(P^{s-k-1/k})\,.$$

(v)
$$r(n) = \mathfrak{S}_\varphi(n)I + I_{\mathfrak{m}} + o(n^{s/k-1})\,,$$

where

$$I_{\mathfrak{m}} = \int_{\mathfrak{m}} f^s(x)e^{-2\pi i n x}\, dx\,.$$

(vi) On $\mathfrak{m}$, $f(x) = O(P^{1-\sigma(1-\delta)+\varepsilon})$.

Finally deduce (*).

16. If $(q_1, q_2) = 1$, show that there exist integers a_1, a_2, such that

$$S_\varphi(a, q_1q_2) = S_\varphi(a_1, q_1)S_\varphi(a_2, q_2)\,.$$

In particular if $q = p_1^{\alpha_1} \cdots p_r^{\alpha_r}$, then

$$S_\varphi(a, q) = \prod_{i=1}^{r} S_\varphi(a_i, p_i^{\alpha_i})\,.$$

17. Let P be a positive integer and let m run through an arbitrary set of positive integers. Let $f(z)$ be an arbitrary function of z and

$$S' = \sum_{(m,P)=1} f(m), \qquad S_d = \sum_{m\equiv 0 (\mathrm{mod}\ d)} f(m)\,.$$

Show that

$$S' = \sum_{d|P} \mu(d)S_d\,.$$

In particular, let $f(z) = e^{2\pi i\alpha z}$ and let P be the product of all primes $\le \sqrt{N}$. If $m \le N$, $(m, P) = 1$, then

$$S' = \sum_{\sqrt{N}<p\le N} e^{2\pi i\alpha p} + e^{2\pi i\alpha} = S + O(\sqrt{N})\,,$$

where the summation is over primes p and where

$$S = \sum_{p\le N} e^{2\pi i\alpha p}\,.$$

Deduce that

$$S = \sum_{d|P} \mu(d)S_d + O(\sqrt{N})\,.$$

18. Suppose that

$$\theta(x) = 1 + 2x + 2x^4 + 2x^9 + \cdots\,.$$

If $x = e^{-\delta+2\pi ia/q}$, $(a, q) = 1$ show that

(i) $$\theta(x) = 1 + 2 \sum_{j=1}^{q} e^{2\pi ij^2a/q} \sum_{l=0}^{\infty} e^{-\delta(lq+j)^2} ,$$

(ii) $$\sum_{l=0}^{\infty} e^{-\delta(lj+q)^2} \sim \int_0^{\infty} e^{-\delta(xq+j)^2} dx \sim \frac{1}{2q}\sqrt{\frac{\pi}{\delta}} , \qquad \text{as } \delta \to 0 ,$$

(iii) $$\theta(x) \sim \frac{1}{q}\sqrt{\frac{\pi}{\delta}} \sum_{j=1}^{q} e^{2\pi iaj^2/q} .$$

$\theta(x)$ is used to investigate the number of representations of n as a sum of squares. The technique is more closely akin to the method of the partition function.

19. Suppose that $r(n)$ is the number of representations of n in the form

$$n = p_1^k + \cdots + p_s^k ,$$

where the p_i are primes. Show by "heuristic" reasoning that

$$r(n) \sim \mathfrak{S}(n)\psi(n) ,$$

where

$$\psi(n) = \int_{-\infty}^{\infty} \left(\int_2^P \frac{e^{2\pi iyk^t}}{\log t} dt \right)^s dy ,$$

and

$$\mathfrak{S}(n) = \sum_{q=1}^{\infty} B(q) ,$$

where

$$B(q) = \sum_{a=1;\ (a,q)=1}^{q} \left(\frac{W(a, q)}{\varphi(q)} \right)^s e^{-2\pi ian/q} ,$$

$$W(a, q) = \sum_{l=1;\ (l,q)=1}^{q} e^{2\pi ialk/q}$$

as follows:

(i) If $f(x) = \sum_{p \leq P} e^{2\pi ipk_x}$, then for any τ

$$r(n) = \int_{\tau-1}^{1-\tau^{-1}} f^s(x) e^{-2\pi inx} dx ,$$

(ii) Subdivide the interval into major and minor arcs, and then show that

$$r(n) \sim \sum_{a,q} \int_{M(a,q)} f^s\left(\frac{a}{q} + y\right) e^{-2\pi in(a/q+y)} dy ,$$

(iii) On $M(a, q)$,

$$f\left(\frac{a}{q}\right) \sim \sum_{p \leq P} e^{2\pi iapk/q} \sim \sum_{1 \leq l \leq q;\ (l,q)=1} e^{2\pi ialk/q} \pi(P, q, l)$$
$$\sim \frac{1}{\varphi(q)} \int_2^P \frac{dt}{\log t} W(a, q) ,$$
$$f\left(\frac{a}{q} + y\right) \sim \frac{W(a, q)}{\varphi(q)} \int_2^P \frac{e^{2\pi iyk^t}}{\log t} dt ,$$

(iv) $$f^s\left(\frac{a}{q}+y\right) \sim \left(\frac{W(a,\, q)}{\varphi(q)}\right)^s \left(\int_2^P \frac{e^{2\pi i y k_t}}{\log t}\,dt\right)^s,$$

(v) $$r(n) \sim \sum_q \sum_a \left(\frac{W(a,\, q)}{\varphi(q)}\right)^s e^{-2\pi i n a} \int_{-\infty}^{\infty} \left(\int_2^P \frac{e^{2\pi i y k_t}}{\log t}\,dt\right)^s dy\,.$$

The complete details are by no means simple.

20. Let $f(x)$ be a real function with continuous and steadily decreasing derivative in (a, b) and $|f(x)| \leqq \theta < 1$. Let $g(x)$ be a real positive decreasing function with $g'(x)$ continuous and $|g'(x)|$ steadily decreasing. Show that

$$\sum_{a \leqq n \leqq b} g(n) e^{2\pi i f(n)} = \int_a^b g(t) e^{2\pi i f(t)}\,dt + O(g(a))\,.$$

21. Using Problem 20, show that if C is any constant > 1, $|t| \leqq 2\pi x/C$, then

$$\zeta(s) = \sum_{n \leqq x} \frac{1}{n^s} - \frac{x^{1-s}}{1-s} + O(x^{-\sigma})$$

uniformly for $\sigma \geqq \sigma_0 > 0$.
From Chapter I, § 3, (21),

$$\zeta(s) = \sum_{n=1}^{N} \frac{1}{n^s} - \frac{N^{1-s}}{1-s} + s\int_N^\infty \frac{[u]-u+\frac{1}{2}}{u^{s+1}}\,du - \frac{N^{-s}}{2}$$
$$= \sum_{1}^{N} \frac{1}{n^s} - \frac{N^{1-s}}{1-s} + O\left(\frac{|s|}{N^\sigma}\right) + O(N^{-\sigma})\,.$$

Apply Problem 20 to

$$\sum_{x<n\leqq N} \frac{1}{n^s}$$

and let $N \to \infty$.

22. Let $(a, q) = 1$ and

$$\Phi(y) = \frac{ay + \psi(y)}{q}\,,$$

where $\psi(y)$ is a real function of y. Let m be an integer and suppose that in the interval $(m, m+q-1)$, $\max \psi(y) - \min \psi(y) \leqq \lambda$ where $\lambda > 0$. If $U > 0$, show that

$$\sum_{y=m}^{m+q-1} \min\left(U, \frac{1}{2\,\|\Phi(y)\|}\right) \leqq (\lambda+3)U + q\log q\,.$$

23. If $r(n)$ is the number of solutions of

$$m_1^k + m_2^k + \cdots + m_s^k = n$$

show that

$$\sum_{1 \leqq n \leqq Q} r(n) \sim \gamma(s, k)\,\frac{k}{s}\,Q^{s/k}\,.$$

24. Use Theorem 5.9 to show that

$$\int_{\mathfrak{m}} g^s(x)e^{-2\pi i n x}\,dx = o(P^{s-k}) ,$$

if $s \geqq k2^{k-1}+1$.

25. Let $a_1, a_2, \cdots, a_k$ be integers, p a prime, $a_1 \not\equiv 0 \pmod p$

$$f(x) = a_1x^k + a_2x^{k-1} + \cdots + a_kx ,$$

$$S = \sum_{m=0}^{p-1} e^{2\pi i f(m)/p} .$$

Show that

$$S = O(p^{1-1/k})$$

as follows (Mordell):

(i) $$|S|^{2k} = \sum_{m_r, n_r;\ r=1,2,\ldots,k}^{0,p-1} e^{2\pi i g/p} ,$$

where $g = \sum_{s=1}^k a_s \sum_{r=1}^k (m_r^{k+1-s} - n_r^{k+1-s})$.

(ii) $$\sum_{a_1=0}^{p-1} |S|^{2k} = Np^k ,$$

where N is the number of solutions of the k congruences

$$\sum_{r=1}^k m_r^s \equiv \sum_{r=1}^k n_r^s \pmod p \qquad s = 1, 2, \cdots, k .$$

(iii) Use Newton's formulae to show that the elementary symmetric functions of m_i are congruent to those of n_i and hence that each $m_i \equiv n_j \pmod p$ for some j.

Deduce that $N \leqq k^k p^k$.

(iv) Find a lower bound for the left-hand side of (ii) as follows. If b, c, run through reduced and complete residues mod p respectively, then

$$|S| = \sum_m e^{2\pi i (f(bm+c)-f(c))/p} .$$

Count the number of times $|S|$ appears in the sum on the left-hand side of (ii). Show that it appears at least $p(p-1)/(k, p-1)$ times and therefore deduce that

$$\frac{p(p-1)}{(k, p-1)} |S|^{2k} \leqq k^k p^{2k} .$$

Notes to Chapter IV

1. Waring's conjecture appeared first in his *Meditationes algebraicae*, 1782. There is no reason to suppose that his conjecture was based on anything but the broadest intuition.

The general literature on $g(k)$ and $G(k)$ and related problems is vast. We cite a few of the best values for $g(k)$ and $G(k)$ for small values of k.

$$g(2) = G(2) = 4 \qquad \text{(Euler and Lagrange)},$$

$$g(3) = 9;\ G(3) \leqq 7 \qquad \text{(G.L. Watson and U.V. Linnik)}.$$

The precise value of $G(3)$ is still not known.

$$g(4) \leqq 37;\ G(4) = 16 \qquad \text{(H. Davenport)},$$

$$g(5) \leqq 58;\ G(5) \leqq 23 \qquad \text{(H. Davenport)}.$$

2 and 4 are the only values of k for which $G(k)$ has been precisely determined.

The first proof that $G(k)$ exists and is independent of n was given by D. Hilbert. A proof was published in Math. Ann. (1909). The upper bound for $G(k)$ inferred from his proof is very large.

U.V. Linnik has given yet another proof of the existence of $G(k)$. His proof depends on the following considerations:

If A is a set of integers, we define the Schnirelman density α as follows:

$$\alpha = \text{g.l.b.} \frac{A(n)}{n},$$

where $A(n) = \sum_{k \leqq n; k \in A} 1$. If $\alpha = 1$, then A comprises all integers. If A and B are two sets of integers, then the set $A + B$ is the set consisting of integers $c = a + b$ with $a \in A$ and $b \in B$. It is proved that if the density α of a set A is $\geqq c > 0$ then the sum of a suitable number of copies of A has density 1. Thus the sum of a suitable number of copies of A comprises all integers. U.V. Linnik proves that if A is the set of kth powers, then there exists an integer m such that the sum of m copies of A has positive density. Thus the sum of a suitable number of copies comprises all integers.

2. The underlying idea of approximating to a function at a rational point, which found its origin in the argument on the partition function, is at the basis of much work in additive number theory.

It is of interest to note that the procedure of Hardy and Littlewood is unexpectedly successful. We are interested in proving the existence of a certain decomposition of an integer. We replace this question by the seemingly more difficult one of determining the number of such representations and thus prove an existence theorem by showing that the number is positive. This replacement of one question by another has altered the character of additive number theory rather substantially.

3. The precise choice of what constitutes the "major arcs" is to a certain extent arbitrary. The reader who encounters the discussion for the first time may be somewhat mystified by the choice. Actually it is determined to a large extent by the ease with which certain later estimates can be made and to balance this ease against the ease with which the estimate on the corresponding minor arc can be made. Roughly speaking, the less we put in the major arcs, the more trouble we have on the minor arcs and vice versa.

4. The discussion on the major arcs or basic intervals is essentially that of Hardy and Littlewood as modified and simplified by Vinogradoff. The theorems of Hardy and Littlewood are found in *On some problems of partitio numerorum*, I-VI:

I. Gottinger Nachrichten (1920).
II. Math. Z. **9.**
III. Acta Math. **44.**
IV. Math. Z. **12.**
V. Proc. London Math. Soc. **22.**
VI. Math. Z. **23.**

Memoirs III and V deal with Goldbach's problem. Vinogradoff's celebrated contributions appeared in a series of memoirs from about 1924 on. A fairly full account may be found in his book *The method of trigonometric sums in the theory of numbers* and in the selections from his collected works in Russian.

5. The method of H. Weyl for estimating trigonometric sums appeared in his famous memoir *Über die Gleichverteilung der Zahlen Mod eins,* in Math. Ann. **77.** The problem of uniform distribution of sets is considered there in some detail.

The deeper estimates of Vinogradoff may be found in the above cited works as well as in Titchmarsh's *The theory of the Riemann Zeta function,* Oxford, 1951.

6. The idea of the asymptotic formula for $r(n)$ is again due to Hardy and Littlewood with the modification of Vinogradoff. Hua's Theorem 6.7 extends the validity of the formula for $r(n)$ to $s \geqq 2^k + 1$. Actually Hardy and Littlewood had already used somewhat the same principle to show the validity of the asymptotic formula for $s \geqq (k-2)2^{k-1} + 5$.

7. The principle of allowing freedom in the choice of the representation of n as a sum of kth powers is due to Vinogradoff as are most of the theorems of this section. Theorem 7.1 however is in the work of Hardy and Littlewood.

8. The theorems of this section are due entirely to Hardy and Littlewood. Some of the original proofs were simplified by Landau, Vinogradoff, and others.

CHAPTER V

Dirichlet L-functions and the Class Number of Quadratic Fields

1. Introduction and algebraic preliminaries. In this chapter we shall study some questions concerning the class number of quadratic fields and the closely related problem of Dirichlet L-series with real characters.

The class number of quadratic fields is intimately related to the class number of quadratic forms, and though this latter topic had been studied for many years, it was not until 1837 that Dirichlet completed a study started by Gauss. Their investigation led to a remarkably compact formula which in certain cases is characterized by great simplicity. In his study of class number, Gauss was led to two conjectures, both of which we shall prove.

We assume known in the first part of this chapter the elements of the theory of quadratic fields. The reader who is not acquainted with this theory will not be seriously handicapped. He may take equation (60), in Theorem 2.8, as the definition of the class number $h(d)$, bearing in mind that it is a positive integer, and most of the subsequent results can be easily interpreted as theorems about Dirichlet L-series with real characters. These latter results have had important applications, among others to the distribution of primes in various arithmetic progressions and consequences thereof.

Let R denote the field of rational numbers and $R(\sqrt{D})$ a quadratic field over R. The introduction of ideals, it will be remembered, was made necessary by the failure of the fundamental theorem of arithmetic for the integers of $R(\sqrt{D})$. The decomposition of integers of $R(\sqrt{D})$ into primes is not unique. Another way of expressing this is to say that in $R(\sqrt{D})$ not all ideals are principal. It is natural then to define a function which represents some measure of dispersion so to speak. The intent is to measure the extent to which the integers of the field deviate from the uniqueness of decomposition. One such (and certainly the most important) is the so-called class number h which is such that if $h = 1$, then all ideals are principal. To define this function, we introduce the concept of equivalence.

DEFINITION 1.1. Two ideals $\mathfrak{a}$ and $\mathfrak{b}$ are said to be equivalent, and we write $\mathfrak{a} \sim \mathfrak{b}$, if there exist integers α and β of the field such that

$$(1) \qquad (\alpha)\mathfrak{a} = (\beta)\mathfrak{b} ,$$

where (η) indicates the principal ideal generated by η.

The first theorem states that this is indeed an equivalence relation.

THEOREM 1.1. (i) $\mathfrak{a} \sim \mathfrak{b}$;

(ii) *If* $\mathfrak{a} \sim \mathfrak{b}$, *then* $\mathfrak{b} \sim \mathfrak{a}$;

(iii) *If* $\mathfrak{a} \sim \mathfrak{b}$ *and* $\mathfrak{b} \sim \mathfrak{c}$, *then* $\mathfrak{a} \sim \mathfrak{c}$.

Proof. The proofs of (i) and (ii) follow at once from the definition. For the proof of (iii), we determine integers α, β, γ, δ such that by (1),

$$(\alpha)\mathfrak{a} = (\beta)\mathfrak{b}, \qquad (\gamma)\mathfrak{b} = (\delta)\mathfrak{c}$$

and therefore $(\alpha\gamma)\mathfrak{a} = (\beta\delta)\mathfrak{c}$ which implies that $\mathfrak{a} \sim \mathfrak{c}$.

This equivalence relation thus decomposes the set of all ideals into equivalence classes.

Definition 1.2. The number of equivalence classes is called the class number and is denoted by h. If we denote by d the discriminant of the field $R(\sqrt{D})$, then $h = h(d)$ is a function of d.

We observe that if $h = 1$, then there is only one class—all ideals are principal.

Actually, under an obvious law of composition, the classes of ideals form a group. We prove

Theorem 1.2. *The classes of ideals form an abelian group* $\mathfrak{G}$.

Proof. We define the law of composition as follows. If $\mathscr{C}_1$ and $\mathscr{C}_2$ are two classes with representatives $\mathfrak{a}_1$ and $\mathfrak{a}_2$, then we define the product of the classes $\mathscr{C}_1$ and $\mathscr{C}_2$ as the class $\mathscr{C}_3$ determined by the product $\mathfrak{a}_1\mathfrak{a}_2$. It is now easy to see that the class $\mathscr{C}_3$ is independent of the representatives $\mathfrak{a}_1$ and $\mathfrak{a}_2$. For if $\mathfrak{b}_1$ and $\mathfrak{b}_2$ are any other ideals in $\mathscr{C}_1$ and $\mathscr{C}_2$, then $\mathfrak{a}_1 \sim \mathfrak{b}_1$, $\mathfrak{a}_2 \sim \mathfrak{b}_2$ and clearly $\mathfrak{a}_1\mathfrak{a}_2 \sim \mathfrak{b}_1\mathfrak{b}_2$; thus $\mathfrak{b}_1\mathfrak{b}_2$ determines the same class $\mathscr{C}_3$. This composition is clearly an associative and commutative one.

Let $\mathscr{C}_0$ be the class of principal ideals, then $\mathscr{C}_0\mathscr{C} = \mathscr{C}\mathscr{C}_0 = \mathscr{C}$ for any class $\mathscr{C}$, and $\mathscr{C}_0$ thus acts as an identity.

One of the fundamental theorems on ideals is that to each ideal $\mathfrak{a}$ there exists an ideal $\mathfrak{b}$ such that $\mathfrak{a}\mathfrak{b}$ is a principal ideal, say (γ). If $\mathfrak{a}$ belongs to $\mathscr{C}$, then the inverse class $\mathscr{C}^{-1}$ is the class determined by this ideal $\mathfrak{b}$. $\mathscr{C}^{-1}$ is once again independent of the choice of the ideal $\mathfrak{a}$. For if $\mathfrak{a}' \sim \mathfrak{a}$ and $\mathfrak{a}'\mathfrak{b}' = (\gamma')$, then we determine integers μ and μ' such that $(\mu)\mathfrak{a} = (\mu')\mathfrak{a}'$. As a result $(\mu')\mathfrak{b}'\mathfrak{a}' = (\gamma'\mu') = (\mu)\mathfrak{a}\mathfrak{b}'$, $(\mu'\gamma')\mathfrak{b} = (\mu)\mathfrak{a}\mathfrak{b}\mathfrak{b}' = (\mu\gamma)\mathfrak{b}'$. This means that $\mathfrak{b} \sim \mathfrak{b}'$.

The class number h is the order of the group $\mathfrak{G}$. One of the first questions which arises from the definition of h is whether h is always finite. The answer is in the affirmative and a proof can be achieved with the help of one of Minkowski's theorems on convex sets. Before stating this theorem, it is helpful to introduce some simple concepts.

In the plane, we call points with integer coordinates *lattice points*.

Let A be a set in the plane. We say that A is a convex set if whenever it contains two points P and Q it contains the line segment joining P to Q. That is, if P is the vector (a, b) and Q the vector (c, d), then if the points P and Q are in the convex set A, $\lambda P + \mu Q$ is in A for all non-negative real numbers λ and μ satisfying $\lambda + \mu = 1$.

A is said to be symmetric about the origin O if whenever it contains P it also contains $-P$.

DEFINITION 1.3. By a convex body is meant an open bounded convex set. We prove the basic theorem of Minkowski.

THEOREM 1.3. *If A is a convex body symmetric about the origin O, and its area is > 4, then there exists inside A a lattice point other than O.*

PROOF. The proof is based on the following lemma: We shall show that if C is an open bounded set with area > 1, then C contains two points P and Q such that $P-Q$ is a lattice point. To show this, we translate all of the squares in the plane with lattice points at the vertices to the unit square carrying any point of C with the square. Since the area of C is > 1, two parts of the translates of C must overlap in the unit square and any two points of C which are translated to the same point in the unit square will satisfy the conclusion of the theorem. To make this precise, let $\phi(x)$ be the characteristic function of C. That is

$$\phi(x) = \begin{cases} 0 & \text{if } x \text{ is not in } C\,, \\ 1 & \text{if } x \text{ is in } C\,, \end{cases}$$

and consider the expression

$$\psi(x) = \sum_g \phi(x+g)\,,$$

where the summation is over all lattice points in the plane. The summation is in reality finite since C is by assumption bounded, and if we go out far enough $\phi(x+g) = 0$. Each $\phi(x+g)$ is integrable and therefore so is $\psi(x)$. Thus integrating over the unit square I, we find, if R denotes the whole plane,

$$\int_I \psi(x)dx = \sum_g \int_I \phi(x+g)dx = \sum_g \int_{I+g} \phi(y)dy$$
$$= \int_R \phi(y)dy = V(C) > 1\,.$$

$I+g$ denotes the unit square translated by g, and $V(C)$ denotes the area of C.

Since $\psi(x)$ takes on only integer values, it attains a maximum m at a point x_1. Thus

$$\int_I \psi(x)dx \leqq m \cdot 1$$

and therefore, from the above inequalities, since m is an integer $m \geqq 2$, that is, $\psi(x_1) \geqq 2$. Thus, from the definition of $\psi(x)$, there exist at least two distinct lattice points g_1 and g_2 such that

$$\phi(x_1+g_1) = \phi(x_1+g_2) = 1\,.$$

This means, however, that $P = x_1 + g_1$ and $Q = x_1 + g_2$ both belong to C and that $P - Q = g_1 - g_2 =$ lattice point.

A proof of Minkowski's theorem now follows easily. Let $B = A/2$, then B has an area > 1, and by what we have just proved, there are two points

P and Q in B such that $P-Q=G$ is a lattice point. Because B is symmetric, $-Q$ is contained in B and therefore by convexity

$$\tfrac{1}{2}P - \tfrac{1}{2}Q = \tfrac{1}{2}G$$

belongs to B. In that event, however, G itself belongs to A.

COROLLARY 1. *If the area of A is precisely 4, then there is a lattice point inside A or on the boundary of A.*

PROOF. Let λ be a real number such that $1<\lambda<2$. Then the body λA has volume $4\lambda^2>4$. Thus λA has a lattice point g_λ inside A. On the other hand λA is contained in $2A$ and therefore g_λ is contained in $2A$. Thus there are only finitely many possibilities for g_λ. Let $\lambda \to 1$ in such a way that g_λ is always the same point g. Then g/λ belongs to A and $g/\lambda \to g$ as $\lambda \to 1$ through the same sequence and therefore g is a limit point of points of A. Hence g belongs to A or the boundary of A.

A consequence of this theorem is the following important corollary.

THEOREM 1.4. *Let*

$$L_i(x) = a_{i1}x_1 + a_{i2}x_2 \qquad (i=1,2) \tag{2}$$

be two linear forms with the provision that if a_{ij} are complex, then $L_2(x)=\overline{L_1(x)}$. If the determinant $D=|a_{ij}|\neq 0$ and λ_1, λ_2 are real numbers such that

$$\lambda_1\lambda_2 \geqq |D|, \tag{3}$$

with $\lambda_1=\lambda_2$ whenever a_{ij} are complex, then there exist integers x_1 and x_2 not both 0 such that

$$|L_i(x)| \leqq \lambda_i \qquad (i=1,2). \tag{4}$$

PROOF. We consider two cases:

Case (i). Suppose a_{ij} are real. Then the region determined by the inequalities (4) is convex and symmetric about the origin; indeed, it is a parallelogram. Its area is

$$A = \iint_{|L_i(x)|\leqq\lambda_i} dx_1dx_2 .$$

If we substitute $y_i=L_i(x)$ $(i=1,2)$, we find by (3),

$$A = \int_{-\lambda_1}^{\lambda_1}\int_{-\lambda_2}^{\lambda_2} \frac{\partial(x_1,x_2)}{\partial(y_1,y_2)}dy_1dy_2 = \frac{1}{|D|}4\lambda_1\lambda_2 \geqq 4 .$$

Therefore by the corollary of Theorem 1.3, it contains a lattice point inside or on the boundary other than the origin. This means that (4) is satisfied by some pair of integers x_1 and x_2 not both 0.

Case (ii). If a_{ij} are complex, then we consider the forms

$$L_1' = \frac{L_1+L_2}{2}, \qquad L_2' = \frac{L_1-L_2}{2i}, \tag{5}$$

and let

$$\lambda_1' = \lambda_2' = \frac{\lambda_1}{\sqrt{2}} .$$

L_1' and L_2' are real forms and the determinant D' of the new system (5) satisfies the relation

$$|D'| = \tfrac{1}{2}|D| ,$$

and therefore

(6) $$\lambda_1'\lambda_2' \geqq |D'| .$$

Thus again by Minkowski's theorem there exists a pair of integers satisfying the inequalities

(7) $$|L_i'(x)| \leqq \lambda_i' \qquad (i = 1, 2)$$

On the other hand, by (5) and (7),

$$|L_1(x)|^2 = L_1'^2 + L_2'^2 \leqq \lambda_1'^2 + \lambda_2'^2 = \lambda_1^2 ,$$

and this completes the proof.

We have now nearly reached our first objective.

THEOREM 1.5. *The class number is finite.*

PROOF. The proof depends on showing that in every class $\mathscr{C}$ of ideals there exists an ideal $\mathfrak{b}$ such that

$$N(\mathfrak{b}) \leqq |\sqrt{d}| ,$$

where d is the discriminant of the field. In fact, let $\mathfrak{a}$ be a representative of the class $\mathscr{C}^{-1}$ and let α_1 and α_2 be a basis for $\mathfrak{a}$, α_1' and α_2' being the conjugates of α_1 and α_2. The determinant

(8) $$D = \alpha_1\alpha_2' - \alpha_2\alpha_1' = N(\mathfrak{a})\sqrt{d} .$$

Let

(9) $$\omega = \alpha_1x_1 + \alpha_2x_2 , \qquad \omega' = \alpha_1'x_1 + \alpha_2'x_2 ,$$

and

(10) $$\lambda_1 = \lambda_2 = |N(\mathfrak{a})\sqrt{d}|^{1/2} .$$

Thus $\lambda_1\lambda_2 \geqq |D|$ and therefore by Theorem 1.4, the system

$$|\omega| \leqq \lambda_1 , \qquad |\omega'| \leqq \lambda_2$$

can be solved for nonzero integers x_1 and x_2. This means by (9) and (10) that the algebraic integer ω satisfies the inequality

$$|N(\omega)| \leqq |N(\mathfrak{a})\sqrt{d}| = N(\mathfrak{a})\,|\sqrt{d}| .$$

On the other hand, by (9), the integer ω belongs to the ideal $\mathfrak{a}$, that is, $\mathfrak{a}\,|\,(\omega)$ and therefore there exists an ideal $\mathfrak{b}$ such that $\mathfrak{a}\mathfrak{b} = (\omega)$. The ideal $\mathfrak{b}$ then belongs to the class $\mathscr{C}$ and

$$N(\mathfrak{a})N(\mathfrak{b}) = |N(\omega)| \leqq N(\mathfrak{a})|\sqrt{d}|$$

and $\mathfrak{b}$ is therefore the required ideal. Since the number of ideals with a given norm is finite, it follows that the class number is finite.

2. The analytic setting and preliminary evaluation of the class number. Our object in this section is to relate the evaluation of the class number $h(d)$ to the evaluation of a Dirichlet L-series with a certain real character. The underlying vehicle for carrying this out is the zeta function for the quadratic field $K = R(\sqrt{D})$. Let $s = \sigma + it$ and

$$\zeta(s, K) = \sum_{\mathfrak{a}} \frac{1}{N(\mathfrak{a})^s}\,; \tag{1}$$

the summation is over all integral ideals $\mathfrak{a}$. We outline the procedure we use to connect the class number with the L-series.

On the one hand, we can write $\zeta(s, K)$ as an ordinary Dirichlet series, namely

$$\zeta(s, K) = \sum_{n=1}^{\infty} \frac{F(n)}{n^s}\,, \tag{2}$$

where $F(n)$ = number of ideals whose norm is precisely n. We shall prove that

$$H(x) = \sum_{n \leqq x} F(n) = \alpha h x + O(x^{1/2})\,, \tag{3}$$

where α is a constant depending only on K and h is the class number. From this we shall show that for $\sigma > \frac{1}{2}$, $\zeta(s, K)$ is analytic except for a simple pole at $s = 1$ with residue αh.

On the other hand, the arithmetic of K will allow us to prove that

$$\zeta(s, K) = \zeta(s)L(s, \chi)\,, \tag{4}$$

where $\zeta(s)$ is the Riemann zeta function and $L(s, \chi)$ is a Dirichlet L function with a real nonprincipal character χ. The residue of $\zeta(s, K)$ is therefore

$$\lim_{s \to 1}\,(s-1)\zeta(s)L(s, \chi) = L(1, \chi)\,, \tag{5}$$

since $\zeta(s)$ has a simple pole at $s = 1$ with residue 1. A comparison of these two calculations of the residue shows then, the important conclusion that

$$\alpha h = L(1, \chi)\,. \tag{6}$$

In the next section we shall sum the series $L(1, \chi)$. We shall begin this section by proving (3). In fact, we prove somewhat more.

THEOREM 2.1. *If $\mathscr{C}$ is any class of ideals and $F(n, \mathscr{C})$ denotes the number of ideals of $\mathscr{C}$ with norm precisely n, then*

$$H(t, \mathscr{C}) = \sum_{N(\mathfrak{a}) \leqq t;\, \mathfrak{a} \in \mathscr{C}} 1 = \sum_{n \leqq t} F(n, \mathscr{C}) = \alpha t + O(t^{1/2})\,. \tag{7}$$

Here

$$\alpha = \begin{cases} \dfrac{2\pi}{w\,|\sqrt{d}\,|} & \text{if } d < 0 \\ \dfrac{2\log \varepsilon}{\sqrt{d}} & \text{if } d > 0, \end{cases} \tag{8}$$

where d is the discriminant, w is the order of the group of roots of unity contained in K ($w = 2$ for $d < -4$, $w = 6$ for $d = -3$, $w = 4$ for $d = -4$) and ε is the fundamental unit of K (ε is the least solution of the equation $x^2 - dy^2 = 4$).

Before proceeding with the proof, we make a few general remarks about counting lattice points in a given domain. Let A be any domain bounded by a suitably smooth curve. Let $M(A)$ be the number of lattice points in A or on the boundary of A. It is reasonable to suppose that

$$M(A) = \text{area of } A + \text{error}.$$

The magnitude of the error certainly does not exceed the area of a "band" of width $\mathscr{F}$, where $\mathscr{F}$ is the maximum distance between two lattice points. We make these observations more general and more precise.

LEMMA 2.1. *Let Γ be a continuous arc such that the radius of curvature at any point of Γ is $\geqq r > 0$ and suppose that about each point of Γ, there is drawn a circle of radius r. Let the resulting domain be denoted by $\Gamma(r)$ and let $|\Gamma|$ be the length of the arc Γ. Then the area $|\Gamma(r)|$ of $\Gamma(r)$ satisfies the inequality*

$$|\Gamma(r)| \leqq 2r\,|\Gamma| + \pi r^2 . \tag{9}$$

PROOF. We give a sketch of the proof; the reader may fill in complete details.

Suppose that (x, y) and (x', y') are two neighboring points on Γ and at each of these points we draw a normal to the curve Γ. In the limit these normals will intersect in the center of curvature. Let the normals intersect in an angle $d\phi$. If R is the radius of curvature then

$$ds = Rd\phi$$

and on the other hand, since $R \geqq r$ the element of area of $\Gamma(r)$ is

$$dA = 2Rrd\phi = 2rds .$$

If we integrate along Γ and supplement this integral by the semicircles at the endpoints of Γ, we find

$$|\Gamma(r)| \leqq 2r\,|\Gamma| + \pi r^2 .$$

Suppose now that the region A is bounded by a curve Γ made up of a finite number n of arcs Γ_i $(i = 1, \cdots, n)$ of curves satisfying the conditions of Lemma 2.1, then the number of lattice points in or on A is obtained as follows. Around each point of the curve Γ we draw a circle of radius r, where r is the maximum distance between lattice points and suppose that $r \leqq$ the radius of curvature at any point of Γ. Then the number of lattice points $M(A)$ in A or on Γ_i $(i = 1, \cdots, n)$ is

(10) $$M(A) = |A| + E\,,$$

where by an obvious extension of Lemma 2.1,

(11) $$E = O(2r\,|\Gamma| + n\pi r^2)\,.$$

We return to a

PROOF OF THEOREM 2.1. Let $\mathfrak{b}$ be a fixed ideal in $\mathscr{C}^{-1}$; then for every $\mathfrak{a}$ in $\mathscr{C}$, there exists γ such that

$$\mathfrak{a}\mathfrak{b} = (\gamma)\,,$$

the principal ideal generated by (γ). Thus γ is an integer in $\mathfrak{b}$ and

(12) $$|N(\gamma)| = N((\gamma)) = N(\mathfrak{a})N(\mathfrak{b}) \leqq tN(\mathfrak{b})\,.$$

If η is a unit in K, then $(\gamma\eta) = (\gamma)$ and therefore from (12)

(13) $$H(t, \mathscr{C}) = \sum_{N(\mathfrak{a}) \leqq t;\, \mathfrak{a} \in \mathscr{C}} 1 = \sum_{|N(\gamma)| \leqq tN(\mathfrak{b});\, \gamma \in \mathfrak{b}}^{*} 1$$

where the asterisk indicates that among all the associates of γ only one is to be chosen. Let γ_1, γ_2 be a basis for the ideal $\mathfrak{b}$. Then the integers of $\mathfrak{b}$ consist of the set

(14) $$\gamma(x) = x_1\gamma_1 + x_2\gamma_2\,,$$

where x_1 and x_2 are rational integers. The range of summation in (13) means therefore that we are to select the set of all pairs of integers (x_1, x_2) satisfying

(15) $$|N(\gamma(x))| \leqq tN(\mathfrak{b})$$

and such that no two of the γ defined by (14) are associates. Let us now regard x_1 and x_2 as real variables and consider the x_1x_2 plane. The condition (15) defines a certain domain W in the x_1x_2 plane whose nature we shall shortly make precise. $H(t, \mathscr{C})$ is therefore a certain number of lattice points having the property that no two lattice points lead to associated γ's. We shall impose a condition which defines essentially uniquely one γ among all its associates. To specify the domain W defined by (12), we note that

$$\begin{aligned} N(\gamma(x)) &= (x_1\gamma_1^{(1)} + x_2\gamma_2^{(1)})(x_1\gamma_1^{(2)} + x_2\gamma_2^{(2)}) \\ &= N(\gamma_1)x_1^2 + (\gamma_1^{(1)}\gamma_2^{(2)} + \gamma_2^{(1)}\gamma_1^{(2)})x_1x_2 + N(\gamma_2)x_2^2\,. \end{aligned}$$

Thus $N(\gamma(x)) = c$ defines a conic section and W is the "interior" of a hyperbola or an ellipse. Since the discriminant of the section is easily seen to be $N(\mathfrak{a})d$, it is a hyperbola when K is real and an ellipse when K is imaginary. Thus each term of the summation (13) corresponds to some lattice point in W or on its boundry. Two lattice points of W may, however, lead to associated γ's. The condition we impose to ensure that no two lattice points of a certain sub-domain of W lead to associated γ's is described as follows.

We consider the case first when K is real, and suppose that ε is a fundamental unit $\varepsilon > 1$, and all units have the form $\pm\varepsilon^k$ $(k = 0, \pm 1, \pm 2, \cdots)$.

We put

$$\log\left|\frac{\gamma^{(1)}}{\sqrt{(N(\gamma))}}\right| = z\log|\varepsilon^{(1)}| \qquad (\varepsilon^{(1)} = \varepsilon). \tag{16}$$

z is a certain real analogue of the argument of a complex number. It is easily seen that (16) holds also for the conjugate, for

$$\log\left|\frac{\gamma^{(1)}}{\sqrt{(N(\gamma))}}\right| + \log\left|\frac{\gamma^{(2)}}{\sqrt{(N(\gamma))}}\right| = 0 = \log|\varepsilon^{(1)}| + \log|\varepsilon^{(2)}|\,.$$

If we replace γ, by its associate $\pm\varepsilon^k\gamma$, then the "argument" is shifted by k. In fact we get

$$\log\left|\frac{\pm\gamma\varepsilon^k}{\sqrt{(N(\gamma\varepsilon^k))}}\right| = (z-k)\log|\varepsilon|\,, \tag{17}$$

the relation holding for both conjugates.

Among the associates of γ, we can therefore choose that unique (up to sign) associate which makes

$$0 \leqq z-k < 1\,.$$

This implies that

$$\log\left|\frac{\pm\gamma^{(i)}\varepsilon^{(i)k}}{\sqrt{(N(\gamma^{(i)}\varepsilon^{(i)k}))}}\right| < \log|\varepsilon^{(i)}| \qquad (i=1,2). \tag{18}$$

If we regard $\gamma^{(i)} = \gamma^{(i)}(x)$ as a function of x_1 and x_2, we then infer that conditions (18) describe two "sectors" of the hyperbolas W. We denote the sectors by A. Then $H(t, \mathscr{C})$ is exactly half the number of lattice points in A since there remained an ambiguity in the sign of the associate.

To apply Lemma 2.1, we shall find the area $|A|$ of the region A. We contract A by a factor $\sqrt{t}$; let

$$y_i = \frac{x_i}{\sqrt{t}} \qquad (i=1,2) \tag{19}$$

and

$$B = \frac{A}{\sqrt{t}}\,, \qquad |B| = \left|\frac{A}{\sqrt{t}}\right| = \frac{|A|}{t}\,. \tag{20}$$

Then (15) and (19) imply that

$$0 < |N(\gamma(y))| \leqq N(\mathfrak{b})\,, \tag{21}$$

while (18) is unchanged. The conditions (18) and (21) now describe the area B and

$$|B| = \iint_B dy_1 dy_2\,.$$

To perform the integration, we change variables by putting

$$z_i = \gamma_1^{(i)} y_1 + \gamma_2^{(i)} y_2 \qquad (i=1,2)\,. \tag{22}$$

The Jacobian is

$$\gamma_1^{(1)}\gamma_2^{(2)} - \gamma_1^{(2)}\gamma_2^{(1)} = N(\mathfrak{b})\,|\sqrt{d}\,| \, . \tag{23}$$

Therefore

$$|B| = \frac{1}{|\sqrt{d}\,|\,N(\mathfrak{b})} \iint dz_1 dz_2 \, , \tag{24}$$

whereas (21) implies that

$$|z_1 z_2| \leqq N(\mathfrak{b}) \, . \tag{25}$$

$|B|$ is then 4 times the area of the domain restricted to $z_i > 0$. We introduce finally the new variables

$$u = z_1 z_2 \, , \tag{26}$$

$$v = \frac{\log \dfrac{z_1}{\sqrt{(z_1 z_2)}}}{\log |\varepsilon^{(1)}|} \tag{27}$$

the Jacobian $\partial(z_1 z_2)/\partial(vu) = \log|\varepsilon|$ and then by (24), (25), (26), (27),

$$|B| = \frac{4\log|\varepsilon|}{\sqrt{|d|}\,N(\mathfrak{b})} \cdot \int_0^{N(\mathfrak{b})}\int_0^1 du dv = \frac{4\log|\varepsilon|}{\sqrt{|d|}} \, . \tag{28}$$

The conditions (14), (15), and (18) describe a sector of a hyperbola when K is real. These curves satisfy the hypothesis of Lemma 2.1. Since the length of arc is $O(\sqrt{t})$, we conclude finally when K is real that

$$H(t, \mathscr{C}) = \frac{1}{2}\,|A| + O(\sqrt{t}) = \frac{2\log|\varepsilon|}{\sqrt{|d|}}\, t + O(\sqrt{t}) \, . \tag{29}$$

The statement (8b) follows since $\varepsilon > 1$. The argument for imaginary fields is simpler since there are only w associates to every γ and we infer without any further difficulty that, in that case,

$$H(t, \mathscr{C}) = \frac{2\pi}{w\sqrt{|d|}}\, t + O(\sqrt{t}) \, . \tag{30}$$

This completes the proof and leads to the following important corollary.

THEOREM 2.2. *If*

$$H(t) = \sum_{\mathscr{C}} H(t, \mathscr{C}) = \sum_{N(\mathfrak{a}) \leqq t} 1 \, , \tag{31}$$

the first summation being over all classes $\mathscr{C}$, *then*

$$H(t) = \alpha h t + O(\sqrt{t}) \, . \tag{32}$$

PROOF. We simply apply Theorem 2.1 summing over all classes. The summation is meaningful since we have shown that the class number is finite.

If we couple this result with a general theorem on ordinary Dirichlet series, we can infer some important properties of the zeta function for K.

THEOREM 2.3. *The series*

$$\sum_{\mathfrak{a}} \frac{1}{N(\mathfrak{a})^s} = \sum_{n=1}^{\infty} \frac{F(n)}{n^s}$$

converges absolutely for $\sigma > 1$; *the function* $\zeta(s, K)$ *it represents is analytic for* $\sigma > \frac{1}{2}$ *except for a simple pole at* $s = 1$ *where the residue is* αh.

PROOF. Because

$$H(t) = \sum_{n \leq t} F(n) = \alpha h t + O(t^{1/2}) ,$$

the abscissa of convergence of $\zeta(s, K)$ is 1 by Theorem 3.4, Chapter I. Applying partial summation (Lemma 3.1, Chapter I), we get readily, if we put $H(t) - \alpha h t = \Delta(t)$,

$$\begin{aligned} \sum_{1 \leq n \leq N} \frac{F(n)}{n^s} &= s\int_1^N \frac{H(x)dx}{x^{s+1}} + \frac{H(N)}{N^s} \\ &= s\int_1^N \frac{\alpha h x dx}{x^{s+1}} + s\int_1^N \frac{\Delta(x)}{x^{s+1}} dx + \frac{H(N)}{N^s} \qquad (33) \\ &= s\alpha h\left(\frac{N^{1-s}}{1-s} + \frac{1}{s-1}\right) + s\int_1^N \frac{\Delta(x)}{x^{s+1}} dx + \frac{H(N)}{N^s} . \end{aligned}$$

If we now let $N \to \infty$, then for $\sigma > 1$,

$$\zeta(s, K) = \frac{s\alpha h}{s-1} + s\int_1^\infty \frac{\Delta(x)}{x^{s+1}} dx .$$

The integral, however, converges if $\sigma > \frac{1}{2}$ since $\Delta(x) = O(x^{1/2})$, which means that it represents an analytic function of s for $\sigma > \frac{1}{2}$. Thus for $\sigma > \frac{1}{2}$, $\zeta(s, K)$ is analytic except for the simple pole at $s = 1$ with residue αh.

The first part of the program we outlined at the beginning of the section is complete. We turn to the second part. We first show that

$$\zeta(s, K) = \prod_{\mathfrak{p}} \left(1 - \frac{1}{N(\mathfrak{p})^s}\right)^{-1} \qquad (34)$$

the product extended over all prime ideals $\mathfrak{p}$, and then use the arithmetic of K, relative to the decomposition of rational primes in K, to show that

$$\zeta(s, K) = \zeta(s)L(s, \chi) , \qquad (35)$$

where

$$\begin{aligned} L(s, \chi) &= \prod_p \left(1 - \frac{\left(\frac{d}{p}\right)}{p^s}\right)^{-1} \\ &= \sum_{n=1}^{\infty} \left(\frac{d}{n}\right) \cdot \frac{1}{n^s} , \end{aligned}$$

and (d/n) represents the Kronecker symbol whose definition and properties we shall recall shortly.

We begin by proving

THEOREM 2.4. *If* $\sigma > 1$,

$$\zeta(s, K) = \prod_{\mathfrak{p}} \left(1 - \frac{1}{N(\mathfrak{p})^s}\right)^{-1} . \tag{37}$$

PROOF. The argument is exactly the same as that used for the Riemann zeta function and uses the fact that the decomposition into prime ideals is unique. Namely, since the series

$$\sum_{k=0}^{\infty} \frac{1}{N(\mathfrak{p}^k)^s}$$

converge absolutely for $\sigma > 1$, we can multiply the series on the right of (37) and rearrange the terms. The fundamental theorem on ideals tells us that

$$\prod_{N(\mathfrak{p}) \leq x} \left(1 - \frac{1}{N(\mathfrak{p})^s}\right)^{-1} = \prod_{N(\mathfrak{p}) \leq x} \sum_{k=0}^{\infty} \frac{1}{N(\mathfrak{p}^k)^s} = \sum_{\mathfrak{a}}{}' \frac{1}{N(\mathfrak{a})^s} , \tag{38}$$

where the sum on the right includes all ideals $\mathfrak{a}$ no one of whose prime ideal factors has norm exceeding x. Allowing $x \to \infty$, we infer the result from (38).

The next step is a proof of (35). We note first that

$$\zeta(s, K) = \prod_{p} \prod_{\mathfrak{p} | p} \left(1 - \frac{1}{N(\mathfrak{p})^s}\right)^{-1} \tag{39}$$

and the problem reduces to that of investigating the manner in which a rational prime p decomposes in the field K. For this purpose, we need several lemmas.

THEOREM 2.5. *The norm of a prime ideal* $\mathfrak{p}$ *is a power of a rational prime* p. *Every principal ideal* (p) *decomposes into at most two prime ideal factors.*

PROOF. Every prime ideal $\mathfrak{p}$ divides some rational prime p. Let

$$\mathfrak{p}\mathfrak{a} = (p) ,$$

then $N((p)) = N(\mathfrak{p})N(\mathfrak{a})$ and $N((p)) = p^2$. This means that $N(\mathfrak{p}) \mid p^2$ which is the first part of the theorem. Furthermore, if

$$(p) = \mathfrak{p}_1\mathfrak{p}_2 \cdots \mathfrak{p}_r , \tag{40}$$

then

$$p^2 = N((p)) = N(\mathfrak{p}_1)N(\mathfrak{p}_2) \cdots N(\mathfrak{p}_r) . \tag{41}$$

However, by the first part, each factor on the right of (41) is a power of a prime which implies that $r \leq 2$.

We recall that if

$$K = R(\sqrt{D})$$

and d is the discriminant of K, then

$$d = \begin{cases} 4D & \text{if } D \equiv 2 \text{ or } 3 \pmod 4 , \\ D & \text{if } D \equiv 1 \pmod 4 . \end{cases} \tag{42}$$

This means that for a quadratic field, the discriminant

(43) $$d \equiv 0 \text{ or } 1 \pmod 4 .$$

Moreover, in both cases a basis for the integers of K is given by 1, $(d + \sqrt{d})/2$.

Before continuing the discussion on the decomposition of rational primes in K, we find it convenient to introduce the Kronecker symbol. This is an extension of the Jacobi symbol and we begin by summarizing some of the properties of the Jacobi and Legendre symbols.

Let p be an odd prime and a an integer prime to p. We define the Legendre symbol

(i) $$\left(\frac{a}{p}\right) = \begin{cases} +1 & \text{if } x^2 \equiv a \pmod p \text{ is solvable,} \\ -1 & \text{if } x^2 \equiv a \pmod p \text{ is not solvable.} \end{cases}$$

It is known that if $(a, p) = (b, p) = 1$, then

(ii) $$\left(\frac{ab}{p}\right) = \left(\frac{a}{p}\right)\left(\frac{b}{p}\right), \qquad \left(\frac{ac^2}{p}\right) = \left(\frac{a}{p}\right).$$

We have the equality

(iii) $$\left(\frac{a}{p}\right) = \left(\frac{b}{p}\right),$$

if $a \equiv b \pmod p$, and the remarkable Gauss-Legendre reciprocity law: If p and q are odd primes, then

(iv) $$\left(\frac{p}{q}\right)\left(\frac{q}{p}\right) = (-1)^{(p-1)(q-1)/4}$$

and the supplementary relations

(v) $$\left(\frac{-1}{p}\right) = (-1)^{(p-1)/2}, \qquad \left(\frac{2}{p}\right) = (-1)^{(p^2-1)/8}.$$

Properties (i), (ii), (iii) assert that (a/p) as a function of a for a fixed p is a character on the group of reduced residues mod p, and is nonprincipal. The Jacobi symbol is an extension of the Legendre symbol and is defined as follows: If $n > 0$, n is odd and $(a, n) = 1$, $n = p_1^{a_1} p_2^{a_2} \cdots p_r^{a_r}$, then we define

(vi) $$\left(\frac{a}{n}\right) = \left(\frac{a}{p_1}\right)^{a_1}\left(\frac{a}{p_2}\right)^{a_2} \cdots \left(\frac{a}{p_r}\right)^{a_r}.$$

In this way, the symbol (a/n) is defined for all integers a and all odd positive integers n.

Multiplicative properties are shared by Jacobi symbols. If m and n are odd positive integers, and $(a, m) = (a, n) = 1$, then

(vii) $$\left(\frac{a}{mn}\right) = \left(\frac{a}{m}\right)\left(\frac{a}{n}\right) \quad \text{and} \quad \left(\frac{ab}{n}\right) = \left(\frac{a}{n}\right)\left(\frac{b}{n}\right),$$

if $(b, n) = 1$.

The reciprocity and supplementary relations hold: If $(a, n) = 1$, and a and n are both odd positive integers, then

(viii) $$\left(\frac{a}{n}\right)\left(\frac{n}{a}\right)=(-1)^{(n-1)(a-1)/4},$$

(ix) $$\left(\frac{-1}{n}\right)=(-1)^{(n-1)/2}; \qquad \left(\frac{2}{n}\right)=(-1)^{(n^2-1)/8}.$$

The restriction that n be odd in the definition of the Jacobi symbol is inconvenient for our purposes and we extend the definition for certain n. We define the Kronecker symbol.

Let d be an integer, positive or negative and not a perfect square, $d \equiv 0$, or 1 (mod 4). We shall use the symbol in the special case when d is the discriminant of a quadratic field. If n is a positive odd integer, we define

(44) $$\left(\frac{d}{n}\right)=\begin{cases}\text{Jacobi symbol} & \text{if } (d, n)=1, \\ 0 & \text{if } (d, n)>1,\end{cases}$$

(45) $$\left(\frac{d}{2}\right)=\begin{cases}0 & \text{if } (d, 2)>1, \\ +1 & \text{if } d \equiv 1 \pmod 8, \\ -1 & \text{if } d \equiv 5 \pmod 8.\end{cases}$$

We further define for m and n both positive,

(46) $$\left(\frac{d}{2^k}\right)=\left(\frac{d}{2}\right)^k, \qquad \left(\frac{d}{mn}\right)=\left(\frac{d}{m}\right)\left(\frac{d}{n}\right).$$

By the supplementary result for the Jacobi symbol,

(47) $$\left(\frac{d}{2}\right)=\left(\frac{2}{|d|}\right),$$

and if $d_1 \equiv d_2 \pmod 8$ then

$$\left(\frac{d_1}{2}\right)=\left(\frac{d_2}{2}\right).$$

Our object is to prove that for fixed d,

$$\chi_d(n)=\left(\frac{d}{n}\right)$$

is a character modulo $|d|$ which is nonprincipal.

We define

$$\operatorname{sgn} d = d/|d|$$

and prove a preliminary result.

Lemma 2.2. *If d is odd and n positive, then*

$$\left(\frac{d}{n}\right)=\left(\frac{n}{|d|}\right).$$

Proof. If d is odd, then $d \equiv 1 \pmod 4$. Let $n = 2^a n_1$ where n_1 is odd; then on noting that $\operatorname{sgn} d = (-1)^{(\operatorname{sgn} d-1)/2}$ and for any odd k and m

$$\frac{km-1}{2} \equiv \frac{k-1}{2}+\frac{m-1}{2} \pmod 2,$$

we get,

$$\left(\frac{d}{n}\right)=\left(\frac{d}{2^a n_1}\right)=\left(\frac{d}{2}\right)^a\left(\frac{d}{n_1}\right)=\left(\frac{2}{|d|}\right)^a\left(\frac{|d|}{n_1}\right)\left(\frac{\operatorname{sgn} d}{n_1}\right)$$

$$=\left(\frac{2}{|d|}\right)^a\left(\frac{n_1}{|d|}\right)\left(\frac{\operatorname{sgn} d}{n_1}\right)(-1)^{(n_1-1)(|d|-1)/4}$$

$$=\left(\frac{n}{|d|}\right)(\operatorname{sgn} d)^{(n_1-1)/2}(-1)^{((n_1-1)/2)((|d|-1)/2)}$$

$$=\left(\frac{n}{|d|}\right)(-1)^{((n_1-1)/2)((\operatorname{sgn} d-1)/2)}(-1)^{((n_1-1)/2)((d-1)/2)+(\operatorname{sgn} d-1)/2}$$

$$=\left(\frac{n}{|d|}\right)(-1)^{(n_1-1)(d-1)/4}=\left(\frac{n}{|d|}\right).$$

With the aid of this lemma, we prove the important

LEMMA 2.3. *If m and n are both positive, then*

$$\left(\frac{d}{m}\right)=\left(\frac{d}{n}\right) \qquad \text{if } m \equiv n \pmod{|d|},$$

$$\left(\frac{d}{m}\right)=\left(\frac{d}{n}\right)\operatorname{sgn} d \qquad \text{if } m \equiv -n \pmod{|d|}.$$

PROOF. Let $d=2^a d_1$, $n=2^b n_1$, $m=2^c m_1$, with d_1, m_1, and n_1 odd.

Case (i). $a>0$. If $b>0$, then c is also greater than 0 and the result is trivial. Thus we consider the case $b=c=0$. Using (46), we get

$$\left(\frac{d}{m}\right)=\left(\frac{2}{m}\right)^a\left(\frac{|d_1|}{m}\right)\left(\frac{\operatorname{sgn} d_1}{m}\right)$$

$$=(-1)^{a(m^2-1)/8}\left(\frac{m}{|d_1|}\right)(-1)^{(m-1)(|d_1|-1)/4}(\operatorname{sgn} d_1)^{(m-1)/2}$$

$$=(-1)^{a(m^2-1)/8}\left(\frac{m}{|d_1|}\right)(-1)^{(m-1)(d_1-1)/4}.$$

The analogue holds for (d/n). Since $a \geqq 2$, then

$$a(m^2-n^2) \equiv 0 \pmod{a\,2^{a+1}}$$
$$\equiv 0 \pmod{16}.$$

Therefore if $m \equiv n \pmod{|d|}$, $(d/m)=(d/n)$, whereas if $m \equiv -n \pmod{|d|}$ the two differ by a factor $\operatorname{sgn} d$.

Case (ii). $a=0$. In this case $d \equiv 1 \pmod 4$ and Lemma 2.2 is applicable. We have

$$\left(\frac{d}{n}\right)=\left(\frac{n}{|d|}\right)$$

and the result follows at once since $(-1/|d|)=(-1)^{(|d|-1)/2}=(-1)^{(\operatorname{sgn} d-1)/2}=\operatorname{sgn} d$.

In virtue of this lemma, it is natural to define

(48) $$\chi_d(n) = \chi_d(-n)\,\mathrm{sgn}\, d$$

in case n negative. With this in mind we now prove

LEMMA 2.4. *If* $d \equiv 0$ *or* 1 (mod 4) *and not a perfect square, then*

$$\chi_d(n) = \left(\frac{d}{n}\right)$$

is a character modulo $|d|$ *which is nonprincipal.*

PROOF. That it is a character is clear from the proceding discussion. It remains to show that it is nonprincipal. We shall show that for any d, there exists n such that $(d/n) = -1$.

Case (i). Suppose that d is odd, $d \equiv 1 \pmod 4$. Let $d = p^k r$ where $(p, r) = 1$, $p \neq 2$, r is odd and k odd. This is possible since d is not a square. We let s be any quadratic nonresidue mod p and we then determine n by the congruences

$$n \equiv s \pmod p, \qquad n \equiv 1 \pmod{|r|}.$$

Using Lemma 2.2, we get

$$\left(\frac{d}{n}\right) = \left(\frac{n}{|d|}\right) = \left(\frac{n}{p}\right)^k \left(\frac{n}{|r|}\right) = \left(\frac{s}{p}\right)^k = (-1)^k = -1.$$

Case (ii). d even, $d = 2^a u$, $(u, 2) = 1$. If a is odd, we solve the congruences

$$n \equiv 5 \pmod 8, \qquad n \equiv 1 \pmod{|u|};$$

then

$$\left(\frac{d}{n}\right) = \left(\frac{2}{n}\right)^a \left(\frac{n}{|u|}\right)(-1)^{(u-1)(n-1)/4} = \left(\frac{2}{n}\right)^a = -1.$$

If a is even, and $u \equiv 3 \pmod 4$, then we solve the congruences

$$n \equiv 3 \pmod 4, \qquad n \equiv 1 \pmod{|u|}, \qquad \text{and} \quad n > 0.$$

Then

$$\left(\frac{d}{n}\right) = (-1)^{(u-1)(n-1)/4}\left(\frac{n}{|u|}\right) = (-1)^{(u-1)/2} = -1.$$

If a is even and $u \equiv 1 \pmod 4$, let $u = p^j v$, where j is odd, v is odd, $(p, v) = 1$, $p \neq 2$. We choose s a nonresidue mod p, and determine n from the congruences

$$n \equiv s \pmod p, \qquad n \equiv 1 \pmod{|v|}, \qquad n \equiv 1 \pmod 2.$$

Then by Lemma 2.1,

$$\left(\frac{d}{n}\right) = \left(\frac{n}{|u|}\right) = \left(\frac{n}{p^j}\right)\left(\frac{n}{|v|}\right) = \left(\frac{s}{p}\right)^j = (-1)^j = -1.$$

We continue by deriving a criterion for the decomposition of rational primes in K.

THEOREM 2.6. *If p is a rational prime, and d is the discriminant of the quadratic field $R(\sqrt{D})$, then if (d/p) is the Kronecker symbol,*
(i) *p decomposes into two distinct prime ideal factors if $(d/p) = 1$,*
(ii) *p remains prime if $(d/p) = -1$,*
(iii) *p is the square of a prime ideal if $(d/p) = 0$.*

PROOF. We know by Theorem 2.5 that (p) has at most two prime ideal factors.

Case (i). Suppose $p \nmid d$, then $(d/p) = 1$ means that the congruence

$$x^2 \equiv d \pmod{4p} \tag{49}$$

is solvable since $d \equiv 0, 1 \pmod 4$. We let b be a solution of (49), put

$$r = \frac{b-d}{2},$$

and consider the ideals

$$\mathfrak{p} = \left(p, r + \frac{d+\sqrt{d}}{2}\right), \tag{50}$$

$$\mathfrak{q} = \left(p, r + \frac{d-\sqrt{d}}{2}\right). \tag{51}$$

We show first that p must decompose. Let $\omega = (b + \sqrt{d})/2$; then ω is an integer but ω/p is not an integer for if it were, then ω'/p would be an integer and $((\omega - \omega')/p)^2 = d/p^2$ would be an integer which is a contradiction. Thus $p \nmid \omega$, $p \nmid \omega'$ but $p \mid \omega\omega' = (b^2 - d)/4$. Therefore (p) is not a prime ideal and hence must split into a product of two prime ideal factors. It remains to show that they are distinct. Because $(r + d/2)^2 - d/4 = (b/2)^2 - d/4 \equiv 0 \pmod p$ by (49),

$$\mathfrak{p}\mathfrak{q} = (p)\left(p, r + \frac{d+\sqrt{d}}{2}, r + \frac{d-\sqrt{d}}{2}, \frac{b^2-d}{4p}\right).$$

The second factor contains the terms p and $\{(r + (d+\sqrt{d})/2) - (r + (d-\sqrt{d})/2\}^2 = d$ and $(p, d) = 1$. Therefore the second factor is (1) and

$$\mathfrak{p}\mathfrak{q} = (p).$$

Moreover $\mathfrak{p} \neq \mathfrak{q}$ since the g.c.d.

$$(\mathfrak{p}, \mathfrak{q}) = \left(p, r + \frac{d+\sqrt{d}}{2}, r + \frac{d-\sqrt{d}}{2}\right) = (1)$$

because it contains the relatively prime integers p and d.

Now we suppose the converse. Suppose that $(p) = \mathfrak{p}\mathfrak{q}$ and $\mathfrak{p} \neq \mathfrak{q}$. Then $N(\mathfrak{p}) = p$. The residue classes $1, 2, \cdots, p-1$, are all distinct modulo $\mathfrak{p}$. For if $a \neq b$ and $a \equiv b \pmod{\mathfrak{p}}$, then

$$c = a - b \equiv 0 \pmod{\mathfrak{p}}. \tag{52}$$

But $(c, p) = 1$ and there exist integers m and n such that $mc + np = 1$. This means that $((c), (p)) = 1$ or that $((c), \mathfrak{p}) = 1$ which contradicts (52). Thus for some rational integer r,

$$\frac{d + \sqrt{d}}{2} \equiv r \pmod{\mathfrak{p}}$$

or

$$(2r - d)^2 \equiv d \pmod{4\mathfrak{p}} .$$

Since this involves only the rational integers $(2r - d)$ and d, it follows that

$$(2r - d)^2 \equiv d \pmod{4\mathfrak{q}}$$

or that

$$(2r - d)^2 \equiv d \pmod{4p} ,$$

since we assumed that $\mathfrak{p} \neq \mathfrak{q}$. This implies however that

$$\left(\frac{d}{p}\right) = 1 .$$

Case (ii). If $p \mid d$, and p is odd, let

$$\mathfrak{q} = \left(p, \frac{d + \sqrt{d}}{2}\right) .$$

The conjugate

$$\mathfrak{q}' = \left(p, \frac{d - \sqrt{d}}{2}\right) = \left(p, \frac{d - \sqrt{d}}{2} - d\right) = \left(p, \frac{d + \sqrt{d}}{2}\right) = \mathfrak{q} ,$$

since $p \mid d$. Therefore

$$\mathfrak{q}^2 = \mathfrak{q}\mathfrak{q}' = (p)\left(p, \frac{d + \sqrt{d}}{2}, \frac{d - \sqrt{d}}{2}, \frac{d(d-1)}{4p}\right) .$$

Since $(p, d(d-1)/4p) = 1$ because d is free of the square of an odd prime, it follows that

$$(p) = \mathfrak{q}^2 .$$

Case (iii). We consider finally the case $2 \mid d$, that is, $D \equiv 2, 3 \pmod 4$; then

$$2 = \begin{cases} (2, \sqrt{D})^2 & \text{if } D \equiv 2 \pmod 4 , \\ (2, 1 + \sqrt{D})^2 & \text{if } D \equiv 3 \pmod 4 . \end{cases}$$

This completes the proof.

We return to a proof of (35).

THEOREM 2.7. *If $K = R(\sqrt{D})$ is a quadratic field with discriminant d and $\zeta(s, K)$, the zeta function of K, then*

$$\zeta(s, K) = \zeta(s)L(s, \chi) , \tag{53}$$

where $\zeta(s)$ is the Riemann zeta function and

$$L(s, \chi) = \sum_{n=1}^{\infty} \frac{\left(\frac{d}{n}\right)}{n^s} . \tag{54}$$

Proof. By Theorem 2.4 and because each prime ideal divides a rational prime p, we have

$$\zeta(s, K) = \prod_{\mathfrak{p}} \left(1 - \frac{1}{N(\mathfrak{p})^s}\right)^{-1} = \prod_{p} \prod_{\mathfrak{p}|p} \left(1 - \frac{1}{N(\mathfrak{p})^s}\right)^{-1} . \tag{55}$$

On the other hand, we use Theorem 2.6 to investigate the inner product. Suppose that $(d/p) = 1$, then $p = \mathfrak{p}\mathfrak{p}'$, $N(\mathfrak{p}) = N(\mathfrak{p}') = p$ and therefore

$$\prod_{\mathfrak{p}|p} \left(1 - \frac{1}{N(\mathfrak{p})^s}\right)^{-1} = \left(1 - \frac{1}{N(\mathfrak{p}')^s}\right)^{-1} \left(1 - \frac{1}{N(\mathfrak{p})^s}\right)^{-1}$$

$$= \left(1 - \frac{1}{p^s}\right)^{-2} = \left(1 - \frac{1}{p^s}\right)^{-1} \left(1 - \frac{\left(\frac{d}{p}\right)}{p^s}\right)^{-1} .$$

If $(d/p) = -1$, p remains prime $(p) = \mathfrak{p}$, $N(\mathfrak{p}) = p^2$ and

$$\begin{aligned} \prod_{\mathfrak{p}|p} \left(1 - \frac{1}{N(\mathfrak{p})^s}\right)^{-1} &= \left(1 - \frac{1}{p^{2s}}\right)^{-1} = \left(1 - \frac{1}{p^s}\right)^{-1} \left(1 + \frac{1}{p^s}\right)^{-1} \\ &= \left(1 - \frac{1}{p^s}\right)^{-1} \left(1 - \frac{\left(\frac{d}{p}\right)}{p^s}\right)^{-1} . \end{aligned} \tag{57}$$

If $(d/p) = 0$, then $(p) = \mathfrak{p}^2$, $N(\mathfrak{p}) = p$ and

$$\prod_{\mathfrak{p}|p} \left(1 - \frac{1}{N(\mathfrak{p})^s}\right)^{-1} = \left(1 - \frac{1}{p^s}\right)^{-1} = \left(1 - \frac{1}{p^s}\right)^{-1} \left(1 - \frac{\left(\frac{d}{p}\right)}{p^s}\right)^{-1} . \tag{58}$$

Thus in every case, by (56), (57), (58),

$$\prod_{\mathfrak{p}|p} \left(1 - \frac{1}{N(\mathfrak{p})^s}\right)^{-1} = \left(1 - \frac{1}{p^s}\right)^{-1} \left(1 - \frac{\left(\frac{d}{p}\right)}{p^s}\right)^{-1}$$

and this completes the proof.

This theorem permits the calculation of the residue of $\zeta(s, K)$ and the deduction of the fundamental relation § 1, (6).

Theorem 2.8. *If*

$$\alpha = \begin{cases} \dfrac{2\pi}{w\sqrt{|d|}} & \text{if } d < 0 , \\[2ex] \dfrac{2 \log \varepsilon}{\sqrt{d}} & \text{if } d > 0 , \end{cases} \tag{59}$$

where $w = 2$ *for* $d \leqq -7$, $w = 6$ *for* $d = -3$, $w = 4$ *for* $d = -4$, *and* ε *is the fundamental unit of* K, *in other words,* ε *is the least positive solution of the equation* $x^2 - dy^2 = 4$, *then*

$$\alpha h(d) = L(1, \chi)\,, \tag{60}$$

where

$$L(1, \chi) = \prod_p \left(1 - \frac{\left(\frac{d}{p}\right)}{p}\right)^{-1} = \sum_{n=1}^{\infty} \frac{\left(\frac{d}{n}\right)}{n}\,. \tag{61}$$

PROOF. By Lemma 2.4, the Kronecker symbol (d/n) is a nonprincipal character modulo $|d|$. Consequently, the series $L(s, \chi)$ converges for $\sigma > 0$ by Theorem 4.1, Chapter I, and is therefore analytic for $\sigma > 0$. Since $\zeta(s)$ has a simple pole at $s = 1$ with residue 1, it follows that the residue of $\zeta(s, K)$ is given by

$$\lim_{s \to 1} (s-1)\zeta(s, K) = \lim_{s \to 1} (s-1)\zeta(s) \cdot \lim_{s \to 1} L(s, \chi) = L(1, \chi)\,.$$

On the other hand, we calculated the residue in another way by Theorem 2.3 and this was $\alpha h(d)$. Thus

$$\alpha h(d) = L(1, \chi)\,. \tag{62}$$

We observe an important and interesting by-product, namely

COROLLARY 1. *If* $\chi = \chi_d$ *is the Kronecker symbol, then*

$$L(1, \chi) > 0\,. \tag{63}$$

The decomposition of primes in K *has therefore provided a new proof of this fundamental fact.*

In the next section, we sum the series for $L(1, \chi)$.

3. The Gauss-Dirichlet formula for the class number. Our object in this section is to sum the series $L(1, \chi)$. This is accomplished as follows. Since, by Lemma 2.4, $\chi(n) = (d/n)$ is a character modulo $|d|$, it follows that $\chi(n)$ is a periodic function on the integers with period $|d|$. We expand $\chi(n)$ in a finite "Fourier" series relative to a suitable set. This set is provided by the roots of unity. Let

$$\rho = e^{2\pi i/|d|}\,, \tag{1}$$

then ρ^n is periodic with period $|d|$. That is,

$$\rho^{n+|d|} = \rho^n\,.$$

Moreover, by Lemma 8.1, Chapter IV,

$$\begin{aligned} \sum_{a=0}^{|d|-1} \rho^{ar}\rho^{-as} = \sum_{a=1}^{|d|} \rho^{ar}\rho^{-as} &= \sum_{a=1}^{|d|} \rho^{a(r-s)} \\ &= \begin{cases} |d| & \text{if } r \equiv s \pmod{|d|} \\ 0 & \text{if } r \not\equiv s \pmod{|d|} \end{cases} = |d|\,\delta_{rs}\,. \end{aligned} \tag{2}$$

Thus the $|d|$th roots of unity have a property of orthogonality mod $|d|$.

With this in mind, we observe that the system of equations

(3) $$\chi(n) = \sum_{r=0}^{|d|-1} c_r \rho^{nr} \qquad (n = 0, 1, \cdots, |d| - 1)$$

always has a unique solution c_r $(r = 0, 1, \cdots, |d| - 1)$ since the determinant of the system is

$$|\rho^{nr}| \qquad (n, r = 0, 1, \cdots, |d| - 1)$$

and this is the well-known van der Monde determinant whose value is

$$\prod_{i \neq j} (\rho^i - \rho^j) \neq 0 .$$

Moreover, if $m \equiv n \pmod d$, then $\chi(n) = \chi(m)$ and

(4) $$c_n = c_m .$$

But since by § 2, (48),

$$\chi(-n) = \chi(n) \operatorname{sgn} d ,$$

we get

(5) $$c_{-n} = c_n \operatorname{sgn} d .$$

If we solve for these "Fourier" coefficients c_n, we get

THEOREM 3.1. *If $c_0, c_1, \cdots, c_{|d|-1}$ are defined by* (3), *then*

(6) $$c_r = \frac{1}{d} \sum_{m=1}^{|d|-1} \chi(m) \rho^{mr} .$$

In particular, $c_0 = 0$.

PROOF. Indeed from (3), we multiply both sides by ρ^{-sn} and sum on n. Then using (2), we get

(7) $$\sum_{n=0}^{|d|-1} \chi(n) \rho^{-sn} = \sum_{r=0}^{|d|-1} c_r \sum_{n=0}^{|d|-1} \rho^{rn} \rho^{-sn} = |d| c_s .$$

Therefore from (7),

$$c_s = \frac{1}{|d|} \sum_{n=0}^{|d|-1} \chi(n) \rho^{-sn} = \frac{\chi(-1)}{|d|} \sum_{n=0}^{|d|-1} \chi(-n) \rho^{-sn} = \frac{1}{d} \sum_{m=0}^{|d|-1} \chi(m) \rho^{sm} .$$

COROLLARY 1. *Suppose that $s \neq 0$, then if $d > 0$, c_s is real, while if $d < 0$, c_s is purely imaginary. In fact*

$$\bar{c}_s = \frac{1}{d} \sum_{n=0}^{|d|-1} \chi(n) \rho^{-sn} = c_{-s} = c_s \operatorname{sgn} d,$$

by (5).

We now sum the series for $L(1, \chi)$.

THEOREM 3.2. *If $c_0, c_1, \cdots, c_{|d|-1}$ are defined by* (3), *then*
(i) *if $d < 0$*,

$$L(1, \chi) = \frac{-\pi i}{d} \sum_{r=1}^{|d|-1} r c_r \,; \tag{8}$$

(ii) *if* $d > 0$,

$$L(1, \chi) = -\sum_{r=1}^{|d|-1} c_r \log \sin \frac{\pi r}{d} \,. \tag{9}$$

PROOF. In the series

$$L(1, \chi) = \sum_{n=1}^{\infty} \frac{\chi(n)}{n} = \sum_{n=1}^{\infty} \frac{\left(\frac{d}{n}\right)}{n} \,,$$

we substitute for $\chi(n)$ from (3),

$$L(1, \chi) = \sum_{n=1}^{\infty} \frac{1}{n} \sum_{r=0}^{|d|-1} c_r \rho^{nr} \,. \tag{10}$$

Then on observing that by Theorem 3.1, $c_0 = 0$, and the series

$$\sum_{m=1}^{\infty} \frac{\rho^{rm}}{m}$$

all converge if $r \neq 0$, we find by (10),

$$L(1, \chi) = \sum_{r=1}^{|d|-1} c_r \sum_{n=1}^{\infty} \frac{\rho^{nr}}{n} = -\sum_{r=1}^{|d|-1} c_r \log (1 - \rho^r) \,. \tag{11}$$

We consider the cases $d > 0$, $d < 0$ separately.

Case (i). $d < 0$. By corollary, Theorem 3.1, c_r is purely imaginary and since $L(1, \chi)$ is real, then by (11)

$$\begin{aligned} L(1, \chi) &= -i \sum_{r=1}^{|d|-1} c_r \mathscr{I} \log (1 - \rho^r) \\ &= -i \sum_{r=1}^{|d|-1} c_r \arg (1 - \rho^r) = \frac{-i\pi}{|d|} \sum_{r=1}^{|d|-1} r c_r \,, \end{aligned}$$

if we use the fact that $\sum_{r=1}^{|d|-1} c_r = 0$.

Case (ii). $d > 0$, then again from (11),

$$\begin{aligned} L(1, \chi) &= -\sum_{r=1}^{d-1} c_r \mathscr{R} \log (1 - \rho^r) \\ &= -\sum_{r=1}^{d-1} c_r \log |1 - \rho^r| \\ &= -\sum_{r=1}^{d-1} c_r \log \sin \frac{\pi r}{d} \,. \end{aligned}$$

The sum which appears in the right-hand side of (6) is the celebrated Gauss sum, which was first introduced by Gauss in connection with cyclotomy. We define

$$G(a, \chi_d) = \sum_{n=0}^{|d|-1} \chi_d(n) \rho^{an} = \sum_{n \bmod |d|} \chi_d(n) \rho^{an} \,, \tag{12}$$

where again $\chi(n) = \chi_d(n) = (d/n)$ is the Kronecker symbol and $\rho = \exp[2\pi i/|d|]$. We shall give a systematic account of Gaussian sums in § 4, but for the moment, we assume known the following theorems

$$G(a, \chi) = \chi(a)G(1, \chi)\,, \tag{13}$$

$$G(1, \chi) = \sqrt{d}\,. \tag{14}$$

See Theorems 4.12, 4.17. With the help of (13) and (14) we can derive the formula for the class number.

Theorem 3.3. *The class number $h(d)$ of a quadratic field with discriminant d satisfies the following relation*:

$$h(d) = \begin{cases} \dfrac{-w}{2|d|} \displaystyle\sum_{r=1}^{|d|-1} r\left(\frac{d}{r}\right) & \textit{if } d < 0, \quad (15) \\ \dfrac{-1}{2\log\varepsilon} \displaystyle\sum_{r=1}^{d-1} \left(\frac{d}{r}\right) \log\sin\frac{\pi r}{d} & \textit{if } d > 0. \quad (16) \end{cases}$$

Here ε and w are as defined in Theorem 2.8.

Proof. Indeed by § 2, (60), of Theorem 2.8,

$$\alpha h(d) = L(1, \chi)\,.$$

Case (i). If $d < 0$, then by Theorem 3.2, and the definition of α we get from (8),

$$\frac{2\pi h(d)}{w\sqrt{|d|}} = -\frac{\pi i}{|d|} \sum_{r=1}^{|d|-1} r c_r\,.$$

But by Theorem 3.1, (13) and (14),

$$c_r = \frac{1}{d} G(r, \chi) = \frac{1}{d} \chi(r) G(1, \chi) = \frac{\chi(r)}{d} \sqrt{d}$$

from which the statement (15) of the theorem follows.

Case (ii). The corresponding formulas for $d > 0$, permit the deduction of (16). Indeed from Theorem 3.2,

$$\frac{2\log\varepsilon}{\sqrt{d}} h(d) = -\sum_{r=1}^{d-1} c_r \log\sin\frac{\pi r}{d}$$

thus

$$h(d) = \frac{-1}{2\log\varepsilon} \sum_{r=1}^{d-1} \chi(r) \log\sin\frac{\pi r}{d}\,.$$

From these formulas, some highly interesting results may be deduced. We derive some here and in the problems.

Consider the case when d is the negative of a prime and $d < -4$. Suppose that $d = -p$ in which case $p \equiv 3 \pmod 4$. It follows from (15) that

$$h(-p) = -\frac{1}{p} \sum_{r=1}^{p-1} r\left(\frac{-p}{r}\right), \tag{17}$$

and we get

THEOREM 3.4. *If p is a prime, $p \equiv 3 \pmod 4$, then*

$$h(-p) = \frac{1}{p}(\Sigma\, n - \Sigma\, r)\,, \tag{18}$$

where the first summation is over the nonresidues modulo p and the second sum over the residues.

PROOF. From (17), we have

$$h(-p) = -\frac{1}{p}\sum_{j=1}^{p-1} j\left(\frac{-p}{j}\right).$$

On the other hand, by Lemma 2.2,

$$\left(\frac{-p}{j}\right) = \left(\frac{j}{p}\right).$$

Hence

$$h(-p) = -\frac{1}{p}\sum_{j=1}^{p-1} j\left(-\frac{p}{j}\right) = -\frac{1}{p}\sum_{j=1}^{p-1} j\left(\frac{j}{p}\right) = \frac{1}{p}(\Sigma\, n - \Sigma\, r)\,,$$

as required.

A further reduction is possible when p is prime.

THEOREM 3.5. *If $-p \equiv 1 \pmod 8$, then*

$$h(-p) = \sum_{0<r<p/2} 1 - \sum_{-p/2<r<0} 1$$

(19) = *number of positive quadratic residues — number of negative quadratic residues in the interval $-p/2 < x < p/2$, where the summation index ranges over quadratic residues modulo p.*

PROOF. Because $p \equiv 7 \pmod 8$, $(2/p) = 1$, and as r ranges over the quadratic residues modulo p, so does $2r$. If r is a residue and $0 < r < p/2$, then

$$0 < 2r < p\,, \tag{20}$$

whereas if $p/2 < r < p$, then

$$0 < 2r - p < p\,. \tag{21}$$

Hence by (20) and (21),

$$\sum_{0<r<p} r = \sum_{0<r<p/2} 2r + \sum_{p>r>p/2} (2r - p) = \sum_{0<r<p} 2r - p\sum_{p>r>p/2} 1\,. \tag{22}$$

In the same way,

$$\sum_{0<n<p} n = \sum_{0<n<p} 2n - p\sum_{p>n>p/2} 1\,. \tag{23}$$

Consequently, from (22) and (23),

$$\sum_{0<n<p} n - \sum_{0<r<p} r = p\Big(\sum_{p/2<n<p} 1 - \sum_{p/2<r<p} 1\Big)\,.$$

But since $(-1/p) = -1$, then if n is a nonresidue, $-n$ is a residue and therefore

$$\begin{aligned}\sum n - \sum r &= p\Big(\sum_{-p<r<-p/2} 1 - \sum_{p>r>p/2} 1\Big)\\ &= p\Big(\sum_{0<r<p/2} 1 - \sum_{p/2<r<p} 1\Big)\\ &= p\Big(\sum_{0<r<p/2} 1 - \sum_{-p/2<r<0} 1\Big),\end{aligned}$$

and this is essentially the enunciation of the theorem.

The case $p \equiv 8 \pmod 3$ is treated similarly.

Theorem 3.6. *If* $-p \equiv 5 \pmod 8$, *then*

$$h(-p) = \frac{1}{3}\Big(\sum_{0<r<p/2} 1 - \sum_{-p/2<r<0} 1\Big) \tag{24}$$

$= \frac{1}{3}$ (*number of positive* − *number of negative quadratic residues in the interval* $-p/2 < x < p/2$).

Proof. The proof proceeds exactly as above except that in this case $(2/p) = -1$ and this introduces the factor $\frac{1}{3}$.

Actually a direct consequence of these theorems is the following purely arithmetic theorem.

Theorem 3.7. *If* $p \equiv 3 \pmod 4$, *then there are more quadratic residues* $< p/2$ *than there are* $> p/2$.

Proof. Since h is by its nature $\geqq 1$, it follows that there are more residues in the interval 0 to $p/2$ than there are in the interval $p/2$ to p, in the case when $p \equiv 3 \pmod 4$.

Actually the only fact we need for this deduction is that $L(1, \chi) \neq 0$.

It is interesting to observe that in spite of the simplicity of its statement, no "elementary" proof of Theorem 3.7 is known.

This remarkable fact for primes $p \equiv 3 \pmod 4$ is in contrast to the case $p \equiv 1 \pmod 4$, where, because $(-1/p) = 1$, there are as many residues in the interval 0 to $p/2$ as there are in the interval $p/2$ to p.

The formulas of Theorems 3.5 and 3.6 may in fact be used to calculate class numbers and are highly efficacious for small values of p.

Example 1. Let θ satisfy the equation

$$x^2 + x + 1 = 0$$

and $K = R(\theta)$; that is, K is the field of cube roots of unity. It is easy to see that $d = -3$. Here we must retain the value $w = 6$, and from (15) and (24), we have

$$h(-3) = \frac{3}{3}(1 - 0) = 1\,.$$

Example 2. Let $K = R(\sqrt{-7})$. Then $d = -7$, $p = 7$, and $h(-7) = 1$ since the quadratic residues of 7 are 1, 2, 4.

EXAMPLE 3. If $K = R(\sqrt{-23})$, then $p = 23 \equiv 7 \pmod 8$. The residues modulo 23 are

$$1,\ 4,\ 9,\ -7,\ 2,\ -10,\ 3,\ -5,\ -11,\ 8,\ 6,$$

and therefore $h(-23) = 3$.

Though these formulas are all highly interesting, there nevertheless remain some outstanding questions about $h(d)$ unanswered by the preceding discussion. Among these is the following:

For what values of d is $h(d) = 1$? In other words, for what quadratic fields is the decomposition into prime integers of the field unique? That is, for what fields is every ideal principal? We shall not enter into details of this question, but it may be mentioned that it has been shown by Heilbronn and Linfoot that in case $d < 0$, there are at most 10 values of d for which $h(d) = 1$. Nine of these are $d = -3,\ -4,\ -7,\ -8,\ -11,\ -19,\ -43,\ -67,\ -163$. Whether or not a tenth value exists is still not known.

In the case $d < 0$, on the contrary, it appears possible that there exist infinitely many d for which $h(d) = 1$.

We pass to the problem of the asymptotic behavior of $h(d)$ as $d \to \pm\infty$.

In the case $d < 0$, Gauss conjectured that $h(d) \to \infty$ as $d \to -\infty$. This was first proved by Heilbronn in 1933. In § 6, we shall prove a stronger theorem due to Siegel from which Heilbronn's theorem follows as an immediate consequence.

On the other hand, for $d > 0$, the behavior of $h(d)$ appears to be intimately related to the fundamental unit.

In the case $d < 0$, Siegel's theorem states that $\log h(d) \sim \frac{1}{2} \log |d|$. Before proving this and its analogue for $d > 0$, we shall consider the problem of the mean value of $h(d)$ but first give a systematic account of Gaussian sums.

4. Characters and Gaussian sums. Let χ be a character modulo k and suppose that

$$\rho = \rho_k = e^{2\pi i/k}\,. \tag{1}$$

We define quite generally a Gaussian sum as follows:

$$G(a, \chi) = \sum_{n=0}^{k-1} \chi(n)\rho^{an}\,. \tag{2}$$

Since each of the functions χ and ρ has period k, it follows that

$$G(a, \chi) = \sum_{n \bmod k} \chi(n)\rho^{an}\,, \tag{3}$$

where n runs through a complete residue system modulo k. Actually, because $\chi(n) = 0$ for $(n, k) > 1$, it suffices to have n run through a reduced residue system modulo k.

It will be observed that χ is a multiplicative function defined on the multiplicative residues modulo k whereas ρ is multiplicative on the additive residues.

From the periodicity of ρ and χ, it follows that if $a \equiv b \pmod{k}$, then

$$G(a, \chi) = G(b, \chi) . \tag{4}$$

Our object is to evaluate the sum $G(a, \chi)$ insofar as it is possible to do so, and the first step is to show that it suffices to evaluate G when k is a power of a prime. The argument used is similar to that used for the sums arising in Chapter IV, § 8.

To explain the decomposition, we recall again some elementary facts from arithmetic.

Let

$$k = k_1 k_2 \cdots k_r \tag{5}$$

be a decomposition of k into pairwise relatively prime integers k_i. That is $(k_i, k_j) = 1$ $(i \neq j)$.

Then by the Chinese remainder theorem the system of congruences

$$x \equiv a_i \pmod{k_i} \qquad i = 1, 2, \cdots, r$$

is solvable for given a_i $(i = 1, 2, \cdots, r)$.

Indeed, if $K_i = k/k_i$, then $(K_i, K_j) = 1$, $(i \neq j)$ and there exist integers c_1, $c_2, \cdots, c_r$ such that

$$c_1 K_1 + c_2 K_2 + \cdots + c_r K_r = 1 .$$

If

$$x = a_1 c_1 K_1 + a_2 c_2 K_2 + \cdots + a_r c_r K_r , \tag{6}$$

then x is the required solution and is uniquely determined modulo k.

Conversely, any residue class a modulo k determines a_i modulo k_i. It will then be recalled that as a_i run through residue systems modulo k_i, then x as determined above, runs through a residue system modulo k and conversely.

If χ is a character modulo k, we shall define the induced character χ_i modulo k_i as follows. If a is a residue class modulo k_i, then by the Chinese remainder theorem for fixed i we determine a solution of the r congruences

$$\begin{aligned} x &\equiv a \pmod{k_i} \\ x &\equiv 1 \pmod{k_j} \qquad j \neq i, j = 1, 2, \cdots, r. \end{aligned} \tag{7}$$

We call the solution a_i. It then follows that

$$a \equiv a_1 a_2 \cdots a_r \pmod{k_j} \qquad j = 1, 2, \cdots, r \tag{8}$$

and hence

$$a \equiv a_1 a_2 \cdots a_r \pmod{k} \tag{9}$$

since $(k_i, k_j) = 1$, $(i \neq j)$. Moreover for any a, the a_i are uniquely determined modulo k_i.

We then define χ_i as follows:

$$\chi_i(a) = \chi(a_i) \tag{10}$$

and it is now easy to see that χ_i is a character modulo k_i. For we have at once that if $a \equiv b \pmod{k}$, then $a_i \equiv b_i \pmod{k_i}$ and

$$\chi_i(a) = \chi_i(b) .$$

Moreover if $l \equiv m \pmod{k_i}$, then $l_i \equiv m_i \pmod{k}$, and

$$\chi_i(l) = \chi(l_i) = \chi(m_i) = \chi_i(m) .$$

By (8)

$$\chi(a) = \chi(a_1 \cdots a_r) = \chi(a_1)\chi(a_2)\cdots\chi(a_r) = \chi_1(a)\chi_2(a)\cdots\chi_r(a) . \tag{12}$$

Thus we have decomposed χ into a product $\chi_1\chi_2\cdots\chi_r$. If

$$\chi = \chi_1'\chi_2'\cdots\chi_r'$$

is another decomposition of χ, into characters χ_i' modulo k_i, then using (7), (8) and (10),

$$\chi_i(a) = \chi(a_i) = \chi_1'(a_i)\cdots\chi_r'(a_i) = \chi_i'(a_i) = \chi_i'(a) .$$

We summarize these remarks in the following

THEOREM 4.1. *If*

$$k = k_1k_2\cdots k_r \tag{13}$$

is a decomposition of k into pairwise coprime integers and if χ is a character modulo k, then there exists a unique decomposition of χ into characters χ_i modulo k_i

$$\chi = \chi_1\chi_2\cdots\chi_r . \tag{14}$$

Moreover χ_i is defined as follows:

$$\chi_i(a) = \chi(a_i) \tag{15}$$

where

$$a_i \equiv a \pmod{k_i} \qquad a_i \equiv 1 \pmod{k_j} \qquad j = 1, 2, \cdots, r, \quad j \neq i. \tag{16}$$

With the help of Theorem 4.1, we prove

THEOREM 4.2. *If $G(a, \chi)$ is the Gaussian sum defined by* (2),

$$k = k_1k_2\cdots k_r , \ (k_i , k_j) = 1 , \qquad i \neq j,$$

and $a_i \equiv a \pmod{k_i}$, then

$$G(a, \chi) = \varepsilon G(a_1 , \chi_1)G(a_2 , \chi_2)\cdots G(a_r , \chi_r) , \tag{17}$$

where $\chi = \chi_1\chi_2\cdots\chi_r$ is the decomposition of χ given by Theorem 4.1 *and*

$$\varepsilon = \chi_1\left(\frac{k}{k_1}\right)\cdots\chi_r\left(\frac{k}{k_r}\right) . \tag{18}$$

PROOF. Let $k = k_1k_2\cdots k_r$ and $K_i = k/k_i$. We determine $g_1 , g_2 , \cdots, g_r$ such that

$$g_1K_1 + g_2K_2 + \cdots + g_rK_r = 1\,. \tag{19}$$

Then if

$$n_i \equiv n \pmod{k_i}, \qquad n_i \equiv 1 \pmod{k_j} \qquad j = 1, 2, \cdots r, \; j \neq i,$$

$a \equiv a_i \pmod{k_i}$, we get from (19),

$$\begin{aligned}\rho^{an} &= e^{2\pi i a n/k} = e^{2\pi i a n g_1/k_1} \cdots e^{2\pi i a n g_r/k_r} \\ &= \rho_{k_1}^{a_1 g_1 n_1} \cdots \rho_{k_r}^{a_r g_r n_r}\,.\end{aligned}$$

Thus using Theorem 4.1,

$$\begin{aligned}G(a, \chi) &= \sum_{n \bmod k} \chi(n)\rho^{an} = \prod_{i=1}^{r} \sum_{n_i \bmod k_i} \chi_i(n_i)\rho_{k_i}^{a_i g_i n_i} \\ &= \prod_{i=1}^{r} \bar{\chi}_i(g_i) \sum_{n_i \bmod k_i} \chi_i(g_i n_i)\rho_{k_i}^{a_i n_i g_i} = \prod_{i=1}^{r} \bar{\chi}_i(g_i) G(a_i, \chi_i)\,.\end{aligned}$$

But from (19), $g_iK_i \equiv 1 \pmod{k_i}$ and therefore

$$\bar{\chi}_i(g_i) = \chi_i(K_i)$$

and the proof is thus complete.

Before proceeding, we shall introduce a concept which divides characters into two classes. The concept is that of primitivity. Its relevance for our purposes stems from a property of Gaussian sums belonging to primitive characters.

Suppose that χ_1 and χ_2 are characters modulo k_1 and k_2 respectively. If n is chosen so that $(n, k_1) = (n, k_2) = 1$, that is $(n, \{k_1, k_2\}) = 1$ where $\{k_1, k_2\}$ is the L.C.M. of k_1 and k_2, then $\chi_1(n) \neq 0$, $\chi_2(n) \neq 0$.

DEFINITION 4.1. We say that the character χ_1 is equivalent to χ_2 and we write

$$\chi_1 \sim \chi_2$$

if $\chi_1(n) = \chi_2(n)$ for $(n, \{k_1, k_2\}) = 1$.

That this is an equivalence relation is a straightforward verification. Moreover, if $\chi_1 \sim \chi_2$, then the function defined as

$$\chi(n) = \begin{cases} \chi_1(n) = \chi_2(n) & \text{if } (n, \{k_1, k_2\}) = 1\,, \\ 0 & \text{otherwise} \end{cases} \tag{20}$$

is a character modulo $\{k_1, k_2\}$.

DEFINITION 4.2. If $\chi_1 \sim \chi_2$, then we say that χ_1 is definable modulo k_2; χ_2 is said to be a representation of χ_1 modulo k_2 and k_2 is called a defining modulus for χ_1.

LEMMA 4.1. *In order that a character $\chi \bmod k$ be definable $\bmod k'$, it is necessary and sufficient that for $(a, k) = 1$, $a \equiv 1 \pmod{k'}$, then $\chi(a) = 1$.*

PROOF. If χ is definable $\bmod k'$, then χ is equivalent to a character $\chi' \bmod k'$. Therefore if $a \equiv 1 \pmod{k'}$, $(a, k) = 1$, $(a, k') = 1$, and

$$\chi(a) = \chi'(a) = 1\,.$$

Suppose conversely that $\chi(a) = 1$ whenever $(a, k) = 1$, and $a \equiv 1 \pmod{k'}$. We shall construct a character χ' equivalent to χ. Let $(a', k') = 1$, then we shall determine b such that $b \equiv a' \pmod{k'}$ and $(b, k) = 1$. It suffices to solve the congruences

$$b \equiv a' \pmod{k'} ,$$
$$b \equiv 1 \pmod{k_0} ,$$

where k_0 contains those primes in k but not in k'. Then we define

$$\chi'(a') = \chi(b) .$$

This definition is meaningful in the sense that it does not depend on the particular b chosen since if

$$b_1 \equiv a' \pmod{k'}, \qquad b_2 \equiv a' \pmod{k'}, \qquad (b_i, k) = 1 \qquad (i = 1, 2),$$

then

$$b_1 \equiv b_2 \pmod{k'}$$

and we can choose b_2^{-1} such that

$$b_1 b_2^{-1} \equiv 1 \pmod{k'}, \qquad \text{and} \qquad (b_2^{-1}, k) = 1;$$

thus $\chi(b_1 b_2^{-1}) = 1$ by hypothesis and hence $\chi(b_1) = \chi(b_2) = \chi'(a')$. $\chi'(a')$ therefore does not depend on the representative of the residue class of a'.

That χ' is a character mod k' is now clear for if $a' \equiv b' \pmod{k'}$, then we find a such that $(a, k) = 1$ and

$$a' \equiv a \equiv b' \pmod{k'} ;$$

therefore

$$\chi'(a') = \chi(a) = \chi'(b') .$$

If $(a_1', k') = (a_2', k') = 1$ then determining $a_i \equiv a_i' \pmod{k'}$, $(a_i, k) = 1$, $i = 1, 2$, we get

$$\chi'(a_1')\chi'(a_2') = \chi(a_1)\chi(a_2) = \chi(a_1 a_2) = \chi'(a_1' a_2') .$$

We complete the definition of χ' by putting $\chi'(a') = 0$ whenever $(a', k') > 1$. χ' is equivalent to χ and the lemma is proved.

Several theorems now follow from the definitions.

THEOREM 4.3. *If χ is a character modulo k and m is any multiple of k, then χ is definable modulo m.*

PROOF. In fact, we define a character χ^* as follows:

$$\chi^*(n) = \begin{cases} \chi(n) & \text{if } (n, m) = 1 , \\ 0 & \text{otherwise.} \end{cases}$$

Then it is clear that χ^* is a character modulo m and

$$\chi^* \sim \chi .$$

Thus every multiple of k is a defining modulus.

The question naturally arises whether there are circumstances under which the factors of k are defining moduli. In this connection, we have

THEOREM 4.4. *If k_1 and k_2 are defining moduli for χ, then so is (k_1, k_2), the greatest common divisor of k_1 and k_2.*

PROOF. By Lemma 4.1 it suffices to prove that if $(n_i, \{k_1, k_2\}) = 1$, $(i = 1, 2)$, and $n_1 \equiv n_2 \pmod{(k_1, k_2)}$, then

$$\chi(n_1) = \chi(n_2) . \tag{21}$$

To prove (21), it is enough to show that there exists an integer n prime to $\{k_1, k_2\}$ such that

$$n \equiv n_1 \pmod{k_1}; \qquad n \equiv n_2 \pmod{k_2} .$$

Indeed, let $d = (k_1, k_2)$ and $n_1 - n_2 = \sigma d$. There exist integers α and β such that

$$\alpha k_1 + \beta k_2 = d ,$$

and

$$\alpha\sigma k_1 + \beta\sigma k_2 = \sigma d = n_1 - n_2 . \tag{22}$$

From (22), let

$$n = -\alpha\sigma k_1 + n_1 = \beta\sigma k_2 + n_2 . \tag{23}$$

Then (23) implies that

$$n \equiv n_1 \pmod{k_1}, \qquad n \equiv n_2 \pmod{k_2} ,$$

and since $(n_i, k_i) = 1$, it follows that $(n, k_i) = 1$ $(i = 1, 2)$. In other words, $\chi(n_1) = \chi(n) = \chi(n_2)$ as required.

With the help of this result, we prove the basic theorem on defining moduli.

THEOREM 4.5. *If χ is a character, then all defining moduli for χ are multiples of the least modulus which is denoted by $f(\chi)$. $f(\chi)$ is called the conductor of χ.*

PROOF. Let $f(\chi) = k_1, k_2, k_3, \cdots$, be the defining moduli for χ arranged in ascending order of magnitude. If for $i \neq 1$, $(k_i, k_1) = d_i < k_1$, then d_i by the previous theorem is a defining modulus for χ. This contradicts the choice of k_1. Therefore $(k_i, k_1) = k_1$ and $k_1 \mid k_i$ as required.

DEFINITION 4.3. A character χ modulo k is said to be primitive if $k = f(\chi)$, the conductor of χ. Otherwise, χ is called imprimitive.

If χ is any character modulo k, and $f(\chi)$ is its conductor, then we can define a character which is equivalent to χ and which is primitive.

THEOREM 4.6. *If χ is a character modulo k, and $f(\chi)$ its conductor, then there exists a unique character χ^* modulo $f(\chi)$ equivalent to χ which is primitive.*

PROOF. The uniqueness is clear. By definition, χ is equivalent to a character $\chi^* \bmod f(\chi)$. χ^* must be primitive for if $f(\chi^*)$ is its conductor, then χ^* is equivalent to a character $\chi_1^* \bmod f(\chi^*)$. This implies that χ is equivalent to χ_1^*;

this means that χ is definable modulo $f(\chi^*)$. In other words $f(\chi^*)=f(\chi)$ by Theorem 4.5.

By the argument of Lemma 4.1, if $(n, f(\chi))=1$, then there exists n^* such that $(n^*, k)=1$, $n^* \equiv n \pmod{f(\chi)}$. χ^* is then given explicitly as follows:

$$\chi^*(n)=\begin{cases}\chi(n^*) & \text{if } (n, f(\chi))=1,\ n^*\equiv n \pmod{f(\chi)},\ (n^*, k)=1\,,\\ 0 & \text{if } (n, f(\chi))>1.\end{cases} \tag{24}$$

As a simple consequence, we get

Theorem 4.7. *If χ is a character* mod k, *$f(\chi)$ its conductor and χ^* the primitive character* mod $f(\chi)$ *equivalent to χ, then*

$$L(s, \chi^*)=\prod_{p\mid k}\left(1-\frac{\chi^*(p)}{p^s}\right)^{-1}L(s, \chi)\,, \tag{25}$$

where $L(s, \chi^*)$ and $L(s, \chi)$ are the Dirichlet L-series belonging to χ^* and χ respectively.

Proof. By Theorem 1.5, Chapter I,

$$\frac{L(s, \chi^*)}{L(s, \chi)}=\frac{\prod_p\left(1-\frac{\chi^*(p)}{p^s}\right)^{-1}}{\prod_p\left(1-\frac{\chi(p)}{p^s}\right)^{-1}}\,. \tag{26}$$

If $(p, k)=1$, then $(p, f(\chi))=1$, and $\chi^*(p)=\chi(p)$. On the other hand, if $p\mid k$, $p\nmid f(\chi)$, then $\chi(p)=0$, but $\chi^*(p)\neq 0$. Therefore cancelling equal factors in (26), we get

$$\frac{L(s, \chi^*)}{L(s, \chi)}=\prod_{p\mid k}\left(1-\frac{\chi^*(p)}{p^s}\right)^{-1}$$

as required since $\chi^*(p)=0$ if $p\mid f(\chi)$.

As a corollary, there follows

Theorem 4.8. *If χ is a character modulo k and χ^* is equivalent to χ modulo the conductor $f(\chi)$, then*

$$\sum_{n\leq N}\chi(n)=\sum_{a\mid k;\ a\leq N}\mu(a)\chi^*(a)\sum_{b\leq N/a}\chi^*(b)\,. \tag{27}$$

Proof. From (25) we get

$$\sum_{n=1}^{\infty}\frac{\chi(n)}{n^s}=\prod_{p\mid k}\left(1-\frac{\chi^*(p)}{p^s}\right)\sum_{n=1}^{\infty}\frac{\chi^*(n)}{n^s}=\sum_{d\mid k}\frac{\mu(d)\chi^*(d)}{d^s}\sum_{n=1}^{\infty}\frac{\chi^*(n)}{n^s}\,. \tag{28}$$

We write the first factor on the right of (28) as an ordinary Dirichlet series by putting

$$\delta(a)=\begin{cases}1 & \text{if } a\mid k,\\ 0 & \text{otherwise.}\end{cases}$$

Then by the multiplication theorem for Dirichlet series,

(29) $$\chi(n) = \sum_{ab=n} \mu(a)\chi^*(a)\delta(a)\chi^*(b) ,$$

and the enunciation follows.

THEOREM 4.9. *Let χ be a character modulo k and suppose that*

(30) $$k = k_1k_2 \cdots k_r \qquad (k_i, k_j) = 1, \ i \neq j$$

and

$$\chi = \chi_1\chi_2 \cdots \chi_r$$

the corresponding decomposition of χ into characters modulo k_i.
Then

(32) $$f(\chi) = f(\chi_1)f(\chi_2) \cdots f(\chi_r) ,$$

where $f(\chi_i)$ is the conductor of χ_i.

PROOF. Let k' be a factor of k and let

(33) $$k' = k_1'k_2' \cdots k_r' ,$$

where

$$k_i' = (k', k_i) .$$

Thus $(k_i', k_j') = 1$, $i \neq j$.

We shall show that k' is a defining modulus for χ if and only if k_i' is a defining modulus for χ_i $(i = 1, 2, \cdots, r)$. Indeed if k' is a defining modulus for χ, then by Lemma 4.1, for $a \equiv 1 \pmod{k'}$, $(a, k) = 1$, $\chi(a) = 1$. To show that k_i' is a defining modulus for χ_i, we determine components $a_i \bmod k_i'$ of a as in (7), (8), (9) such that

$$a_i \equiv 1 \pmod{k_i'} \qquad (i = 1, 2, \cdots, r),\ a_i \equiv 1 \pmod{k'}$$

and then $a \equiv 1 \pmod{k_i'}$, and by definition of χ_i,

$$\chi_i(a) = \chi(a_i) = 1 ;$$

that is

$$\chi_i(a) = 1 \text{ if } a \equiv 1 \pmod{k_i'} \qquad i = 1, 2, \cdots, r,$$

as required. Conversely, suppose that χ_i is definable mod k_i', then

$$\chi_i(a) = 1 \text{ for } a \equiv 1 \pmod{k_i'} \qquad i = 1, 2, \cdots, r.$$

Thus $a \equiv 1 \pmod{k'}$ and by Theorem 4.1,

$$\chi(a) = \chi_1(a)\chi_2(a) \cdots \chi_r(a) = 1 .$$

Therefore $\chi(a) = 1$ if $a \equiv 1 \pmod{k'}$.

We have therefore shown that χ is definable mod k' if and only if χ_i is definable mod k_i'.

Therefore, if $f = f(\chi)$ is the conductor of χ, then $f \mid k$ by Theorem 4.5, and we write

$$f = k_1'k_2' \cdots k_r' ,$$

where

$$k_i' = (f, k_i) .$$

It follows that $k_i' = f(\chi_i)$; for if not, then by Theorem 4.5 $f(\chi_i) \mid k_i'$, $f(\chi_i) \neq k_i'$ and χ_i is definable modulo $f(\chi_i)$. Thus by what we have just shown χ must be definable modulo m, where

$$m = k_1'k_2' \cdots k_{i-1}' f(\chi_i) k_{i+1}' \cdots k_r' .$$

Then m is a proper factor of $f(\chi)$, which contradicts the choice of $f(\chi)$.

We shall apply some of these considerations to the Kronecker symbol.

Let d be the discriminant of a quadratic field. That is, if D is square free,

$$d = \begin{cases} D & \text{if } D \equiv 1 \pmod 4, \\ 4D & \text{if } D \equiv 2, 3 \pmod 4). \end{cases} \tag{34}$$

That is $d \equiv 0, 1 \pmod 4$. We shall call integers d satisfying (34) fundamental discriminants.

The following are fundamental discriminants.

$$d = \begin{cases} (-1)^{(p-1/2}p & \text{where } p \text{ is an odd prime,} \\ -4, \pm 8. \end{cases} \tag{35}$$

We put for simplicity

$$p^* = (-1)^{(p-1)/2}p = \begin{cases} p & \text{if } p \equiv 1 \pmod 4, \\ -p & \text{if } p \equiv 3 \pmod 4). \end{cases} \tag{36}$$

Then d defined in (35) are the discriminants of the quadratic fields $R(\sqrt{p^*})$, $R(\sqrt{-1})$, $R(\sqrt{\pm 2})$ respectively.

We call the d defined in (35) prime discriminants. We have at once

THEOREM 4.10. *A product of relatively prime, prime discriminants is a fundamental discriminant. If d is a fundamental discriminant, then it is a product of distinct prime discriminants.*

PROOF. Clearly a product of relatively prime, prime discriminants is a fundamental discriminant. Suppose conversely that d is fundamental. Then

$$d = \begin{cases} D & \text{if } D \equiv 1 \pmod 4, \\ 4D & \text{if } D \equiv 2, 3 \pmod 4 \end{cases}$$

and D is square free.

Let $D > 0$; the case $D < 0$ is treated in exactly the same way.

Case (i). $D \equiv 1 \pmod 4$, then

$$d = p_1 p_2 \cdots p_r ,$$

where p_i are distinct odd primes and the number of primes $\equiv 3 \pmod 4$ must be even, for otherwise d would be $\equiv 3 \pmod 4$. Thus (say)

$$d = p_1 \cdots p_j p_{j+1} \cdots p_r ,$$

where

$$p_i \equiv 3 \pmod 4 \qquad i = 1, 2, \cdots, j, j \equiv 0 \pmod 2$$
$$p_i \equiv 1 \pmod 4 \qquad i = j+1, \cdots, r.$$

Then

$$\begin{aligned} d &= ((-1)^{(p_1-1)/2}p_1)\cdots((-1)^{(p_j-1)/2}p_j)p_{j+1}\cdots p_r \\ &= p_1^* p_2^* \cdots p_j^* p_{j+1}^* \cdots p_r^* \end{aligned}$$

as required.

Case (ii). $D \equiv 3 \pmod 4$. Then

$$d = 4p_1p_2 \cdots p_r ,$$

where the number of primes p_i which are $\equiv 3 \pmod 4$ must be odd. Thus

$$d = (-4)p_1^* \cdots p_r^*$$

as required. Finally

Case (iii). $D \equiv 2 \pmod 4$. Then

$$d = 8p_1p_2 \cdots p_r = 8p_1^* \cdots p_r^*$$

if the number of primes $\equiv 3 \pmod 4$ is even, and

$$d = -8p_1^* \cdots p_r^*$$

if the number of primes $\equiv 3 \pmod 4$ is odd.

With the aid of this result, we prove

THEOREM 4.11. *If d is a fundamental discriminant, that is*

$$d = \begin{cases} D & \text{if } D \equiv 1 \pmod 4, \\ 4D & \text{if } D \equiv 2, 3 \pmod 4. \end{cases}$$

and D is square free, then

$$\chi_d(n) = \left(\frac{d}{n}\right) = \textit{Kronecker symbol}$$

is a primitive character modulo $|d|$.

PROOF. *Case* (i). $D \equiv 1 \pmod 4$. Then by Theorem 4.10

$$d = p_1^* \cdots p_r^* .$$

We write

$$\chi^{(i)}(n) = \left(\frac{i}{n}\right). \tag{37}$$

By Theorem 4.1,

$$\chi_d = \chi^{(p_1^*)} \cdots \chi^{(p_r^*)}, \text{ where } \chi_d(n) = \left(\frac{d}{n}\right) = \left(\frac{p_1^*}{n}\right) \cdots \left(\frac{p_r^*}{n}\right).$$

By Lemma 4.4, (m/n) is the principal character mod m if and only m is a square. Therefore the characters $\chi^{(p_i^*)}$ are not principal and the conductor $f(\chi^{(p_i^*)}) = |p_i^*|$.

By Theorem 4.7, then

$$f(\chi_d) = f(\chi^{(p_1^*)}) \cdots f(\chi^{(p_r^*)}) = |p_1^*| \cdots |p_r^*| = |d|$$

as required.

Case (ii). $D \equiv 3 \pmod 4$. Then

$$d = (-4)p_1^* \cdots p_r^*$$

and

$$f(\chi_d) = f(\chi^{(-4)})f(\chi^{(p_1^*)}) \cdots f(\chi^{(p_r^*)})$$

and it suffices to show that

$$\chi^{(-4)}(n) = \left(\frac{-4}{n}\right)$$

is primitive. If not, then $f(\chi^{(-4)}) = 2$ and this would imply that $\chi^{(-4)}(3) = 1$; but $\chi^{(-4)}(3) = -1$, which is a contradiction.

Case (iii). $D \equiv 2 \pmod 4$. Here it suffices (using the same reasoning as in Cases (i) and (ii)) to show that

$$f(\chi^{(\pm 8)}) = 8 .$$

Clearly $f(\chi^{(\pm 8)}) \neq 2$, for this would imply that

$$\left(\frac{\pm 8}{n}\right) = 1 \qquad \text{for all odd } n.$$

If $f(\chi^{(8)}) = 4$, this would imply that $\chi^{(8)}$ is definable mod 4, which means that if a is odd and

$$a \equiv 1 \pmod 4 ,$$

then $\chi^{(8)}(a) = 1$. But $\chi^{(8)}(5) = (8/5) = -1$, which is a contradiction. Similarly for $\chi^{(-8)}$ and the proof is complete.

For primitive characters, Gaussian sums satisfy a particular simple relation.

It can be shown that the Kronecker symbol is essentially the only type of real primitive character.

THEOREM 4.12. *If χ is a primitive character* mod k, *then*

$$G(ab, \chi) = \bar{\chi}(a)G(b, \chi) .$$

PROOF. If $(c, k) = 1$, then

$$G(bc, \chi) = \sum_{n \bmod k} \chi(n)e^{2\pi ibcn/k}$$

(38)

$$= \bar{\chi}(c) \sum_{n \bmod k} \chi(cn)e^{2\pi ibcn/k} .$$

However, an n ranges over a residue system mod k, then so does cn. Therefore from (38)

(39) $$G(bc, \chi) = \bar{\chi}(c) \sum_{m \bmod k} \chi(m) e^{2\pi i b m/k} = \bar{\chi}(c) G(b, \chi) .$$

Thus if $(a, k) = 1$, then the theorem is proved. If $(m, k) = d > 1$, then we show that $G(m, \chi) = 0$. Suppose on the contrary that $G(m, \chi) \neq 0$; then for all c for which $mc \equiv m \pmod{k}$, it follows from the definition of $G(a, \chi)$ that

$$G(mc, \chi) = G(m, \chi) .$$

Therefore for these values of c such that $(c, k) = 1$, $mc \equiv m \pmod{k}$, it follows from (39) that $\chi(c) = 1$.

Let $k = k_0 d$, $m = m_0 d$, then $c \equiv 1 \pmod{k_0}$ and conversely if $c \equiv 1 \pmod{k_0}$, $cm \equiv m \pmod{k}$, and $\chi(c) = 1$. We have therefore shown that if $(c, k) = 1$, $c \equiv 1 \pmod{k_0}$ then $\chi(c) = 1$. By Lemma 4.1, this means that χ is definable modulo k_0, which contradicts the fact that χ is primitive. Thus, if $(m, k) \neq 1$, $G(m, \chi) = 0$ and the theorem holds in every case.

In particular

$$G(a, \chi) = \bar{\chi}(a) G(1, \chi) ,$$

and in order to evaluate $G(a, \chi)$ it suffices to evaluate $G(1, \chi)$. We can in fact measure $|G(1, \chi)|$.

Theorem 4.13. *If χ is a primitive character modulo k, then*

(40) $$|G(1, \chi)|^2 = k .$$

Proof. By Theorems 4.2 and 4.12 it is enough to assume that k is a power of a prime say $k = p^\alpha$, and χ a primitive character modulo p^α.

Then

(41) $$|G(1, \chi)|^2 = \sum_{a \bmod p^\alpha; (a, p)=1} \ \sum_{b \bmod p^\alpha; (b, p)=1} \chi(a)\bar{\chi}(b) \exp\left[\frac{2\pi i(a-b)}{p^\alpha}\right] .$$

Since $b \not\equiv 0 \pmod{p}$, then we can solve the congruence

(42) $$bt \equiv a \pmod{p^\alpha} ,$$

and as a runs through a residue system mod p^α, so does t. Therefore, from (41) and (42)

(43) $$\begin{aligned} |G(1, \chi)|^2 &= \sum_{t \bmod p^\alpha} \ \sum_{b \bmod p^\alpha;\ b \not\equiv 0 (\bmod p)} \chi(bt)\bar{\chi}(b) \exp\left[\frac{2\pi i b(t-1)}{p^\alpha}\right] \\ &= \sum_{t \bmod p^\alpha} \chi(t) \sum_{b \bmod p^\alpha} \exp\left[\frac{2\pi i b(t-1)}{p^\alpha}\right] \\ &\quad - \sum_{t \bmod p^\alpha} \chi(t) \sum_{b \equiv 0 (p);\ b \bmod p^\alpha} \exp\left[\frac{2\pi i b(t-1)}{p^\alpha}\right] . \end{aligned}$$

By Lemma 8.1, Chapter IV, the inner sum of the first term of (43) is 0 if $t \not\equiv 1 \pmod{p^\alpha}$ and p^α otherwise. The second term on the right of (43) is, again by Lemma 8.1, Chapter IV,

$$\sum_{t \bmod p^\alpha} \chi(t) \sum_{c \bmod p^{\alpha-1}} \exp\left[\frac{2\pi i c(t-1)}{p^{\alpha-1}}\right] = p^{\alpha-1} \sum_{t \bmod p^\alpha;\ t \equiv 1 (\bmod p^{\alpha-1})} \chi(t) .$$

The residues $t \equiv 1 \pmod{p^{\alpha-1}}$ form a group and $\chi(t)$ is a character defined on this group. Thus, by Chapter I, Theorem 2.6, this last sum is 0 unless χ is the principal character on this group. χ cannot be principal on this group for this would imply that $\chi(t) = 1$ if $t \equiv 1 \pmod{p^{\alpha-1}}$ and by Lemma 4.1, this means that χ is definable modulo $p^{\alpha-1}$. By hypothesis however, χ is primitive and therefore the second sum on the right of (43), is 0. Thus

$$|G(1, \chi)|^2 = p^\alpha$$

which completes the proof.

We return to the special case where the character is the symbol (d/n) for a fundamental discriminant d. In this case, we shall evaluate $G(1, \chi_d)$ explicitly.

Let

$$\chi_d(n) = \left(\frac{d}{n}\right).$$

We recall by Lemma 2.4 that $\chi_d(n)$ is a character modulo $|d|$ which is, by Theorem 4.11, primitive.

By Theorem 4.12,

$$G(a, \chi_d) = \chi(a) G(1, \chi_d)$$

and by Theorem 4.2, the evaluation of $G(1, \chi_d)$ can be reduced to the evaluation of $G(1, \chi^{(p^*)})$ for odd p, and to $G(1, \chi^{(-4)})$, $G(1, \chi^{(\pm 8)})$.

We shall, accordingly, study these sums. Here we have

$$\chi^{(p^*)}(n) = \left(\frac{p^*}{n}\right),$$

where again we recall that

$$p^* = (-1)^{(p-1)/2} p.$$

But by Lemma 2.2

$$\left(\frac{p^*}{n}\right) = \left(\frac{n}{|p^*|}\right) = \left(\frac{n}{p}\right);$$

it is, therefore, sufficient to evaluate

$$G(1, \chi^{(p^*)}) = \sum_{n \bmod p} \left(\frac{n}{p}\right) \exp\left[\frac{2\pi i n}{p}\right]. \tag{44}$$

We replace this sum by one more amenable to evaluation.

Theorem 4.14. *If p is an odd prime,*

$$G(1, \chi^{(p^*)}) = \sum_{m=0}^{p-1} e^{2\pi i m^2/p}.$$

Proof. On the one hand, by (44),

$$G(1, \chi^{(p^*)}) = \sum_r e^{2\pi i r/p} - \sum_n e^{2\pi i n/p}, \tag{45}$$

where r and n run over the quadratic residues and quadratic nonresidues modulo p respectively. On the other hand

$$1 + \sum_{r} e^{2\pi i r/p} + \sum_{n} e^{2i\pi n/p} = \sum_{m=0}^{p-1} e^{2\pi i m/p} = 0 \tag{46}$$

and therefore from (45) and (46)

$$G(1, \chi^{(p^*)}) = 1 + 2 \sum_{r} e^{2\pi i r/p} . \tag{47}$$

The quadratic residues, however, can be chosen as $1^2, 2^2, \cdots, ((p-1)/2)^2$; consequently from (47),

$$G(1, \chi^{(p^*)}) = 1 + 2 \sum_{m=1}^{(p-1)/2} e^{2\pi i m^2/p} . \tag{48}$$

But since

$$\sum_{a=1}^{(p-1)/2} e^{2\pi i (p-a)^2/p} = \sum_{a=1}^{(p-1)/2} e^{2\pi i a^2/p} , \tag{49}$$

the statement of the theorem follows from (48) and (49).

We have therefore to evaluate the sum

$$G(p) = \sum_{m=0}^{p-1} e^{2\pi i m^2/p} .$$

Actually we prove a more general result.

THEOREM 4.15. *If*

$$G(k) = \sum_{m=0}^{k-1} e^{2\pi i m^2/k} , \tag{50}$$

then

$$G(k) = \begin{cases} (1+i)\sqrt{k} & \text{if } k \equiv 0 \pmod 4 , \\ \sqrt{k} & \text{if } k \equiv 1 \pmod 4 , \\ 0 & \text{if } k \equiv 2 \pmod 4 , \\ i\sqrt{k} & \text{if } k \equiv 3 \pmod 4 . \end{cases} \tag{51}$$

PROOF. Of the many possible proofs, we select here one due to Kronecker which uses the calculus of residues. In fact, it is natural to apply Cauchy's theorem to the function

$$f(z) = \frac{e^{2\pi i z^2/k}}{1 - e^{2\pi i z}} \tag{52}$$

which has simple poles at $z = 0, \pm 1, \pm 2, \cdots$, with residue

$$R_m = -\frac{1}{2\pi i} e^{2\pi i m^2/k} \tag{53}$$

at the simple pole at $z = m$.

To evaluate a sum of the type (50), we integrate $f(z)$ around the contour C indicated in the diagram. It is a rectangle with vertices at $k/2 \pm iT$ and $\pm iT$; there are indentations at 0 and $k/2$ by means of semicircles of radius

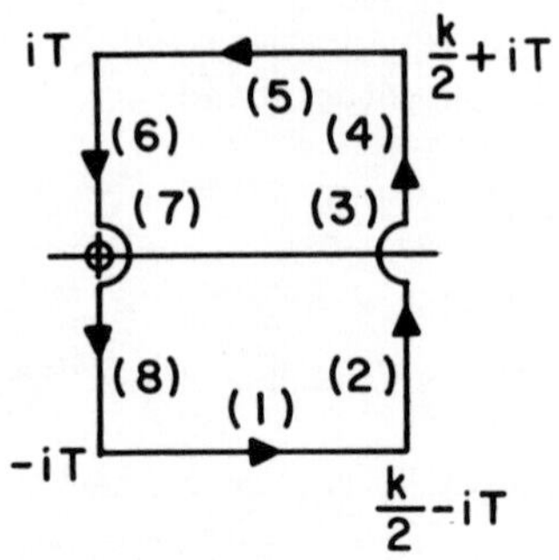

ρ. The elements of the path C are indicated by numbers (1) to (8). The integrand has a pole at $z=0$ and at $z=k/2$ if k is even. We have, therefore, by Cauchy's theorem and (53)

$$I=\int_C f(z)dz=-\sum_{m=1}^{[(k-1)/2]} e^{2\pi i m^2/k} . \tag{54}$$

On the other hand,

$$I=\sum_{j=1}^{8}\int_{(j)} f(z)dz=\sum_{j=1}^{8} I_j .$$

It is easy to see, however, that

$$\sum_{m=1}^{[(k-1)/2]} e^{2\pi i m^2/k}=\frac{1}{2}\sum_{m=1}^{k-1} e^{2\pi i m^2/k} , \tag{55}$$

with the understanding that if k is even, the term

$$\exp\left[\frac{2\pi i}{k}\left(\frac{k}{2}\right)^2\right]$$

is missing on the right-hand side.

By a simple calculation

$$I_6+I_8=-i\int_\rho^T e^{-2\pi i y^2/k}dy . \tag{56}$$

By a similar but more complicated calculation,

$$I_2+I_4=(-i)^{k+1}\int_\rho^T e^{-2\pi i y^2/k}dy . \tag{57}$$

Along the horizontal sides

$$\begin{aligned} I_5 &= O\left(\int_0^{k/2}\frac{\exp\left[\frac{2\pi i(x+iT)^2}{k}\right]}{1-\exp[2\pi i(x+iT)]}dx\right)=O\left(\int_0^{k/2}\frac{\exp\left[\frac{-4\pi xT}{k}\right]}{1-\exp[-2\pi T]}dx\right) \\ &= O\left(\frac{1}{T}\right)=o(1) , \end{aligned} \tag{58}$$

as $T\to\infty$.

By the same token,

(59) $$I_1 = o(1) \quad \text{as } T \to \infty .$$

Thus letting $T \to \infty$, we get from (54), (56), (57), (58), (59),

(60) $$I = -i(1 + (-i)^k) \int_\rho^\infty e^{-2\pi i y^2/k} dy + I_3 + I_7$$

since the integral on the right of (60) converges.

On the other hand, it is readily seen that

(61) $$\lim_{\rho \to 0} I_3 = \begin{cases} 0 & \text{if } k \text{ is odd,} \\ -\dfrac{1}{2} \exp\left[\dfrac{2\pi i}{k}\left(\dfrac{k}{2}\right)^2\right] & \text{if } k \text{ is even;} \end{cases}$$

whereas

(62) $$\lim_{\rho \to 0} I_7 = -\tfrac{1}{2} .$$

Therefore from (55), (60), (61), (62), on letting $\rho \to 0$,

$$-\frac{1}{2} \sum_{m=0}^{k-1} e^{2\pi i m^2/k} = -i(1 + (-i)^k) \int_0^\infty e^{-2\pi i y^2/k} dy .$$

In other words substituting $u^2 = (y^2/k)$ in the integral, we get

(63) $$G(k) = 2i(1 + (-i)^k)\sqrt{k} \int_0^\infty e^{-2\pi i u^2} du .$$

If $k = 1$, $G(k) = 1$ and therefore from (63)

(64) $$\int_0^\infty e^{-2\pi i u^2} du = \frac{1}{2i(1-i)}$$

that is, putting (64) in (63), we conclude that

$$G(k) = \sqrt{k}\left(\frac{1 + (-i)^k}{1 - i}\right) .$$

Taking the four possibilities modulo 4, we get the statement of the theorem.

COROLLARY.

(65) $$G(1, \chi^{(p^*)}) = \begin{cases} \sqrt{p} & \text{if } p \equiv 1 \pmod 4, \\ i\sqrt{p} & \text{if } p \equiv 3 \pmod 4 \end{cases} = \sqrt{p^*} .$$

Our object, it will be recalled, is to evaluate

$$G(1, \chi_d) .$$

We prove a preliminary lemma.

THEOREM 4.16. *Let*

(66) $$g(d) = \frac{1}{\sqrt{d}} G(1, \chi_d) ;$$

then $g(d)$ is multiplicative. That is, if $(d_1, d_2) = 1$, then

(67) $$g(d_1 d_2) = g(d_1)g(d_2)\,.$$

PROOF. By Theorems 4.1, 4.10 and 4.2,

(68) $$\begin{aligned} g(d_1d_2) &= \frac{1}{\sqrt{(d_1d_2)}} G(1, \chi_{d_1d_2}) = \frac{\varepsilon}{\sqrt{(d_1d_2)}} G(1, \chi_{d_1})G(1, \chi_{d_2}) \\ &= \frac{\varepsilon\sqrt{d_1}\sqrt{d_2}}{\sqrt{(d_1d_2)}} g(d_1)g(d_2)\,, \end{aligned}$$

where

(69) $$\varepsilon = \left(\frac{d_2}{|d_1|}\right)\left(\frac{d_1}{|d_2|}\right).$$

Thus, it suffices from (68) to show that

(70) $$\sqrt{(d_1d_2)} = \varepsilon\sqrt{d_1}\sqrt{d_2}\,.$$

Case (i). $d_1 < 0$, $d_2 < 0$.
In this case,

$$\sqrt{d_1}\sqrt{d_2} = -\sqrt{(d_1d_2)}$$

and we must, therefore, show that

$$\varepsilon = -1\,.$$

Indeed, since $(d_1, d_2) = 1$, we may assume because of symmetry that d_1 is odd. Then, by Lemma 2.2,

(71) $$\left(\frac{d_1}{|d_2|}\right) = \left(\frac{|d_2|}{|d_1|}\right).$$

Thus, from (69) and (71)

$$\varepsilon = \left(\frac{|d_2|}{|d_1|}\right)\left(\frac{d_2}{|d_1|}\right) = \left(\frac{|d_2|}{|d_1|}\right)\left(\frac{-1}{|d_1|}\right)\left(\frac{|d_2|}{|d_1|}\right) = (-1)^{(|d_1|-1)/2} = -1\,,$$

since $d_1 \equiv 1 \bmod 4$.

Case (ii). $d_1 > 0$, $d_2 < 0$.
Then, by (71)

$$\varepsilon = \left(\frac{|d_2|}{d_1}\right)\left(\frac{d_2}{d_1}\right) = \left(\frac{-1}{d_1}\right) = (-1)^{(d_1-1)/2} = +1\,.$$

Case (iii). $d_1 < 0$, $d_2 > 0$, then $\varepsilon = +1$ by symmetry from (ii).
Case (iv). $d_1 > 0$, $d_2 > 0$.
Then from (71)

$$\varepsilon = \left(\frac{d_2^2}{d_1}\right) = +1\,.$$

This completes the proof.

THEOREM 4.17.

$$G(1, \chi_d) = \sqrt{d}\,.$$

PROOF. We apply Theorem 4.10 and the corollary of Theorem 4.15.
Case (i). $d \equiv 1 \pmod 4$.
Then by Theorem 4.10,

$$d = p_1^* \cdots p_r^*\,,$$

where p_i are odd primes, and hence by Theorems 4.10 and 4.16,

$$G(1, \chi_d) = \sqrt{(p_1^* \cdots p_r^*)} = \sqrt{d}\,.$$

Case (ii). $d \equiv 0 \pmod 4$.
In this case, either

$$d = -4p_1^* \cdots p_r^*$$

or

$$d = \pm 8p_1^* \cdots p_r^*\,,$$

where p_i^* are odd. We have, therefore, to evaluate

$$G(1, \chi^{(-4)}) \quad \text{and} \quad G(1, \chi^{(\pm 8)})\,.$$

Indeed

$$G(1, \chi^{(-4)}) = \sum_{n \bmod 4} \left(\frac{-4}{n}\right) e^{2\pi i n/4} = i - i^3 = 2i = \sqrt{-4}\,.$$

Let $\rho = e^{\pi i/4} = (1+i)/\sqrt{2}$

$$G(1, \chi^{(\pm 8)}) = \sum_{n \bmod 8} \left(\frac{\pm 8}{n}\right) e^{2\pi i n/8} = \rho \mp \rho^3 - \rho^5 \pm \rho^7 = \rho(1 \mp \rho^2 - \rho^4 \pm \rho^6)\,.$$

Since $\rho^2 = i$, we get

$$G(1, \chi^{(\pm 8)}) = \rho(1 \mp i - i^2 \pm i^3) = \frac{1+i}{\sqrt{2}}(2 \mp 2i) = \sqrt{2}(1+i)(1 \mp i)$$

$$= \begin{Bmatrix} 2\sqrt{2} & \text{if } d = 8, \\ 2i\sqrt{2} & \text{if } d = -8 \end{Bmatrix} = \sqrt{\pm 8}\,.$$

If, therefore, we again apply the corollary of Theorem 4.15 and Theorem 4.16, we get

$$G(1, \chi_d) = \sqrt{d}\,.$$

Thus, in every case we have

$$G(1, \chi_d) = \sqrt{d}$$

as required.

5. The mean value of $h(d)$**.** In connection with quadratic forms, Gauss conjectured that the mean value of the class number $h_0(d)$ of binary quadratic forms of discriminant d satisfies the following relations:

(a) If $d > 0$, $d = 4k$, then

$$\sum_{4k \leq N} h_0(4k) \log \varepsilon_{4k} \sim \frac{4\pi^2}{21\zeta(3)} N^{3/2} ; \tag{1}$$

(b) If $d < 0$, $d = -m$, $m > 0$, then

$$\sum_{m \leq N} h_0(-m) \sim \frac{\pi}{18\zeta(3)} N^{3/2} . \tag{2}$$

The relation (2) was first proved by Mertens, whereas (1) was proved by Siegel. We shall state and prove the analogous result for quadratic fields basing our argument on Siegel's proof which is applicable both for $d > 0$ and $d < 0$.

It may again be pointed out that the precise nature of $h(d)$ is not strictly necessary for an understanding of what follows. It is enough to take the relation

$$\alpha h(d) = L(1, \chi_d) , \tag{3}$$

where α is defined in Theorem 2.8, as the definition of $h(d)$ and then interpret our results as theorems about $L(1, \chi_d)$.

The argument we use requires a theorem about characters. The result we need, due to Pólya, is the following:

THEOREM 5.1. *If χ is a nonprincipal character modulo k, and*

$$S(n) = \sum_{1 \leq m \leq n} \chi(m) , \tag{4}$$

then

$$S(n) = O(k^{1/2} \log k) , \tag{5}$$

the constant implied by the O being independent of n and k.

PROOF. The proof is divided into two cases according as the character χ is or is not primitive.

Case (i). We suppose that χ is a primitive character mod k and we make the abbreviation

$$\rho = e^{2\pi i/k} . \tag{6}$$

By Theorem 4.12, we have

$$G(m, \chi) = \bar{\chi}(m) G(1, \chi) . \tag{7}$$

Summing over m in (7), we get

$$\begin{aligned} \overline{S(n)} G(1, \chi) &= \sum_{m=1}^{n} G(m, \chi) = \sum_{m=1}^{n} \sum_{r=1}^{k-1} \chi(r) \rho^{rm} \\ &= \sum_{r=1}^{k-1} \chi(r) \rho^r \left(\frac{1 - \rho^{nr}}{1 - \rho^r} \right) . \end{aligned} \tag{8}$$

Since for k even, $\chi(k/2) = 0$, and $\rho^k = 1$, and since $\chi(k-r) = \chi(-1)\chi(r)$, then (8) becomes

$$\overline{S(n)}G(1, \chi) = \sum_{r=1}^{[(k-1)/2]} \chi(r)\left\{\rho^r \frac{1-\rho^{nr}}{1-\rho^r} + \chi(-1)\rho^{-r}\frac{1-\rho^{-nr}}{1-\rho^{-r}}\right\} \tag{9}$$

$$= \sum_{r=1}^{[(k-1)/2]} \chi(r)\frac{\rho^r - \chi(-1) + \chi(-1)\rho^{-nr} - \rho^{(n+1)r}}{1-\rho^r}.$$

On the other hand, since $|1-\rho^r| = 2\sin \pi r/k > 4r/k$, for $r < k/2$ (since $\sin\theta > 2\theta/\pi$ for $0 < \theta < \pi/2$), it follows from (9) that

$$|\overline{S(n)}|\,|G(1, \chi)| = O\left\{\sum_{r=1}^{[(k-1)/2]} \frac{1}{|1-\rho^r|}\right\} = O\left\{\sum_{r=1}^{[(k-1)/2]} \frac{1}{\sin\frac{r\pi}{k}}\right\} \tag{10}$$

$$= O\left(\sum_{r=1}^{[(k-1)/2]} \frac{k}{r}\right) = O(k\log k).$$

By Theorem 4.13 $|G(1, \chi)| = \sqrt{k}$, and with (10), this means that

$$S(n) = O(k^{1/2}\log k). \tag{11}$$

Case (ii). Suppose that χ is an imprimitive character mod k and let $f = f(\chi)$ be its conductor. By Theorem 4.8,

$$S(n) = \sum_{d|k} \mu(d)\chi^*(d)\sum_{r=1}^{[n/d]} \chi^*(r). \tag{12}$$

By Case (i), since χ^* is primitive mod f, the inner sum is $O(f^{1/2}\log f)$ and therefore from (12),

$$S(n) = O(M(k)f^{1/2}\log f), \tag{13}$$

where $M(k)$ is the number of square free numbers of which every prime factor is in k but not in f. On the other hand, $M(k) \leqq$ number of divisors of k/f and this is $O(\sqrt{(k/f)})$. Thus from (13), it follows that

$$S(n) = O(k^{1/2}\log k).$$

As a useful corollary, we get

THEOREM 5.2. *If N is a positive integer and χ is a nonprincipal character* mod k, *then*

$$\sum_{n=N+1}^{\infty} \frac{\chi(n)}{n} = O\left(\frac{k^{1/2}\log k}{N}\right). \tag{14}$$

PROOF.

$$\sum_{n=N+1}^{M} \frac{\chi(n)}{n} = \sum_{n=N+1}^{M} \frac{S(n)-S(n-1)}{n} = \sum_{n=N+1}^{M-1} \frac{S(n)}{n(n+1)} - \frac{S(N)}{N} + \frac{S(M)}{M}$$

$$= O(k^{1/2}\log k)\sum_{n=N}^{M-1}\frac{1}{n^2} + O\left(\frac{k^{1/2}\log k}{N}\right) + O\left(\frac{k^{1/2}\log k}{M}\right)$$

$$= O\left(\frac{k^{1/2}\log k}{N}\right) + O\left(\frac{k^{1/2}\log k}{M}\right).$$

If we let $M \to \infty$, the theorem follows.

We return to the question of the mean value of $h(d)$.

Let $K = R(\sqrt{D})$ be a quadratic field with discriminant d. Thus D is square free and

$$d = \begin{cases} D & \text{if } D \equiv 1 \pmod 4, \\ 4D & \text{if } D \equiv 2, 3 \pmod 4. \end{cases}$$

Let $h(d)$ be the class number of K. Our main object is to prove the following mean value theorem.

THEOREM 5.3. (a) *If* $d < 0$,

$$\sum_{0<-d\leq N} \frac{h(d)}{\sqrt{|d|}} = \frac{N}{2\pi} C + O(N^{3/4} \log N).$$

(b) *If* $d > 0$,

$$\sum_{0<d\leq N} \frac{h(d)\log \varepsilon}{\sqrt{d}} = \frac{N}{4} C + O(N^{3/4} \log N)$$

where

$$C = \prod_p \left(1 - \frac{1}{p^2(p+1)}\right)$$

and the summation is over all fundamental discriminants in the indicated range.

PROOF. We shall consider the case $d > 0$; the case $d < 0$ is proved in exactly the same way.

We prove the theorem starting from Theorem 2.8 and the relation

$$\alpha h(d) = L(1, \chi_d).$$

That is

$$\alpha h(d) = \sum_{n=1}^{\infty} \frac{\chi_d(n)}{n} \tag{15}$$

where, in case $d < -4$, from the definition of α,

$$\alpha = \frac{\pi}{\sqrt{|d|}} \tag{16}$$

and when $d > 0$, $\alpha = (2 \log \varepsilon)/\sqrt{d}$ and

$$\chi_d(n) = \left(\frac{d}{n}\right) = \text{Kronecker symbol.}$$

Since d is not a square, $\chi_d(n)$ is not principal and Theorem 5.2 is applicable. We get from (15), and Theorem 5.2,

$$\alpha h(d) = \sum_{n=1}^{N} \frac{\chi_d(n)}{n} + O\left(\frac{|d|^{1/2} \log |d|}{N}\right). \tag{17}$$

We sum (17) over fundamental discriminants.

$$(18)\qquad \sum_{0<d\leqq N;\ d\ \mathrm{fund.}} \alpha h(d) = \sum_{0<d\leqq N;\ d\ \mathrm{fund.}} \sum_{n=1}^{N} \frac{\chi_d(n)}{n} + O\Bigl(\sum_{0<d\leqq N} \frac{|d|^{1/2}\log|d|}{N}\Bigr).$$

The second term of (18) is easily seen to be

$$O(N^{1/2}\log N).$$

Thus from (18) interchanging the order of summation, we get

$$(19)\qquad \sum_{0<d\leqq N;\ d\ \mathrm{fund.}} \alpha h(d) = \sum_{n=1}^{N} \frac{1}{n} \sum_{0<d\leqq N;\ d\ \mathrm{fund.}} \Bigl(\frac{d}{n}\Bigr) + O(N^{1/2}\log N).$$

Let

$$(20)\qquad S(n) = \sum_{0<d\leqq N;\ d\ \mathrm{fund.}} \Bigl(\frac{d}{n}\Bigr).$$

Since

$$d = \begin{cases} D & \text{if } D \equiv 1 \pmod 4, \\ 4D & \text{if } D \equiv 2, 3 \pmod 4, \end{cases}$$

we write

$$(21)\qquad \begin{aligned} S(n) &= \sum_{0<d\leqq N;\ d\equiv 1 (\mathrm{mod}\ 4);\ d\ \mathrm{fund.}} \Bigl(\frac{d}{n}\Bigr) + \sum_{0<d\leqq N;\ d/4\equiv 2 (\mathrm{mod}\ 4);\ d\ \mathrm{fund.}} \Bigl(\frac{d}{n}\Bigr) \\ &\quad + \sum_{0<d\leqq N;\ d/4\equiv 3 (\mathrm{mod}\ 4);\ d\ \mathrm{fund.}} \Bigl(\frac{d}{n}\Bigr) \\ &= S_1(n) + S_2(n) + S_3(n). \end{aligned}$$

We consider these sums separately. For S_1, we have, since d is square free,

$$(22)\qquad S_1(n) = \sum_{0<d\leqq N;\ d\equiv 1 (\mathrm{mod}\ 4)} \Bigl(\frac{d}{n}\Bigr)\mu^2(d).$$

We can write

$$(23)\qquad \mu^2(d) = \sum_{l^2|d} \mu(l),$$

$$(24)\qquad S_1(n) = \sum_{0<d\leqq N;\ d\equiv 1 (\mathrm{mod}\ 4)} \Bigl(\frac{d}{n}\Bigr) \sum_{l^2|d} \mu(l).$$

If we put $d = l^2k$, in (24) we find

$$(25)\qquad S_1(n) = \sum_{0<l^2k\leqq N;\ l^2k\equiv 1 (\mathrm{mod}\ 4)} \Bigl(\frac{l^2k}{n}\Bigr)\mu(l).$$

If l is even, $l^2k \equiv 0 \pmod 4$ which is impossible; if l is odd $l^2 \equiv 1 \pmod 4$ and accordingly from (25),

$$(26)\qquad \begin{aligned} S_1(n) &= \sum_{0<l^2k\leqq N;\ k\equiv 1 (\mathrm{mod}\ 4);\ (l,n)=(l,2)=1} \Bigl(\frac{k}{n}\Bigr)\mu(l) \\ &= \sum_{0<l\leqq \sqrt{N};\ (l,2n)=1} \mu(l) \sum_{0<k\leqq N/l^2;\ k\equiv 1 (\mathrm{mod}\ 4)} \Bigl(\frac{k}{n}\Bigr). \end{aligned}$$

By exactly the same argument,

$$S_2(n) = \left(\frac{4}{n}\right) \sum_{0<l\leq\sqrt{N}/2;\ (l,\,2n)=1} \mu(l) \sum_{0<k\leq N/4l^2;\ k\equiv 2 \pmod 4} \left(\frac{k}{n}\right), \tag{27}$$

$$S_3(n) = \left(\frac{4}{n}\right) \sum_{0<l\leq\sqrt{N}/2;\ (l,\,2n)=1} \mu(l) \sum_{0<k\leq N/4l^2;\ k\equiv 3 \pmod 4} \left(\frac{k}{n}\right). \tag{28}$$

Let

$$P(r, n, M) = \sum_{0<k\leq N;\ k\equiv r \pmod 4} \left(\frac{k}{n}\right). \tag{29}$$

We notice first that if n is even, then

$$S_2(n) = S_3(n) = 0\,. \tag{30}$$

Case (i). Suppose then that n is odd and not a square. In this case (k/n) is a character modulo n which is not principal. Moreover,

$$P(1, n, M) = \frac{1}{2}\sum_{0<k\leq M} \left(\frac{k}{n}\right)\{\chi_1(k) + \chi_3(k)\}\,, \tag{31}$$

where χ_1 and χ_3 are the two characters modulo 4, χ_1 being the principal one. The products $(k/n)\chi_i(k)$ $(i = 1, 2)$ are characters modulo $4n$ which are evidently nonprincipal. Theorem 5.1 is applicable to each of the sums on the right of (31), and we infer that

$$P(1, n, M) = O(\mathrm{Min}\,(n^{1/2}\log n, M))\,. \tag{32}$$

Case (ii). If n is even and not a square, we have only to consider $P(1, n, M)$. Let $n = ls$ with s odd. Then since $k \equiv 1 \pmod 4$,

$$\left(\frac{k}{n}\right) = \left(\frac{k}{l}\right)\left(\frac{k}{s}\right) = \left(\frac{l}{k}\right)\left(\frac{k}{s}\right). \tag{33}$$

We can write

$$\begin{gathered} \chi_1(k) = \left(\frac{4}{k}\right), \qquad \chi_3(k) = \left(\frac{-4}{k}\right), \\ P(1, n, M) = \frac{1}{2}\sum_{0<k\leq M}\left\{\left(\frac{4l}{k}\right)\left(\frac{k}{s}\right) + \left(\frac{-4l}{k}\right)\left(\frac{k}{s}\right)\right\}. \end{gathered} \tag{34}$$

Each of the terms in the parentheses is a character modulo $4n$ and therefore Theorem 5.1 is applicable and yields from (34)

$$P(1, n, M) = O(\mathrm{Min}\,(n^{1/2}\log n, M))\,.$$

In all cases, therefore, if n is not a square,

$$P(r, n, M) = O(\mathrm{Min}\,(n^{1/2}\log n, M))\,. \tag{35}$$

We use this estimate in (26), (27) and (28) and infer from (21) that if n is not a square,

$$
\begin{aligned}
S(n) &= O\left(\sum_{0<l\leqq\sqrt{N}} \operatorname{Min}\left(n^{1/2}\log n,\ \frac{N}{l^2}\right)\right)\\
&= O\left(\sum_{0<l\leqq\sqrt{N}/\sqrt{(n^{1/2}\log n)}} \operatorname{Min}\left(n^{1/2}\log n,\ \frac{N}{l^2}\right)\right)\\
&\quad + O\left(\sum_{l>\sqrt{N}/\sqrt{(n^{1/2}\log n)}} \operatorname{Min}\left(n^{1/2}\log n,\ \frac{N}{l^2}\right)\right)\\
&= O\left(\sum_{0<l\leqq\sqrt{N}/\sqrt{(n^{1/2}\log n)}} n^{1/2}\log n\right) + O\left(\sum_{l>\sqrt{N}/\sqrt{(n^{1/2}\log n)}} \frac{N}{l^2}\right)\\
&= O(N^{1/2}n^{1/4}\log^{1/2}n)\ .
\end{aligned}
\tag{36}
$$

Case (iii). Suppose now that n is a square,

$$n = m^2\ .$$

(a) If m is odd

$$P(1, m^2, M) = \sum_{0<k\leqq M;\ k\equiv 1 (\mathrm{mod}\ 4)} \left(\frac{k}{m^2}\right) = \frac{1}{2}\sum_{0<k\leqq M}\left(\frac{k}{m^2}\right)\{\chi_1(k) + \chi_3(k)\}\ . \tag{37}$$

The product $(k/m^2)\chi_1(k)$ is the principal character mod $4m$, while $(k/m^2)\chi_3(k)$ is a nonprincipal character mod $4m$.

If in (37) we break the interval of summation into intervals of length $4m$, we find using Theorem 2.6, of Chapter I,

$$\sum_{0<k\leqq M}\left(\frac{k}{m^2}\right)\chi_1(k) = \frac{\varphi(4m)M}{4m} + O(m) \tag{38}$$

and

$$\sum_{0<k\leqq M}\left(\frac{k}{m^2}\right)\chi_3(k) = O(m)\ . \tag{39}$$

Thus from (37), (38) and (39)

$$P(1, m^2, M) = \frac{\varphi(4m)M}{8m} + O(m) = \frac{\varphi(m)M}{4m} + O(m)\ .$$

In exactly the same way, for $r = 2, 3$,

$$P(r, m^2, M) = \frac{\varphi(m)M}{4m} + O(m)\ . \tag{40}$$

(b) If m is even, say $m = 2^l m_1$, with m_1 odd, then it suffices to calculate $P(1, m^2, M)$ since by (27), (28), when n is even, $S_2 = S_3 = 0$. Now

$$P(1, m^2, M) = \frac{1}{2}\sum_{0<k\leqq M}\left(\frac{k}{m^2}\right)(\chi_1(k) + \chi_3(k)) \tag{41}$$

and $(k/m^2)\chi_i(k)$ $(i = 1, 3)$ is a character modulo $2m$ or m according as $l = 1$ or $l > 1$. In either case, we infer as in (38) above, that

$$P(1, m^2, M) = \frac{\varphi(m)M}{2m} + O(m)\ . \tag{42}$$

Accordingly, when n is odd and a square, $n = m^2$ we get by (21), (26), (27), (28), (40),

$$(43)\qquad \begin{aligned} S(n) &= S_1(n) + S_2(n) + S_3(n) \\ &= \frac{\varphi(m)N}{8m} \sum_{0<l\leq\sqrt{N/2};\,(l,\,2n)=1} \frac{\mu(l)}{l^2} + \frac{\varphi(m)N}{4m} \sum_{0<l\leq\sqrt{N};\,(l,\,2n)=1} \frac{\mu(l)}{l^2} + O(m\sqrt{N}) \\ &= \frac{3\varphi(m)N}{8m} \sum_{l=1;\,(l,\,2n)=1}^{\infty} \frac{\mu(l)}{l^2} + O\left(\frac{\varphi(m)N}{m} \sum_{l>\sqrt{N}} \frac{1}{l^2}\right) + O(m\sqrt{N}) \\ &= \frac{3\varphi(m)N}{8m} \sum_{l=1;\,(l,\,2m)=1}^{\infty} \frac{\mu(l)}{l^2} + O(\sqrt{N}) + O(m\sqrt{N}) . \end{aligned}$$

If on the other hand n is even, then $S_2 = S_3 = 0$ and by (42),

$$(44)\qquad S(n) = \frac{\varphi(m)N}{2m} \sum_{l=1;\,(l,\,m)=1}^{\infty} \frac{\mu(l)}{l^2} + O(\sqrt{N}) + O(m\sqrt{N}) .$$

Consider now the sum in (43). Evidently by Theorems 1.4 and 1.5 of Chapter I,

$$(45)\qquad \begin{aligned} \sum_{l=1;\,(l,\,2m)=1}^{\infty} \frac{\mu(l)}{l^2} &= \prod_{p\nmid 2m}\left(1 + \frac{\mu(p)}{p^2}\right) = \prod_{p}\left(1 - \frac{1}{p^2}\right) \prod_{p\mid 2m}\left(1 - \frac{1}{p^2}\right)^{-1} \\ &= \frac{1}{\zeta(2)} \cdot \frac{4}{3} \cdot \prod_{p\mid m}\left(1 - \frac{1}{p}\right)^{-1}\left(1 + \frac{1}{p}\right)^{-1} = \frac{4m}{3\zeta(2)\varphi(m)} \cdot g(m) , \end{aligned}$$

where $g(m) = \prod_{p\mid m} (1 + 1/p)^{-1}$.

By exactly the same argument,

$$(46)\qquad \sum_{l=1;\,(l,\,m)=1}^{\infty} \frac{\mu(l)}{l^2} = \frac{m}{\zeta(2)\varphi(m)}\, g(m) .$$

Therefore we have from (43), (44), (45) and (46), if n is a square, $n = m^2$,

$$(47)\qquad S(n) = \frac{N}{2\zeta(2)}\, g(m) + O(\sqrt{N}) + O(m\sqrt{N}) .$$

Consequently, from (19), (36), and (47),

$$(48)\qquad \begin{aligned} \sum_{0<d\leq N;\ d \text{ fund.}} \alpha h(d) &= \sum_{n=1}^{N} \frac{1}{n} S(n) + O(N^{1/2} \log N) \\ &= \sum_{n=m^2;\ 1\leq n\leq N} \frac{1}{n} S(n) + \sum_{n\neq m^2;\ 1\leq n\leq N} \frac{1}{n} S(n) + O(N^{1/2}\log N) \\ &= \frac{N}{2\zeta(2)} \sum_{1\leq m\leq\sqrt{N}} \frac{g(m)}{m^2} + O\Bigl(\sqrt{N} \sum_{1\leq m\leq\sqrt{N}} \frac{1}{m^2}\Bigr) \\ &\quad + O\Bigl(\sqrt{N} \sum_{1\leq m\leq\sqrt{N}} \frac{1}{m^2}\Bigr) + O\Bigl(N^{1/2} \sum_{1\leq n\leq N} \frac{\log^{1/2} n}{n^{3/4}}\Bigr) + O(N^{1/2} \log N) \\ &= \frac{N}{2\zeta(2)} \sum_{1\leq m\leq\sqrt{N}} \frac{g(m)}{m^2} + O(N^{3/4} \log N) . \end{aligned}$$

On the other hand, it is easy to see that

$$g(m) = \prod_{p|m}\left(1+\frac{1}{p}\right)^{-1} = \prod_{p|m}\left(1-\frac{1}{p+1}\right)$$

and therefore

$$\sum_{1\leq m\leq \sqrt{N}} \frac{g(m)}{m^2} = \sum_{m=1}^{\infty}\frac{g(m)}{m^2} + O\left(\frac{1}{\sqrt{N}}\right). \tag{49}$$

Moreover, $g(m)$ is clearly multiplicative and again using Theorem 1.5, of Chapter I, we get

$$\begin{aligned}\frac{1}{\zeta(2)}\sum_{m=1}^{\infty}\frac{g(m)}{m^2} &= \frac{1}{\zeta(2)}\prod_p\left(1+\sum_{r=1}^{\infty}\frac{g(p^r)}{p^{2r}}\right) = \frac{1}{\zeta(2)}\prod_p\left(1+\left(1-\frac{1}{p+1}\right)\sum_{r=1}^{\infty}\frac{1}{p^{2r}}\right)\\ &= \prod_p(1-p^{-2})\left(1+\left(1-\frac{1}{p+1}\right)\frac{p^{-2}}{1-p^{-2}}\right) = \prod_p\left(1-\frac{1}{p^2(p+1)}\right).\end{aligned} \tag{50}$$

We conclude finally from (48), (49) and (50) that

$$\sum_{0<d\leq N;\ d \text{ fund.}} \alpha h(d) = \frac{N}{2}\prod_p\left(1-\frac{1}{p^2(p+1)}\right) + O(N^{3/4}\log N).$$

Inserting the value of α, we get the enunciation of the theorem. The case $d<0$ is treated in exactly the same way.

6. Siegel's theorem on the class number. In this section, we prove Siegel's celebrated theorem on the class number. As we stated previously, Gauss conjectured that in the case $d<0$, $h(d)\to\infty$ as $d\to-\infty$ and though many steps had been taken toward a proof of this conjecture, it was not until 1933 that Heilbronn first succeeded in filling in the gaps which remained. Shortly thereafter, there followed the significant generalization of Siegel. Not only does this result generalize that of Gauss-Heilbronn, but Walfisz has shown that it has far-reaching implications to the distribution of primes in arithmetic progressions.

Let

$$R = \begin{cases}\dfrac{\pi}{w} & \text{if } d<0,\\ \log\varepsilon & \text{if } d>0,\end{cases} \tag{1}$$

where w and ε were defined in Theorem 2.8. Then our object is to prove the following

THEOREM 6.1.

$$\log Rh(d) \sim \tfrac{1}{2}\log|d| \tag{2}$$

as $d\to\infty$ $(d>0)$ *or* $d\to-\infty$ $(d<0)$.

Our first observation is that this theorem is equivalent to one on L series.

THEOREM 6.2. *If* $\chi_d(n)=(d/n)$, *then*

$$\log L(1,\chi_d) = o(\log|d|), \tag{3}$$

if and only if

$$\log Rh(d) \sim \tfrac{1}{2}\log|d| \,. \tag{4}$$

Suppose that (4) holds, then, since by Theorem 2.8

$$\alpha h(d) = L(1, \chi_d)\,, \tag{5}$$

where

$$\alpha = \frac{2R}{\sqrt{|d|}}\,,$$

it follows that

$$\log 2 - \tfrac{1}{2}\log|d| + \log Rh(d) = \log L(1, \chi_d) \tag{6}$$

and therefore from (6)

$$L(1, \chi_d) = o(\log|d|)\,.$$

Conversely, a direct reversal of the argument yields (4).

Several proofs of (3) are known though, in general, the underlying idea is essentially that given in Siegel's original proof.

This proof was based on a formula due to Hecke for the zeta function of an algebraic number field and used the elements of class field theory. With the help of a theorem of Heilbronn, we shall bypass these results from the general theory of algebraic number fields according to the following scheme:

The Riemann zeta function satisfies the following relation as is shown in Appendix B, (41),

$$\Phi(s) = \pi^{-s/2}\Gamma\left(\frac{s}{2}\right)\zeta(s) = \frac{1}{s(s-1)} + \int_1^\infty (x^{s/2} + x^{(1-s)/2})\omega(x)\frac{dx}{x}\,, \tag{7}$$

where

$$\omega(x) = \sum_{n=1}^\infty e^{-n^2\pi x}\,.$$

Moreover, as a consequence, $\Phi(s) = \Phi(1-s)$.

Hecke derived the analogue of (7) for the zeta function of an algebraic number field. Since in Siegel's proof, Hecke's formula is applied to a relatively simple product of L functions, Heilbronn derived a type of converse applicable to a wide class of functions incorporating products of L functions. Here is the result.

THEOREM 6.3. *Suppose that*

$$\varphi(s) = \sum_{n=1}^\infty \frac{a(n)}{n^s} \tag{8}$$

is a Dirichlet series satisfying the following conditions:

(a) *the series has a half plane of convergence;*

(b) *$\varphi(s)$ is a meromorphic function;*

(c) *there exists an integer $k > 0$ and real numbers $A > 0$, $\lambda > 0$, such that if*

(9) $$\Phi(s) = A^{-s}\Gamma^k\left(\frac{s}{\lambda}\right)\varphi(s)$$

then

(10) $$\Phi(s) = \Phi(1-s)\ ;$$

(d) $\Phi_0(s)$ *is a rational function of s which vanishes at* ∞ *and makes*

$$\Phi(s) - \Phi_0(s)$$

an entire function of s;

(11)(e) $$\varphi(s) = O(|t|^{\nu})$$

for some constant ν *uniformly for* $\sigma \geqq \frac{1}{2}$. *If* $x_1, x_2, \cdots, x_k$ *are positive real variables and if for simplicity we write*

(12) $$S(x) = x_1 + x_2 + \cdots + x_k\ ,\quad N(x) = x_1 x_2 \cdots x_k\ ,\quad dx = dx_1 dx_2 \cdots dx_k\ ,$$

(13) $$\mu = \frac{\lambda}{k}\ ,$$

then for all s,

(14) $$\Phi(s) = \Phi_0(s) + \sum_{n=1}^{\infty} a(n) \int_{N(x)\geqq 1} (N(x)^{s/\lambda} + N(x)^{(1-s)/\lambda}) e^{-A^{\mu} n^{\mu} S(x)} \frac{dx}{N(x)}\ .$$

In particular (14) holds for $\zeta(s, K)$ the zeta function of a quadratic field and for a certain product of L functions as we shall show in Theorem 6.4.

To prove the theorem, we let

(15) $$\Delta(x) = \Phi(s) - \Phi_0(s) - \sum_{n=1}^{\infty} a(n) \int_{N(x)\geqq 1} (N(x)^{s/\lambda} + N(x)^{(1-s)/\lambda}) e^{-A^{\mu} n^{\mu} S(x)} \frac{dx}{N(x)}\ .$$

We shall show that $\Delta(x)$

(i) is an entire function of s;

(ii) is bounded in absolute value of σ is bounded;

(iii) satisfies the functional equation

$$\Delta(s) = \Delta(1-s)\ ;$$

(iv) tends to 0 as $\sigma \to \infty$.

From these facts it follows by Liouville's theorem that $\Delta(s)$ is identically 0, whence the enunciation of the theorem. For, by (ii) it suffices to show that $\Delta(x) \to 0$ as $\sigma \to \pm\infty$ and by (iii) it is enough to consider the case $\sigma \to \infty$.

We start with two lemmas which will help us to prove (i) to (iv).

LEMMA 6.1. *If* $a(n) = O(n^{\alpha})$ *for some* $\alpha \geqq 0$, *and if* $c,\ \mu > 0$, *then the series*

(16) $$\sum_{n=1}^{\infty} a(n) \int_{N(x)\geqq 1} N(x)^s e^{-cn^{\mu} S(x)} dx$$

converges absolutely for arbitrary s and is an entire function of s which tends to 0 *as* $\sigma \to -\infty$.

LEMMA 6.2. *Under the hypothesis of Lemma* 6.1, *the series*

$$\sum_{n=1}^{\infty} a(n) \int_{0 \leqq N(x) \leqq 1} N(x)^s e^{-cn^{\mu} S(x)} dx \tag{17}$$

is absolutely convergent if σ *is sufficiently large, say*

$$\sigma \geqq \sigma_0 , \tag{18}$$

and tends to 0 *as* $\sigma \to \infty$.

PROOF OF LEMMA 6.1. For simplicity, let

$$f(s, x, c) = N(x)^s e^{-cS(x)} \tag{19}$$

and let D denote the domain $N(x) \geqq 1$, C_R the sphere $x_1^2 + \cdots + x_k^2 \leqq R$, and $D_R = D \cap C_R$. Let

$$I(s, c) = \int_D f(s, x, c) dx , \tag{20}$$

$$I_R(s, c) = \int_{D_R} f(s, x, c) dx . \tag{21}$$

Since $f(s, x, c)$ is a continuously differentiable function of s for x in the bounded domain D_R, it follows readily that $I_R(s, c)$ is an entire function of s.

Furthermore, for fixed σ,

$$f(s, x, c) = N(x)^s e^{-cS(x)} = O(N(x)^{\sigma} e^{-cS(x)}) = O(e^{-(c/2)S(x)}) \tag{22}$$

as $x_i \to \infty$.

Therefore,

$$\begin{aligned} I(s, c) &= O\left(\int_0^{\infty} \cdots \int_0^{\infty} e^{-(c/2)S(x)} dx\right) \\ &= O\left(\int_0^{\infty} e^{-(c/2)t} dt\right)^k = O(1) , \end{aligned} \tag{23}$$

where the constant implied by the O depends only on c and k.

Thus if σ is bounded, then $I(s, c)$ is bounded in absolute value.

Furthermore, if $|s| \leqq r$, then by (22) and (23),

$$\begin{aligned} I(s, c) - I_R(s, c) &= \int_{D-D_R} f(s, x, c) dx \\ &= O\left(\int_{D-D_R} e^{-(c/2)S(x)} dx\right) = o(1) \end{aligned} \tag{24}$$

as $R \to \infty$.

Consequently $I_R(s, c)$ converges uniformly to $I(s, c)$ in the domain $|s| \leqq r$ and $I(s, c)$ is therefore, analytic in this domain. Since r is arbitrary, $I(s, c)$ is entire. We consider now the series (16). We have

$$\left|\sum_{n=1}^{\infty} a(n)I(s, cn^{\mu})\right| \leqq \sum_{n=1}^{\infty} |a(n)| I(\sigma, cn^{\mu})$$

$$(25) \qquad = \lim_{M\to\infty} \int_D N(x)^{\sigma} \sum_{n=1}^{M} |a(n)| e^{-cn^{\mu}S(x)} dx$$

$$\leqq \lim_{M\to\infty} \int_D N(x)^{\sigma} e^{-(c/2)S(x)} \sum_{n=1}^{M} |a(n)| e^{-(c/2) n^{\mu}S(x)} dx .$$

By assumption $a(n) = O(n^{\alpha})$ and since $N(x) \geqq 1$, it follows that $S(x) \geqq 1$ and consequently,

$$(26) \qquad \sum_{n=1}^{M} |a(n)| e^{-(c/2) n^{\mu}S(x)} = O\left(\sum_{n=1}^{M} n^{\alpha} e^{-(c/2) n^{\mu}}\right) = O(1)$$

as $M \to \infty$.

Accordingly, from (25) and (26),

$$(27) \qquad \sum_{n=1}^{\infty} |a(n)| I(\sigma, cn^{\mu}) = O\left(\int_D N(x)^{\sigma} e^{-(c/2) S(x)} dx\right) .$$

If $|s| \leqq r$, then from (23), we infer that the series

$$\sum_{n=1}^{\infty} a(n)I(s, cn^{\mu})$$

is absolutely convergent and is bounded in absolute value if σ is bounded. The convergence, moreover, is uniform in $|s| \leqq r$. For, as above, we have

$$\sum_{n=M+1}^{Q} a(n)I(s, cn^{\mu}) = O\left(\int_D N(x)^{\sigma} e^{-(c/2)S(x)} \sum_{n=M+1}^{Q} |a(n)| e^{-(c/2) n^{\mu}S(x)} dx\right) .$$

On the other hand,

$$\sum_{n=M+1}^{Q} |a(n)| e^{-(c/2) n^{\mu}S(x)} = O\left(\sum_{n=M+1}^{Q} n^{\alpha} e^{-(c/2) n^{\mu}}\right) = o(1) \qquad \text{as } M \to \infty$$

uniformly in s. Thus the convergence is uniform in $|s| \leqq r$ and this implies that the function

$$(28) \qquad g(s) = \sum_{n=1}^{\infty} a(n)I(s, cn^{\mu})$$

is entire.

It remains to show that

$$(29) \qquad \lim_{\sigma\to-\infty} g(s) = 0 .$$

To do this, we prove that

$$I\left(\sigma, \frac{c}{2}\right) \to 0 \qquad \text{as } \sigma \to -\infty$$

and (29) will follow from (27).

Indeed, suppose that $\varepsilon > 0$, then

$$I\left(\sigma, \frac{c}{2}\right) = \int_{N(x) \geqq 1} N(x)^{\sigma} e^{-(c/2)S(x)} dx$$

(30)
$$= \int_{1+\varepsilon \geqq N(x) \geqq 1} N(x)^{\sigma} e^{-(c/2)S(x)} dx + \int_{N(x) \geqq 1+\varepsilon} N(x)^{\sigma} e^{-(c/2)S(x)} dx$$

$$= I_1 + I_2 .$$

Since $\sigma \to -\infty$, we can assume that $\sigma < 0$ and infer that

(31)
$$I_2 \leqq (1+\varepsilon)^{\sigma} \int_{N(x) \geqq 1+\varepsilon} e^{-(c/2)S(x)} dx \leqq (1+\varepsilon)^{\sigma} \left(\frac{2}{c}\right)^k .$$

On the other hand,

$$I_1 \leqq \int_{1+\varepsilon \geqq N(x) \geqq 1} e^{-(c/2)S(x)} dx$$

$$\leqq \int_0^{\infty} \cdots \int_0^{\infty} \int_{(x_1 \cdots x_{k-1})^{-1}}^{(1+\varepsilon)(x_1 \cdots x_{k-1})^{-1}} e^{-(c/2)(x_1 + \cdots + x_k)} dx_1 \cdots dx_k$$

$$\leqq \int_0^{\infty} e^{-(c/2)x_1} dx_1 \cdots \int_0^{\infty} e^{-(c/2)x_{k-1}} e^{-(c/2)(x_1 \cdots x_{k-1})^{-1}} \varepsilon (x_1 \cdots x_{k-1})^{-1} dx_{k-1} .$$

However, since $ye^{-y} \leqq e^{-1}$, we deduce that

(32)
$$I_1 \leqq \frac{2\varepsilon}{ce} \left(\int_0^{\infty} e^{-(c/2)t} dt\right)^{k-1} = \frac{2\varepsilon}{ce} \left(\frac{2}{c}\right)^{k-1} .$$

Consequently from (31) and (32),

$$I\left(\sigma, \frac{c}{2}\right) \leqq \left(\frac{2}{c}\right)^k \left(\frac{\varepsilon}{e} + (1+\varepsilon)^{\sigma}\right) .$$

If $\sigma \to -\infty$,

$$\lim_{\sigma \to -\infty} I\left(\sigma, \frac{c}{2}\right) \leqq \left(\frac{2}{c}\right)^k \frac{\varepsilon}{e}$$

and since ε is arbitrary, the assertion (29) and hence, the lemma is completely proved.

Proof of Lemma 6.2. A proof of this lemma can be achieved along lines very similar to those used in Lemma 6.1.

Indeed, from (17) and (19),

(33)
$$\sum_{n=1}^{\infty} a(n) \int_{0 \leqq N(x) \leqq 1} f(s, x, cn^{\mu}) = O\left(\sum_{n=1}^{\infty} |a(n)| \int_0^{\infty} \cdots \int_0^{\infty} N(x)^{\sigma} e^{-cn^{\mu} S(x)} dx_1 \cdots dx_k\right) .$$

Putting $cn^{\mu} x_i = y_i$ and using Theorem A.7, of Appendix A, we get from (33)

(34)
$$\sum_{n=1}^{\infty} a(n) \int_{0 \leqq N(x) \leqq 1} f(s, x, cn^{\mu}) dx = O\left(c^{-k(\sigma+1)} \Gamma^k(\sigma+1) \sum_{n=1}^{\infty} \frac{n^{\alpha}}{n^{\mu k(\sigma+1)}}\right) .$$

The sum on the right of (34), however, converges if σ is sufficiently large, say $\sigma \geqq \sigma_0$. Thus, the series (17) converges absolutely. To show that the sum tends to 0 as $\sigma \to \infty$, let

$$0 < \varepsilon < \tfrac{1}{2}\,.$$

Then

$$\begin{aligned}
&\sum_{n=1}^{\infty} a(n) \int_{0 \leqq N(x) \leqq 1} f(s, x, cn^{\mu}) dx \\
(35) \qquad &= \sum_{n=1}^{\infty} a(n) \int_{0 \leqq N(x) \leqq 1-\varepsilon} f(s, x, cn^{\mu}) dx + \sum_{n=1}^{\infty} a(n) \int_{1-\varepsilon \leqq N(x) \leqq 1} f(s, x, cn^{\mu}) dx \\
&= S_1 + S_2\,.
\end{aligned}$$

We have

$$(36) \qquad S_1 = O\left((1-\varepsilon)^{\sigma-\sigma_0} \sum_{n=1}^{\infty} |a(n)| \int_{N(x) \leqq 1} f(\sigma_0, x, cn^{\mu}) dx\right) = O((1-\varepsilon)^{\sigma-\sigma_0})$$

since we showed that the series converges absolutely for $\sigma \geqq \sigma_0$, the constant implied by the O being independent of ε and σ.

For an estimate of S_2, we observe that since $\varepsilon < \frac{1}{2}$, $N(x) \geqq \frac{1}{2}$, and hence $S(x) \geqq \frac{1}{2}$. Accordingly, we get for S_2,

$$S_2 \leqq \lim_{M \to \infty} \int_{1-\varepsilon \leqq N(x) \leqq 1} N(x)^{\sigma} e^{-(c/2) S(x)} \sum_{n=1}^{M} |a(n)|\, e^{-(c/4) n^{\mu}} dx\,.$$

As above, in Lemma 6.1, the inner sum is $O(1)$ as $M \to \infty$, and, therefore,

$$(37) \qquad S_2 = O\left(\int_{1-\varepsilon \leqq N(x) \leqq 1} N(x)^{\sigma} e^{-(c/2) S(x)} dx\right).$$

Again, as in Lemma 6.1,

$$(38) \qquad \int_{1-\varepsilon \leqq N(x) \leqq 1} f\left(\sigma, x, \frac{c}{2}\right) dx = O(\varepsilon)\,.$$

Thus, from (36), (37), and (38), we infer that

$$h(s) = \sum a(n) \int_{N(x) \leqq 1} f(s, x, cn^{\mu}) dx = O((1-\varepsilon)^{\sigma-\sigma_0} + \varepsilon)\,.$$

Consequently, as $\sigma \to \infty$.

$$\lim_{\sigma \to \infty} h(s) = O(\varepsilon)$$

and, therefore, $\lim_{\sigma \to \infty} h(s) = 0$, since ε is arbitrary.

We return to proofs of the assertions (i) to (iv).

(i) follows from Lemma 6.1 with $c = A^{\mu}$ since $a(n)$ is clearly $O(n^{\alpha})$ for some α, $\varphi(s)$ having by assumption a half plane of convergence. Furthermore, by assumption $\Phi(s) - \Phi_0(s)$ is entire.

(ii) By Lemma 6.1, again, the series on the right of (15) is bounded if σ is bounded. $\Phi_0(s)$ is bounded if σ is bounded. On the other hand, by (9) and hypothesis (e), and Theorem A.11 of Appendix A,

$$(39) \qquad \Phi(s) = A^{-s} \Gamma^{k}\left(\frac{s}{\lambda}\right) \varphi(s) = O(A^{-\sigma}\, |t|^{\nu}\, e^{-\pi |t|/2\lambda} |t|^{\sigma-1/2}) = O(1)$$

if σ is bounded.

Thus $\Delta(s)$ is bounded if σ is bounded.

(iii) The integral in (15) is evidently invariant under the substitution $s \to 1-s$.

Further, since $\Phi(s) = \Phi(1-s)$, then (6) implies that $\Phi_0(s) - \Phi_0(1-s)$ is an entire function of s. But $\Phi_0(s)$ is a rational function and, therefore,

$$\Phi_0(s) = \Phi_0(1-s) .$$

Consequently $\Delta(s)$ is invariant under the transformation $s \to 1-s$.

(iv) To prove this assertion, we start from Theorem A.7 of Appendix A

$$\Gamma(s) = \int_0^\infty e^{-u}u^{s-1}du .$$

We replace u by $A^\mu n^\mu x$ and s by s/λ and we get, recalling that $\lambda = \mu/k$,

$$A^{-s/k}\Gamma\left(\frac{s}{\lambda}\right)n^{-s/k} = \int_0^\infty x^{s/\lambda}e^{-A^\mu n^\mu x}\frac{dx}{x} . \tag{40}$$

Taking a product of k copies of (40), we get

$$A^{-s}\Gamma^k\left(\frac{s}{\lambda}\right)n^{-s} = \int_{N(x)\geqq 0} N(x)^{s/\lambda}e^{-A^\mu n^\mu S(x)}\frac{dx}{N(x)} .$$

Multiplying by $a(n)$ and summing on n, we infer using (8) and (9), that

$$\Phi(s) = \sum_{n=1}^\infty a(n)\int_{N(x)\geqq 0} N(x)^{s/\lambda}e^{-A^\mu n^\mu S(x)}\frac{dx}{N(x)} . \tag{41}$$

Using (41) and (15), we see that

$$\begin{aligned} \Delta(x) = \Phi_0(s) &+ \sum_{n=1}^\infty a(n)\int_{0\leqq N(x)\leqq 1} N(x)^{s/\lambda}e^{-A^\mu n^\mu S(x)}\frac{dx}{N(x)} \\ &- \sum_{n=1}^\infty a(n)\int_{N(x)\geqq 1} N(x)^{(1-s)/\lambda}e^{-A^\mu n^\mu S(x)}\frac{dx}{N(x)} . \end{aligned} \tag{42}$$

As $\sigma \to \infty$, $\Phi_0(s) \to 0$ and by Lemmas 6.1 and 6.2, both the sums on the right-hand side of (42) tend to 0 as $\sigma \to \infty$.

Thus the proof of (iv) and, therefore Theorem 6.3, is complete.

As examples of functions which fulfill the hypotheses of Theorem 6.3, we mention two important classes.

THEOREM 6.4. *The following functions satisfy the conditions of Theorem* 6.3:

(A) $\zeta(s, K) = \zeta(s)L(s, \chi_d)$ *where d is the discriminant of the field* $K = R(\sqrt{D})$, $k = \frac{1}{2}(3 + \operatorname{sgn} d)$, $\lambda = k$, $A = 2^{2-k}\pi\,|d|^{-1/2}$;

(B) $\varphi(s) = \zeta(s)L(s, \chi_{d_1})L(s, \chi_{d_2})L(s, \chi_{d_3})$, *where $d_1d_2d_3$ is a perfect square and $\chi_{d_i}(n)$ is the Kronecker symbol* (d_i/n), $k = \frac{1}{2}(5 + \sum_{i=1}^3 \operatorname{sgn} d_i)$, $\lambda = k/2$, $A = 2^{4-k}\pi^2\,|d_1d_2d_3|^{-1/2}$. *In case* (A),

$$\Phi_0(s) = \frac{A^{-1}\Gamma^k\left(\frac{1}{k}\right)L(1, \chi_d)}{s(s-1)} . \tag{43}$$

In case (B),

$$\Phi_0(s) = \frac{A^{-1}\Gamma^k\left(\frac{1}{\lambda}\right)L(1, \chi_{d_1})L(1, \chi_{d_2})L(1, \chi_{d_3})}{s(s-1)} . \tag{44}$$

PROOF. We prove the theorem for the more difficult class (B), restricting our attention to the possibility $d_1 < 0$, $d_2 < 0$, $d_3 > 0$. The other possibilities are done in exactly the same way; so, in fact, is class (A). We show that hypotheses (a), (b), (c), (d) and (e) of Theorem 6.3 are satisfied.

(a) We show that the series for

$$\varphi(s) = \zeta(s)L(s, \chi_{d_1})L(s, \chi_{d_2})L(s, \chi_{d_3})$$

has a half plane of convergence. Let

$$\varphi(s) = \sum_{n=1}^{\infty} \frac{a(n)}{n^s} .$$

It suffices to show that $a(n) = O(n^\alpha)$ for some α. Indeed, if

$$\varphi_1(s) = \zeta(s)L(s, \chi_{d_1}) = \sum \frac{a_1(n)}{n^s} ,$$

then $a_1(n) = \sum_{b|n}\chi_{d_1}(b) = O(d(n)) = O(n^\varepsilon)$ by Lemma 5.1, Chapter IV, where $d(n)$ denotes the number of divisors of n.

Let

$$\varphi_2(s) = \varphi_1(s)L(s, \chi_{d_2}) = \sum_{n=1}^{\infty} \frac{a_2(n)}{n^s} .$$

Then using Lemma 5.1, Chapter IV again

$$a_2(n) = \sum_{lm=n} a_1(l)\chi_{d_2}(m) = \sum_{l|n} |a_1(l)| = \sum_{l|n} l^\varepsilon = O(n^{2\varepsilon}) .$$

Proceeding in this way for $\varphi_3(s) = \varphi_2(s)L(s, \chi_{d_2})$ and $\varphi(s) = \varphi_4(s) = \varphi_3(s)L(s, \chi_{d_3})$, we conclude that condition (a) of Theorem 6.3 is fulfilled.

(b) We show that $\varphi(s)$ is meromorphic. This follows directly from Theorems B.6 and B.7, of Appendix B and the hypothesis (b) of Theorem 6.3 is satisfied.

(c) To show that there exists constants k, λ, A such that, if

$$\Phi(s) = A^{-s}\Gamma^k\left(\frac{s}{\lambda}\right)\varphi(s) ,$$

then $\Phi(s) = \Phi(1-s)$, we note that, if $d_1 < 0$, $\chi_{d_1}(-1) = -1$ by Lemma 2.3 and therefore by Theorem B.7 of Appendix B,

$$\Phi_1(s) = \left(\frac{|d_1|}{\pi}\right)^{(s+1)/2}\Gamma\left(\frac{s+1}{2}\right)L(s, \chi_{d_1}) \tag{45}$$

satisfies the relation

$$\Phi_1(s) = \Phi_1(1-s) .$$

Similarly for

(46) $$\Phi_2(s) = \left(\frac{|d_2|}{\pi}\right)^{(s+1)/2} \Gamma\left(\frac{s+1}{2}\right) L(s, \chi_{d_2}) .$$

For $d_3 > 0$, $\chi_{d_3}(-1) = +1$, and

(47) $$\Phi_3(s) = \left(\frac{|d_3|}{\pi}\right)^{s/2} \Gamma\left(\frac{s}{2}\right) L(s, \chi_{d_3}) ,$$

(48) $$\Phi_4(s) = \left(\frac{1}{\pi}\right)^{s/2} \Gamma\left(\frac{s}{2}\right) \zeta(s)$$

all satisfy the relation $\Phi_i(s) = \Phi_i(1-s)$. In addition if we put $\varphi(s) = L(s, \chi_{d_1}) L(s, \chi_{d_2}) L(s, \chi_{d_3}) \zeta(s)$, then by (45) to (48),

$$\left(\frac{|d_1|}{\pi}\right)^{s/2} \left(\frac{|d_2|}{\pi}\right)^{s/2} \left(\frac{|d_3|}{\pi}\right)^{s/2} \left(\frac{1}{\pi}\right)^{s/2} \frac{(|d_1|\,|d_2|)^{1/2}}{\pi} \Gamma^2\left(\frac{s+1}{2}\right) \Gamma^2\left(\frac{s}{2}\right) \varphi(s)$$
$$= \left(\frac{1}{\pi}\right)^{(1-s)/2} \left(\frac{|d_1|}{\pi}\right)^{(1-s)/2} \left(\frac{|d_2|}{\pi}\right)^{(1-s)/2} \left(\frac{|d_3|}{\pi}\right)^{(1-s)/2} \frac{(|d_1|\,|d_2|)^{1/2}}{\pi}$$
$$\times \Gamma^2\left(\frac{1-s}{2} + \frac{1}{2}\right) \Gamma^2\left(\frac{1-s}{2}\right) \varphi(1-s)$$

and therefore

$$(|d_1 d_2 d_3|)^{s/2} \pi^{-2s} \Gamma^2\left(\frac{s+1}{2}\right) \Gamma^2\left(\frac{s}{2}\right) \varphi(s)$$
$$= (|d_1 d_2 d_3|)^{(1-s)/2} \pi^{-2(1-s)} \Gamma^2\left(\frac{1-s}{2} + \frac{1}{2}\right) \Gamma^2\left(\frac{1-s}{2}\right) \varphi(1-s) .$$

But since, by Theorem A.6, of Appendix A,

$$\Gamma(s+\tfrac{1}{2}) \Gamma(s) = 2\sqrt{\pi} 2^{-2s} \Gamma(2s) ,$$

it follows from (49) that $\varphi(s)$ satisfies the conditions (c) Theorem 6.3 with $k = 2$, $\lambda = 1$, $A = |d_1 d_2 d_3|^{-1/2} (2\pi)^2$.

(d) Moreover, if

$$\Phi(s) = A^{-s} \Gamma^k\left(\frac{s}{\lambda}\right) \varphi(s) ,$$

then $\Phi(s)$ has simple poles at $s = 0$ and $s = 1$ and is otherwise analytic. This is because in the case $d > 0$,

$$L(0, \chi_d) = 0$$

by Corollary 1, Theorem B.7 (a) of Appendix B. Accordingly,

(51) $$\Phi_0(s) = \frac{A^{-1} \Gamma^k\left(\frac{1}{\lambda}\right) L(1, \chi_{d_1}) L(1, \chi_{d_2}) L(1, \chi_{d_3})}{s-1} + \frac{R}{s} ,$$

where R is the residue of $\Phi(s)$ at $s = 0$. But because $\Phi(s) = \Phi(1-s)$, it follows from (51) that

$$\Phi_0(s) = \frac{A^{-1}\Gamma^k\left(\frac{1}{\lambda}\right)L(1, \chi_{d_1})L(1, \chi_{d_2})L(1, \chi_{d_3})}{s(s-1)}$$

as required. Thus condition (d) is fulfilled.

(e) Finally for hypothesis (e), we know by Corollary 2, Theorem 4.2, of Chapter II, that $\zeta(s) = O(|t|^{1/2})$. For the L function with characters, we apply partial summation. If χ is a character mod k

$$L(s, \chi) = \sum_{n=1}^{\infty} \frac{\chi(n)}{n^s}$$

and $T(x) = \sum_{m \leqq x} \chi(m)$ then for $\sigma \geqq \frac{1}{2}$,

$$L(s, \chi) = s\int_1^{\infty} \frac{T(x)dx}{x^{s+1}} = O\left(|s| \int_1^{\infty} \frac{dx}{x^{\sigma+1}}\right) = O(|t|).$$

Consequently, $\varphi(s) = O(|t|^{\nu})$ for some ν uniformly for $\sigma \geqq \frac{1}{2}$ as required. In the next theorem, we obtain additional information about the coefficients of $\varphi(s)$.

Theorem 6.5. *If $d_1d_2d_3$ is a square and*

$$\varphi(s) = \sum_{n=1}^{\infty} \frac{a(n)}{n^s}$$

is the Dirichlet series for $L(s, \chi_{d_1})L(s, \chi_{d_2})L(s, \chi_{d_3})\zeta(s)$, then $a(1) = 1$, $a(n) \geqq 0$ for $n \geqq 2$.

Proof. Since

$$\log L(s, \chi_{d_i}) = \sum_{m,\,p} \frac{\chi_{d_i}(p^m)}{mp^{ms}} \qquad (i = 1, 2, 3), \tag{52}$$

it follows that

$$\varphi(s) = \exp\left(\sum_i \sum_{m,\,p} \frac{\chi_{d_i}(p^m)}{mp^{ms}}\right) = \exp\left(\sum_{m,p} \frac{b(m, p)}{mp^{ms}}\right), \tag{53}$$

where

$$b(m, p) = 1 + \chi_{d_1}(p^m) + \chi_{d_2}(p^m) + \chi_{d_3}(p^m).$$

On the other hand, since $\chi_{d_3}(n) = \chi_{d_1}(n)\chi_{d_2}(n)$, for $(n, d_1d_2d_3) = 1$, it follows that $b(m, p) \geqq 0$ if $(p, d_1d_2d_3) = 1$. If $(p, d_1d_2d_3) > 1$, then because $d_1d_2d_3$ is a square, an easy calculation shows that $b(m, p) \geqq 0$. Thus from (53) $a(n) \geqq 0$ if $n \geqq 2$, $a(1)$ is clearly 1.

We note in passing that the Dirichlet series for $\zeta(s, K) = \zeta(s)L(s, \chi_d)$ also satisfies the condition $a(1) = 1$, $a(n) \geqq 0$. This is an immediate consequence of the definition of $\zeta(s, K)$ as the zeta function of the field K. It also follows in the same way as in Theorem 6.5.

The function $\varphi(s) = \zeta(s)\prod_{i=1}^{3} L(s, \chi_{d_i})$ is actually the zeta function of a certain biquadratic field F. Theorem 6.3 as applied to $\varphi(s)$ is Hecke's analogue, for the zeta function of F of Riemann's (7) for the ordinary zeta function. This remark may serve as a useful guide.

The next theorem is an inequality from above for $L(1, \chi_d)$. More generally, we prove

THEOREM 6.6. *If* χ *is any real character* mod k *which is not principal, then*

$$0 < L(1, \chi) < 3 \log k . \tag{54}$$

PROOF. The proof uses Lemma 3.1 of Chapter I. Indeed

$$\sum_{n=1}^{M} \frac{\chi(n)}{n} = \frac{S(M)}{M} + \int_1^M \frac{S(x)}{x^2}\, dx ,$$

where $S(x) = \sum_{n \leqq x} \chi(n)$.

Therefore since $S(x) = O(k)$

$$\begin{aligned} |L(1, \chi)| &= \left|\int_1^\infty \frac{S(x)}{x^2} dx\right| \leqq \int_1^k \frac{|S(x)|}{x^2}\, dx + \int_k^\infty \frac{|S(x)|}{x^2}\, dx \\ &\leqq \int_1^k \frac{dx}{x} + \varphi(k) \int_k^\infty \frac{dx}{x^2} = \log k + \frac{\varphi(k)}{k} < 3 \log k . \end{aligned} \tag{55}$$

It remains to show that $L(1, \chi) > 0$. We know from Theorem 4.4, Chapter I that $L(1, \chi) \neq 0$. Let

$$\theta(s) = \zeta(s) L(s, \chi) = \sum_{n=1}^{\infty} \frac{a(n)}{n^s} . \tag{56}$$

Then $a(n)$ is multiplicative and it is easy to see as in the above proof that

$$a(p^r) = \sum_{m \mid p^r} \chi(m) \geqq 0 .$$

Therefore by (56),

$$\begin{aligned} L(1, \chi) &= \lim_{s \to 1+0} L(s, \chi) = \lim_{s \to 1+0} (s-1)\zeta(s) L(s, \chi) \\ &= \lim_{s \to 1+0} (s-1)\theta(s) \geqq 0 \end{aligned}$$

because for real s, $\theta(s) \geqq 0$.

Since $L(1, \chi) \neq 0$, the result follows.

We note that the inequality $L(1, \chi) > 0$ is contained in Corollary 1, Theorem 2.8 for χ the Kronecker symbol. The above proof is independent of the concept of class number.

Our object in proving Theorems 6.3 and 6.4 is to derive an inequality satisfied by the residues of the functions $\varphi(s) = \zeta(s) \prod_{i=1}^{3} L(s, \chi_{d_i})$ and $\zeta(s, K)$. These residues involve the functions $L(1, \chi_d)$ which are our primary objective.

We therefore prove in this connection

THEOREM 6.7. *If*

(a) $\varphi(s) = \zeta(s) L(s, \chi_d)$

or

(b) $\varphi(s) = \zeta(s)\prod_{i=1}^{3} L(s, \chi_{d_i})$,
where $d_1d_2d_3$ *is the square of an integer,* $\Phi(s)$, $\Phi_0(s)$ *are as defined in Theorems* 6.3 *and* 6.4, s *is a real number such that* $0 < s < 1$. *Then the following inequalities are satisfied*:

$$\Phi(s) - \Phi_0(s) \geqq 2^{-2}e^{-4\pi}|d|^{s/2} \tag{57)(a}$$

$$\Phi(s) - \Phi_0(s) \geqq 2^{-4}e^{-8\pi}\Delta^{s/2}, \tag{58)(b}$$

where $\Delta = |d_1d_2d_3|$.

PROOF. We prove the more difficult case (b) and it is in this proof that we use Theorem 6.3. The explicit value of the constants on the right is of no essential significance. By (14) of Theorem 6.3,

$$\Phi(s) - \Phi_0(s) = \sum_{n=1}^{\infty} a(n) \int\cdots\int_{N(x)\geqq 1} (N(x)^{s/\lambda} + N(x)^{(1-s)/\lambda})e^{-(nA)^{\lambda/k}S(x)} \frac{dx}{N(x)} .$$

Because s is real and by Theorem 6.5, $a(1) = 1$, $a(n) \geqq 0$, then we get, since $\lambda/k = \frac{1}{2}$,

$$\Phi(s) - \Phi_0(s) \geqq \int\cdots\int_{N(x)\geqq 1} N(x)^{-1+2s/k}e^{-A^{1/2}S(x)}dx . \tag{59}$$

If we denote by W the domain

$$\Delta^{1/4} \leqq x_i \leqq 2\Delta^{1/4} \qquad (i = 1, 2, \cdots, k) \tag{60}$$

then from (59)

$$\Phi(s) - \Phi_0(s) \geqq \int\cdots\int_{W} N(x)^{-1+2s/k}e^{-A^{1/2}S(x)}dx . \tag{61}$$

In W, the integrand is

$$\geqq 2^{-k}\Delta^{-k/4}\Delta^{s/2}e^{-A^{1/2}2k\Delta^{1/4}} . \tag{62}$$

Consequently, since by Theorem 6.4,

$$A = 2^{4-k}\pi^2\Delta^{-1/2} , \tag{63}$$

we get from (61), (62), (63),

$$\Phi(s) - \Phi_0(s) \geqq 2^{-k}\Delta^{-k/4}\Delta^{s/2}e^{-2k\pi 2^{2-(k/2)}\Delta^{-1/4}\Delta^{1/4}}\Delta^{k/4} \geqq 2^{-k}e^{-2k\pi 2^{2-(k/2)}}\Delta^{s/2} .$$

In case (b), k is either 2 or 4 and the required inequality is therefore established.

The argument in case (a) is very much the same—except that W is the domain defined by $|d|^{1/2} \leqq x_i \leqq 2|d|^{1/2}$.

The preliminaries are now complete for a

PROOF OF THEOREM 6.1. We wish to show that if

$$\chi_d(n) = \left(\frac{d}{n}\right)$$

then

$$\log L(1, \chi_d) = o(\log |d|) .$$

The proof is indirect; suppose that $\log L(1, \chi_d)$ is not $o(\log |d|)$. Then there exists $\varepsilon > 0$, and an infinite sequence of d such that either

$$L(1, \chi_d) > |d|^{\varepsilon} \tag{64}$$

or

$$L(1, \chi_d) < |d|^{-\varepsilon} . \tag{65}$$

The possibility in (64) is excluded by (54) of Theorem 6.6 since $|d|^{\varepsilon}$ increases infinitely more rapidly than $\log |d|$. In fact if we choose $d_0 > 0$ such that

$$3 \log d_0 < d_0^{\varepsilon}$$

then for $|d| > d_0$

$$L(1, \chi_d) > 3 \log |d| ,$$

and this contradicts (54).

The alternative to (64) is

$$L(1, \chi_d) < |d|^{-\varepsilon}$$

for $d > d_0$. We shall show that on this hypothesis there exists σ_d

$$1 - \varepsilon < \sigma_d < 1$$

such that if $\zeta(s, K) = \zeta(s)L(s, \chi_d)$, then $\zeta(\sigma_d, K) = 0$.

Indeed suppose that for $0 < s < 1$, $\zeta(s, K) \leqq 0$, then from (58) of Theorem 6.7 and the definition (43) of $\Phi_0(s)$, we get

$$\frac{L(1, \chi_d) A^{-1} \Gamma^k\left(\frac{1}{k}\right)}{s(s-1)} + 2^{-2} e^{-4\pi} |d|^{s/2} \leqq 0 , \tag{66}$$

where A, k are defined as in Theorem 6.4. Thus from (66),

$$L(1, \chi_d) \geqq s(1-s) 2^{-2} e^{-4\pi} A \Gamma^{-k}\left(\frac{1}{k}\right) |d|^{s/2} .$$

Since $k = 1$ or 2, we infer that

$$L(1, \chi_d) \geqq s(1-s) e^{-4\pi} |d|^{(s-1)/2} ,$$

and in particular with $s = 1 - \varepsilon$,

$$L(1, \chi_d) \geqq \varepsilon(1-\varepsilon) e^{-4\pi} |d|^{-\varepsilon/2} . \tag{67}$$

But coupled with (65) this is contradictory if d is chosen sufficiently large. In fact we need only choose $|d| > d_0'$, where d_0' is chosen so as to make

$$|d_0'|^{-\varepsilon} < \varepsilon(1-\varepsilon) e^{-4\pi} |d_0'|^{-\varepsilon/2} .$$

We have therefore shown that if $|d| > \max(d_0, d_0')$, then

$$\zeta(1-\varepsilon, K) > 0 .$$

By Theorem 6.6, however, $L(1, \chi_d) > 0$, hence

$$\lim_{s\to 1-0} \zeta(s, K) = \lim_{s\to 1-0} L(s, \chi_d)\zeta(s) = -\infty$$

since $\lim_{s\to 1-0} \zeta(s) = -\infty$.

Therefore for s sufficiently close to 1, $\zeta(s, K) < 0$. Consequently there exists σ_d such that

$$1-\varepsilon < \sigma_d < 1 \tag{68}$$

and

$$\zeta(\sigma_d, K) = \zeta(\sigma_d)L(\sigma_d, \chi_d) = 0 . \tag{69}$$

We use this inference as follows: we put $d = d_1$, we let d_2 be a discriminant satisfying (65) with $|d_2| > |d_1|$ and we suppose that d_3 is the discriminant of the quadratic field generated by $\sqrt{(d_1 d_2)}$. It is then easy to see that $d_1 d_2 d_3$ is a square and we consider the function

$$\varphi(s) = \zeta(s)L(s, \chi_{d_1})L(s, \chi_{d_2})L(s, \chi_{d_3}) .$$

(Actually it would suffice to consider the character $\chi_{d_1}\chi_{d_2}$ and denote it by χ_{d_3}.) Our object in considering $\varphi(s)$ is that it is the simplest function involving $\zeta(s, K)$ and $L(s, \chi_{d_2})$ as factors which at the same time satisfies the hypotheses of Theorem 6.3. We apply (69) and Theorem 6.7 (b) to this function. Indeed since $\varphi(\sigma_d) = 0$, and if $\Phi_0(s)$ is defined by (44) we get

$$-\Phi_0(s) \geqq 2^{-4}e^{-8\pi} |d_1 d_2 d_3|^{\sigma_d/2} .$$

This is the same as

$$\frac{L(1, \chi_{d_1})L(1, \chi_{d_2})L(1, \chi_{d_3})\Gamma^k\left(\frac{1}{\lambda}\right)A^{-1}}{\sigma_d(1-\sigma_d)} \geqq 2^{-4}e^{-8\pi} |d_1 d_2 d_3|^{\sigma_d/2} . \tag{70}$$

In other words,

$$L(1, \chi_{d_1})L(1, \chi_{d_2})L(1, \chi_{d_3}) \geqq 2^{-4}e^{-8\pi}A\Gamma^{-k}\left(\frac{1}{\lambda}\right) |d_1 d_2 d_3|^{\sigma_d/2}\sigma_d(1-\sigma_d) . \tag{71}$$

If we take account of the definition (63) of A and of the fact that $k = 2$ or 4, we infer from (71) that

$$L(1, \chi_{d_1})L(1, \chi_{d_2})L(1, \chi_{d_3}) \geqq 2^{-4}e^{-8\pi} |d_1 d_2 d_3|^{(\sigma_d-1)/2}\sigma_d(1-\sigma_d) . \tag{72}$$

Using the fact that

$$|d_3| \leqq |d_1 d_2|$$

and applying Theorem 6.6 to $L(1, \chi_{d_1})$ and $L(1, \chi_{d_3})$, we get from (72),

$$L(1, \chi_{d_2}) > \frac{\sigma_d(1-\sigma_d) |d_1 d_2|^{\sigma_d-1}}{3^2 2^4 e^{8\pi} \log |d_1| \log |d_1 d_2|} . \tag{73}$$

This inequality coupled with (68) implies that if d_2 is chosen sufficiently large, then

$$L(1, \chi_{d_2}) > |d_2|^{-\varepsilon}$$

contradicting (65). The proof is thus complete.

Problems

1. Show that if $\zeta(s, K)$ is the zeta function of the field $K = R(\sqrt{D})$, then

$$\log \zeta(s, K) = \log \frac{1}{s-1} + r(s) ,$$

where $r(s) = O(1)$ as $s \to 1$.

2. We say that a prime ideal is of the first degree if its norm is a rational prime and of the second degree if its norm is the square of a rational prime.

(a) Deduce from (1) that

$$\sum_{\mathfrak{p}_1} \frac{1}{N(\mathfrak{p}_1)^s} = \log \frac{1}{s-1} + r_1(s) ,$$

where $r_1(s) = O(1)$ as $s \to 1$, the summation being over all prime ideals of the first degree. As a result, there exist infinitely many prime ideals of the first degree.

(b) Using the decomposition

$$\zeta(s, K) = L(s, \chi)\zeta(s)$$

prove that there exist infinitely many prime ideals of the second degree.

3. (a) Use Theorem 2.6, to show that if $\mathfrak{p}$ is an ideal of $R(i)$ of the first degree, then $\mathfrak{p} = (p)$ where p is a rational prime $p \equiv 1 \pmod 4$. As a consequence of 2(a), there exist infinitely many primes $p \equiv 1 \pmod 4$.

(b) Use (b) of Problem 2 to show that there are infinitely many primes of the form $3k + 1$.

4. If

$$\zeta(s, K) = \sum_{n=1}^{\infty} \frac{F(n)}{n^s} = \sum_{\mathfrak{a}} \frac{1}{N(\mathfrak{a})^s} ,$$

then Theorem 2.1 shows that

$$H(x) = \sum_{n \leq x} F(n) = \alpha h x + \Delta(x) ,$$

where $\Delta(x) = O(x^{1/2})$.

What interpretation is to be given to $H(x)$ in the case when

$$K = R(i)?$$

The order of $\Delta(x)$ may be improved by complex integration. Show that

$$H(x) = \frac{1}{2\pi i} \int_{a-i\infty}^{a+i\infty} \frac{\zeta(s, K)x^s}{s} \, ds \qquad a > 1.$$

Shift the line of integration to $\sigma = \sigma_0$ and assume a suitable order condition on $\zeta(s, K)$ in the region $\sigma_0 \leqq \sigma \leqq a$. Draw an inference about $\Delta(x)$.

5. A set $\mathfrak{a}$ of elements of a field $K = R(\sqrt{D})$ is called a fractional ideal if (i) $\mathfrak{a}$ is closed under subtraction and closed under multiplication by integers of K, (ii) there exists an integer λ of K such that $\lambda\alpha$ is an integer for every α in $\mathfrak{a}$. The quotient of two ideals is thus meaningful.

We define the different (ramification ideal) of K. Let $\mathfrak{b}$ denote the set of numbers μ of K such that for every integer α of K,

$$S(\mu\alpha) = \text{rational integer} .$$

$S(\sigma)$ denotes the trace of the number σ. Prove that $\mathfrak{b}$ is an ideal and that its reciprocal is an integral ideal $\mathfrak{d}$. $\mathfrak{d}$ is called the different. Choose a basis ω_1, ω_2 for K and solve the system $S(\mu\omega_i) = n_i$.

6. Let ω be a number of K, and

$$\mathfrak{d}\omega = \frac{\mathfrak{b}}{\mathfrak{a}} \qquad (\mathfrak{a}, \mathfrak{b}) = 1 .$$

Consider the sum

$$G(\omega) = \sum_{\mu \bmod \mathfrak{a}} e^{2\pi i S(\mu^2\omega)} ,$$

where μ runs through a residue system mod $\mathfrak{a}$. Show that $G(\omega)$ is independent of the particular residue system chosen.

7. If $\mathfrak{a} \neq 1$, and $\mathfrak{d}\omega$ has denominator $\mathfrak{a}$ show that

$$\sum_{\mu \bmod \mathfrak{a}} e^{2\pi i S(\mu\omega)} = 0 .$$

8. Let $\omega\mathfrak{d}$ have denominator $\mathfrak{a}$ and α_1, α_2, α be integers of K prime to $\mathfrak{a}$. Show that

$$G(\alpha_1\omega) = G(\alpha_2\omega) \qquad \text{if } \alpha_1 \equiv \alpha_2\alpha^2 \pmod{\mathfrak{a}} .$$

9. Show that if $\mathfrak{a} = \mathfrak{a}_1\mathfrak{a}_2$ with $(\mathfrak{a}_1, \mathfrak{a}_2) = 1$, and $\mathfrak{r}_1$, $\mathfrak{r}_2$ are chosen so that

$$\mathfrak{a}_1\mathfrak{r}_1 = \alpha_1 , \qquad \mathfrak{a}_2\mathfrak{r}_2 = \alpha_2 .$$

$$\omega = \frac{\beta}{\alpha_1\alpha_2} , \qquad \beta = \frac{\mathfrak{b}\mathfrak{r}_1\mathfrak{r}_2}{\mathfrak{d}} ,$$

$\mathfrak{b}$ being the numerator of $\omega\mathfrak{d}$, then

$$G(\omega) = G\left(\frac{\beta}{\alpha_1\alpha_2}\right) = G\left(\frac{\alpha_2\beta}{\alpha_1}\right)G\left(\frac{\alpha_1\beta}{\alpha_2}\right) .$$

10. Let ρ_1, ρ_2 be a basis for $1/\mathfrak{d}$ and if x_1 and x_2 are real variables we write

$$\xi^{(i)} = \rho_1^{(i)}x_1 + \rho_2^{(i)}x_2 \qquad (i = 1,\ 2).$$
$$S(\alpha\xi) = \alpha^{(1)}\xi^{(1)} + \alpha^{(2)}\xi^{(2)} .$$

Show that

$$\int_0^1\int_0^1 e^{2\pi i S(\alpha\xi)}\, dx_1 dx_2 = \begin{cases} 0 & \text{if } \alpha \neq 0 , \\ 1 & \text{if } \alpha = 0 , \end{cases}$$

where α is an integer of K.

11. Let

$$\Lambda(\mathfrak{a}) = \begin{cases} \log N(\mathfrak{p}) & \text{if } \mathfrak{a} = \mathfrak{p}^m , \\ 0 & \text{otherwise} , \end{cases}$$

$$\mu(\mathfrak{a}) = \begin{cases} (-1)^r & \text{if } \mathfrak{a} = \mathfrak{p}_1\mathfrak{p}_2\cdots\mathfrak{p}_r , \quad \mathfrak{p}_i \neq \mathfrak{p}_j , \\ 0 & \text{otherwise} . \end{cases}$$

Show that

(i) $$\frac{1}{\zeta(s, K)} = \sum_{\mathfrak{a}} \frac{\mu(\mathfrak{a})}{N(\mathfrak{a})^s} ;$$

(ii) $$\zeta'(s, K) = -\sum_{\mathfrak{a}} \frac{\log N(\mathfrak{a})}{N(\mathfrak{a})^s} ;$$

(iii) $$\frac{-\zeta'(s, K)}{\zeta(s, K)} = \sum_{\mathfrak{a}} \frac{\Lambda(\mathfrak{a})}{N(\mathfrak{a})^s} .$$

Show that if $a > 1$

$$\psi_K(x) = \sum_{N(\mathfrak{a}) \leq x} \Lambda(\mathfrak{a}) = \frac{1}{2\pi i} \int_{a-i\infty}^{a+i\infty} \left(\frac{-\zeta'(s, K)}{\zeta(s, K)} \right) \frac{x^s}{s} \, ds .$$

It can be shown by the methods of Chapter II that

$$\psi_K(x) \sim x$$

and is thus asymptotically independent of K.

12. Show that if p is a prime, then the fields

$$R(\sqrt{-p}) \qquad \text{for } -p \equiv 1 \pmod 4$$

have odd class number. It suffices to show that

$$\sum_{n=1}^{p-1} n\left(\frac{-p}{n}\right)$$

is odd, or use Theorems 3.5 and 3.6.

13. Show that if ε is a fundamental unit of a real quadratic field, then

$$\varepsilon^{2h} = e^{\sqrt{d}L(1,\chi_d)} .$$

Since ε is an integer of K, its trace is a rational integer. Deduce the surprising fact that

$$2 \cosh \sqrt{d}L(1, \chi) = e^{\sqrt{d}L(1,\chi_d)} + e^{-\sqrt{d}L(1,\chi_d)} = \text{rational integer.}$$

14. Let $\zeta(s, K)$ be the zeta function of the quadratic field $K = R\sqrt{D}$ of discriminant $d < 0$. Deduce from Theorem 6.6 and Theorem 2.8 the inequality

$$(2\pi\,|d|^{-1/2})^{-s}\Gamma(s)\zeta(s, K) > \frac{h(d)}{s(s-1)} + 2^{-2}e^{-4\pi}\,|d|^{s/2} \qquad 0 < s < 1 .$$

Hence show that if $\zeta(s, K) \neq 0$ for $1 - c_1/\log|d| \leqq s < 1$, then

$$h(d) > c_2 \frac{\sqrt{d}}{\log |d|} .$$

Use the fact that $\zeta(s, K) \to -\infty$ as $s \to 1^{-0}$.

15. Let χ_{k_1} and χ_{k_2} be real primitive characters mod k_1 and k_2 respectively and

$$F(s) = \zeta(s)L(s, \chi_{k_1})L(s, \chi_{k_2})L(s, \chi_{k_1 k_2}) = \sum_{n=1}^{\infty} \frac{a(n)}{n^s} .$$

As in Theorem 6.5, it can be shown that $a(1) = 1$, $a(n) \geqq 0$ $(n \geqq 2)$.

Let

$$G(x) = \sum_{n=1}^{\infty} a(n)e^{-nx} .$$

Using the Mellin transform, show that

$$G(x) = \frac{1}{2\pi i}\int_{3/2-i\infty}^{3/2+i\infty} \Gamma(s)F(s)x^{-s}ds .$$

By moving the line of integration to $\sigma = -\frac{1}{2}$, show (by obtaining a suitable estimate for $F(s)$ in accordance with the method used for $\zeta(s)$), that

$$G(x) = \frac{L^*}{x} + O(\sqrt{x}(k_1k_2)^c) ,$$

where

$$L^* = L(1, \chi_{k_1})L(1, \chi_{k_2})L(1, \chi_{k_1 k_2})$$

and c is some constant.

16. Show that for $\sigma > 0$

$$(k_1k_2)^s\Gamma(s)F(s) - \frac{k_1k_2L^*q^{s-1}}{s-1}$$
$$= \int_q^{\infty} x^{s-1}G\left(\frac{x}{k_1k_2}\right)dx + \int_0^q x^{s-1}\left\{G\left(\frac{x}{k_1k_2}\right) - \frac{L^*k_1k_2}{x}\right\} dx .$$

17. By choosing $q = (k_1k_2)^{-A}$, and using (15) and (16), show that

$$(k_1k_2)^s\Gamma(s)F(s) > \frac{k_1k_2L^*}{(s-1)(k_1k_2)^{(s-1)}} + c(k_1k_2)^s .$$

18. Using the fact that if $L(1, \chi_k) < k^{-\varepsilon}$, then $L(\sigma, \chi_k) = 0$ for some value of σ such that $1 > \sigma > 1 - \varepsilon/(A+1)$, deduce that

$$L(1, \chi_k) > k^{-\varepsilon} .$$

This proof is due to Chowla.

19. Let χ be a primitive character mod k and $\rho = e^{2\pi i/k}$. If $f(z) = \sum_{j=1}^{k} \chi(j)z^j$, then we know that

$$f(\rho^m) = \bar{\chi}(m)f(\rho)$$

by Theorem 4.12. Let $1 \leqq a < b \leqq k-1$ and

$$\Phi(x) = \begin{cases} 1 & \text{for } \dfrac{2\pi a}{k} < x < \dfrac{2\pi b}{k}, \\ \dfrac{1}{2} & \text{for } x = \dfrac{2\pi a}{k} \text{ or } x = \dfrac{2\pi b}{k}, \\ 0 & \text{for } 0 \leqq x < \dfrac{2\pi a}{k} \text{ or } \dfrac{2\pi b}{k} < x \leqq 2\pi . \end{cases}$$

Show that

$$\frac{1}{2}\chi(a) + \chi(a+1) + \cdots + \chi(b-1) + \frac{1}{2}\chi(b) = \sum_{s=1}^{k} \Phi\left(\frac{2\pi s}{k}\right)\chi(s),$$

and if we expand $\Phi(x)$ in a Fourier series, we get

$$\begin{aligned} \Phi(x) &= a_0 + \sum_{m=1}^{\infty} (a_m \cos mx + b_m \sin mx) \\ &= \frac{b-a}{k} + \frac{1}{\pi} T\left(x - \frac{2\pi a}{k}\right) - \frac{1}{\pi} T\left(x - \frac{2\pi b}{k}\right), \end{aligned}$$

where $T(x) = \sum_{m=1}^{\infty} (\sin mx)/m$. Then show that

$$\begin{aligned} \sum_{s=1}^{k} \Phi\left(\frac{2\pi s}{k}\right)\chi(s) &= f(\rho) \sum_{m=1}^{\infty} a_m \bar{\chi}(m) \qquad \text{if } \chi(-1) = 1 \\ &= \frac{1}{i} f(\rho) \sum_{m=1}^{\infty} b_m \bar{\chi}(m) \qquad \text{if } \chi(-1) = -1. \end{aligned}$$

20. If

$$R_n(x) = \sum_{m=n+1}^{\infty} \frac{\sin mx}{m}$$

show that if $0 < x \leqq \pi$,

$$| R_n(x) | < \frac{\pi}{nx}.$$

$\sum_{m=1}^{n} (\sin mx)/m = (\pi - x)/2 - \int_x^{\pi} (\sin((2n+1)t/2)/2\sin(t/2))dt$ and use the second mean value theorem. Deduce that

$$\sum_{s=1}^{k} \left| R_n\left(\frac{2\pi s}{k}\right) \right| < \frac{k \log k}{n} \qquad \text{if } k \geqq 3 .$$

21. Show that according to the case $\chi(-1) = 1$ and $\chi(-1) = -1$, respectively,

$$\begin{aligned} \left| \sum_{m=a}^{b} \chi(m) \right| &= \left| \frac{1}{2}(\chi(a) + \chi(b)) + f(\rho) \sum_{m=1}^{n} \begin{Bmatrix} a_m \\ -ib_m \end{Bmatrix} \bar{\chi}(m) \right. \\ &\quad \left. + \frac{1}{\pi} \sum_{s=1}^{k} \left\{ R_n\left(\frac{2\pi(s-a)}{k}\right) - R_n\left(\frac{2\pi(s-b)}{k}\right) \right\} \chi(s) \right| \\ &\leqq 1 + \frac{2}{\pi}\sqrt{k}(1 + \log n) + \frac{2}{\pi}\frac{k \log k}{n} . \end{aligned}$$

Let $n = [k^{1/2+\varepsilon}]$ and infer that

$$\sum_{m=a}^{b} \chi(m) = O(k^{1/2} \log k) .$$

This proof is due to Pólya.

22. Let K be an imaginary quadratic field with discriminant $-p$ and class number 1. Then it can be shown that if $q(m, n) = m^2 + mn + \frac{1}{4}(p+1)n^2$, then

$$\zeta(s, K) = \frac{1}{2} \sum_{m,n \neq 0,0} \frac{1}{(q(m, n))^s} .$$

Deduce from this, using the Euler-MacLaurin formula, that for $\sigma > 1$,

(a) $$\zeta(s, K) = \zeta(2s) + \sum_{n=1}^{\infty} \int_{-\infty}^{\infty} q(x, n)^{-s} dx + \sum_{n=1}^{\infty} \int_{-\infty}^{\infty} \left(x - [x] - \frac{1}{2}\right) \frac{d}{dx} q(x, n)^{-s} dx ;$$

(b) $$\sum_{n=1}^{\infty} \int_{-\infty}^{\infty} q(x, n)^{-s} dx = 2^{2s-1} p^{1/2-s} \zeta(2s-1) \int_{-\infty}^{\infty} (u^2 + 1)^{-s} du .$$

(c) Show that

$$\left| \sum_{n=1}^{\infty} \int_{-\infty}^{\infty} \left(x - [x] - \frac{1}{2}\right) \frac{d}{dx} q(x, n)^{-s} dx \right| \leqq \frac{|s|}{\sigma} 4^{\sigma} p^{-\sigma} \zeta(2\sigma) .$$

23. As in Problem 15, let

$$F(s) = \zeta(s) L(s, \chi_{k_1}) L(s, \chi_{k_2}) L(s, \chi_{k_1 k_2}) ,$$
$$\lambda = L(1, \chi_{k_1}) L(1, \chi_{k_2}) L(1, \chi_{k_3})$$

then $g(s) = F(s) - \lambda/(s-1)$ is regular for $\sigma > 0$. Expand the functions $F(s)$ and $g(s)$ in a Taylor series about the point $s = 2$.

$$\left.\begin{aligned} F(s) &= \sum_{m=0}^{\infty} b_m (2-s)^m \\ g(s) &= \sum_{m=0}^{\infty} (b_m - \lambda)(2-s)^m \end{aligned}\right\} \qquad |s-2| < 1 .$$

and show that $b_m \geqq 0$, $b_0 \geqq 1$.

24. Using partial summation, show that

$$L(s, \chi_k) = O(k^{1/2}) \qquad \text{for } \sigma \geqq \tfrac{1}{2}$$

and deduce that for some constants c_1, c_2, c_3

$$L(s, \chi_{k_1}) L(s, \chi_{k_2}) L(s, \chi_{k_1} \chi_{k_2}) = O((k_1 k_2)^{c_1})$$
$$L(1, \chi_{k_1}) L(1, \chi_{k_2}) L(1, \chi_{k_1 k_2}) = O((k_1 k_2)^{c_2})$$

in the region $|s-2| \leqq \frac{3}{2}$ and moreover

$$g(s) = O((k_1 k_2)^{c_3}) \qquad \text{for } |s-2| \leqq \tfrac{3}{2} .$$

25. Show that for some constants c_1 and c_2, $|a_m - \lambda| \leqq c_1 (k_1 k_2)^{c_2} (\frac{2}{3})^m$ ($m = 0, 1, 2, \cdots$). Since

$$F(\sigma) - \frac{\lambda}{\sigma - 1} = \sum_{0 \leqq m < M} (b_m - \lambda)(2-\sigma)^m + \sum_{m \geqq M} (b_m - \lambda)(2-\sigma)^m ,$$

by choosing M appropriately, show that there exist constants c_1 and c_2 so that for $1 - c_1 \leqq \sigma < 1$,

$$F(\sigma) > \frac{1}{2} - \frac{\lambda}{1-\sigma}(k_1 k_2)^{c_2(1-\sigma)} .$$

26. Show that for a real character χ,

$$L(\sigma, \chi_k) > k^{-\varepsilon}$$

as follows. Let c be a constant to be chosen.

Case (i). If $1 > \varepsilon > 0$, and $L(\sigma_0, \chi) = 0$ for $1 - c\varepsilon < \sigma_0 < 1$, then

$$F(\sigma_0) = 0 .$$

Case (ii). $L(\sigma, \chi) \neq 0$ for $1 - c\varepsilon < \sigma < 1$, then $F(\sigma) < 0$ for $1 - c\varepsilon < \sigma < 1$. Use (25) and the inequality

$$L(s, \chi) < 2 + \log k .$$

This proof is due to T. Estermann.

27. From the inequality

$$L(\sigma, \chi) > k^{-\varepsilon}, \qquad \text{for } k > k_\varepsilon ,$$

deduce that there exists a constant $c(\varepsilon)$ such that

$$L(\sigma, \chi) \neq 0 \qquad \text{for } \sigma > 1 - \frac{c(\varepsilon)}{k^\varepsilon} , \qquad k \geqq 1.$$

28. Show that if $G(k) = \sum_{n=0}^{k-1} e^{(2\pi i/k)n^2}$, then

$$|G(k)|^2 = k .$$

29. In the following, we assume that k is odd. Let $A = [\rho^{lm}/\sqrt{k}]$ $(l, m = 0, 1, 2, \cdots, k-1)$ be a $k \times k$ matrix, where $\rho = e^{2\pi i/k}$. Then

$$\mathrm{Tr}(A) = \frac{G(k)}{k} = S(k)$$

(say), where $\mathrm{Tr}(A)$ is the trace of the matrix A.

Prove as follows.

(i) $A^2 = [a_{l,m}]$ where

$$a_{l,m} = \begin{cases} 1 & \text{if } k \mid l + m , \\ 0 & \text{otherwise} . \end{cases}$$

(ii) $\mathrm{Tr} A^2 = 1$.

(iii) $A^4 = I$.

(iv) The characteristic roots of A are i^r $(r = 0, 1, 2, 3)$.

(v) If m_r is the multiplicity of the root i^r, then

$$S(k) = m_0 - m_2 + i(m_1 - m_3) .$$

Using (28), deduce that $m_0 - m_2 = 0$, $m_1 - m_3 = \pm 1$ or $m_0 - m_2 = \pm 1$, $m_1 - m_3 = 0$ and $S(k) = uv$ where $u = \pm 1$, $v = 1$ or i.

(vi) From (ii), show that

$$m_0 - m_1 + m_2 - m_3 = 1$$

and infer the following equations for m_r

$$m_0 + m_1 + m_2 + m_3 = n\,,$$
$$m_0 - im_1 - m_2 - im_3 = 1\,,$$
$$m_0 - im_1 - m_2 + im_3 = uv^{-1}\,.$$

Deduce that

$$v = \begin{cases} 1 & \text{if } k \equiv 1 \pmod 4\,, \\ i & \text{if } k \equiv 3 \pmod 4\,. \end{cases}$$

(vii) To show that $u = +1$, calculate det A in two ways. Show on the one hand that

(a) det A = product of the characteristic roots $= ui^{k(k-1)/2}$ and on the other hand using van der Monde's formula

(b) $\det A = \prod_{0 \leq l < m \leq k-1} 2i \sin(\pi(m-l)/k) = i^{k(k-1)/2} \prod_{0 \leq l < m \leq k-1} 2 \sin(\pi(m-l)/k)$.

Notes to Chapter V

1. The concept of class number has its origin in the theory of binary quadratic forms. Let $f = ax^2 + bxy + cy^2$ and $F = AX^2 + BXY + CY^2$ be two quadratic forms with the same discriminant $d = b^2 - 4ac = B^2 - 4AC$. We say that f and F are equivalent if there exists a transformation $X = \alpha x + \beta y$, $Y = \gamma x + \delta y$ with α, β, γ, δ rational integers $\alpha\delta - \beta\gamma = 1$, which takes F into f. This is indeed an equivalence relation which partitions the forms with the same discriminant into classes. The importance of the concept for diophantine equations is that forms in the same class represent the same integers. With a restriction placed on equivalence of ideals, it is shown that there is a one-to-one correspondence between the classes of forms of discriminant d and classes of ideals of a quadratic field of discriminant d.

The proof we have given here of the finiteness of the class number is a specialization of a general method which was used by Dedekind and Minkowski. In the case of quadratic fields and forms, however, proofs had been given by Gauss, Dirichlet, Cayley, H. J. S. Smith and others.

2. Theorem 2.1 is a specialization of a general theorem on $H(t, \mathscr{C})$ which was first given by Dedekind for a general algebraic number field, *Über die Anzahl der ideal Classen in den verschiedenen Ordnung eines endlischen Körpers*, Collected Works, Vol. I.

The theorems on the decomposition of rational primes in a quadratic field are given in the works of Dirichlet and Dedekind—see for example the *Vorlesungen über Zahlentheorie*, Supplement II.

The general problem of decomposing primes or prime ideals in an algebraic extension was one of the problems which initiated a study of class fields, though in the contemporary treatment of class field theory, the significance of this problem has virtually disappeared.

Though in much current literature the symbol (a/b) is called the Kronecker symbol, it is difficult to find complete justification for this designation. In any event, Kronecker would perhaps have preferred to be known for his deep mathematical theorems than for two trivial notations (the other being the Kronecker delta)!

As we noted in Chapter I, the fact that $L(1, \chi) \neq 0$ for a real character χ was proved by Dirichlet essentially by the argument given here—viz that $L(1, \chi)$ is a factor of the class number of quadratic forms of a certain discriminant.

3. The derivation of the class number formula was started by Gauss in a manuscript which he never published but which was edited by R. Dedekind and printed in his Collected Works, Vol. 2, under the title *De nexu inter multitudinem classium in quas formae binariae secundi gradus distribuantur earumque determinantem*. In editing the manuscript, Dedekind points out the gaps in the proof (of which Gauss was undoubtedly aware). The proof applied to quadratic forms and is effected by counting in two ways the average number of representations of an integer m prime to d by properly primitive forms of discriminant d.

The completed proof was given first by Dirichlet in his famous memoir *Recherches sur diverses applications de l'analyse infinitesimal à la théorie des nombres* in Crelle, Vol. 19. The theorem of Heilbronn and Linfort referred to appears in the Quart. J. Math. Oxford **5**, *On imaginary quadratic corpora of class number* 1.

4. Gaussian sums arose first in connection with Gauss's treatment of cyclotomy.

The theorems on the decomposition of Gaussian sums and on the decomposition of characters are inherent in the works of Gauss and Dirichlet.

There are numerous proofs of the fundamental Theorem 4.15. Gauss himself gave a proof in *Summatio quarundum seriem*, Collected Works, Vol. 2, and proofs have been given by Dirichlet, Mertens, Schur, Kronecker, Mordell and others. A simple proof of the quadratic reciprocity law follows from the corollary of Theorem 4.15. The reader can easily supply it by coupling Theorem 4.16 with this corollary and the easily proved fact that

$$G(p, \chi^{(q)})G(q, \chi^{(p)}) = G(1, \chi^{(pq)}) .$$

5. Gauss's conjecture on the mean value of the class number appears in the *Disquisitiones arithmeticae* arts. 301 and 302. He appears to attach considerable importance to the result and implies that he has a proof, though this was never published. He must in any event have been aware of the underlying principle for he says, "Per disquisitionem theoreticam satis difficilem quam hic explicare nimis prolixum foret...."

Theorem 5.1 is due to Pólya though the proof we have given is due to Schur. Pólya's proof is outlined in the problems.

The proof of Theorem 5.3 is due in essence to C. L. Siegel; the result for quadratic fields appears here for the first time.

6. Gauss's conjecture that for negative discriminants $h(d) \to \infty$ is made in *Disquitiones* arts. 303 and 304. The following results prior to Heilbronn's proof may be mentioned.

(1) Hecke proved that if $L(s, \chi_d) \neq 0$ for $1 - c/\log|d| \leqq s < 1$, then

$$h(d) > \frac{c\sqrt{|d|}}{\log|d|}.$$

This was based on his analogue for $\zeta(s, K)$ of Riemann's formula for $\zeta(s)$. A proof appears in Landau's paper *Über die Klassenzahl imaginärquadratische Zahlkörper*, Gottinger Nachrichten 1918. See Problem 14.

(2) Deuring proved that if $\zeta(s) = 0$ for some s for which $\sigma > \frac{1}{2}$ that is, if the Riemann hypothesis is false, then

$$\liminf h(d) \geqq 2,$$

Imaginärquadratische Zahlkörper mit Klassenzahl 1, Math Z. **37** (1933), 405–415.

(3) Mordell proved that if the Riemann hypothesis is false, then $\lim h(d) \to \infty$. *On the Riemann hypothesis and imaginary quadratic fields with a given class number*, J. London Math. Soc. **9**. (1934), 289-298. There therefore remained one step in the completion of the proof that $h(d) \to \infty$ viz if $L(s, \chi) = 0$ for some s for which $\sigma > \frac{1}{2}$, then $h(d) \to \infty$ and this was carried out by Heilbronn.

We have in this series of steps the interesting logical situation in which a theorem follows both from the assumption of the generalized Riemann hypothesis and its denial. A similar situation arises in the case of Littlewood's theorem referred to in the notes to Chapter II.

7. Siegel's proof appears in the Acta Arith. **1**, *Über die Klassenzahl imaginärquadratische Zahlkörper*.

As we noted in the text, Siegel used the theory of algebraic number fields and asserted the possibility of proving the more general theorem that if F/Q is a finite extension of the rationals of fixed degree n whose Galois group is solvable, then

$$\log Rh(d) \sim \tfrac{1}{2}\log|d| \qquad (|d| \to \infty)$$

where R denotes the regulator and d the discriminant of F.

He conjectured the truth of this result for an arbitrary F and this conjecture was confirmed by R. Brauer in 1947 in the Amer. J. Math. **69** (1947), 243–250.

Appendix A

The gamma function and the Mellin transform. Though there are many equivalent definitions of the gamma function, one of the most convenient starting points is the Weierstrass product formula. For all s, we define

$$\frac{1}{\Gamma(s)} = se^{\gamma s} \prod_{n=1}^{\infty} \left(1 + \frac{s}{n}\right) e^{-s/n} , \tag{1}$$

where γ is Euler's constant, $\gamma = \lim_{N\to\infty} (\sum_{n=1}^{N} 1/n - \log N)$. We show that this is analytic for all s.

THEOREM A.1. *The product*

$$se^{\gamma s} \prod_{n=1}^{\infty} \left(1 + \frac{s}{n}\right) e^{-s/n}$$

represents an analytic function of s for all values of s.

PROOF. Let k be arbitrary and suppose that $|s| < k/2$. Then for $n > k$,

$$\begin{aligned}\left|\log\left(1+\frac{s}{n}\right) - \frac{s}{n}\right| &\leqq \left|-\frac{1}{2}\frac{s^2}{n^2} + \frac{1}{3}\frac{s^3}{n^3} - \cdots\right| \\ &\leqq \frac{|s|^2}{n^2}\left(1 + \left|\frac{s}{n}\right| + \left|\frac{s}{n}\right|^2 + \cdots\right) \\ &\leqq \frac{|s|^2}{n^2}\left(1 + \frac{1}{2} + \frac{1}{2^2} + \cdots\right) \leqq \frac{k^2}{4n^2}\cdot 2 = \frac{1}{2}\frac{k^2}{n^2} .\end{aligned}$$

It follows that

$$\sum_{n=k+1}^{\infty} \left|\log\left(1+\frac{s}{n}\right) - \frac{s}{n}\right| \leqq \frac{1}{2} \sum_{n=k+1}^{\infty} \frac{k^2}{n^2} = O(1) ,$$

and therefore

$$\sum_{n=k+1}^{\infty} \left(\log\left(1+\frac{s}{n}\right) - \frac{s}{n}\right) \tag{2}$$

is an absolutely and uniformly convergent series of analytic functions which is therefore itself analytic. Consequently its exponential

$$\prod_{n=k+1}^{\infty} \left(1 + \frac{s}{n}\right) e^{-s/n}$$

is analytic; hence

$$se^{s\gamma} \prod_{n=1}^{\infty} \left(1 + \frac{s}{n}\right) e^{-s/n} \tag{3}$$

is analytic for $|s| < \frac{1}{2}k$. However, k was arbitrarily chosen and therefore (3) is analytic for all s.

From this definition of $\Gamma(s)$, we see that $1/\Gamma(s)$ has zeros at $s = 0, -1, -2,$

$\cdots$, and therefore that $\Gamma(s)$ itself is analytic everywhere except for poles at $0, -1, -2, \cdots$.

THEOREM A.2.

$$\Gamma(s) = \frac{1}{s}\prod_{n=1}^{\infty}\left(1+\frac{1}{n}\right)^{s}\left(1+\frac{s}{n}\right)^{-1}, \tag{4}$$

the formula being valid except for $s = 0, -1, -2, \cdots$.

PROOF. The proof is a straightforward consequence of (1):

$$\begin{aligned}\frac{1}{\Gamma(s)} &= s\lim_{m\to\infty}\left[\exp s\left(\sum_{n=1}^{m}\frac{1}{n} - \log m\right)\right]\prod_{n=1}^{m}\left(1+\frac{s}{n}\right)e^{-s/n}\\ &= s\lim_{m\to\infty} m^{-s}\prod_{n=1}^{m}\left(1+\frac{s}{n}\right) = s\lim_{m\to\infty}\prod_{n=1}^{m-1}\left(1+\frac{1}{n}\right)^{-s}\prod_{n=1}^{m}\left(1+\frac{s}{n}\right)\\ &= s\lim_{m\to\infty}\prod_{n=1}^{m}\left(1+\frac{1}{n}\right)^{-s}\left(1+\frac{s}{n}\right)\left(1+\frac{1}{m}\right)^{s}.\end{aligned}$$

Since $(1+1/m)^s \to 1$, the proof is complete.

Two important corollaries follow.

THEOREM A.3.

$$\Gamma(s) = \lim_{n\to\infty}\frac{(n-1)!}{s(s+1)\cdots(s+n-1)}\,n^s. \tag{5}$$

PROOF. From (4),

$$\begin{aligned}\Gamma(s) &= \frac{1}{s}\lim_{n\to\infty}\prod_{k=1}^{n-1}\left(\frac{k+1}{k}\right)^{s}\left(\frac{k}{k+s}\right) = \frac{1}{s}\lim_{n\to\infty} n^s\prod_{k=1}^{n-1}\left(\frac{k}{k+s}\right)\\ &= \frac{1}{s}\lim_{n\to\infty} n^s\frac{(n-1)!}{(s+1)(s+2)\cdots(s+n-1)}.\end{aligned}$$

The next corollary exhibits $\Gamma(s)$ as an interpolation formula for $s!$.

THEOREM A.4.

$$\Gamma(s+1) = s\Gamma(s). \tag{6}$$

In particular, if s *is a positive integer,*

$$\Gamma(s+1) = s!. \tag{7}$$

PROOF. Again from (4),

$$\begin{aligned}\frac{\Gamma(s+1)}{\Gamma(s)} &= \frac{s}{s+1}\lim_{m\to\infty}\prod_{n=1}^{m}\left(1+\frac{1}{n}\right)^{s+1}\left(1+\frac{s+1}{n}\right)^{-1}\left(1+\frac{1}{n}\right)^{-s}\left(1+\frac{s}{n}\right)\\ &= \frac{s}{s+1}\lim_{m\to\infty}\prod_{n=1}^{m}\left(1+\frac{1}{n}\right)\left(\frac{n+s}{n+s+1}\right)\\ &= \frac{s}{s+1}\lim_{m\to\infty}(m+1)\prod_{n=1}^{m}\left(\frac{n+s}{n+s+1}\right) = s\lim_{m\to\infty}\frac{m+1}{m+s+1} = s.\end{aligned}$$

The next result is a functional relation which establishes a connection with the circular functions.

THEOREM A.5.

$$\Gamma(s)\Gamma(1-s) = \frac{\pi}{\sin \pi s}\,. \tag{8}$$

PROOF. From the definition (1),

$$\Gamma(s)\Gamma(-s) = -\frac{1}{s^2}\prod_{n=1}^{\infty}\left(1+\frac{s}{n}\right)^{-1}e^{s/n}\prod_{n=1}^{\infty}\left(1-\frac{s}{n}\right)^{-1}e^{-s/n} = -\frac{1}{s^2}\prod_{n=1}^{\infty}\left(1-\frac{s^2}{n^2}\right)^{-1}.$$

On the other hand, the Weierstrass product for $(\sin \pi s)/\pi s$ is $\prod_{n=1}^{\infty}(1-s^2/n^2)$, and therefore

$$\Gamma(s)\Gamma(-s) = -\frac{1}{s^2}\frac{\pi s}{\sin \pi s} = \frac{-\pi}{s \sin \pi s}\,. \tag{9}$$

From (6), however,

$$\Gamma(1-s) = -s\,\Gamma(-s)\,,$$

and the theorem follows from (9).

In particular, if $s = \frac{1}{2}$,

$$\Gamma\left(\tfrac{1}{2}\right)^2 = \pi\,, \qquad \Gamma\left(\tfrac{1}{2}\right) = \pm\sqrt{\pi}\,,$$

but from the definition, $\Gamma(\frac{1}{2}) > 0$, and therefore

$$\Gamma\left(\tfrac{1}{2}\right) = \sqrt{\pi}\,. \tag{10}$$

We prove Legendre's duplication formula in the following:

THEOREM A.6.

$$\Gamma(2s) = \pi^{-1/2}\,2^{2s-1}\,\Gamma(s)\,\Gamma\left(s+\tfrac{1}{2}\right). \tag{11}$$

PROOF. The proof starts from (5) of Theorem A.3.

$$\Gamma(2s) = \lim_{n\to\infty}\frac{(2n-1)!\,(2n)^{2s}}{2s(2s+1)\cdots(2s+2n-1)}\,,$$

and therefore

$$\frac{2^{2s-1}\Gamma(s)\Gamma(s+\frac{1}{2})}{\Gamma(2s)}$$

$$= \lim_{n\to\infty}\frac{2^{2s-1}((n-1)!)^2 n^{2s+1/2}(2s)(2s+1)\cdots(2s+2n-1)}{(2n)^{2s}(2n-1)!\,s(s+1)\cdots(s+n-1)(s+\frac{1}{2})(s+\frac{3}{2})\cdots(s+\frac{1}{2}+n-1)}$$

$$= \lim_{n\to\infty}\frac{2^{2n-1}((n-1)!)^2 n^{1/2}(2s)(2s+1)\cdots(2s+2n-1)}{2s(2s+2)\cdots(2s+2n-2)(2s+1)(2s+3)\cdots(2s+2n-1)(2n-1)!}$$

$$= \lim_{n\to\infty}\frac{2^{2n-1}((n-1)!)^2 n^{1/2}}{(2n-1)!} = \lim_{n\to\infty}\varphi(n) \qquad \text{(say).}$$

We notice that the right-hand side is independent of s. Hence its value may be determined by giving s some convenient value. For example, we let $s = \frac{1}{2}$, then

$$\lim_{n\to\infty} \varphi(n) = \frac{\Gamma(\frac{1}{2})\Gamma(1)}{\Gamma(1)} = \Gamma(\tfrac{1}{2}) = \sqrt{\pi}\,,$$

by (10). This observation completes the proof.

We can convert $\Gamma(s)$ into what is, perhaps, a more familiar integral formula.

THEOREM A.7. *If $s = \sigma + it$, and $\sigma > 0$, then*

$$\Gamma(s) = \int_0^\infty e^{-x}x^{s-1}dx\,. \tag{12}$$

PROOF. Because

$$e^{-x} = \lim_{n\to\infty}\left(1 - \frac{x}{n}\right)^n,$$

we can expect that

$$\gamma(s, n) = \int_0^n \left(1 - \frac{x}{n}\right)^n x^{s-1}\,dx$$

will converge to the integral in (12). On the other hand, we evaluate $\gamma(s, n)$ explicitly. In fact, if $u = x/n$, then

$$\gamma(s, n) = n^s \int_0^1 (1 - u)^n u^{s-1}\,du\,.$$

If n is an integer > 0, we integrate by parts n times and an easy calculation gives

$$\begin{aligned} \gamma(s, n) &= n^s \cdot \frac{n}{s} \cdot \frac{n-1}{s+1} \cdots \frac{1}{s+n-1}\int_0^1 u^{s+n-1}\,du \\ &= \frac{n^s n!}{s(s+1)\cdots(s+n-1)(s+n)}\,. \end{aligned} \tag{13}$$

Thus on the one hand, the right-hand side of (13) converges to $\Gamma(s)$ by Theorem A.3. On the other hand, it remains to show that $\gamma(s, n)$ converges to the integral in (12). This is seen as follows:

$$\begin{aligned} \lim_{n\to\infty}\left\{\int_0^\infty e^{-x}x^{s-1}dx - \gamma(s, n)\right\} &= \lim_{n\to\infty}\left\{\int_0^n \left(e^{-x} - \left(1 - \frac{x}{n}\right)^n\right) x^{s-1}dx + \int_n^\infty e^{-x}x^{s-1}dx\right\} \\ &= \lim_{n\to\infty}(j_1 + j_2)\,. \end{aligned}$$

Since $\sigma > 0$, the integral in (12) converges and therefore $\lim_{n\to\infty} j_2 = 0$. To show that j_1 tends to 0, we notice that the sequence $(1 - x/n)^n$ converges to e^{-x} from below while $(1 + x/n)^n$ converges to e^x also from below; therefore

$$0 \leqq e^{-x} - \left(1 - \frac{x}{n}\right)^n \leqq e^{-x}\left\{1 - e^x\left(1 - \frac{x}{n}\right)^n\right\}$$
$$\leqq e^{-x}\left\{1 - \left(1 - \frac{x}{n}\right)^n\left(1 + \frac{x}{n}\right)^n\right\} \leqq e^{-x}\left\{1 - \left(1 - \frac{x^2}{n^2}\right)^n\right\}$$
$$\leqq e^{-x}\frac{x^2}{n^2}\cdot n = \frac{x^2 e^{-x}}{n} .$$

Consequently,

$$j_1 = O\left(\frac{1}{n}\right)\int_0^n e^{-x}x^{\sigma+1}\,dx = O\left(\frac{1}{n}\right) = o(1) .$$

This completes the proof.

The integral of Theorem A.6 is valid only for $\sigma > 0$; we derive a contination of the integral of (12) which is valid for all s (we bypass the singularities of $\Gamma(s)$).

THEOREM A.8. *If $\mathscr{C}$ denotes a path which starts at ∞, circles the origin in a counter-clockwise direction and returns to ∞, then*

$$\Gamma(s) = -\frac{1}{2i\sin\pi s}\int_{\mathscr{C}}(-t)^{s-1}e^{-t}\,dt . \tag{14}$$

PROOF. The proof incorporates the principle of the so-called Hankel transform. Let D be a contour which starts at α on the real axis, circles

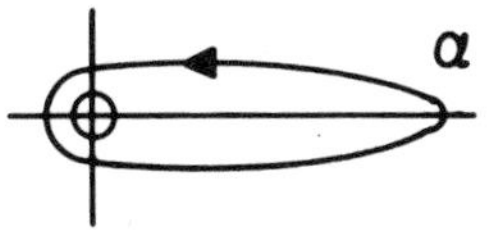

the origin in a counter-clockwise direction and returns to α. We consider the integral

$$\int_D (-u)^{s-1}e^{-u}\,du ,$$

with $\sigma > 0$ and s not an integer. The many-valued function $(-u)^{s-1} = \exp[(s-1)\log(-u)]$ is made precise by choosing that branch of the logarithm which is real when $u < 0$; that is to say, on D, $-\pi \leqq \arg(-u) \leqq \pi$. We transform D itself into a path which starts at α, proceeds along the real axis to a point δ, circles the origin counter-clockwise by a circle of radius δ and returns to α along the lower part of the real axis. On the upper part of the real axis, we have

$$\arg(-u) = -\pi ,$$

so that

$$(-u)^{s-1} = \exp[(s-1)\log(-u)] = \exp[(s-1)(-\pi i + \log u)] = u^{s-1}e^{-i\pi(s-1)} \tag{15}$$

and on the lower part, by the same reasoning,

$$(- u)^{s-1} = u^{s-1} e^{i\pi(s-1)} \, . \tag{16}$$

On the circle, write

$$- u = \delta e^{i\theta} \, ,$$

and then by (15) and (16)

$$\begin{aligned} \int_D (- u)^{s-1} e^{-u} \, du &= \int_\alpha^\delta e^{-i\pi(s-1)} u^{s-1} e^{-u} \, du + \int_\delta^\alpha e^{i\pi(s-1)} u^{s-1} e^{-u} \, du \\ &\quad + \int_{-\pi}^{\pi} (\delta e^{i\theta})^{s-1} e^{\delta(\cos\theta + i \sin\theta)} \delta e^{i\theta} i \, d\theta \, . \end{aligned} \tag{17}$$

The first and second integrals combine to give

$$- 2i \sin \pi s \int_\delta^\alpha u^{s-1} e^{-u} du \, ,$$

while the third integral clearly tends to 0 as $\delta \to 0$. Consequently, from (17)

$$\int_D (- u)^{s-1} e^{-u} du = - 2i \sin \pi s \int_0^\alpha u^{s-1} e^{-u} du \, .$$

This relation holds for all $\alpha > 0$. We let $\alpha \to \infty$ and we let $\mathscr{C}$ be the "limit" of the path D, then

$$\int_{\mathscr{C}} (- u)^{s-1} e^{-u} du = - 2i \sin \pi s \int_0^\infty u^{s-1} e^{-u} du \, .$$

In other words,

$$\Gamma(s) = - \frac{1}{2i \sin \pi s} \int_{\mathscr{C}} (- u)^{s-1} e^{-u} du \, ,$$

as was to be proved.

The importance of this representation stems from the fact that since $\mathscr{C}$ does not pass through the origin, the integral is a single-valued and analytic function of s for all s. The restriction $\sigma > 0$ is no longer necessary. The formula (14) holds for all s except for $s = 0, \pm 1, \pm 2, \cdots$.

The next theorems concern the asymptotic behavior of $\Gamma(s)$. We prove first a somewhat debased form of Stirling's formula.

Theorem A.9. *If N is an integer, then there exists a constant c such that*

$$\log N! = \sum_{n \le N} \log n = \left(N + \frac{1}{2} \right) \log N - N + c + O\left(\frac{1}{N} \right) . \tag{18}$$

Proof. We use the Euler-MacLaurin formula,

$$\begin{aligned} \sum_{n \le N} \log n &= \frac{1}{2} \log N + \int_1^N \log x \, dx + \int_1^N \frac{x - [x] - \frac{1}{2}}{x} dx \\ &= \frac{1}{2} \log N + N \log N - N + \int_1^N \frac{x - [x] - \frac{1}{2}}{x} dx \, . \end{aligned} \tag{19}$$

On the other hand, if we put

$$\varphi(x) = \int_1^x \left(u - [u] - \frac{1}{2}\right) du ,$$

then because the integrand has period 1 and $\varphi(2) = \varphi(1) = 0$, it follows that $\varphi(x)$ is bounded, in fact,

$$|\varphi(x)| \leqq \tfrac{1}{2} .$$

If now we integrate by parts the integral in (19), we get

$$\begin{aligned}\int_1^N \frac{u - [u] - \frac{1}{2}}{u} du &= \frac{\varphi(N)}{N} + \int_1^N \frac{\varphi(x)}{x^2} dx \\ &= \frac{\varphi(N)}{N} + \int_1^\infty \frac{\varphi(x)}{x^2} dx - \int_N^\infty \frac{\varphi(x)}{x^2} dx \\ &= O\left(\frac{1}{N}\right) + c + O\left(\int_N^\infty \frac{dx}{x^2}\right) \\ &= O\left(\frac{1}{N}\right) + c .\end{aligned}$$

We have used the fact that $\int_1^\infty \varphi(x)/x^2$ converges and have denoted its value by c. This proves the theorem.

We pass to the general case.

THEOREM A.10. *There exists an absolute constant* a *such that if* s *is not on the negative real axis, i.e.,*

$$-\pi + \delta \leqq \arg s \leqq \pi - \delta , \tag{20}$$

for $\delta > 0$, *then*

$$\log \Gamma(s) = \left(s - \frac{1}{2}\right) \log s - s + a + O\left(\frac{1}{|s|}\right) . \qquad (s \neq 0) \tag{21}$$

PROOF. By definition,

$$\begin{aligned}\log \Gamma(s) &= \lim_{N\to\infty} \left\{ \sum_{n=1}^N \left(\frac{s}{n} - \log\left(1 + \frac{s}{n}\right)\right)\right\} - \gamma s - \log s \\ &= \lim_{N\to\infty} \left\{ \sum_{n=1}^N \frac{s}{n} - \sum_{n=0}^N \log(n+s) + \sum_{n=1}^N \log n\right\} - \gamma s .\end{aligned} \tag{22}$$

We apply the Euler-MacLaurin formula to the second sum:

$$\begin{aligned}\sum_{n=0}^N \log(n+s) &= \frac{1}{2}\log(N+s) + \frac{1}{2}\log s + \int_0^N \log(x+s)\,dx + \int_0^N \frac{x - [x] - \frac{1}{2}}{x+s} dx \\ &= \frac{1}{2}\log(N+s) + \left(\frac{1}{2} - s\right)\log s + s + (N+s)\log(N+s) \\ &\quad - (N+s) + \int_0^N \frac{x - [x] - \frac{1}{2}}{x+s} dx .\end{aligned} \tag{23}$$

Accordingly, if we use (18) and the fact, proved previously Chapter II,

Theorem 2.4, that

$$\sum_{n=1}^{N} \frac{1}{n} = \log N + \gamma + O\left(\frac{1}{N}\right),$$

we get from (22) and (23)

$$\begin{aligned} \log \Gamma(s) &= \left(s - \frac{1}{2}\right)\log s + c \\ &\quad + \lim_{N\to\infty}\Big\{s(\log N - \log(N+s)) + N(\log N - \log(N+s)) \\ &\quad + \frac{1}{2}(\log N - \log(N+s)) - \int_0^N \frac{x-[x]-\frac{1}{2}}{x+s}\,dx\Big\} \\ &= \left(s - \frac{1}{2}\right)\log s - s + a - \int_0^\infty \frac{x-[x]-\frac{1}{2}}{x+s}\,dx\,. \end{aligned} \tag{24}$$

As in the previous theorem, we integrate the integral in (24) by parts:

$$\begin{aligned} \int_0^\infty \frac{x-[x]-\frac{1}{2}}{x+s}\,dx &= \int_0^\infty \frac{\varphi(x)}{(x+s)^2}\,dx = O\left(\int_0^\infty \frac{dx}{x^2+2x\sigma+|s|^2}\right) \\ &= O\left(\int_0^\infty \frac{dx}{x^2+2x|s|\cos\arg s+|s|^2}\right) \\ &= O\left(\int_0^\infty \frac{dx}{x^2-2x|s|\cos\delta+|s|^2}\right), \end{aligned}$$

where we have used the fact (which follows from (20)) that $\cos\arg s \geqq -\cos\delta$. The substitution $x/|s| = u$ gives

$$\int_0^\infty \frac{dx}{x^2-2x|s|\cos\delta+|s|^2} = O\left(\frac{1}{|s|}\right)\int_0^\infty \frac{du}{u^2-2u\cos\delta+1} = O\left(\frac{1}{|s|}\right),$$

as required.

As a corollary, we deduce an important result concerning the behavior of $\Gamma(\sigma+it)$ for fixed σ and large t.

THEOREM A.11. *If*

$$\sigma_1 \leqq \sigma \leqq \sigma_2\,,$$

then for some constant K, and for $|t| > 1$,

$$|\Gamma(\sigma+it)| = K|t|^{\sigma-1/2}e^{-\pi|t|/2}\left(1 + O\left(\frac{1}{|t|}\right)\right), \tag{25}$$

the constant implied by O depending only on σ_1 and σ_2.

PROOF. From (21) of Theorem A.9,

$$\log \Gamma(\sigma+it) = \left(\sigma+it-\frac{1}{2}\right)\log(\sigma+it) - (\sigma+it) + a + O\left(\frac{1}{|t|}\right), \tag{26}$$

but

$$\log(\sigma + it) = \log(\sigma^2 + t^2)^{1/2} + i \arctan \frac{t}{\sigma};$$

hence

$$\mathscr{R}\left(\left(\sigma + it - \frac{1}{2}\right)\log(\sigma + it)\right) = \left(\sigma - \frac{1}{2}\right)\log(\sigma^2 + t^2)^{1/2} - t \arctan \frac{t}{\sigma}. \tag{27}$$

On the other hand,

$$\log(\sigma^2 + t^2) - \log t^2 = \log\left(1 + \left(\frac{\sigma}{t}\right)^2\right) = O\left(\frac{\sigma}{t}\right)^2 = O\left(\frac{1}{t^2}\right),$$

that is,

$$\log(\sigma^2 + t^2)^{\frac{1}{2}} = \log|t| + O\left(\frac{1}{t^2}\right). \tag{28}$$

Moreover, because

$$\arctan \frac{t}{\sigma} + \arctan \frac{\sigma}{t} = \begin{cases} \pi/2 & \text{if } t > 0, \\ -\pi/2 & \text{if } t < 0, \end{cases}$$

it follows that

$$\arctan \frac{t}{\sigma} = \pm \frac{\pi}{2} - \arctan \frac{\sigma}{t} = \pm \frac{\pi}{2} - \frac{\sigma}{t} + O\left(\frac{1}{t^2}\right)$$

on expanding the arc tan in a power series. This, together with (27) and (28) gives us

$$\mathscr{R}\left\{\left(\sigma + it - \frac{1}{2}\right)\log(\sigma + it)\right\} = \left(\sigma - \frac{1}{2}\right)\log|t| - \frac{\pi}{2}|t| + \sigma + O\left(\frac{1}{|t|}\right). \tag{29}$$

Therefore from (29),

$$\log|\Gamma(\sigma + it)| = \left(\sigma - \frac{1}{2}\right)\log|t| - \frac{\pi}{2}|t| + a + O\left(\frac{1}{|t|}\right),$$

or

$$\begin{aligned} |\Gamma(\sigma + it)| &= K|t|^{\sigma - 1/2} e^{-\pi|t|/2} e^{O(1/|t|)} \\ &= K|t|^{\sigma - 1/2} e^{-\pi|t|/2} \left(1 + O\left(\frac{1}{|t|}\right)\right). \end{aligned}$$

Actually, it can be shown that $K = \sqrt{2\pi}$ but we never need this fact.

Finally, concerning the gamma function, we prove

THEOREM A.12. *The residue of* $\Gamma(s)$ *at the pole* $s = -k$ *is* $(-1)^k/k!$.

PROOF. The residue at $s = -k$ is

$$\lim_{s \to -k} (s + k)\Gamma(s),$$

which, by Theorem A.3, is

$$\lim_{s\to -k}(s+k)\lim_{n\to\infty}\frac{n!n^s}{s(s+1)\cdots(s+n)}$$

$$=\lim_{s\to -k}\lim_{n\to\infty}\frac{n!n^s(s+k)}{s(s+1)\cdots(s+k-1)(s+k)(s+k+1)\cdots(s+n)}$$

$$=\lim_{n\to\infty}\lim_{s\to -k}\frac{n!n^s}{s(s+1)\cdots(s+k-1)(s+k+1)\cdots(s+n)}$$

$$=\lim_{n\to\infty}\frac{n!n^{-k}}{(-k)(-k+1)\cdots(-1)(1)(2)\cdots(n-k)}$$

$$=\lim_{n\to\infty}\frac{(-1)^k}{k!}\frac{n!}{n^k\cdot(n-k)!}$$

$$=\frac{(-1)^k}{k!}\lim_{n\to\infty}\frac{n(n-1)\cdots(n-k+1)}{n^k}=\frac{(-1)^k}{k!}\,.$$

We are now in a position to prove Mellin's formula which was stated without proof and used in § 6, Chapter II.

THEOREM A.13. *If $c > 0$, then*

$$e^{-x}=\frac{1}{2\pi i}\int_{c-i\infty}^{c+i\infty}\Gamma(s)x^{-s}\,ds\,. \tag{30}$$

PROOF. The formula is, so to speak, an inversion of formula (12) of Theorem A.6. The proof uses contour integration. The right-hand side is

$$\lim_{T\to\infty}\frac{1}{2\pi i}\int_{c-iT}^{c+iT}\Gamma(s)x^{-s}\,ds\,. \tag{31}$$

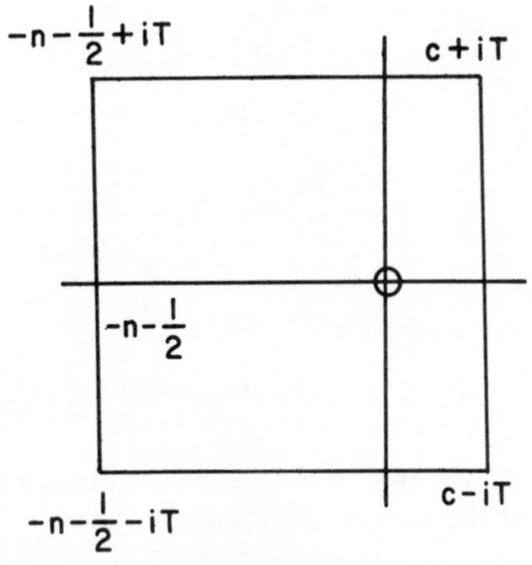

We consider the contour shown in the diagram. Then

$$\begin{aligned}\frac{1}{2\pi i}\int_{c-iT}^{c+iT}\Gamma(s)x^{-s}\,ds&=\frac{1}{2\pi i}\int_{c-iT}^{-n-1/2-iT}\Gamma(s)x^{-s}ds+\frac{1}{2\pi i}\int_{-n-1/2-iT}^{-n-1/2+iT}\Gamma(s)x^{-s}ds\\&\quad+\frac{1}{2\pi i}\int_{-n-1/2+iT}^{c+iT}\Gamma(s)x^{-s}ds+\text{sum of the residues}\,.\end{aligned} \tag{32}$$

The integrand has simple poles at $s=0,-1,\cdots,-n$, and the residue at $s=-k$ is $(-1)^k x^k/k!$. We call the integrals in (32) I_1, I_2, I_3, respectively. Then

$$\frac{1}{2\pi i}\int_{c-iT}^{c+iT}\Gamma(s)x^{-s}ds = I_1+I_2+I_3+\sum_{k=0}^{n}\frac{(-1)^k}{k!}x^k. \tag{33}$$

It remains to show that I_1, I_2, I_3 converge to 0 as $n, T\to\infty$. We consider first I_3; I_1 is treated in the same way:

$$\begin{aligned} I_3 &= \frac{1}{2\pi i}\int_{-n-1/2+iT}^{c+iT}\Gamma(s)x^{-s}ds = \frac{1}{2\pi i}\int_{-n-1/2}^{c}\Gamma(\sigma+iT)x^{-\sigma-iT}d\sigma \\ &= O\left(\int_{-n-1/2}^{c} e^{-\pi|T|/2}\,|T|^{\sigma-1/2}x^{-\sigma}\,d\sigma\right), \end{aligned} \tag{34}$$

by Theorem A.11. The integral in (34), however, is

$$O\left\{\frac{e^{-\pi|T|/2}}{T^{1/2}}\left(\frac{(|T|x^{-1})^c}{\log|T|x^{-1}}-\frac{(|T|x^{-1})^{-n-1/2}}{\log|T|x^{-1}}\right)\right\}=o(1) \qquad \text{as } T\to\infty. \tag{35}$$

We have therefore shown that

$$\frac{1}{2\pi i}\int_{c-i\infty}^{c+i\infty}\Gamma(s)x^{-s}ds=\sum_{k=0}^{n}\frac{(-1)^k}{k}x^k+\int_{-n-1/2-i\infty}^{-n-1/2+i\infty}\Gamma(s)x^{-s}ds. \tag{36}$$

It remains to show that the integral on the right converges to 0 as $n\to\infty$. Indeed

$$I=\int_{-n-1/2-i\infty}^{-n-1/2+i\infty}\Gamma(s)x^{-s}ds=\int_{-\infty}^{\infty}\Gamma\left(-n-\frac{1}{2}+it\right)x^{n+1/2-it}dt. \tag{37}$$

Using the functional equation for $\Gamma(s)$ in the integrand on the right, we find

$$\Gamma\left(-n-\frac{1}{2}+it\right)=\frac{\Gamma(\frac{1}{2}+it)}{(-n-\frac{1}{2}+it)\cdots(-\frac{1}{2}+it)}=O\left(\frac{|\Gamma(\frac{1}{2}+it)|}{(n+1)!}\right). \tag{38}$$

Then using (25), we get from (37) and (38),

$$\begin{aligned} I &= O\left(\int_{-1}^{1}\frac{|\Gamma(\frac{1}{2}+it)|}{(n+1)!}x^{n+1/2}dt\right)+O\left(\int_{1}^{\infty}\frac{e^{-\pi t/2}x^{n+1/2}}{(n+1)!}dt\right) \\ &= O\left(\frac{x^{n+1/2}}{(n+1)!}\right)\int_{-1}^{1}\left|\Gamma\left(\frac{1}{2}+it\right)\right|dt+O\left(\frac{x^{n+1/2}}{(n+1)!}\right). \end{aligned} \tag{39}$$

The constants implied by the O are independent of n and t. On the other hand

$$\int_{-1}^{1}\left|\Gamma\left(\frac{1}{2}+it\right)\right|dt=O(1). \tag{40}$$

Letting $n\to\infty$, the assertion of the theorem follows from (39) and (40).

APPENDIX B

The functional equations of the functions $\zeta(s)$ and $L(s,\chi)$. In Theorem 3.5, of Chapter I, we showed that $\zeta(s)$ is analytic for $\sigma > 0$ except for a simple pole at $s = 1$. We shall show here that $\zeta(s)$ is a meromorphic function whose only singularity is at $s = 1$ and moreover that it satisfies a relatively simple functional equation.

In addition, the same ideas applied to $L(s,\chi)$ show that $L(s,\chi)$ for $\chi \neq \chi_1$, is entire and satisfies a similar type of functional equation.

The proof for the zeta function stems from Riemann. The starting point is the gamma function. Since

$$\Gamma\left(\frac{s}{2}\right) = \int_0^\infty e^{-t} t^{s/2-1} dt\,, \qquad \sigma > 0\,, \tag{1}$$

we replace t by $\pi n^2 u$ and find directly that

$$\pi^{-s/2}\Gamma\left(\frac{s}{2}\right) n^{-s} = \int_0^\infty e^{-\pi n^2 u} u^{s/2-1} du \tag{2}$$

therefore

$$\xi(s) = \pi^{-s/2}\Gamma\left(\frac{s}{2}\right)\zeta(s) = \int_0^\infty \sum_{n=1}^\infty e^{-\pi n^2 u} u^{s/2-1} du\,, \tag{3}$$

the interchange of integration and summation being clearly justified. Riemann's object in (3) is to introduce the function

$$\omega(u) = \sum_{n=1}^\infty e^{-\pi n^2 u}\,,$$

which is closely allied to the function

$$\theta(u) = \sum_{r=-\infty}^\infty e^{-\pi r^2 u}\,, \tag{4}$$

which is an elliptic function satisfying the simple functional equation

$$\theta(u) = \frac{1}{\sqrt{u}}\,\theta\left(\frac{1}{u}\right). \tag{5}$$

The integral in (3) is well behaved for $\sigma > 0$ but for $\sigma \leqq 0$, trouble occurs in the neighborhood of the lower end point. The object of (5) is to improve matters. Before proceeding therefore, we study in more detail the function $\theta(u)$ defined in (4) or rather a slight generalization of it.

We consider the function

$$\Psi(\tau,\alpha) = \sum_{n=-\infty}^\infty e^{-\pi(n+\alpha)^2\tau}\,, \tag{6}$$

for real α and $\tau > 0$. The series converges absolutely. It is our first object to prove the following

THEOREM B.1.

$$\Psi(\tau, \alpha) = \frac{1}{\sqrt{\tau}} \sum_{n=-\infty}^{\infty} e^{-\pi n^2/\tau - 2\pi i n\alpha} . \tag{7}$$

The formula will then hold by analytic continuation for all τ such that $\mathscr{R}(\tau) > 0$.

PROOF. The left-hand side of (7) is

$$\sum_{n=-\infty}^{\infty} e^{-\pi n^2\tau - 2\pi n\alpha\tau - \pi\alpha^2\tau} .$$

We are therefore required to prove that

$$\sum_{n=-\infty}^{\infty} e^{-\pi n^2\tau - 2n\pi\alpha\tau} = \frac{e^{\pi\alpha^2\tau}}{\sqrt{\tau}} \sum_{n=-\infty}^{\infty} e^{-\pi n^2/\tau - 2\pi i n\alpha} . \tag{8}$$

Our natural recourse is Cauchy's theorem and the calculus of residues. In fact if z is the complex variable $x + iy$, then the function

$$f(z) = \frac{e^{-\pi z^2\tau - 2\pi\alpha z\tau}}{e^{2\pi i z} - 1} \tag{9}$$

has simple poles at $z = 0, \pm 1, \pm 2, \cdots$ with residue

$$\frac{1}{2\pi i} e^{-\pi r^2\tau - 2\pi r\alpha\tau} \tag{10}$$

at the simple pole $z = r$.

We consider the rectangle $\mathscr{C}$ in the z plane with vertices at $N + \frac{1}{2} \pm i$,

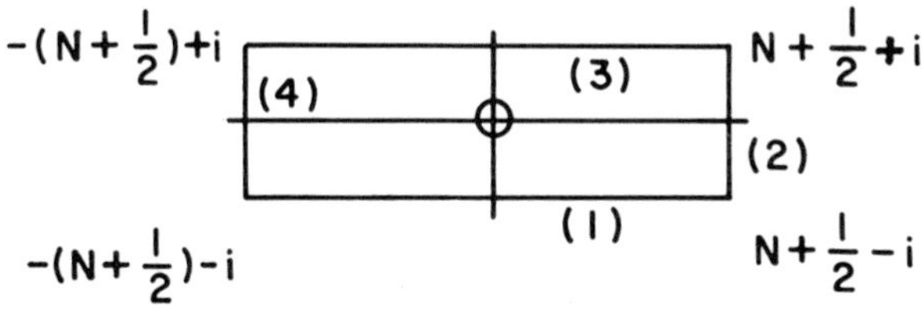

$-(N + \frac{1}{2}) \pm i$ where N is a positive integer. We label the segments of the path (1), (2), (3), (4). By Cauchy's theorem, we get from (9) and (10),

$$\int_{\mathscr{C}} \frac{e^{-\pi\tau z^2 - 2\pi\alpha\tau z}}{e^{2\pi i z} - 1} dz = \sum_{n=-N}^{N} e^{-\pi n^2\tau - 2\pi n\alpha\tau} . \tag{11}$$

The integrals along the vertical sides (2) and (4) are $o(1)$ as $N \to \infty$. Along (2), $z = N + \frac{1}{2} + iy$, and a simple calculation shows that for some constant c

$$\begin{aligned} \int_{(2)} \frac{e^{-\pi\tau z^2 - 2\pi\alpha\tau z}}{e^{2\pi i z} - 1} dz &= O\left(\int_{-1}^{1} \frac{e^{-cN}}{\left|\,|e^{-2\pi y} \cdot e^{2\pi i (N+1/2)}| - 1\right|} dy\right) \\ &= O\left(\frac{e^{-cN}}{e^{-2\pi y} + 1}\right) = o(1) . \end{aligned} \tag{12}$$

A similar argument holds for the integral along (4). Thus letting $N \to \infty$, we conclude from (11) and (12) that

$$e^{\pi\alpha^2\tau}\Psi(\tau, \alpha) = \int_{-\infty-i}^{\infty-i} f(z)dz - \int_{-\infty+i}^{\infty+i} f(z)dz\,, \tag{13}$$

the integrals being absolutely convergent as a simple calculation will show. Since along the path in the first integral of (13)

$$|e^{2\pi iz}| = e^{2\pi} > 1,$$

it follows that

$$\sum_{n=-1}^{-\infty} e^{2\pi inz} = \frac{1}{e^{2\pi iz} - 1}\,,$$

the series converging uniformly and therefore

$$\int_{-\infty-i}^{\infty-i} f(z)dz = \sum_{n=-1}^{-\infty} \int_{-\infty-i}^{\infty-i} e^{-\pi\tau z^2 - 2\pi z(\alpha\tau - ni)}\,dz\,. \tag{14}$$

A similar argument shows that

$$\int_{-\infty+i}^{\infty+i} f(z)dz = \sum_{n=0}^{\infty} \int_{-\infty+i}^{\infty+i} e^{-\pi\tau z^2 - 2\pi z(\alpha\tau - ni)}\,dz\,. \tag{15}$$

On the other hand, completing the square in z, we get

$$e^{\pi\tau(\alpha - ni/\tau)^2} \int_{-\infty\pm i}^{\infty\pm i} e^{-\pi\tau(z+\alpha-ni/\tau)^2}\,dz = e^{\pi\tau(\alpha-ni/\tau)^2} \int_L e^{-\pi\tau u^2}du\,, \tag{16}$$

where the path L is along a line parallel to the real axis with imaginary part μ (say). Applying Cauchy's theorem again to the rectangle with vertices $\pm W$, $\pm W + i\mu$ (with real W) we find as $W \to \infty$

$$\int_L e^{-\pi\tau u^2} du = \int_{-\infty}^{\infty} e^{-\pi\tau u^2} du\,. \tag{17}$$

Thus since

$$\int_{-\infty}^{\infty} e^{-\pi\tau u^2} du = \frac{1}{\sqrt{(\pi\tau)}} \cdot \sqrt{\pi} = \frac{1}{\sqrt{\tau}}\,, \tag{18}$$

we get from (13), (14), (15), (16), (17), (18)

$$\begin{aligned} e^{\pi\alpha^2\tau}\Psi(\tau, \alpha) &= \frac{1}{\sqrt{\tau}} \sum_{n=-\infty}^{\infty} e^{\pi\tau(\alpha - ni/\tau)^2} \\ &= \frac{1}{\sqrt{\tau}}\, e^{\pi\tau\alpha^2} \sum_{n=-\infty}^{\infty} e^{-\pi n^2/\tau - 2\pi in\alpha}\,, \end{aligned}$$

and this is what we set out to prove.

Several corollaries follow readily.

THEOREM B.2.

$$\Psi(\tau, \alpha) = \frac{1}{\sqrt{\tau}} \sum_{n=-\infty}^{\infty} e^{-\pi n^2/\tau} \cos 2\pi n\alpha\,. \tag{19}$$

PROOF. The proof is an immediate consequence of (7) and the fact that

$$e^{-\pi n^2/\tau}\sin 2\pi n\alpha\ ,$$

is an odd function in n, for then the series

$$\sum_{n=-\infty}^{\infty} e^{-\pi n^2/\tau}\sin 2\pi n\alpha$$

must vanish.

If we specialize α, we get at once

THEOREM B.3. *If*

$$\Psi(\tau, 0) = \theta(\tau)\ ,$$

then

$$\theta(\tau) = \frac{1}{\sqrt{\tau}}\,\theta\left(\frac{1}{\tau}\right). \tag{20}$$

If we differentiate both sides of (19) with respect to α, we get

THEOREM B.4.

$$\sum_{n=-\infty}^{\infty} (n+\alpha)e^{-\pi\tau(n+\alpha)^2} = \frac{1}{\tau\sqrt{\tau}}\sum_{n=-\infty}^{\infty} ne^{-n^2\pi/\tau}\sin(2\pi n\alpha)\ . \tag{21}$$

PROOF. The proof follows from the uniform convergence of both sides in α.

For dealing with the L functions, we shall require series similar to the above but involving characters. Let χ be a primitive character modulo k. Two cases arise in a natural way. In the first place $\chi(-1) = \pm 1$; we therefore consider

Case (i). Suppose that

$$\chi(-1) = 1\ . \tag{22}$$

We define

$$\psi(\tau, \chi) = 2\sum_{n=1}^{\infty} \chi(n)e^{-\pi n^2\tau/k} \tag{23}$$

and shall show that $\psi(\tau, \chi)$ satisfies a functional equation.

In fact since

$$\chi(n)e^{-\pi n^2\tau/k}$$

is, by (22), an even function of n and since $\chi(0) = 0$, we get

$$\psi(\tau, \chi) = \sum_{n=-\infty}^{\infty} \chi(n)e^{-\pi n^2\tau/k}\ . \tag{24}$$

We break the summation in (24) into residue classes modulo k by putting $n = mk + r$, and we get

$$\psi(\tau, \chi) = \sum_{r=0}^{k} \chi(r) \sum_{m=-\infty}^{\infty} e^{-\pi(m+r/k)^2 k\tau} = \sum_{r=0}^{k} \chi(r) \Psi\left(k\tau, \frac{r}{k}\right), \tag{25}$$

where $\Psi(k\tau, r/k)$ is defined by (6).

If we apply (19) to $\Psi(k\tau, r/k)$, we find from (25)

$$\begin{aligned} \psi(\tau, \chi) &= \sum_{r=0}^{k} \chi(r) \frac{1}{\sqrt{(k\tau)}} \sum_{m=-\infty}^{\infty} e^{-\pi m^2/k\tau} \cos \frac{2\pi rm}{k} \\ &= \frac{1}{\sqrt{(k\tau)}} \sum_{m=-\infty}^{\infty} e^{-\pi m^2/k\tau} \sum_{r=0}^{k} \chi(r) \cos \frac{2\pi rm}{k} . \end{aligned} \tag{26}$$

On the other hand, since $\chi(-1) = 1$, and therefore $\chi(k-n) = \chi(n)$ and since $\sin(2\pi m(k-n)/k) = -\sin(2\pi mn/k)$, it follows that

$$\sum_{r=0}^{k} \chi(r) \sin \frac{2\pi mr}{k} = 0 . \tag{27}$$

Accordingly from (26) and (27),

$$\psi(\tau, \chi) = \frac{1}{\sqrt{(k\tau)}} \sum_{m=-\infty}^{\infty} e^{-\pi m^2/k\tau} \sum_{r=0}^{k} \chi(r) e^{2\pi imr/k} . \tag{28}$$

The inner sum, however, is the familiar Gaussian sum

$$G(m, \chi) = \sum_{r=0}^{k} \chi(r) e^{2\pi imr/k} .$$

By Theorem 4.12,

$$G(m, \chi) = \bar{\chi}(m) G(1, \chi) \tag{29}$$

and therefore from (27), (28) and (29),

$$\psi(\tau, \chi) = \frac{1}{\sqrt{\tau}} \frac{G(1, \chi)}{\sqrt{k}} \sum_{m=-\infty}^{\infty} \bar{\chi}(m) e^{-\pi m^2/k\tau} .$$

Consequently we get

THEOREM B.5. *If $\psi(\tau, \chi)$ is defined by* (23) *and $G(1, \chi)$ is a Gaussian sum, then*

$$\psi(\tau, \chi) = \frac{1}{\sqrt{\tau}} \frac{G(1, \chi)}{\sqrt{k}} \psi\left(\frac{1}{\tau}, \bar{\chi}\right) . \tag{30}$$

For simplicity, we put

$$\varepsilon(\chi) = \frac{G(1, \chi)}{\sqrt{k}} ; \tag{31}$$

then, by Theorem 4.13, Chapter V, we get

$$| \varepsilon(x) | = \frac{| G(1, \chi) |}{\sqrt{k}} = 1 . \tag{32}$$

Moreover, since

$$G(1, \bar{\chi}) = \sum_{r=0}^{k} \bar{\chi}(r) e^{2\pi i r/k} = \sum_{r=0}^{k} \bar{\chi}(r) e^{-2\pi i r/k} = \overline{G(1, \chi)} ,$$

because $\chi(-1) = 1$. Therefore it follows that

$$\overline{\varepsilon(\chi)} = \varepsilon(\bar{\chi}) .$$

Thus by (32),

$$\varepsilon(\bar{\chi}) = \frac{1}{\varepsilon(\chi)} . \tag{33}$$

Case (ii). $\chi(-1) = -1$. In this case we modify the function $\psi(\tau, \chi)$ for later application. Let

$$\psi_1(\tau, \chi) = 2 \sum_{n=1}^{\infty} n\chi(n) e^{-\pi n^2 \tau/k} ; \tag{34}$$

then exactly as in Case (i), we show using (21) that

$$\begin{aligned} \psi_1(\tau, \chi) &= \sum_{n=-\infty}^{\infty} n\chi(n) e^{-\pi n^2 \tau/k} = \frac{1}{i\tau\sqrt{(k\tau)}} \sum_{m=-\infty}^{\infty} m e^{(-\pi m^2/k)\tau} \sum_{r=0}^{k} \chi(r) e^{2\pi i m r/k} \\ &= \frac{-i\, G(1, \chi)}{\tau\sqrt{\tau}\sqrt{k}} \psi_1\left(\frac{1}{\tau}, \bar{\chi}\right) = \varepsilon_1(\chi) \frac{1}{\tau\sqrt{\tau}} \psi_1\left(\frac{1}{\tau}, \bar{\chi}\right) , \end{aligned} \tag{35}$$

where

$$\varepsilon_1(\chi) = \frac{-\, iG(1, \chi)}{\sqrt{k}} .$$

In this case because $\chi(-1) = -1$,

$$\overline{G(1, \chi)} = \sum_{r=0}^{k} \bar{\chi}(r) e^{-2\pi i r/k} = - \sum_{r=0}^{k} \bar{\chi}(r) e^{2\pi i r/k} = - G(1, \bar{\chi}) .$$

Therefore

$$\overline{\varepsilon_1(x)} = \frac{i\, \overline{G(1, \chi)}}{\sqrt{k}} = \frac{-i\, G(1, \bar{\chi})}{\sqrt{k}} = \varepsilon_1(\bar{\chi}) ,$$

and since as above

$$| \varepsilon_1(\chi) | = 1 ,$$

we get

$$\varepsilon_1(\bar{\chi}) = \frac{1}{\varepsilon_1(\chi)} . \tag{36}$$

We return to proofs of the functional equations for $\zeta(s)$ and $L(s, \chi)$.

THEOREM B.6. *If*

$$\xi(s) = \pi^{-s/2}\, \Gamma\left(\frac{s}{2}\right) \zeta(s) \tag{37}$$

then $\xi(s)$ *is regular for all* s *except for simple poles at* $s = 0$, $s = 1$. $\xi(s)$ *satisfies the functional equation* $\xi(s) = \xi(1 - s)$.

PROOF. We had from (3),

$$\xi(s) = \int_0^\infty \omega(u)\, u^{s/2-1} du\ ,$$

where

$$\omega(u) = \sum_{n=1}^{\infty} e^{-\pi n^2 u}\ .$$

We break the interval of integration

$$\xi(s) = \int_0^1 \omega(u) u^{s/2-1} du + \int_1^\infty \omega(u) u^{s/2-1} du\ . \tag{38}$$

In the first integral we replace u by $1/u$, and find from (38),

$$\xi(s) = \int_1^\infty \omega\left(\frac{1}{u}\right) u^{-s/2-1} du + \int_1^\infty \omega(u) u^{s/2-1} du\ . \tag{39}$$

Now

$$1 + 2\omega(u) = \theta(u)$$

and using Theorem B.3, we get

$$1 + 2\omega(u) = \frac{1}{\sqrt{u}}\left(1 + 2\omega\left(\frac{1}{u}\right)\right)\ . \tag{40}$$

Inserting $\omega(1/u)$ from (40) in the first integral of (39), we deduce, on performing the simple integrations,

$$\xi(s) = \frac{1}{s-1} - \frac{1}{s} + \int_1^\infty \omega(u)(u^{s/2} + u^{(1-s)/2}) \frac{du}{u}\ . \tag{41}$$

The integral in (41) is regular for all s and the right-hand side is clearly invariant on replacing s by $1-s$. This completes the proof.

We turn to the functional equation for $L(s, \chi)$ for χ a primitive character modulo k. The argument is much the same as the one we used for $\xi(s)$. Naturally there are added complications but we have prepared for these.

We consider again 2 cases.

Case (i). $\chi(-1) = 1$. We start from the gamma function and get

$$\left(\frac{\pi}{k}\right)^{-s/2} \Gamma\left(\frac{s}{2}\right) n^{-s} = \int_0^\infty e^{-\pi n^2 u/k} u^{s/2-1} du$$

and therefore using (23),

$$\begin{aligned} \xi(s, \chi) = \left(\frac{\pi}{k}\right)^{-s/2} \Gamma\left(\frac{s}{2}\right) L(s, \chi) &= \int_0^\infty \sum_{n=1}^{\infty} \chi(n) e^{-\pi n^2 u/k} u^{s/2-1} du \\ &= \frac{1}{2}\int_0^\infty \psi(u, \chi) u^{s/2-1} du \qquad (42) \\ &= \frac{1}{2}\int_0^1 \psi(u, \chi) u^{s/2-1} du + \frac{1}{2}\int_1^\infty \psi(u, \chi) u^{s/2-1} du\ . \end{aligned}$$

We apply (30) to the first integral of (42) after replacing u by $1/u$,

$$\xi(s, \chi) = \frac{\varepsilon(\chi)}{2}\int_1^\infty \psi(u, \bar{\chi})u^{(1-s)/2}\frac{du}{u} + \frac{1}{2}\int_1^\infty \psi(u, \chi)u^{s/2}\frac{du}{u} . \tag{43}$$

The integrals on the right of (43) are regular for all s and therefore so is $\xi(s, \chi)$. Moreover

$$\xi(1 - s, \bar{\chi}) = \frac{\varepsilon(\bar{\chi})}{2}\int_1^\infty \psi(u, \chi)u^{s/2}\frac{du}{u} + \frac{1}{2}\int_1^\infty \psi(u, \bar{\chi})u^{(1-s)/2}\frac{du}{u} .$$

Using (33), however, it follows that

$$\varepsilon(\chi)\ \xi(1 - s, \bar{\chi}) = \xi(s, \chi) .$$

Case (ii). $\chi(-1) = -1$. In this case we start from

$$\left(\frac{\pi}{k}\right)^{-(s+1)/2}\Gamma\left(\frac{s+1}{2}\right)n^{-s} = \int_0^\infty ne^{-\pi n^2 u/k}u^{(s+1)/2-1}du .$$

Then it follows that

$$\xi_1(s, \chi) = \left(\frac{\pi}{k}\right)^{-(s+1)/2}\Gamma\left(\frac{s+1}{2}\right)L(s, \chi) = \frac{1}{2}\int_0^\infty \psi_1(u, \chi)u^{(s+1)/2}\frac{du}{u} ,$$

where $\psi_1(u, \chi)$ is defined by (34). We break the interval of integration as before and apply (35) and deduce

$$\xi_1(s, \chi) = \frac{\varepsilon_1(\chi)}{2}\int_1^\infty \psi_1(u, \bar{\chi})u^{-s/2}du + \frac{1}{2}\int_1^\infty \psi_1(u, \chi)u^{-(1-s)/2}du .$$

Again the right-hand side is regular in s and using (36), we deduce

$$\xi_1(s, \chi) = \varepsilon_1(\chi)\,\xi_1(1 - s, \bar{\chi}) . \tag{44}$$

We combine these two into the same

THEOREM B.7. *If χ is a primitive character modulo k which is nonprincipal,*

$$a = \begin{cases} 0 & \text{if } x(-1) = 1 , \\ 1 & \text{if } \chi(-1) = -1 \end{cases}$$

and

$$\xi(s, \chi) = \left(\frac{\pi}{k}\right)^{-(s+a)/2}\Gamma\left(\frac{s+a}{2}\right)L(s, \chi) , \tag{45}$$

then $\xi(s, \chi)$ is an entire function of s and satisfies the functional equation

$$\xi(s, \chi) = \varepsilon(\chi)\xi(1 - s, \bar{\chi})$$

where

$$\varepsilon(\chi) = \begin{cases} \dfrac{G(1, \chi)}{\sqrt{k}} & \text{if } a = 0 , \\[2ex] \dfrac{-iG(1, \chi)}{\sqrt{k}} & \text{if } a = 1 . \end{cases}$$

In the particular case when $\chi(n) = \chi_d(n) = (d/n)$, we have by Theorem 4.17

$$G(1, \chi) = \begin{cases} i\sqrt{|d|} & \text{if } d < 0 . \\ \sqrt{d} & \text{if } d > 0 \end{cases}$$

Therefore in either case ,

$$\varepsilon(\chi) = 1 . \tag{46}$$

CoROLLARY 1. *If* $a = 0$, *the function* $L(s, \chi)$ *vanishes for* $s = 0, -2, -4, \cdots$. *If* $a = 1$, $L(s, \chi)$ *vanishes for* $s = -1, -3, -5, \cdots$.

PROOF. We showed that $L(s, \chi)$ is analytic for $\sigma \geqq \delta > 0$. The poles of $\Gamma((s + a)/2)$ must be cancelled by zeros of $L(s, \chi)$.

If χ is not primitive, we reduce the case to the primitive one by using Theorem 4.7 of Chapter V.

References

The following is a list of books on number theory which are devoted to analytic theory of numbers or which contain sections devoted to the analytic theory.

If the reference contains material relevant to one or more of the five chapters of this book, we indicate this by one or more numbers I to V after the reference.

1. Bachmann, P. *Analytische Zahlentheorie*, 2nd ed., B. G. Teubner, 1921; I, II and III.

2. Bohr, H. and Cramer, H. *Die neuere Entwicklung der analytischen Zahlentheorie*, Enzyklopädie der Math. Wiss. II, C, 1922; I and II.

3. Dirichlet, P. G. and Dedekind, R. *Vorlesungen über Zahlentheorie*, 4th ed., Vieweg, 1894; I and V.

4. Estermann, T. *Modern prime number theory*, Cambridge, 1950; I, II and V.

5. Hardy, G. H. *Lectures on Ramanujan*, Cambridge, 1940; II and III.

6. ———. *Ramanujan's work*, Institute for Advanced Study, 1936.

7. Hardy, G. H. and Riesz, M. *The general theory of Dirichlet series*, Cambridge, reprinted 1952; I and II.

8. Hardy, G. H. and Wright, E. M. *An introduction to the theory of numbers*, Oxford, 1938, 4th ed., 1960; II and III.

9. Hasse, H. *Vorlesungen über Zahlentheorie*, Springer, 1950; I and V.

10. Hecke, E. *Vorlesungen über die Theorie der algebraischen Zahlen*, Akad. Verlag, Leipzig, 1923, reprinted by Chelsea 1952; V.

11. Hua, L. K. *Additive Primzahltheorie*, Teubner, 1959; IV.

12. ———. *Exponentialsummen und ihre Anwendung in der Zahlentheorie*, Enzyklopädie der Math. Wiss. I, § 13, Part 1, 1959; IV.

13. Ingham, A. E. *The distribution of primes*, Cambridge, 1932; I and II.

14. Landau, E. *Handbuch der Lehre von der Verteilung der Primzahlen*, 2 vols., Teubner, 1909, reprinted by Chelsea, 1953; I and II.

15. ———. *Vorlesungen über Zahlentheorie*. 3 vols., S. Hirzel, 1927, reprinted by Chelsea, 1947; I, II and IV.

16. ———. *Über einige neuere Fortschritte der additiven Zahlentheorie*, Cambridge Univ. Press, 1937; IV and V.

17. ———. *Einführung in die elementare und analytische Theorie der algebraischen Zahlen und der Ideale*, reprinted by Chelsea, 1949; V.

18. Leveque, W. J. *Topics in number theory*, Vol. II, Addison Wesley, 1956; I and II.

19. Matthews, G. B. *Theory of numbers*, reprinted by Chelsea, 1962; II and V.

20. Ostmann, H. H. *Additive Zahlentheorie*, 2 vols., Springer, 1956; II and III.

21. Prachar, K. *Primzahlverteilung*, Springer, 1957; I, II and V.

22. Rademacher, H. *Lectures on analytic number theory*, Tata Institute of Fundamental Research, Bombay, 1955; III.

23. Specht, W. *Elementare Beweis der Primzahlsätze*, V. E. B. Deutsche Verlag, 1956; II.

24. Titchmarsh, E. C. *The zeta function of Riemann*, Cambridge, 1930; II.

25. ———. *The theory of the Riemann zeta function*, Oxford, 1951; II.

26. Trost, E. *Primzahlen,* Birkhauser, 1953; II.
27. Tschudakoff, A. *Dirichlet L-functions,* GITTL, Moscow, 1947; I, II and V. (Russian)
28. Vinogradoff, I. M. *The method of trigonometric sums in the theory of numbers,* translated by K. F. Roth and Anne Davenport, Interscience, 1954; IV.
29. Walfisz, A. *Die Weyl-Vinogradoffschen exponential Summen in der Zahlentheorie,* V. E. B. Deutsche Verlag, Berlin, 1962; IV.
30. Weyl, H. *Algebraic theory of numbers,* Princeton, 1940; V.

Index of Symbols Used

Subject Index